The Regulation of
Acid–Base Balance

Raven Press books by
Donald W. Seldin and Gerhard Giebisch

The Regulation of Potassium Balance
The Regulation of Acid–Base Balance
The Regulation of Sodium Chloride Balance
The Kidney (2 volumes)

The Regulation of
Acid–Base Balance

Editors

Donald W. Seldin, M.D.

William Buchanan and Systems Professor of Internal Medicine
Department of Internal Medicine
The University of Texas Southwestern Medical Center at Dallas
Dallas, Texas

Gerhard Giebisch, M.D.

Sterling Professor
Department of Cellular and Molecular Physiology
Yale University School of Medicine
New Haven, Connecticut

Raven Press  New York

Raven Press, 1185 Avenue of the Americas, New York, New York 10036

Made in the United States of America

Library of Congress Cataloging-in-Publication Data

The Regulation of acid–base balance.

    Includes bibliographies and index.
      1. Acid–base imbalances.   2. Acid–base equilibrium.
I. Seldin, Donald W., 1920- . II. Giebisch,
Gerhard H. [DNLM: 1. Acid–Base Equilibrium.
2. Acid–Base Imbalance. 3. Acidosis.   WD 220 R344]
RC630.R44   1989   616.3'9   86-40396
ISBN 0-88167-480-X

9 8 7 6 5 4 3 2 1

Preface

The present volume begins with a consideration of the general principles governing the cellular and extracellular buffering of acids and bases, as well as the specialized behavior of key organ systems. Then the mechanisms whereby the lungs and kidneys regulate acid–base balance are delineated. The second section of the book involves a detailed portrayal of the different forms of acid–base disturbances, their recognition, and treatment.

It is hoped that an appreciation of deranged acid–base balance as an expression of disturbances in pulmonary, renal, metabolic, and circulatory dysfunction will permit deeper understanding of causal mechanisms and, therefore, better clinical diagnosis and treatment.

The pH of the blood is given by the ratio of HCO_3^- to CO_2 according to the Henderson-Hasselbalch equation.

$$pH = 6.1 + \log\frac{[HCO_3^-]}{[CO_2]}$$

The pH is kept remarkably constant by a variety of mechanisms serving to stabilize the concentrations of HCO_3^- and CO_2. These mechanisms are of four types: closed buffer systems, metabolic processes, open buffer systems, and physiologic regulation.

The major buffer system of plasma is HCO_3^-/CO_2. As a closed buffer, it is relatively weak, since the pK is far removed from the normal blood pH of 7.4. Metabolic processes also serve to mitigate pH changes. Lactic acid, for example, is generated by intracellular alkalosis, thereby reducing the blood HCO_3^- concentration and blunting the rise of blood pH that results from hyperventilation. Such metabolic adjustments may have a critical role in stabilizing intracellular pH, but they are of only modest potency in affecting the HCO_3^-/CO_2 buffer ratio. The pivotal role of this system stems from the fact that it is an open buffer system under physiologic regulation. Its powerful buffering effect depends on the discrete regulation of its components by two different organ systems, the lungs serving to control the elimination of CO_2 and the kidneys regulating the HCO_3^- concentration.

Two features characterize this dual control system. First, acid–base balance can be influenced by disturbances in renal function or pulmonary function or both. Second, the two organ systems interact in such a manner that there is no pure acid–base disturbance. A primary change in one member of the buffer pair automatically elicits a compensatory change in the other.

Since the kidneys and lungs are responsible for stabilizing the HCO_3^-/CO_2 concentrations, it follows that disturbances in these concentrations usually are critical signposts of serious abnormalities in pulmonary, renal, or circulatory function or in a variety of metabolic processes. Very often, elimination of these underlying disturbances is more valuable in remedying the acid–base imbalance than direct intervention to restore the blood pH. Extreme acid–base disturbances are important in their own right and may require aggressive treatment with alkali or acid. Even more important, however, are the physiologic derangements that lead to a failure of regulatory function on the part of an organ or organ systems, the correction of which may restore both organ function and acid–base balance. Lactic acidosis may signal circulatory collapse and require administration of salt or antibiotics, ketonemic acidosis is treated with insulin and other measures to reinstitute normal intermediary metabolism, the acidosis associated with ethylene glycol poisoning requires measures designed to accelerate elimination and prevent its conversion to toxic metabolites; the metabolic alkalosis of vomiting can usually be corrected by administration of saline; and respiratory acidosis is often amenable to measures restoring a patent airway. In all these instances, the acid–base derangement may constitute a vital clue to the basic disturbance, the treatment of which may be the most effective way to manage the acid–base derangement. The physician must be alerted, therefore, to recognize the significance of an acid–base disturbance as evidence of an underlying pathophysiologic disturbance.

For the students of physiology and internal medicine, we hope this volume will provide a stimulus to future research, and for the urologists, nephrologists and internists, provide a deeper insight into some of the causes and consequences of the clinical syndromes encountered.

Donald W. Seldin, M.D.
Gerhard Giebisch, M.D.

Contents

Contributors

Allen I. Arieff, M.D., F.A.C.P.
Professor of Medicine
Department of Internal Medicine/
  Nephrology/Geriatrics
University of California, San
  Francisco, and
Veterans Administration Medical
  Center
4150 Clement Street, 111
San Francisco, California 94121

Daniel C. Batlle, M.D., F.A.C.P.
Associate Professor of Medicine
Department of Medicine
Northwestern University Medical School
303 East Chicago Avenue
Chicago, Illinois 60611

Walter F. Boron, M.D., Ph.D.
Professor of Cellular and Molecular
  Physiology
Department of Cellular and Molecular
  Physiology
Yale University School of Medicine
333 Cedar Street
New Haven, Connecticut 06510

David A. Bushinsky, M.D.
Associate Professor of Medicine
Department of Medicine
Section of Nephrology
University of Chicago Pritzker School
  of Medicine
5841 South Maryland Avenue, Box 28
Chicago, Illinois 60637

Alan N. Charney, M.D.
Professor of Medicine
Department of Medicine
New York University School of
  Medicine
408 First Avenue
New York, New York 10010

Robert O. Crapo, M.D.
Associate Professor of Medicine
Department of Medicine
University of Utah School of Medicine
  and *Medical Director*
Pulmonary Laboratory
LDS Hospital
325 Eighth Avenue
Salt Lake City, Utah 84143

Thomas D. DuBose, Jr., M.D.
Professor of Medicine, Physiology and
  Biophysics
Chief, Division of Nephrology
University of Texas Medical Branch at
  Galveston
E-62, 4.200 Old John Sealy
Galveston, Texas 77550

C. Gregory Elliott, M.D.
Associate Professor of Medicine
University of Utah School of Medicine
  and *Department of Medicine*
LDS Hospital
325 Eighth Avenue
Salt Lake City, Utah 84143

Michael Emmett, M.D., F.A.C.P.
Ralph Tompsett Professor of Medicine
Division of Nephrology/Metabolism
Baylor University Medical Center
3500 Gaston Avenue
Dallas, Texas 75246

George M. Feldman, M.D.
Assistant Professor of Medicine
University of Pennsylvania School of
  Medicine
Chief, Renal Electrolyte Section
Veterans Administration Medical
  Center
University and Woodland Avenues
Philadelphia, Pennsylvania 19104

Gerhard Giebisch, M.D.
Sterling Professor
Department of Cellular and Molecular
  Physiology
Yale University School of Medicine
333 Cedar Street
New Haven, Connecticut 06510

David W. Good, Ph.D.
Assistant Professor of Physiology,
  Biophysics, and Internal Medicine
University of Texas Medical Branch
John Sealy Hospital
4.200 Route E-62
Galveston, Texas 77550-2778

Robert B. Gunn, M.D.
Professor of Physiology and
Chairman, Department of Physiology
Emory University School of Medicine
Atlanta, Georgia 30322

William L. Henrich, M.D.
Professor of Medicine
The University of Texas Southwestern
  Medical Center
Veterans Administration Medical
  Center
4500 South Lancaster Road
Dallas, Texas 75216

Harry R. Jacobson, M.D.
Professor of Medicine
Director, Division of Nephrology
Vanderbilt University School of
  Medicine
1161-21st Avenue, South
Nashville, Tennessee 37232

Bruce M. Koeppen, M.D., Ph.D.
Associate Professor of Medicine and
  Physiology
Division of Nephrology
University of Connecticut Health
  Center
Farmington, Connecticut 06032-9984

Jeffrey A. Kraut, M.D.
Associate Professor of Medicine
Department of Nephrology

Wadsworth Veterans Administration
  Medical Center
Sawtelle and Wilshire Boulevards
Los Angeles, California 90073

Neil A. Kurtzman, M.D.
Arnett Professor of Medicine
Professor of Physiology
Chief, Section of Nephrology
Chairman, Department of Internal
  Medicine
Texas Tech University Health Sciences
  Center
3601 4th Street
Lubbock, Texas 79430

Melvin E. Laski, M.D.
Assistant Professor of Medicine
Departments of Internal Medicine and
  Physiology
Texas Tech University Health Sciences
  Center
4th and Indiana
Lubbock, Texas 79430

Nicolaos E. Madias, M.D.
Associate Professor of Medicine
Tufts University School of Medicine
  and Chief, Division of Nephrology
New England Medicine Center
  Hospitals
750 Washington Street
Boston, Massachusetts 02111

Alan H. Morris, M.D.
Professor of Medicine
University of Utah School of Medicine
  and Director of Research
Pulmonary Division
LDS Hospital
325 Eighth Avenue
Salt Lake City, Utah 84143

Sandra Sabatini, M.D., Ph.D.
Professor of Medicine
Department of Internal Medicine
Texas Tech University Health Sciences
  Center
3601 Fourth Street
Lubbock, Texas 79430

Donald W. Seldin, M.D.

*William Buchanan and Systems
  Professor of Internal Medicine
Department of Internal Medicine
The University of Texas Southwestern
  Medical Center at Dallas
5323 Harry Hines Boulevard
Dallas, Texas 75235-9030*

Jeffrey R. Thompson, M.D.

*Assistant Professor of Medicine
Department of Internal Medicine
The University of Texas Southwestern
  Medical Center at Dallas
5323 Harry Hines Boulevard
Dallas, Texas 75235-9030*

Normal Acid–Base Balance

The Regulation of Acid–Base Balance, edited
by Donald W. Seldin and Gerhard Giebisch,
Raven Press, Ltd., New York © 1989.

1

Chemistry of Buffer Equilibria in Blood Plasma

Walter F. Boron

*Department of Cellular and Molecular Physiology,
Yale University School of Medicine, New Haven, Connecticut 06510*

---

pH
Carbon Dioxide
Equilibria
  Interactions of Carbon Dioxide with Aqueous Solutions • Henderson-Hasselbalch Equation
Alteration of P_{CO_2} or Addition of HCO_3^- in a Buffer-free System
  Increasing $[CO_2]$ • Increasing $[HCO_3^-]$ • Increasing $[CO_2]$ and $[HCO_3^-]$ Proportionally
Buffering Power
  Buffering Power in a Closed System • Buffering Power in an Open System
Alterations of $[CO_2]$ or $[HCO_3^-]$
  Constructing a Davenport Diagram • Respiratory Acid-Base Disturbances • Metabolic Acid-Base Disturbances • Compensations for Acid-Base Disturbances
References

Because problems in acid-base balance arise in both clinical settings and the research laboratory, buffer equilibria are important for the practicing physician and the biomedical scientist. The purpose of this chapter is to provide an overview of buffer equilibria in the blood plasma. However, the principles that guide one's approach to problems of acid-base chemistry in the blood plasma also apply to acid-base problems in numerous other areas. It should be noted that in whole blood, there is an intimate relationship between the acid-base chemistry of the blood plasma and the acid-base physiology of erythrocytes, a subject discussed in Chapter 3.

Although cell pH probably has far more influence on cell function than does plasma pH, the latter has traditionally been viewed as the primary clinical barometer of acid-base disturbances. This is probably valid because disturbances in plasma pH either cause or reflect disturbances in cellular acid-base balance. Intracellular pH, as well as the interaction between intracellular and extracellular pH, is discussed in Chapter 2.

pH (1–3,6,9)

In aqueous solutions, hydrogen ions do not truly exist as free protons but are associated with one or probably more H_2O molecules to form extended complexes. Strictly speaking, it is not the concentration of these proton–water complexes that is important but their thermodynamic activity. For the sake of simplicity, we refer to hydrogen ions as if they were free in solution and generally refer to concentrations of H^+ and other ions rather than to activities.

Because $[H^+]$ varies over several orders of magnitude in biologic fluids (e.g., from 10^{-1} M in gastric fluids to 10^{-8} M and below in mitochondria), Sorensen attempted to simplify the notation of hydrogen ion concentrations by devising a pH scale based on powers of 10:

$$pH \equiv -\log_{10}[H^+] \qquad [1]$$

For example, when $[H^+]$ is 10^{-7} M, the pH is 7.0. Note that a tenfold change in $[H^+]$ corresponds to a pH shift of 1, whereas a twofold change in $[H^+]$ corresponds to a pH shift of very nearly 0.3. Table 1 lists the pH values for several H^+ concentrations to which we refer in this chapter. Although acid-base data sometimes are reported in terms of $[H^+]$, particularly in the clinical literature, this is to be discouraged. For thermodynamic reasons, it is impossible to specify precisely the $[H^+]$ in the solutions used to calibrate pH electrodes. Thus, a pH value (i.e., the primary measurement) cannot be converted precisely to a value of $[H^+]$ (i.e., a derived quantity). The pH scale is, therefore, the preferred method for quantitating the relative acidity or alkalinity of an aqueous solution.

Although $[H^+]$ is exceedingly low in most biologic fluids, H^+ is extremely important biochemically. This is because many proteins and other molecules have buffer groups that bind H^+ with an extremely high affinity. Altering pH causes the degree of protonation of such groups to change. Sometimes this produces profound changes in function. Because pH is such an important factor for many enzymes and structural proteins, it is not surprising that the body has gone to great lengths to regulate the pH in various compartments. For example, although the pH of neutral water at 37°C is about 6.81, the pH of mammalian blood plasma normally is kept very close to 7.4. This regulation of the pH of blood plasma is accomplished by controlling the concentrations of CO_2 and HCO_3^-, the two components of the major buffer in plasma.

TABLE 1. *Relationship between [H$^+$] and pH*

[H$^+$]	pH
1×10^{-6}	6.0
1×10^{-7}	7.0
8×10^{-8}	7.1
4×10^{-8}	7.4
2×10^{-8}	7.7
1×10^{-8}	8.0

CARBON DIOXIDE EQUILIBRIA (8)

Interactions of Carbon Dioxide with Aqueous Solutions

Imagine that a beaker of pure water (pH = 6.81 at 37°C) is brought into contact with air containing CO_2 (Fig. 1). CO_2 from the air dissolves in the water, thereby raising the concentration of dissolved CO_2 ($[CO_2]_{Dis}$). On the other hand, some of the newly dissolved CO_2 leaves the water and enters the atmosphere. When the rates of CO_2 entering and leaving the water are equal, the system is in equilibrium, and $[CO_2]_{Dis}$ is given by Henry's law:

$$[CO_2]_{Dis} = sP_{CO_2} \qquad [2]$$

where s is the solubility of CO_2 in water (units: mmoles·l^{-1}·torr^{-1}) and P_{CO_2} is the partial pressure of CO_2 in the atmosphere. The aqueous chemistry of CO_2, however, is complicated by the fact that CO_2 participates in a solvolysis reaction. That is, CO_2 reacts with the solvent (i.e., H_2O) to form carbonic acid.

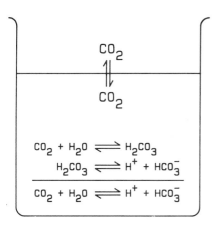

FIG. 1. Fate of dissolved CO_2 is an aqueous solution. When an aqueous solution is exposed to an atmosphere containing CO_2, the concentration of dissolved CO_2 at equilibrium is given by Henry's Law: $[CO_2]_{Dis} = sP_{CO_2}$. The dissolved CO_2 can react with H_2O to form H_2CO_3, which in turn dissociates to form H^+ plus HCO_3^-.

$$CO_2 + H_2O \rightleftharpoons H_2CO_3 \qquad [3]$$

Because this reaction does not involve the formation or consumption of H^+, it has no direct effect on pH. However, H_2CO_3 is a weak acid, as indicated by the following reaction.

$$H_2CO_3 \rightleftharpoons H^+ + HCO_3^- \qquad [4]$$

Because the dissociation of H_2CO_3 results in the formation of an H^+, the pH of the solution falls. HCO_3^- is a weak base, the conjugate weak base of H_2CO_3. Conversely, H_2CO_3 is the conjugate weak acid of HCO_3^-. Students are sometimes confused by Eq. 4, reasoning that because both H^+ and a base (i.e., HCO_3^-) are formed simultaneously, there should be no change in pH. However, the disposition of H^+ is the only factor of consequence for an acid-base problem. Thus, because H^+ is formed in this example, pH must fall. HCO_3^- itself is an amphiprotic substance: it can accept a proton to form its conjugate weak acid (i.e., H_2CO_3) or release a proton to form its conjugate base (i.e., CO_3). This latter reaction is of only minor significance physiologically (its pK is substantially greater than plasma pH) and hereafter in this chapter is ignored. The net effect of exposing pure water to CO_2 can be obtained by combining Eqs. 3 and 4.

$$CO_2 + H_2O \rightarrow H_2CO_3 \rightarrow H^+ + HCO_3^- \qquad [5]$$

In summary, raising P_{CO_2} produces a rise in $[H^+]$ and a fall of pH.

It should be noted that the hydration of CO_2 (Eq. 3) normally is a very slow reaction. As discussed in Chapter 3, the enzyme carbonic anhydrase is present at high levels in erythrocytes and certain other cells. It is thought to catalyze the reaction

$$CO_2 + OH^- \rightleftharpoons HCO_3^- \qquad [6]$$

Because the OH^- in Eq. 6 is provided by the dissociation of water ($H_2O \rightleftharpoons H^+ + OH^-$), Eq. 6 is equivalent to Eq. 5 and, in effect, bypasses the slow reaction of CO_2 hydration (Eq. 3).

Henderson-Hasselbalch Equation

Although two separate equilibria link CO_2 and H_2O, on the one hand, to H^+ and HCO_3^-, on the other, we may treat the system for the purpose of thermodynamics as if only one reaction were involved.

$$CO_2 + H_2O \rightleftharpoons H^+ + HCO_3^- \qquad [7]$$

The equilibrium constant for this reaction is

$$K = \frac{[H^+][HCO_3^-]}{[CO_2]\ [H_2O]} \qquad [8]$$

The equation can be simplified by combining K and $[H_2O]$ into a new term, the apparent equilibrium constant K'.

$$K\,[H_2O] \;=\; K' \;=\; \frac{[H^+][HCO_3^-]}{[CO_2]} \tag{9}$$

Taking the log of each side of this equation, we have

$$\log K' \;=\; \log[H^+] \;+\; \log\frac{[HCO_3^-]}{[CO_2]} \tag{10}$$

Because $\log[H^+] = -pH$ and $\log K' = -pK'$

$$pH \;=\; pK' \;+\; \log\frac{[HCO_3^-]}{[CO_2]} \tag{11}$$

Finally, Henry's law (Eq. 2) may be used to express $[CO_2]$ in terms of P_{CO_2}.

$$pH \;=\; pK' \;+\; \log\frac{[HCO_3^-]}{s P_{CO_2}} \tag{12}$$

This is the Henderson-Hasselbalch equation, which describes the CO_2/HCO_3^- equilibrium (Eq. 7) in logarithmic form. In human blood plasma at 37°C, where pK' is approximately 6.1, and s is about 0.03 mM CO_2/torr, this equation becomes

$$pH \;=\; 6.1 \;+\; \log\frac{[HCO_3^-]}{(0.03)\,P_{CO_2}} \tag{13}$$

The normal arterial P_{CO_2} is about 40 torr, and the normal HCO_3^- is about 24 mM. Thus

$$pH \;=\; 6.1 \;+\; \log\frac{24\text{ mM}}{1.2\text{ mM}} \;=\; 7.4 \tag{14}$$

which is the normal pH of arterial blood.

ALTERATION OF P_{CO_2} OR ADDITION OF HCO_3^- IN A BUFFER-FREE SYSTEM

Increasing $[CO_2]$

In this and the following sections, we examine how the pH of an unbuffered solution is affected by altering P_{CO_2} or by adding HCO_3^-. Inasmuch as the analysis is greatly simplified when buffers other than CO_2/HCO_3^- are absent, we treat this case first. The more complicated (but more physiologic) case, in which non-HCO_3^- buffers are present, is the subject of the next section.

The Henderson-Hasselbalch equation (Eq. 12) states that, when CO_2/HCO_3^- is the only buffer present, pH depends solely on the ratio $[HCO_3^-]/P_{CO_2}$. Consider the consequences of doubling $[CO_2]_{Dis}$ from 1.2 mM to 2.4 mM in a system with no buffers other than the CO_2/HCO_3^- buffer pair. The doubling of $[CO_2]_{Dis}$ is achieved by increasing the P_{CO_2} in the atmosphere from 40 torr to 80 torr. CO_2 enters the solution until $[CO_2]_{Dis}$ reaches 2.4 mM. The total amount of CO_2 entering is the CO_2 flux. As $[CO_2]_{Dis}$ increases, the CO_2/HCO_3^- equilibrium is driven to the right.

$$CO_2 + H_2O \rightarrow H^+ + HCO_3^- \qquad [15]$$

The flux of CO_2 through this reaction, as well as the new pH, can be calculated from Eq. 12 if we make the provisional assumption that $[HCO_3^-]$ remains unchanged at 24 mM.

$$pH = 6.1 + \log \frac{24 \text{ mM}}{2.4 \text{ mM}} = 7.1 \qquad [16]$$

Thus, doubling $[CO_2]_{Dis}$ causes the pH to decrease by 0.3. (Recall the discussion of Table 1 and the observation that a factor of 2 corresponds to a pH change of 0.3.) How much CO_2 had to enter the solution from the atmosphere and undergo the reaction of Eq. 15 in order to produce this pH change? Equation 15 states that for each CO_2 consumed, one H^+ and one HCO_3^- are produced. Thus, the CO_2 flux must be the same as the production of H^+ ($\Delta[H^+]$), which is easily computed from the initial and final pH values (Table 1):

$$\begin{aligned} \Delta[H^+] &= 10^{-7.1}M - 10^{-7.4}M \\ &= 8 \times 10^{-8}M - 4 \times 10^{-8}M \\ &= 4 \times 10^{-8}M \\ &= 0.00004 \text{ mM} \end{aligned}$$

Because $[H^+]$ increased by only 0.00004 mM, the flux of CO_2 through the reaction also must have been only 0.00004 mmole per liter of solution. The CO_2 flux for this example and others is summarized in Table 2.

We are now in a position to assess the validity of our assumption that doubling $[CO_2]$ did not alter $[HCO_3^-]$. According to Eq. 15, the production of HCO_3^- ($\Delta[HCO_3^-]$) must be the same as the production of H^+ (i.e., $\Delta[H^+]$).

$$\Delta[HCO_3^-] = 0.00004 \text{ mM}$$

Thus, the final $[HCO_3^-]$ is actually 24.00004 mM, an increase of about 0.00017% over the initial $[HCO_3^-]$. Our assumption that $[HCO_3^-]$ remains constant was, therefore, very nearly correct. In underestimating the final $[HCO_3^-]$ by 0.00017%, we underestimated the final pH by only 0.0000007.

TABLE 2. *CO_2 flux through the reaction, $CO_2 + H_2O \rightarrow H^+ + HCO_3^-$, when P_{CO_2} is increased from 40 (pH = 7.4) to 80 torr*

β (mM)	CO_2 flux (mM)
0	0.00004
5	1.38
25	5.34
∞	23.94

In summary, when $[CO_2]$ is increased in the absence of non-HCO_3^- buffers, the fractional change in $[H^+]$ is the same as the fractional change in $[CO_2]$, and there is no appreciable change in $[HCO_3^-]$. If the fractional change in $[CO_2]$ is α, the initial (i) and final conditions can be summarized as follows.

Initial conditions

$$K' = \frac{[H^+]^i [HCO_3^-]^i}{[CO_2]^i}$$

Final conditions

$$K' = \frac{(\alpha[H^+]^i) [HCO_3^-]^i}{(\alpha[CO_2]^i)}$$

Why is the CO_2 flux through the reaction only 0.00004 mM? The flux of CO_2 is just large enough to reestablish the equilibrium $K' = [H^+] [HCO_3^-]/[CO_2]$. If the denominator is doubled (i.e., $[CO_2]$ increased from 1.2 to 2.4 mM), the numerator must also be doubled. In general, this doubling can take place in an infinite number of ways. However, in an unbuffered solution for which $[HCO_3^-] >> [H^+]$, even an extremely small CO_2 flux causes $[H^+]$ to double before $[HCO_3^-]$ has changed appreciably. As we shall see, the situation is very different when non-HCO_3^- buffers are present.

Increasing $[HCO_3^-]$

Consider now the consequences of adding 24 mmoles of HCO_3^- to one liter of a solution initially buffered to pH 7.40 with 1.2 mM CO_2 and 24 mM HCO_3^-. No other buffers are present. Raising $[HCO_3^-]$ must drive the reaction

$$H^+ + HCO_3^- \rightarrow CO_2 + H_2O \qquad [17]$$

to the right. We will make the simplifying assumption that $[CO_2]_{Dis}$ remains constant. Although such a constraint at first may seem artificial, this is usually the way the reaction is carried out in a beaker, and it is almost always the way in which it is carried out in the body. In a beaker, $[CO_2]_{Dis}$ is maintained at a constant value by equilibrating the solution with an atmosphere having a fixed P_{CO_2}, as illustrated in Fig. 1. In the blood plasma, $[CO_2]_{Dis}$ is fixed by equilibrating the plasma with the air in the alveoli, the P_{CO_2} of which is maintained by adjusting alveolar ventilation. Thus, excess CO_2 formed in the reaction of Eq. 17 is evolved to an atmosphere that serves as an infinite reservoir of CO_2. A buffer system in which one member of the buffer pair can exchange with the environment is said to be an "open system."

Although the addition of 24 mM HCO_3^- may cause $[HCO_3^-]$ to double initially, we know that, according to Eq. 17, some of the newly added HCO_3^- will be consumed. If we provisionally assume that the amount of HCO_3^- so consumed is negligible, the final pH can be calculated from the Henderson-Hasselbalch equation.

$$pH = 6.1 + \log \frac{48 \text{ mM}}{1.2 \text{ mM}} = 7.7 \qquad [18]$$

Thus, doubling $[HCO_3^-]$ causes the pH to increase by 0.3. The flux of HCO_3^- through the reaction is the opposite of the change in $[H^+]$, which is computed easily from the initial and final pH values (Table 1):

$$\begin{aligned} \Delta[H^+] &= 10^{-7.7} - 10^{-7.4} \\ &= 2 \times 10^{-8}\text{M} - 4 \times 10^{-8}\text{M} \\ &= -2 \times 10^{-8}\text{M} \\ &= -0.00002 \text{ mM} \end{aligned}$$

Because one HCO_3^- is consumed for each H^+ consumed

$$\Delta[HCO_3^-] = -0.00002 \text{ mM}$$

Thus, because the flux of HCO_3^- through the reaction is 0.00002 mM, the final $[HCO_3^-]$ is actually 47.99998 mM, a fractional increase of 1.999999 over the initial value of 24 mM. Thus, our assumption that $[HCO_3^-]$ remained unchanged after its initial doubling was very nearly correct. In overestimating the final $[HCO_3^-]$ by 0.00004%, we overestimated the final pH by only 0.0000002.

In summary, when $[HCO_3^-]$ is increased in the absence of non-HCO_3^- buffers and $[CO_2]$ is held constant, the fractional change in $[H^+]$ is the reciprocal of the fractional change in $[HCO_3^-]$. If this fractional change in $[HCO_3^-]$ is α, the initial (i) and final conditions can be summarized as follows.

Initial conditions	Final conditions
$K' = \dfrac{[H^+]^i [HCO_3^-]^i}{[CO_2]^i}$	$K' = \dfrac{([H^+]^i/\alpha)(\alpha[HCO_3^-]^i)}{[CO_2]^i}$

Why was the HCO_3^- flux through the reaction only 0.00002 mM? The flux of HCO_3^- is just large enough to reestablish the equilibrium $K' = [H^+]$ $[HCO_3^-]/[CO_2]$. If the denominator is fixed, an initial doubling of $[HCO_3^-]$

must be compensated for by a reciprocal decrease in $[H^+]$. In general, this compensation can take place in an infinite number of ways. However, in a solution lacking other buffers and in which $[HCO_3^-] >> [H^+]$, even an extremely small HCO_3^- flux causes $[H^+]$ to halve before $[HCO_3^-]$ has changed appreciably. The situation is very different when non-HCO_3^- buffers are present.

Increasing $[CO_2]$ and $[HCO_3^-]$ Proportionally

If $[CO_2]$ and $[HCO_3^-]$ are changed by the same fraction, there is no effect on pH. For example, if $[CO_2]$ were doubled from 1.2 to 2.4 mM and $[HCO_3^-]$ were simultaneously doubled from 24 to 48 mM, pH would remain at 7.4.

$$pH = 6.1 + \log \frac{48 \text{ mM}}{2.4 \text{ mM}} = 7.4 \qquad [19]$$

When $[HCO_3^-]$ and P_{CO_2} are changed by the same fraction, there is no change in pH. If this fractional change in $[HCO_3^-]$ and P_{CO_2} is α, the initial (i) and final conditions can be summarized as follows.

Initial conditions	Final conditions
$K' = \dfrac{[H^+]^i [HCO_3^-]^i}{[CO_2]^i}$	$K' = \dfrac{[H^+]^i (\alpha[HCO_3^-]^i)}{(\alpha[CO_2]^i)}$

Because $[HCO_3^-]$ and $[CO_2]_{Dis}$ are changed by the same fraction, the CO_2/HCO_3^- buffer pair remains in equilibrium without any net flux of CO_2, HCO_3^-, or H^+ through the reaction sequence of Eq. 17.

In summary, it is not $[CO_2]$ or $[HCO_3^-]$ per se that determines pH in a simple CO_2/HCO_3^- buffer system, but the ratio $[CO_2]/[HCO_3^-]$. For the blood plasma, $[CO_2]$ is controlled primarily by the lungs via alveolar ventilation, and $[HCO_3^-]$ is controlled primarily by the kidneys via HCO_3^- reabsorption. This can be represented by the following, somewhat whimsical, relationship.

$$pH_{plasma} = \text{Constant} + \frac{\text{kidney}}{\text{lung}} \qquad [20]$$

BUFFERING POWER (4,5)

In the example in the preceding section, the analysis was simplified by assuming that CO_2 and HCO_3^- were the only buffers present. The situation is more complicated, however, if the solution contains other, non-HCO_3^- buffers. This is the case for blood plasma, for which the non-HCO_3^- buffers include titratable groups on proteins as well as inorganic phosphate. A buffer pair is a weak acid and its conjugate weak base. By consuming or releasing protons, the buffer pair minimizes changes in pH. Consider a neutral weak acid (HA) and its conjugate weak base (A^-).

$$HA \rightleftharpoons H^+ + A^- \qquad [21]$$

Examples of such buffer pairs include acetic acid and acetate as well as carboxyl groups on proteins. Another example of a buffer pair is a neutral weak base (B) and its conjugate weak acid (BH^+):

$$BH^+ \rightleftharpoons B + H^+ \qquad [22]$$

Some examples are NH_3 and NH_4^+ and imidazole groups in proteins. Of course, buffers exist for which both members of the conjugate pair are charged, such as inorganic phosphate ($H_2PO_4^- \rightleftharpoons HPO_4^= + H^+$). In the general case

$$BufH^{(n+1)} \rightleftharpoons Buf^n + H^+ \qquad [23]$$

for which n is the valence of the deprotonated species. Thus, Buf^n buffers acid loads by combining with some of the added H^+ to form $BufH^{(n+1)}$. Conversely, $BufH^{(n+1)}$ buffers alkali loads by dissociating to form Buf^n and H^+, which in turn neutralizes some of the added OH^-. The quantity of OH^- that is so neutralized is described by the buffering power, β. For example, when 5 mmoles of OH^- is added to 1 liter of separated blood plasma, the plasma pH rises by 1 pH unit. Conversely, when 5 mmoles of H^+ is added, the pH falls by 1. β is defined as

$$\beta \equiv \frac{\text{Moles } OH^- \text{ added/liter}}{\text{Resultant pH increase}} \qquad [24a]$$

$$\beta = \frac{\text{Moles } H^+ \text{ added/liter}}{\text{Resultant pH increase}} \qquad [24b]$$

Thus, for blood plasma, β = 5 mM per pH unit. Because a pH unit is dimensionless, buffering power is usually given in the units mM. The total buffering power of a solution that contains several buffers is the sum of the buffering powers of the individual buffers:

$$\beta_{total} = \sum_{j=1}^{n} \beta_j. \qquad [25]$$

For each buffer, the buffering power can be calculated from first principles. Buffering falls into two major classes, based on the ability of one member of the buffer pair to exchange with the environment: closed-system buffering and open-system buffering.

Buffering Power in a Closed System

A closed system is one in which neither member of the buffer pair can exchange with the environment, so that the concentration of total buffer ($[TBuf] = [BufH^{(n+1)}] + [Buf^n]$) is fixed. As in Eq. 24a, buffering power can be defined in terms of the macroscopic amount of strong base (e.g., OH^-) necessary to produce a given increase in pH. In differential notation, this definition becomes

$$\beta \equiv \frac{d(OH^-)}{dpH} \tag{26}$$

where (OH^-) refers to the amount of added OH^- (given in mM). To determine the buffering power of the buffer pair $Buf^n/BufH^{(n+1)}$, we must calculate how much added OH^- is consumed in the following reaction sequence.

$$
\begin{array}{c}
H^+ + Buf^n \leftarrow BufH^{(n+1)} \\
OH^- \dashv \downarrow \\
H_2O
\end{array}
\tag{27}
$$

Because one Buf^n is produced for each OH^- consumed

$$\beta = \frac{d[Buf^n]}{dpH} \tag{28}$$

From the law of mass action, it is easy to show[1] that $[Buf^n] = [TBuf]K'/(H + K')$. Substituting this expression for $[Buf^n]$ into Eq. 28, we have

$$\beta = \frac{d}{dpH} \frac{[TBuf]K'}{([H^+] + K')} \tag{29}$$

We now make the assumption that $[TBuf]$ is constant (i.e., that the system is closed). Therefore, the constants $[TBuf]$ and K' both can be removed as arguments of d/dpH, so that

---

[1] If $K' = [Buf^n][H^+]/[BufH^{(n+1)}]$ and $[BufH^{(n+1)}] = [TBuf] - [Buf^n]$, then

$$K' = \frac{[Buf^n][H^+]}{[TBuf] - [Buf^n]}$$

Rearranging, we have

$$K'[TBuf] - K'[Buf^n] = [Buf^n][H^+]$$

from which

$$[Buf^n] = \frac{K'}{[H^+] + K'}[TBuf]$$

$$\beta = [\text{TBuf}]K' \; \frac{d}{d\text{pH}} \; \frac{1}{[\text{H}^+] + K'} \qquad [30]$$

from which it follows that

$$\beta = - \; \frac{[\text{TBuf}]K'}{([\text{H}^+] + K')^2} \cdot \frac{d[\text{H}^+]}{d\text{pH}} \qquad [31]$$

It is easily shown[2] that $d[\text{H}^+]/d\text{pH} = -2.3[\text{H}^+]$. Thus, the final expression for the closed-system buffering power becomes

$$\beta = 2.3 \; \frac{[\text{H}^+]\,K'}{([\text{H}^+] + K')^2} \; [\text{TBuf}] \qquad [32]$$

For the most part, the non-HCO_3^- buffers of the blood plasma behave as closed-system buffers, inasmuch as they cannot freely exchange between the plasma and another compartment. Figure 2 includes plots of β versus pH for five closed-system buffers, each at a concentration of 10 mM, having pK' values of 5, 6, 7, 8, and 9. The buffering power of a closed-system buffer is maximal when $[\text{H}^+]$ equals K' (i.e., when pH equals pK'). That is, the derivative of β with respect to $[\text{H}^+]$ in Eq. 32 is zero when $[\text{H}^+] = K'$. The expression for the maximal buffering power can be obtained by inserting this value for $[\text{H}^+]$ into Eq. 32.

$$\beta^{\text{max}} = 0.58\,[\text{TBuf}] \qquad [33]$$

Note that β^{max} is independent of pK'. Equation 33 states that, when present in identical concentrations, all closed-system buffers have the same maximal buffering power. The only difference among buffers is the pH at which this maximal β is achieved. As noted in connection with Eq. 25, the total buffering power (β_{total}) of a solution is the sum of the buffering powers of the individual buffers. Figure 2 includes a plot of β_{total} versus pH for a solution containing the five closed-system buffers discussed previously, each at 10 mM. It is apparent that even though the pK' values of the buffers are spaced one pH unit apart from 5 to 9, there is very little variation of β_{total} with pH between pH values of 6 and 8.

---

[2] By definition, $\text{pH} = -\log_{10}[\text{H}^+] = -(\ln[\text{H}^+])/\ln 10$. Therefore,

$$[\text{H}^+] = e^{-(\ln 10)\text{pH}}$$

and

$$\frac{d[\text{H}^+]}{d\text{pH}} = -(\ln 10)e^{-(\ln 10)\text{pH}} = -(\ln 10)\,[\text{H}^+].$$

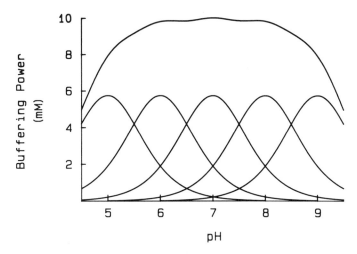

FIG. 2. Dependence of closed-system buffering power on pH. In the bottom portion of the figure are plotted the buffering powers for five closed-system buffers, each present at a concentration of 10 mM. They are assumed to have pK' values of 5, 6, 7, 8, and 9. For each buffer, the closed-system buffering power is maximal when pH = pK'. The total buffering power at any pH is the sum of the buffering powers of the five individual buffers. As indicated by the top curve, the total buffering power is very insensitive to pH changes when pH is in the middle range of the buffer pK' values, 6 to 8.

Buffering Power in an Open System

For an open-system buffer, one of the members of the buffer pair equilibrates with the environment. The most physiologically important example of such a buffer is CO_2/HCO_3^-, for which adjustments in alveolar ventilation maintain a constant plasma P_{CO_2}. Thus, added OH^- is buffered by CO_2/HCO_3^- according to the reaction

$$OH^- \begin{array}{c} H^+ + HCO_3^- \leftarrow CO_2 + H_2O \\ \downarrow \\ H_2O \end{array} \qquad [34]$$

The CO_2 consumed in this reaction is replenished as CO_2 enters the solution from the atmosphere, so that P_{CO_2} remains constant. Because this prevents the depletion of the key reactant, the net flux of CO_2 through the reaction sequence is considerably greater at pH values above 7 than if CO_2/HCO_3^- behaved as a closed-system buffer (i.e., if the sum $[CO_2] + [HCO_3^-]$ were constant). Conversely, when added H^+ is buffered by CO_2/HCO_3^-, the CO_2 produced is lost to the atmosphere, so that the consumption of H^+ is not limited by the buildup of the key reaction product.

Equation 34 predicts that one HCO_3^- is formed for each OH^- buffered by the open-system CO_2/HCO_3^- buffer pair. Therefore, from the differential notation definition of buffering power (Eq. 26) we have

$$\beta \equiv \frac{d(OH^-)}{dpH} = \frac{d[HCO_3^-]}{dpH} \qquad [35]$$

From the Henderson-Hasselbalch equation (Eq. 12), we know that $[HCO_3^-] = sP_{CO_2} \cdot 10^{(pH-pK)}$. Inserting this expression for $[HCO_3^-]$ into Eq. 35

$$\beta = \frac{d}{dpH} sP_{CO_2} \cdot 10^{(pH-pK)} \qquad [36]$$

If we make the assumption that P_{CO_2} is fixed (i.e., the system is open), s and P_{CO_2} can be removed as arguments of d/dpH, so that

$$\beta = sP_{CO_2} \frac{d}{dpH} 10^{(pH-pK)}$$

$$= sP_{CO_2}(\ln 10) \, 10^{(pH-pK)}$$

$$= 2.3 \, [HCO_3^-] \qquad [37]$$

As an example, consider a solution for which the initial pH is 7.4, $[HCO_3^-]$ is 24 mM, and $[CO_2]$ is 1.2 mM. If this is titrated in an open system having a P_{CO_2} of 40 torr, the buffering power (computed from Eq. 37) would be described by the curve labeled "Open" in Fig. 3. As can be seen, the open-system buffering power has no maximum but rises exponentially with pH. If the original solution at pH 7.4 (i.e., [total CO_2] = 25.2 mM) were placed in a closed system (e.g., a capped syringe) and then titrated, the buffering power computed from Eq. 32) would be described by the "Closed" curve in Fig. 3. At a pH of 6.1 (i.e., pH = pK'), $[HCO_3^-] = [CO_2] = 12.6$ mM, and the closed-system buffering power would achieve its maximal value of 14.5 mM. On the other hand, in the open-system example, $[CO_2] = [HCO_3^-] = 1.2$ mM, and β^{open} would be only 2.8 mM. At higher pHs, however β^{closed} would gradually fall and β^{open} would rise, until β^{open} would far exceed β^{closed} at physiologic values for plasma pH.

It is perhaps worth noting that, in the preceding example, the relatively high value of β^{closed} for pH values in the vicinity of pK' was a consequence of the design of the experiment. Because the system was initially closed at a pH of 7.4, the [total CO_2] was 25.2 mM throughout the closed-system experiment but only 2.4 mM at a pH of 6.1 in the open-system experiment. If the closed system had been constrained to have a [total CO_2] of 2.4 mM at a pH of 6.1, the maximal β^{closed} would have been only 1.4 mM, half the open-system value of 2.8 mM. Thus, when compared at equal [total CO_2] values, the open-system CO_2/HCO_3^- buffering power is twice the closed-system value even at the pK' and substantially greater at higher pH values.

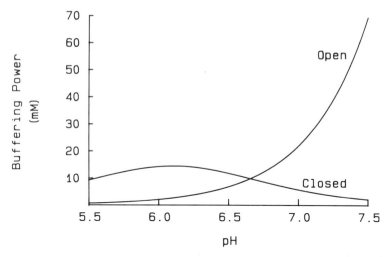

FIG. 3. Dependence of CO_2/HCO_3^- open-system and closed-system buffering powers on pH. For the calculation of open-system buffering power. P_{CO_2} is assumed to be fixed at 40 torr, regardless of pH. Thus, for a pK' of 6.1 and a solubility of 0.03 mM/torr, $[HCO_3^-] = \sim 24$ mM when pH = 7.40. Note that the open-system buffering power, described by the equation $\beta^{open} = 2.3\ [HCO_3^-]$, has no maximum but rises exponentially with pH. For the calculation of closed-system buffering power, total CO_2 is assumed to be that prevailing at pH 7.4 when $P_{CO_2} = 40$ torr (i.e., [total CO_2] = $[HCO_3^-] + [CO_2]$ = 24.0 mM + 1.2 mM = 25.2 mM). Note that closed-system buffering power is maximal at pH = pK'.

ALTERATIONS OF [CO₂] OR [HCO₃⁻] IN A BUFFERED SYSTEM (7)

Constructing a Davenport Diagram

The analysis of acid-base problems involving both CO_2/HCO_3^- and non-HCO_3^- buffers is much easier if the problems are approached graphically. Perhaps the most straightforward graphic method, and certainly the one most solidly grounded in theory, is the approach of Davenport. A Davenport diagram consists of plots of [base] versus pH for two classes of buffers: (a) the open-system CO_2/HCO_3^- buffer pair and (b) the sum of all closed-system non-HCO_3^- buffers. The plot of $[HCO_3^-]$ versus pH is obtained by using the Henderson-Hasselbalch equation to calculate $[HCO_3^-]$ at various pH values, always at a fixed value of P_{CO_2}. For example, the Henderson-Hasselbalch equation is easily rearranged for calculating $[HCO_3^-]$ from pH at a fixed P_{CO_2} of 40 torr.

$$[HCO_3^-] = (0.03\ mM/torr)\ (40\ torr)\ 10^{(pH-6.1)} \qquad [38]$$

The result of such a computation for pH values between 7.05 and 7.75 is the middle, upwardly sloping curve in Fig. 4. This curve is called a CO_2 isopleth (from the Greek *isos* = equal, and *plethos* = quantity) and is a plot of all possible combinations of $[HCO_3^-]$ and pH when P_{CO_2} is 40 torr. Equations

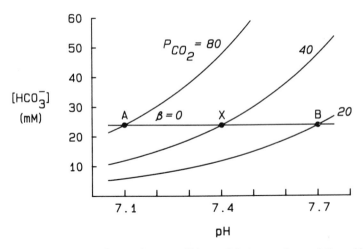

FIG. 4. Davenport diagram for respiratory acid-base disturbances in a solution with a non-HCO_3^- buffering power of zero. The CO_2 isopleths at Pco_2 values of 20, 40, and 80 torr are computed from the equation $[HCO_3^-] = sPco_2\ 10^{(pH - pK')}$ where $s = 0.03$ mM/torr and $pK' = 6.1$. The non-HCO_3^- buffer line has a slope of zero, and passes through point X, which describes the initial conditions ($pH = 7.40$ and $[HCO_3^-] = 23.94$ mM). When Pco_2 is doubled to 80 torr, the system is described by point A, so that pH falls by 0.3 and $[HCO_3^-]$ essentially is unchanged. Conversely, when Pco_2 is halved to 20 torr, the system is described by point B, so that pH rises by 0.3 and $[HCO_3^-]$ once again is almost unchanged.

analogous to Eq. 38 can be used to obtain CO_2 isopleths for the Pco_2 values of 20 and 80 torr (Fig. 4). Note that, for any value of pH, the $[HCO_3^-]$ at a Pco_2 of 20 torr is half that at 40 torr, whereas the $[HCO_3^-]$ at 80 torr is twice that at 40 torr. The slope of a CO_2 isopleth at any pH is the open-system buffering power provided by the CO_2/HCO_3^- buffer pair. Indeed, the derivative of $[HCO_3^-]$ with respect to pH (Eq. 38) is $2.3[HCO_3^-]$. Notice that the slope of the isopleth rises continuously with pH, consistent with the plot of open-system CO_2/HCO_3^- buffering power in Fig. 3.

The second component of a Davenport diagram describes the total buffering power of non-HCO_3^- buffers and is termed the non-HCO_3^- buffer curve. Assume that all non-HCO_3^- buffers are grouped together and thought of as a single buffer: $BufH^{(n+1)} \rightleftharpoons Buf^n + H^+$. The non-$HCO_3^-$ buffer curve is a plot of relative $-[Buf^n]$ versus pH. Thus, its slope is the negative of the total non-HCO_3^- buffering power, a value that is determined empirically. Only the slope of this buffer curve has significance, not its displacement from the abscissa. Plotting the buffer curve as a line implies that the non-CO_2 buffering power is constant over the pH range of interest. Indeed, the buffering power of separated blood plasma is roughly constant over the physiologic range, having a value of about 5 mM/pH. This insensitivity of total buffering power to pH changes is not surprising given the example of Fig. 2, which demonstrates that it is easy to design a mixture of closed-system buffers having a total buffering power that is rather pH insensitive. The non-HCO_3^-

buffer line of Fig. 4 has a slope of zero, indicating that the total non-HCO_3^- buffering power ($\beta_{non-HCO_3}$) is zero. This line also passes through point X, which describes the normal acid-base status of mammalian blood plasma (i.e., $[HCO_3^-] = 24$ mM, pH $= 7.40$, and $P_{CO_2} = 40$ torr) and the initial conditions for the acid-base disturbances described subsequently.

This Davenport diagram can be used in the graphic solution of acid-base problems involving either changes in P_{CO_2} (i.e., respiratory disturbances) or additions of HCO_3^-, strong acids, or strong bases (i.e., metabolic disturbances). The pH changes produced by alterations in P_{CO_2} are termed "respiratory" acid-base disturbances because in the intact animal the changes in P_{CO_2} usually are brought about by alterations in the respiratory apparatus. The pH changes produced by the addition of HCO_3^- or of strong acids or bases are termed "metabolic" acid-base disturbances because in the intact animal these are often brought about by derangements in metabolism. We now consider examples of both respiratory and metabolic acid-base disturbances. Keep in mind that, in using the Davenport diagram, one makes the assumption that CO_2 is exchanged freely with the environment (i.e., that the system is open for CO_2).

Respiratory Acid-Base Disturbances

Raising P_{CO_2} When the Non-HCO_3^- Buffering Power is Zero

As an illustration of how the Davenport diagram can be used to solve a problem in which the primary insult is a change in P_{CO_2}, let us reconsider an example presented previously. A solution that is devoid of buffers other than CO_2/HCO_3^- has an initial pH of 7.4, a P_{CO_2} of 40 torr, and a $[HCO_3^-]$ of 24 mM. What is the new pH and $[HCO_3^-]$ when the P_{CO_2} is doubled to 80 torr?

The status of the system before the increase in P_{CO_2} is given by point X in Fig. 4. X must be on the 40-torr P_{CO_2} isopleth because the prevailing P_{CO_2} is 40 torr. Furthermore, X must be at the intersection of the lines pH $= 7.4$ and $[HCO_3^-] = 24$ mM. Note that only two of these three parameters must be known; the third can be computed from Eq. 38. The slope of the non-HCO_3^- buffer curve must be zero because the non-HCO_3^- buffering power is zero, and it is constrained to pass through X. The rule for using the Davenport diagram to solve a respiratory acid-base problem is the following:

Rule 1: How to solve a respiratory acid-base problem

The final conditions are described by the point at the intersection of the original non-HCO_3^- buffer line and the isopleth for the new P_{CO_2}.

In our example, the final P_{CO_2} is 80 torr, so that the final conditions must be described by point A, which is at the intersection of the 80-torr CO_2 isopleth and the original non-HCO_3^- buffer line. One can graphically determine that the new pH is 7.1 and that the new [HCO_3^-] is approximately 24 mM. That is, in the absence of non-HCO_3^- buffers, a twofold increase in P_{CO_2} causes pH to fall by 0.3 but causes [HCO_3^-] to rise by only a trivial amount. Note that the graphic correlate of this stability of [HCO_3^-] is the horizontal non-HCO_3^- buffer line. Because a change in P_{CO_2} has produced a fall in pH, the acid-base disturbance is termed "respiratory acidosis."

The same problem was solved mathematically in a previous section, yielding values of 7.1 for pH and 24.00004 mM for [HCO_3^-]. Thus, when P_{CO_2} is raised from 40 to 80 torr in a system free of other buffers and initially at a pH of 7.40, the flux of CO_2 through the reaction $CO_2 + H_2O \rightarrow HCO_3^- + H^+$ is 0.00004 mM, as indicated in Table 2.

Lowering P_{CO_2} When the Non-HCO_3^- Buffering Power Is Zero

The preceding example illustrated how to solve a problem in respiratory acidosis. A similar approach can be used to predict the pH increase brought about by lowering P_{CO_2} (i.e., respiratory alkalosis). As an example, imagine that the initial conditions are described once again by point X (i.e., P_{CO_2} = 40 torr, pH = 7.40, and [HCO_3^-] = 24 mM), but that P_{CO_2} is now halved to 20 torr. According to the preceding rule, the final conditions are described by point B at the intersection of the non-CO_2 buffer curve and the 20-torr CO_2 isopleth. Note that, in the absence of non-CO_2 buffers, halving P_{CO_2} causes pH to increase by 0.3 to 7.7 but causes only a trivial change in [HCO_3^-].

Raising P_{CO_2} When the non-HCO_3^- Buffering Power is 5 mM

When non-HCO_3^- buffers are present, the H^+ produced or consumed by a change in P_{CO_2} is buffered by the non-HCO_3^- buffers. For this reason, the change in pH is smaller than if these non-HCO_3^- were absent. As we shall see, however, the change in [HCO_3^-] is substantially larger. What is the pH change caused by increasing P_{CO_2} from 40 to 80 torr for a solution having the same non-HCO_3^- buffering power as blood plasma (i.e., 5 mM/pH)? Before solving the problem graphically, let us examine the chemical reactions involved when P_{CO_2} is increased. For simplicity, we make the standard assumption that all non-HCO_3^- buffers are grouped together into one hypothetical buffer ($BufH^{(n+1)} \rightleftharpoons Buf^n + H^+$).

$$CO_2 + H_2O \rightarrow HCO_3^- + H^+$$

$$\cdot \quad \overset{\displaystyle \vphantom{x}}{\underset{\textstyle BufH^{(n+1)}}{\big\downarrow}}\!\!- Buf^n \qquad\qquad [39]$$

When P_{CO_2} is increased from 40 to 80 torr in our example, HCO_3^- and H^+ are formed in equal quantities (*see* Eq. 39). Almost all of the newly formed H^+ is taken up by non-HCO_3^- buffers in the blood plasma (i.e., proteins and phosphate). The tiny amount of H^+ not buffered remains free and is responsible for the small increase in $[H^+]$.

This problem can be solved graphically by employing *Rule 1*. The initial conditions are given by point X in Fig. 5: P_{CO_2} = 40 torr and pH = 7.40. For the sake of accuracy, we compute the initial $[HCO_3^-]$ from Eq. 13 and express the result to two decimal places, 23.94 mM. The final conditions are arrived at by following the non-HCO_3^- buffer line (slope = -5 mM/pH) to the new CO_2 isopleth (P_{CO_2} = 80 torr) at point A. The coordinates of this point are pH = 7.123 and $[HCO_3^-]$ = 25.32 mM. Thus, for a non-HCO_3^- buffering power of 5 mM, doubling P_{CO_2} caused pH to fall by 0.277 and $[HCO_3^-]$ to rise by 1.38 mM. We can see from Eq. 39 that in each liter of solution 1.38 mmoles of CO_2 combined with 1.38 millimoles of H_2O to form 1.38 mmoles of HCO_3^- and 1.38 mmoles of H^+. Virtually all of this H^+ was buffered as ~1.38 mmoles of Buf^n formed a like amount of $BufH^{(n+1)}$. What fraction of the newly formed H^+ was buffered? Because the pH fell from 7.40 to 7.123, we can calculate that $[H^+]$ rose from $10^{-7.4}$ M to $10^{-7.123}$ M, or that the change in free $[H^+]$ was 0.0000355 mM. If ~1.38 mmoles of H^+ was formed and 0.0000355 mmoles of this H^+ remained free, more than 99.997% of the newly formed H^+ was buffered.

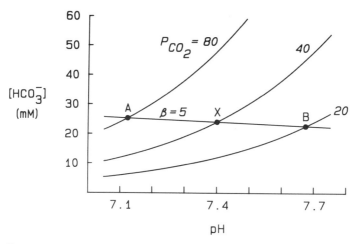

FIG. 5. Davenport diagram for respiratory acid-base disturbances in a solution with a non-HCO_3^- buffering power ($\beta_{non-HCO_3}$) of 5 mM. The non-HCO_3^- buffer line has a slope of 5 mM per pH unit and passes through point X, which describes the initial conditions (pH = 7.40 and $[HCO_3^-]$ = 23.94 mM). When P_{CO_2} is doubled to 80 torr (point A), pH falls but by a smaller amount than when $\beta_{non-HCO_3}$ = 0 (*see* Fig. 4). In addition, the rise in $[HCO_3^-]$, nearly 1.4 mM, is several orders of magnitude greater than would occur with $\beta_{non-HCO_3}$ = 0. The opposite changes occur when P_{CO_2} is halved to 20 torr (point B).

Although the non-HCO_3^- buffers in this example buffered virtually all of the newly formed H^+, the pH change (i.e., 0.277) was only slightly less than that predicted when no non-HCO_3^- buffers were present (i.e., 0.3). The major effect of the non-HCO_3^- buffers was that the flux of CO_2 through Eq. 39, and thus the formation of HCO_3^-, was increased substantially. As summarized in Table 2, raising P_{CO_2} from 40 to 80 torr caused a CO_2 flux of only 0.00004 mM in the absence of HCO_3^- buffers, but a flux of 1.38 mM in a solution having a $\beta_{non-HCO_3}$ of 5 mM.

If we had not known $\beta_{non-HCO_3}$, we could have calculated it from the data of this example. From the definition of buffering power given in Eq. 24

$$\beta = \frac{\text{Amount of acid added}}{\text{Resultant pH decrease}}$$

the amount of acid added is the same as the amount of HCO_3^- formed

$$\beta = \frac{\Delta[HCO_3^-]}{-\Delta pH} = \frac{1.38 \text{ mM}}{0.277} = 5 \text{ mM/pH}$$

This is an approach by which the non-HCO_3^- buffering power of blood plasma can be determined empirically.

Lowering P_{CO_2} When the Non-HCO_3^- Buffering Power is 5 mM

Also summarized in Fig. 5 is the graphic solution to the respiratory alkalosis problem in which P_{CO_2} is halved from 40 torr to 20 torr in a solution having a non-HCO_3^- buffering power of 5 mM. The pH increases from 7.40 to 7.675 ($\Delta pH = 0.275$), and [HCO_3^-] falls from 24 mM to 22.56 mM ($\Delta[HCO_3^-]$ = -1.44 mM). These values contrast with those of the example in which $\beta_{non-HCO_3}$ was zero. In that case, the pH increase (i.e., $\Delta pH = 0.3$) was larger, whereas the change in [HCO_3^-] (i.e., $\sim$0 mM) was very much smaller.

Respiratory Acid-Base Disturbances at Non-HCO_3^- Buffering Powers of 25 mM and Infinity

Figure 6 summarizes the graphic solutions for the respiratory acid-base disturbances already discussed for the cases in which $\beta_{non-HCO_3}$ was 0 mM and 5 mM, as well as two others in which $\beta_{non-HCO_3}$ is 25 mM (the value in whole blood) and infinity. For a given ΔP_{CO_2}, an increase in $\beta_{non-HCO_3}$ causes the magnitude of ΔpH to be smaller and of the flux of CO_2 (i.e., $\Delta[HCO_3^-]$) to be larger. These data are summarized in Table 2.

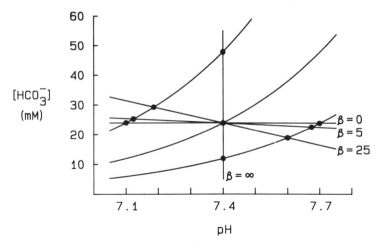

FIG. 6. Davenport diagram for respiratory acid-base disturbances in solutions having non-HCO_3^- buffering powers ($\beta_{non-HCO_3}$) of 0 mM, 5 mM, 25 mM, and ∞. All non-HCO_3^- buffer lines pass through point X, which describes the initial conditions (pH = 7.40 and [HCO_3^-] = 23.94 mM). When PCO_2 is doubled to 80 torr, the decline in pH becomes progressively smaller at higher values of $\beta_{non-HCO_3}$ until finally, when $\beta_{non-HCO_3} = \infty$, increasing PCO_2 has no effect on pH whatsoever. Because Δ[HCO_3^-] is an index of non-HCO_3^- buffering power in respiratory disturbances, Δ[HCO_3^-], increases as $\beta_{non-HCO_3}$ increases. Similar changes, though in the opposite direction, are observed when PCO_2 is decreased.

Metabolic Acid-Base Disturbances

The respiratory acid-base disturbances discussed in the preceding section are the result of CO_2 titrations. Because the production or consumption of H^+ is brought about by changes in PCO_2, the resulting acid or alkali loads cannot be buffered by the CO_2/HCO_3^- buffer system, only by non-HCO_3^- buffers. With metabolic acid-base disturbances, the solution is titrated with HCO_3^- or with strong acids (e.g., HCl) or bases (e.g., NaOH). In these cases, the H^+ generated or consumed is buffered both by non-HCO_3^- buffers and by the CO_2/HCO_3^- buffer system. The magnitude of the pH change produced by a metabolic acid-base disturbance depends on the amount of acid or base added, the HCO_3^- buffering power (β_{HCO_3}), and the non-HCO_3^- buffering power ($\beta_{non-HCO_3}$). In the following discussion, we assume that the CO_2 in the solution freely exchanges with CO_2 in the atmosphere, so that PCO_2 remains constant.

Addition of HCl When $\beta_{non-HCO_3} = 0$

The addition of a strong acid to a solution or the removal of HCO_3^- produces a metabolic acidosis. The simplest case is one in which no non-HCO_3^-

buffers are present. As an example, consider the addition of 10 millimoles of HCl to a liter of a solution that has the same initial condition as in the examples discussed previously: pH = 7.40, P_{CO_2} = 40 torr, and $[HCO_3^-]$ = 23.94 mM. The chemical reaction taking place is the following.

$$10\,H^+ \; + \; 10\,HCO_3^- \; \rightarrow \; 10\,CO_2 \; + \; 10\,H_2O \qquad\qquad [40]$$

Virtually all of the added H^+ combines with HCO_3^-, so that the decrease in $[HCO_3^-]$ is the same as the amount of added H^+. Moreover, the newly formed CO_2 is lost to the atmosphere, so that P_{CO_2} remains at 40 torr. The new pH is easily calculated without resorting to a Davenport diagram.

$$\text{pH} \; = \; 6.1 \; + \; \log \frac{13.94 \text{ mM}}{1.2 \text{ mM}} \; = \; 7.165$$

Thus, ΔpH is -0.235 and, as summarized in Table 3, the flux of CO_2 through Eq. 40 is nearly 10 mM.

However, this problem also can be solved using a Davenport diagram. One must construct a CO_2 isopleth for a P_{CO_2} of 40 torr, as well as a non-HCO_3^- buffer line intersecting this isopleth at the initial pH and having the appropriate slope. This is illustrated for the case in which $\beta_{\text{non-HCO}_3} = 0$ in Fig. 7. The approach for solving a metabolic acid-base disturbance problem is the following.

Rule 2: How to solve a metabolic acid-base problem

The final conditions are described by the point at the intersection of the CO_2 isopleth and a new non-HCO_3^- buffer line. For a metabolic acidosis, this new buffer line is obtained by displacing the old one downward by an amount equal to the amount of strong acid added. For an alkalosis, the lime is displaced upward by an amount equal to the amount of strong base added.

The initial conditions are described by X in Fig. 7. Because 10 mmoles HCl is added to one liter of solution, the alkali load (ΔB) is -10 mM, and the non-HCO_3^- buffer line is displaced downward by 10 mM. The final conditions are described by A. Note that A is on the original CO_2 isopleth because P_{CO_2} is

TABLE 3. *Changes produced by adding 10 mmoles HCl to a solution initially at pH 7.4 and equilibrated with a P_{CO_2} of 40 torr*

β (mM)	ΔpH	H^+ buffered by HCO_3^- (mM)	Mean β_{HCO_3} (mM)	Mean β_{Total} (mM)
0	0.235	9.99997	42.6	42.6
5	0.204	8.98	44.0	49.0
25	0.138	6.55	47.5	72.5
∞	0	0	—	∞

unchanged at 40 torr. This graphic solution produces the same results as the calculation: pH = 7.165 and $[HCO_3^-]$ = 13.94 mM. The open-system CO_2/HCO_3^- buffering power in this experiment can be computed at any pH from Eq. 37. The mean value in the interval between pH 7.165 and 7.400 also can be determined graphically from Fig. 7. It is simply the mean slope of the CO_2 isopleth in the pH range between the initial and final conditions.

$$\text{Mean } \beta_{HCO_3} = \frac{\Delta[HCO_3^-]}{\Delta pH} = \frac{-10 \text{ mM}}{-0.235} = 42.6 \text{ mM}$$

$$\text{Mean } \beta_{non\text{-}HCO_3} = \frac{\Delta B - \Delta[HCO_3^-]}{\Delta pH} = \frac{-10 \text{ mM} - (-10 \text{ mM})}{-0.235} = 0.0 \text{ mM}$$

$$\text{Mean } \beta_{total} = \frac{\Delta B}{\Delta pH} = \frac{-10 \text{ mM}}{-0.235} = 42.6 \text{ mM}$$

Addition of NaOH When $\beta_{non\text{-}HCO_3}$ Equals 0

The addition of HCO_3^- or a strong base to a solution produces a metabolic alkalosis. Consider the example in which 10 millimoles of NaOH is added to a liter of solution having an initial pH of 7.40, a fixed P_{CO_2} of 40 torr, and a $[HCO_3^-]$ of 23.94 mM. The chemical reactions taking place are the following.

$$10H^+ + 10 \text{ HCO}_3^- \leftarrow 10 \text{ CO}_2 + 10 \text{ H}_2\text{O}$$
$$10 \text{ OH}^- \downarrow \qquad\qquad\qquad\qquad\qquad [41]$$
$$10 \text{ H}_2\text{O}$$

Thus, virtually all of the added OH^- is consumed by the CO_2/HCO_3^- buffer system. In this process, one HCO_3^- is generated for each OH^- consumed. The final pH in this example is

$$pH = 6.1 + \log \frac{33.94 \text{ mM}}{1.2 \text{ mM}} = 7.552$$

The problem also can be solved graphically, as illustrated in Fig. 7. Because 10 mmoles NaOH is added, ΔB is +10 mM, and the non-HCO_3^- buffer line is displaced 10 mM upward. The final conditions are given by B. Note that the outcome would have been the same whether HCO_3^-, instead of OH^-, had

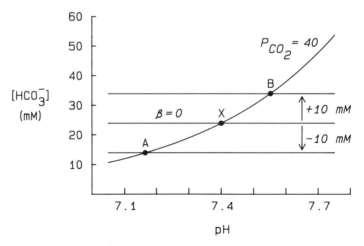

FIG. 7. Davenport diagram for metabolic acid-base disturbances in a solution having non-HCO_3^- buffering power $\beta_{non\text{-}HCO_3}$ of 0 mM. It is assumed that this is an open system, with the P_{CO_2} fixed at 40 torr. The non-HCO_3^- buffer line has a slope of 0 mM per pH unit and passes through point X, which describes the initial conditions (pH = 7.40 and $[HCO_3^-]$ = 23.94 mM). When 10 mmoles of a strong acid is added to a liter of solution, the final conditions are described by point A. This lies at the intersection of the original 40-torr P_{CO_2} isopleth and the non-HCO_3^- buffer line, which has been displaced downward by 10 mM. Conversely, when 10 mmoles of a strong base is added to the solution, the final conditions are described by B. In the absence of non-HCO_3^- buffers, all buffering is done by the CO_2/HCO_3^- buffer system.

been added to the solution. In either case, the final $[HCO_3^-]$ is incremented by 10 mM.

Addition of HCl When $\beta_{non\text{-}HCO_3}$ Equals 5 mM

The situation is more complex when both CO_2/HCO_3^- buffers and non-HCO_3^- buffers are present, inasmuch as the two buffer systems compete for the added H^+. Although the outcome can be predicted mathematically, it is much easier to solve the problem using the Davenport diagram. As noted in Fig. 8, for the example in which 10 mmoles HCl is added to a liter of isolation, the final conditions (A) are obtained by displacing the non-HCO_3^- buffer line downward by 10 mM. The final pH is 7.196, and the final $[HCO_3^-]$ is 14.96 mM. We know that virtually all of the added H^+ was neutralized by either the CO_2/HCO_3^- buffer pair or the non-HCO_3^- buffers. However, what were their relative contributions? Because $[HCO_3^-]$ fell from ~24 mM to ~15 mM, ~9 mmoles of HCO_3^- must have been consumed as the CO_2/HCO_3^- buffer system neutralized 9 mmoles of the added H^+. The remaining 1 mmole of the added H^+ must have been buffered by non-HCO_3^- buffers.

$$9\,H^+ + 9\,HCO_3^- \rightarrow 9\,CO_2 + 9\,H_2O \qquad [42a]$$

$$1\,H^+ + 1\,Buf^n \rightarrow 1\,BufH^{(n+1)} \qquad [42b]$$

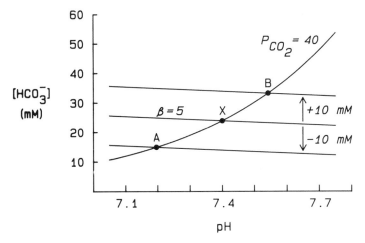

FIG. 8. Davenport diagram for metabolic acid-base disturbances in a solution having non-HCO_3^- buffering power ($\beta_{\text{non-HCO}_3}$) of 5 mM. It is assumed that this is an open system, with the P_{CO_2} fixed at 40 torr. The non-HCO_3^- buffer line has a slope of 5 mM per pH unit and passes through point X, which describes the initial conditions (pH = 7.40 and $[HCO_3^-]$ = 23.94 mM). When 10 millimoles of a strong acid is added to a liter of solution (point A), both pH and $[HCO_3^-]$ fall by smaller amounts than under similar conditions when $\beta_{\text{non-HCO}_3}$ = 0 (*see* Fig. 7). Because $\Delta[HCO_3^-]$ is an index of the CO_2/HCO_3^- buffering power for metabolic acid-base disturbance, the magnitude of $\Delta[HCO_3^-]$ is expected to be smaller when $\beta_{\text{non-HCO}_3}$ = 5 mM than when $\beta_{\text{non-HCO}_3}$ = 0. The opposite changes occur when 10 mmoles of a strong base is added to the solution (point B).

From these data we can compute the mean values for β_{HCO_3} and $\beta_{\text{non-HCO}_3}$.

$$\text{Mean } \beta_{\text{HCO}_3} = \frac{\Delta[HCO_3^-]}{\Delta pH} = \frac{-9 \text{ mM}}{-0.204} = 44.0 \text{ mM}$$

$$\text{Mean } \beta_{\text{non-HCO}_3} = \frac{\Delta B - \Delta[HCO_3^-]}{\Delta pH} = \frac{-10 \text{ mM} - (-9 \text{ mM})}{-0.204} = 5.0 \text{ mM}$$

$$\text{Mean } \beta_{\text{total}} = \frac{\Delta B}{\Delta pH} = \frac{-10 \text{ mM}}{-0.204} = 49.0 \text{ mM}$$

When this example is compared to the one in which 10 mmole HCl was added to a solution for which $\beta_{\text{non-HCO}_3}$ = 0 mM, four interesting trends emerge. First of all, in the presence of non-HCO_3^- buffers, the pH decrease is smaller (0.204 versus 0.235; *see* Table 3). Second, the mean β_{HCO_3} is larger (44.0 mM versus 42.6 mM) in the presence of non-HCO_3^- buffers. Although this may seem counterintuitive, the explanation is straightforward. The added non-HCO_3^- buffers prevent pH from falling as far as it otherwise would have. Thus, because the mean pH is higher (i.e., [7.40 + 7.196]/2 = 7.298 versus [7.40 + 7.165]/2 = 7.283), the mean β_{HCO_3} must be higher, as required by Eq.

37. Third β_{total} is larger (49.0 mM versus 42.6 mM). This is caused by the increase in $\beta_{non-HCO_3}$, which in turn also increases β_{HCO_3}. Finally, a smaller fraction of the total buffering is done by the CO_2/HCO_3^- system. These trends continue with further increases in the non-HCO_3^- buffering power. In the extreme, with a $\beta_{non-HCO_3}$ of infinity, there is no pH at all, and all of the buffering is done by non-HCO_3^- buffers.

Addition of NaOH When $\beta_{non-HCO_3}$ Equals 5 mM

The same approach that was used to predict the outcome of metabolic alkalosis in the absence of non-HCO_3^- buffers can be used in the presence of such buffers. For example, if 10 mmoles NaOH is added to one liter of a solution with an initial pH of 7.40, a fixed P_{CO_2} of 40 torr and a $[HCO_3^-]$ of 23.94 mM, ΔB is $+10$ mM and the non-HCO_3^- buffer line is displaced 10 mM upward. The final conditions are given by B in Fig. 8: pH $= 7.542$ and $[HCO_3^-] = 33.23$ mM. Because $[HCO_3^-]$ rose from 23.94 mM to 33.23 mM, ~9.3 mmoles of HCO_3^- must have been formed as the CO_2/HCO_3^- buffer system neutralized ~9.3 millimoles of the added OH^-. The remaining 0.7 mmole must have been buffered by non-HCO_3^- buffers.

$$9.3\,H^+ + 9.3\,HCO_3^- \leftarrow 9.3\,CO_2 + 9.3\,H_2O$$

$$9.3\,OH^- \rightharpoondown \qquad\qquad\qquad\qquad\qquad\qquad\qquad [43a]$$

$$9.3\,H_2O$$

$$0.7\,H^+ + 0.7\,Buf^n \leftarrow 0.7\,BufH^{(n+1)}$$

$$0.7\,OH^- \rightharpoondown \qquad\qquad\qquad\qquad\qquad\qquad\qquad [43b]$$

$$0.7\,H_2O$$

From these data we can compute the mean values for β_{HCO_3} and $\beta_{non-HCO_3}$.

$$\text{Mean } \beta_{HCO_3} = \frac{\Delta[HCO_3^-]}{\Delta pH} = \frac{9.3\text{ mM}}{0.142} = 65.4\text{ mM}$$

$$\text{Mean } \beta_{non-HCO_3} = \frac{\Delta B - \Delta[HCO_3^-]}{\Delta pH} = \frac{10\text{ mM} - (9.3\text{ mM})}{0.142} = 5.0\text{ mM}$$

$$\text{Mean } \beta_{total} = \frac{\Delta B}{\Delta pH} = \frac{10\text{ mM}}{0.142} = 70.4\text{ mM}$$

This total buffering power is substantially higher than that of the previous example of metabolic acidosis for a $\beta_{non-HCO_3}$ of 5 mM. The difference can be attributed exclusively to the increased contribution by the open-system $CO_2/$ HCO_3^- buffer. This occurs because the mean pH for this example of metabolic alkalosis (i.e., $[7.542 + 7.400]/2 = 7.471$) is far higher than for the example of metabolic acidosis (i.e., $[7.40 + 7.196]/2 = 7.298$). Thus, as is evident from Eq. 37, the mean β_{HCO_3} must be higher for metabolic alkalosis than for metabolic acidosis.

Compensations for Acid-Base Disturbances

In the preceding two sections, we discussed the four primary acid-base disturbances: respiratory acidosis and alkalosis and metabolic acidosis and alkalosis. Their representation on a Davenport diagram is summarized in Fig. 9. To use the Davenport diagram to solve a problem dealing with a respiratory acid-base disturbance, move along the non-HCO_3^- buffer line to the intersection with the new CO_2 isopleth. For a metabolic acid-base disturbance, displace the non-HCO_3^- buffer line appropriately, and then move along the CO_2 isopleth to the intersection with the new non-HCO_3^- buffer line. In the intact animal, these primary acid-base disturbances can be compensated by processes that tend to return plasma pH toward normal. We will now consider the chemistry behind the compensation for each of the primary acid-base disturbances.

Respiratory Acidosis

Assuming that normal conditions are represented by X in Fig. 9 (i.e., pH = 7.40, $[HCO_3^-] = 24$ mM, $P_{CO_2} = 40$ torr), A represents a simple respiratory acidosis in which P_{CO_2} is increased to 80 torr in a solution with a $\beta_{non\text{-}HCO_3}$ of 25 mM. The only way to compensate for this decrease in pH at a fixed but elevated P_{CO_2} is to increase $[HCO_3^-]$. The body can increase plasma $[HCO_3^-]$ by increasing renal HCO_3^- reabsorption. *In vitro*, this can be achieved by adding either HCO_3^- or a strong base, such as NaOH. Such an addition of base is in effect a metabolic alkalosis. However, because this metabolic alkalosis helps alleviate a preexisting respiratory acidosis, the disturbance is termed "respiratory acidosis with metabolic compensation." On a Davenport diagram, this compensation is represented by elevating the non-HCO_3^- buffer line by 1 mM for each millimole of base added to a liter of solution. Thus, the point describing the system moves upward along the elevated CO_2 isopleth ($P_{CO_2} = 80$ torr in this example), as indicated by the broken arrow near point A in Fig. 9.

If sufficient base were added, the pH could be restored to its original level. In the example of Fig. 9, the initial disturbance was a respiratory acidosis generated by doubling the P_{CO_2}. If 24 mmoles of base also were

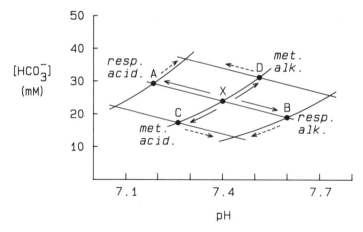

FIG. 9. Summary of the use of the Davenport diagram to solve respiratory and metabolic acid-base disturbances. Point X represents the initial conditions for mammalian blood plasma (pH = 7.4, [HCO$_3^-$] = 23.94 mM, and P$_{CO_2}$ = 40 torr) and lies at the intersection of the 40-torr P$_{CO_2}$ isopleth and the non-HCO$_3^-$ buffering line (shown here for a $\beta_{non-HCO_3}$ of 25 mM). **A:** Increasing P$_{CO_2}$ to 80 torr causes the system to move along the non-HCO$_3^-$ buffer line from X to A (respiratory acidosis). This acidification can be reduced by the addition of strong base (metabolic compensation), which causes the system to move in the alkaline direction along the 80-torr P$_{CO_2}$ isopleth (broken arrow). **B:** Decreasing P$_{CO_2}$ to 20 torr causes the system to move along the buffer line from X to B (respiratory alkalosis). This alkalinization can be reduced by the addition of strong acid (metabolic compensation), which causes the system to move in the acid direction along the 20-torr P$_{CO_2}$ isopleth (broken arrow). **C:** Adding 10 mmoles of strong acid to a liter of solution causes the system to move along the 40-torr P$_{CO_2}$ isopleth from X to the downwardly displaced buffer line at C (metabolic acidosis). This acidosis can be reduced by lowering the P$_{CO_2}$ (respiratory compensation), which causes the system to move in the alkaline direction along the displaced buffer line (broken arrow). **D:** Adding 10 mmoles of strong base to the solution causes the system to move along the 40-torr P$_{CO_2}$ isopleth from X to the upwardly displaced buffer line at D (metabolic alkalosis). This alkalosis can be reduced by raising the P$_{CO_2}$ (respiratory compensation), which causes the system to move in the acid direction along the displaced buffer line (broken arrow).

added to the solution, the non-HCO$_3^-$ buffer line would be elevated by 24 mM. The intersection of this line with the isopleth for P$_{CO_2}$ = 80 torr would be at a pH of 7.4 and a [HCO$_3^-$] of 48 mM. This outcome is not unexpected: if both the P$_{CO_2}$ and the [HCO$_3^-$] are doubled, the final pH is unchanged. Such a condition is termed "isohydric hypercapnia," isohydric because the pH is unchanged, hypercapnia because the P$_{CO_2}$ is elevated.

Respiratory Alkalosis

In the example of Fig. 9, the respiratory alkalosis is generated by reducing P$_{CO_2}$ to 20 torr (point B). The only way to compensate for this increase in pH at a fixed but reduced P$_{CO_2}$ is to lower [HCO$_3^-$]. This can be achieved by adding an acid, such as HCl, to the solution or by removing HCO$_3^-$. In the intact animal, a reduction of plasma $[HCO_3^-]$ could be achieved by decreasing the amount of acid secreted by the kidneys, producing a metabolic acidosis in the blood plasma. On a Davenport diagram, such a respiratory alkalosis with metabolic compensation is represented by displacing the non-HCO_3^- buffer line downward 1 mM for each millimole of acid added to (or HCO_3^- removed from) a liter of solution. This is indicated by the broken arrow near point B in Fig. 9. If sufficient acid is added in this example to reduce $[HCO_3^-]$ to half its normal value, the pH would return to 7.40. The fully compensated acid-base disturbance would be termed "isohydric hypocapnia."

Metabolic Acidosis

In the example of Fig. 9, the metabolic acidosis (point C) is generated by adding 10 mmoles HCl to one liter of a solution for which the P_{CO_2} is fixed at 40 torr and $\beta_{non-HCO_3}$ is 25 mM. To compensate for this decrease in pH, we must reduce P_{CO_2}. *In vitro*, this can be accomplished by lowering the P_{CO_2} of the gas mixture with which the solution is equilibrated. In the intact animal, the P_{CO_2} of the blood plasma can be reduced by increasing alveolar ventilation (provided the rate of metabolic CO_2 production is unchanged). Such a reduction of P_{CO_2} is a respiratory alkalosis. On a Davenport diagram, this metabolic acidosis with respiratory compensation is represented by drawing a new CO_2 isopleth and moving along the depressed non-HCO_3^- buffer line until that line intersects with the new isopleth. This is indicated in Fig. 9 by the broken arrow near point C. If the P_{CO_2} is reduced sufficiently, the pH can be returned to normal, a situation that can be termed "isohydric hypocapnia."

Metabolic Alkalosis

In the example of Fig. 9, the metabolic alkalosis (point D) is generated by adding 10 mmoles NaOH to one liter of a solution having a P_{CO_2} fixed at 40 torr and a $\beta_{non-HCO_3}$ of 25 mM. In order to compensate for this increase in pH, we must increase P_{CO_2}. *In vitro*, this can be accomplished by raising the P_{CO_2} of the gas mixture with which the solution is equilibrated. In the intact animal, the P_{CO_2} of the blood plasma can be increased by reducing alveolar ventilation (provided the rate of metabolic CO_2 production is fixed). Such an increase in P_{CO_2} is a respiratory acidosis. On a Davenport diagram, this metabolic alkalosis with respiratory compensation is represented by drawing a new CO_2 isopleth and moving along the elevated non-HCO_3^- buffer line until that line intersects with the new isopleth. This is indicated in Fig. 9 by the broken arrow near point D. Sufficiently increasing the P_{CO_2} will return pH to normal, a condition that can be described as isohydric hypercapnia.

ACKNOWLEDGMENTS

I thank Eleanor Savage for her excellent secretarial assistance.

REFERENCES

1. Bates, R. G. (1973): *Determination of pH. Theory and Practice*. Wiley, New York.
2. Bockris, J. O., and Reddy, A. K. N. (1970): *Modern Electrochemistry. Vol 1*. Plenum Press, New York.
3. Edsall, J. T., and Wyman, J. (1958): *Biophysical Chemistry. Vol. 1*. Academic Press, New York.
4. Roos, A., and Boron, W. F. (1980): The buffer value of weak acids and bases: Origin of the concept, and first mathematical derivation and application of physico-chemical systems. The work of M. Koppel and K. Spiro (1914). *Respir. Physiol.*, 40:1–32.
5. Van Slyke, D. D. (1922): On the measurement of buffer values and on the relationship of buffer value to the dissociation constant of the buffer and the concentration and the reaction of the buffer solution. *J. Biol. Chem.*, 52:525–570.

General Review Articles

6. Boron, W. F. (1988): Cellular buffering and intracellular pH. In: *The Regulation of Acid-Base Balance*, edited by D. W. Seldin and G. Giebisch. Raven Press, New York.
7. Davenport, H. W. (1958): *The ABC of Acid-Base Chemistry*, 4th ed. University of Chicago Press, Chicago.
8. Gunn, R. B. (1988): Buffer equilibrium in red blood cells. In: *The Regulation of Acid-Base Balance*, edited by D. W. Seldin and G. Giebisch. Raven Press, New York.
9. Roos, A., and Boron, W. F. (1981): Intracellular pH. *Physiol. Rev.*, 61:296–434.

The Regulation of Acid–Base Balance, edited
by Donald W. Seldin and Gerhard Giebisch,
Raven Press, Ltd., New York, © 1989.

2

Cellular Buffering and Intracellular pH

Walter F. Boron

*Department of Cellular and Molecular Physiology, Yale University School of
Medicine, New Haven, Connecticut 06510*

Because almost every cellular process is sensitive to changes in pH, it is vitally important that cells have a mechanism or mechanisms for appropriately regulating their cytoplasmic pH (pH_i). In this chapter, we discuss methods for measuring pH_i as well as factors that affect the regulation of pH_i. The acid-base insults to which cells are subjected can be divided into two broad groups: (a) acute (i.e., those with a limited duration) and (b) chronic (i.e., those with an indefinite duration). An acute acid-base disturbance is produced, for example, by injecting the cell with acid. The rapid fall in pH_i caused by such an acute acid load, however, is minimized by the actions of cytoplasmic buffers. Altering the concentration of a permeant weak acid or

33

base also can produce an acute intracellular acid or alkali load. Because acute acid or alkali loads are one-time-only events, the disturbances in pH_i that they cause eventually are corrected by the acid-base transport mechanisms that regulate pH_i.

In the longer term, pH_i regulation is not dependent on buffering power and is unaffected by acute acid-base disturbances. pH_i reaches a steady state when a balance is achieved between the rates of acid loading and acid extrusion. The value of pH_i in the steady state is determined solely by factors that permanently modulate the rate at which acid is added to or removed from the cytoplasm.

METHODS FOR MEASURING INTRACELLULAR pH

The regulation of pH_i can be studied only by monitoring pH_i. Several techniques are available for measuring pH_i, each having a unique profile of advantages and disadvantages. Three of the major techniques in current use are pH-sensitive microelectrodes, pH-sensitive dyes, and nuclear magnetic resonance. All of these techniques are accurate and are capable of continuously recording pH_i.

pH-Sensitive Microelectrodes

The sensor in a pH-sensitive microelectrode can be a thin layer of pH-sensitive glass or an organic ionophore dissolved in a hydrophobic solvent. A single cell, or two electrically coupled cells, must be impaled with two electrodes, a pH-sensitive one and a reference electrode that completes the electrical circuit between the pH-sensitive electrode and the voltage meter. Alternatively, a single double-barreled electrode can be employed. The measured voltage varies linearly with pH_i. The advantage of the microelectrode approach is that it is capable of monitoring rapid pH_i changes and can be applied to a single cell or small group of cells. The disadvantage is that the cells must be sufficiently large and rugged to withstand the impalements, and that fabricating and using the electrodes requires some skill.

pH-Sensitive Dyes

Fluorescein derivatives have become popular probes for monitoring pH_i. One can exploit the pH sensitivity of either the dye's absorbance spectrum or the fluorescence excitation spectrum. Dye techniques are relatively easy to use, appear to be reasonably accurate, and are capable of monitoring very rapid pH_i changes. The techniques can be applied to a single cell in culture, to an *in vitro* preparation of a few cells (e.g., a single perfused renal tubule), to tens of thousands of cells attached to a coverslip, or to hundreds of thousands of cells in suspension. Fluorescence also can be applied to cells on the surface of a solid *in vivo* preparation (e.g., the surface of a kidney). Finally, dyes attached to macromolecules can be used to study the pH of endocytic vesicles. When the dye technique is applied to many cells in a cuvette, disadvantages can include leakage of dye from cells into a stagnant extracellular fluid and difficulty in making rapid solution changes. When dyes are used with single cells, higher light intensities per cell generally are used in order to produce a greater fluorescence intensity. Side effects of this include dye bleaching and photodynamic damage to the cell.

Nuclear Magnetic Resonance

The basis of the nuclear magnetic resonance (NMR) approach for measuring pH_i is that the chemical shift of ^{31}P or ^{19}F incorporated into weak acids or bases (e.g., inorganic phosphate in the case of ^{31}P or F-containing amino acid analogs in the case of ^{19}F) is sensitive to pH changes. The technique offers the advantages of being able to monitor pH_i in *in-vivo* tissues (e.g., a human forearm) over very long periods of observation. In addition, ^{31}P NMR provides information on the levels of various P-containing metabolites (e.g., ATP). The disadvantages are that a relatively large mass of tissue is required and that there is a trade-off between time resolution and signal/noise ratio. A typical time resolution is on the order of several tens of seconds, and a typical pH_i resolution is about 0.05. In *in vitro* experiments, care must be taken to ensure that nutrients (e.g., O_2) are delivered continuously to the cells and that wastes are removed.

CELLULAR BUFFERING

In the broadest sense, pH buffering is performed by any process that reversibly consumes or releases H^+. Thus, a buffer reduces the size of a pH change produced by an acute acid or alkali load. The pH of the cytoplasm can be buffered by three classes of processes: weak acids and bases (physicochemical buffering), biochemical reactions (biochemical buffering), and transport of acid-base equivalents across organellar membranes (organellar buffering). Regardless of the mechanism, the efficacy of buffering can be quantitated by the buffering power (β), defined as the amount of strong base that must be added to a solution in order to raise pH by one pH unit.

$$\beta \equiv \frac{\text{Amount of strong base added}}{\text{Resultant } pH_i \text{ increase}} = \frac{\text{Amount of strong acid added}}{\text{Resultant } pH_i \text{ decrease}} \quad [1]$$

Thus, the greater the buffering power, the more strong acid or base that must be added in order to alter pH_i. Buffers also can be described as being intrinsic or extrinsic to the cell. Intrinsic buffers are those that are confined to the cell, including close-system physicochemical buffers, biochemical buffers, and organellar buffers. Extrinsic buffers include open-system physicochemical buffers.

Physicochemical Buffering

Chapter 1 contains a detailed discussion of buffering by weak acids and bases. The principles involved in the physicochemical buffering of the cytoplasm are the same as those that pertain to the buffering of extracellular fluids. Cytoplasmic physicochemical buffers can be divided into two groups, those that cannot permeate the cell membrane and behave as closed-system buffers, and those whose neutral form freely permeates the cell membrane and that behave as open-system buffers.

As noted previously, closed-system buffers are those that cannot permeate the cell membrane, such as the weak acid-base moieties of proteins. The buffering power of any single closed-system buffer $(HA \rightleftharpoons H^+ + A^-)$ is given by the Michaelis-Van Slyke modification to the Koppel-Spiro equation discussed in Chapter 1.

$$\beta^{closed} = 2.3 \frac{[H^+] K'}{([H^+] + K')^2} [TA] \qquad [2]$$

where K' is the apparent dissociation constant of the weak acid, and $[TA]$ is the total amount of buffer (i.e., $[TA] = [HA] + [A^-]$). β is maximal when $[H^+] = K'$ (i.e., when $pH = pK'$), at which point $\beta \cong 0.58 \, [TA]$. When several closed-system buffers are present simultaneously, the total physicochemical buffering power of closed-system buffers is the sum of individual buffering powers calculated from Eq. 2.

Open-system buffers are those for which the neutral form freely permeates the cell membrane. Consider, for example, a weak acid HA that equilibrates across the cell membrane. If H^+ is added to the cytoplasm, it is buffered in the usual way.

$$H^+ + A^- \rightarrow HA \qquad [3]$$

In a closed system, buffering of H^+ is limited by the accumulation of HA and availability of A^-. Conversely, buffering of OH^- is limited by accumulation of A^- and availability of HA. If the cell membrane is freely permeable to HA, however, the HA formed after addition of H^+ exits the cell, so that buffering is no longer limited by buildup of HA. Thus, an increase in $[HA]$ is prevented (i.e., [HA] is fixed), and the buffering reaction can proceed to a much greater extent. Conversely, on addition of OH^- to the cytoplasm, depletion of HA is avoided because HA diffuses into the cell. The buffering power of an open-system weak acid (see Chapter 1) is

$$\beta^{open} = 2.3 \, [A^-] \qquad [4]$$

Note that, unlike the closed-system buffering power, the open-system buffering power does not peak at the pK' but increases steadily as pH_i (i.e., $[A^-]_i$) increases. If [HA] is fixed and independent of pH_i, both $[A^-]_i$ and β^{open} double each time pH_i increases by 0.3. It is instructive to compare closed-system and open-system buffering powers when $pH_i = pK'$ and the closed-system buffering power is maximal. As noted previously, the maximal β^{closed} is about 0.58 [TA]. For an open system containing the same amount of total buffer, $[A^-] = [TA]/2$ when $pH = pK'$. Thus, β^{open} is about 1.15 [TA] or about twice as great as β^{closed}. At higher pH_i values, the ratio of open-system to closed-system buffering powers is even greater. Thus, open-system buffers are in a position to make a substantial contribution to total intracellular buffering power. Physiologically, the most important open-system buffer is CO_2/HCO_3^-. Indeed, when a typical cell is exposed to 5% CO_2, the open-system CO_2/HCO_3^- buffering power at a normal pH_i is larger than the buffering power of all other cellular buffers combined.

Biochemical Buffering

Biochemical reactions can function as pH buffers by consuming (or producing) protons in response to acute intracellular acid (or alkali) loads. For example, when mammalian brain cells are acid loaded, the concentrations of lactate, pyruvate, citrate, and several other carboxylates decrease. These weak bases, together with protons, are converted to neutral products (i.e., glucose) or products that are freely diffusible (i.e., CO_2). Thus, the relevant biochemical reactions respond to the acid load by a net consumption of acid. Conversely, an acute alkali load is followed by a net production of biochemical buffering, at least under certain conditions, may be about half of that of closed-system physicochemical buffers.

Organellar Buffering

Several intracellular organelles are known to actively transport acid-base equivalents across the organellar membrane. It is expected that a decrease in cytoplasmic pH would increase the transport of H^+ into acidic vesicles (e.g., via an H^+ pump, ATPase) and decrease the transport of H^+ out of alkaline organelles. Such changes in transport would be equivalent to transferring cytoplasmic H^+ to organelles, thereby buffering the cytoplasm. However, the contribution of such organellar processes to total cellular buffering has not been determined.

EFFECTS ON pH_i OF PERMEANT WEAK ACIDS AND BASES

One of the major mechanisms by which a change in a cell's environment can affect pH_i is by fluxes across the cell membrane of permeant buffers. The general rule is that the membrane is far more permeable to a neutral species of a buffer pair than to its charged counterpart. This difference reflects the relative solubilities of the two buffer species in the lipid phase of the membrane. Thus, if a cell is exposed to a buffer, the neutral species of which is a weak base (e.g., NH_3), the predominant early effect will be a cell alkalinization. If the conjugate weak acid (e.g., NH_4^+) also can enter the cell, this pH_i increase may be followed by a slower decline. Conversely, if a cell is exposed to a buffer, the neutral species of which is a weak acid (e.g., CO_2), the predominant early effect will be a cell acidification. The time course of pH_i on exposure of a cell to a permeant buffer depends on the effective permeability of the membrane to each of the buffer species, the external concentrations of these buffer species, intracellular buffering power, and the initial pH_i. We now consider two examples of buffer permeation, exposure of a cell to NH_3/NH_4^+ and to CO_2/HCO_3^-.

Effect of Exposing a Cell to NH_3/NH_4^+

Imagine that a cell is exposed to a solution containing NH_3 and NH_4^+ ($NH_4^+ \rightleftharpoons NH_3 + H^+$). If we make the reasonable assumption that NH_3 enters the cell far more rapidly than NH_4^+, we can ignore the early effects of NH_4^+ entry. As illustrated in Fig. 1A, the influx of NH_3 produces a rapid pH_i increase as incoming NH_3 consumes protons in forming NH_4^+. The speed of this increase is approximately proportional to the membrane's permeability to NH_3 and inversely proportional to the cell's buffering power. As the NH_3 influx continues $[NH_3]_i$ and $[NH_4^+]_i$ gradually rise and $[H^+]_i$ gradually falls until the intracellular reaction $NH_3 + H^+ \rightleftharpoons NH_4^+$ is in equilibrium, and $[NH_3]_i = [NH_3]_o$. At this point, there is no further net entry of NH_3, and pH_i has reached its maximal value (Fig. 1B). The magnitude of the intracellular alkalinization caused by NH_3 entry is increased by increasing $[NH_3]_o$, decreasing pH_i, and decreasing intracellular buffering power.

If the exposure to NH_3/NH_4^+ is maintained past the point indicated in Fig. 1B, the transport of NH_4^+ plays a major role in the subsequent time course of pH_i. All cells thus far examined have a finite permeability to NH_4^+. Because the electrochemical gradient governing the passive movement of NH_4^+ is inward, NH_4^+ slowly enters the cell and produces a fall in pH_i, as depicted in Fig. 1C. This period of slow pH_i change has been termed the "plateau phase." Although in some cells simple diffusion may be the only significant pathway by which NH_4^+ enters, in others the Na, K pump can carry NH_4^+ into the cell, with NH_4^+ substituting for K^+. There is also evidence that the Na/K/ Cl cotransporter may be capable of NH_4^+ transport. Regardless of the mechanism of NH_4^+ entry, the accumulation of NH_4^+ drives $[NH_4^+]_i$ above the value necessary for NH_4^+ to remain in equilibrium with NH_3 and H^+ inside the cell. As a result, a small fraction of entering NH_4^+ dissociates into NH_3 and H^+. This fraction, typically 1% to 5%, is determined by the difference between pH_i and the pK' governing the equilibrium $NH_4^+ \rightleftharpoons NH_3 + H^+$. As NH_3 is formed in this reaction, $[NH_3]_i$ is driven above $[NH_3]_o$, so that there is a net efflux of NH_3. Thus, there is a recycling of NH_3/NH_4^+ across the membrane shuttling protons into the cell and producing an intracellular acidification.

When the external NH_4^+/NH_3 finally is removed from the external solution, virtually all intracellular NH_4^+ (including that NH_4^+ that had entered previously as NH_4^+ and not previously dissociated) now dissociates. The newly formed NH_3 exits from the cell, but the H^+ remains trapped inside. Thus, there is a rapid fall of pH_i (Fig. 1D) to a value far below the initial one. The net effect of applying and then withdrawing external NH_4^+/NH_3 is the same as injecting the cell with H^+. Indeed, a brief application of NH_4^+/NH_3 is a popular method of experimentally acid loading cells.

Effect of Exposing a Cell to CO_2/HCO_3^-

Imagine that a cell is exposed to a solution containing CO_2 and HCO_3^- ($CO_2 + H_2O \rightleftharpoons HCO_3^- + H^+$). If the cell membrane is far more permeable to CO_2 than to HCO_3^-, the movement of CO_2 will dominate the early course of pH_i. As illustrated in Fig. 2A, the influx of CO_2 produces a rapid pH_i decrease as incoming CO_2 combines with H_2O to form H_2CO_3, which in turn dissociates into H^+ and HCO_3^-. The speed of this intracellular acidification is approximately proportional to the CO_2 permeability and inversely proportional to intracellular buffering power. As the CO_2 influx continues $[CO_2]_i$, $[HCO_3^-]_i$, and $[H^+]_i$ gradually rise until the intracellular reaction $CO_2 + H_2O \rightleftharpoons HCO_3^- + H^+$ is in equilibrium, and $[CO_2]_i = [CO_2]_o$. At this point, there is no further net entry of CO_2 (Fig. 2B). This acid-base disturbance is an intracellular respiratory acidosis and can be analyzed in the same way as respiratory acidosis in the blood plasma (see Chapter 1). The magnitude of the CO_2-induced intracellular acidification is increased by increasing $[CO_2]_o$ or the initial pH_i, and by decreasing intracellular buffering power.

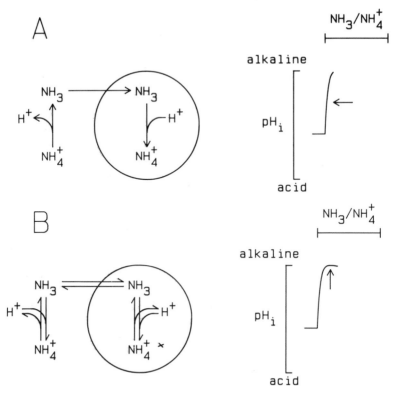

FIG. 1. Effect of NH_3/NH_4^+ on intracellular pH. **A**: The initial phase of an exposure to a solution containing NH_3/NH_4^+ is dominated by the influx of the highly permeant, neutral weak base NH_3. The entering NH_3 combines with intracellular H^+ to form NH_4^+, thereby causing a rapid rise of intracellular pH (pH_i). **B**: The second phase of the exposure to NH_3/NH_4^+ is characterized by the equilibration of NH_3 across the cell membrane. At this point, there is no net flux of NH_3 across the cell membrane nor any change in pH_i.

If the exposure to CO_2/HCO_3^- is maintained past the point indicated in Fig. 2B, one might expect the transport of HCO_3^- to play a role analogous to that played by NH_4^+ in the NH_4^+/NH_3 experiment of Fig. 1. However, experience has taught us that the course of pH_i during the plateau phase of a CO_2/HCO_3^- exposure is highly dependent on cell type. If the cell membrane were permeable to HCO_3^-, the passive movement of HCO_3^- would be governed by the electrochemical gradient for this ion, which generally favors an efflux. Thus, one might expect the passive movement of HCO_3^- to produce a slow intracellular acidification, as indicated in Fig. 2C. However, there is little evidence that a simple HCO_3^- permeability plays a major role in determining pH_i in any cell. Nevertheless, at least two ion-transport systems are known to mediate a net HCO_3^- efflux (*see next section*). As long as HCO_3^- efflux were to dominate possible alkalinizing influences, the cell would slowly acidify during the plateau phase, as indicated in Fig. 2C. Such an acidification

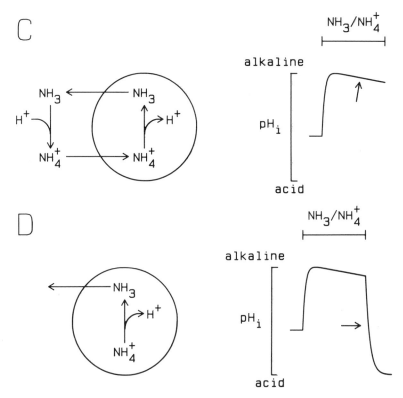

FIG. 1. (*Continued.*) **C**: The third, or plateau, phase of the exposure to NH_3/NH_4^+ is dominated by the influx of NH_4^+, either as a simple passive process or mediated by a transporter such as the Na, K pump. The net effect is a slow decline in pH_i as a small fraction of incoming NH_4^+ dissociates into NH_3 and H^+. **D**: The washout of intracellular NH_4^+ is initiated by the removal of extracellular NH_3/NH_4^+. Because the cell membrane is far more permeable to NH_3 than to NH_4^+, almost all of the internal NH_4^+ dissociates into NH_3 (which diffuses from the cell) and H^+ (which is trapped within).

is a metabolic acidosis superimposed on a respiratory acidosis and can be analyzed in the same way as similar acid-base disturbances in the blood plasma.

A second possible outcome for pH_i during the plateau phase of a CO_2/HCO_3^- exposure is for pH_i to stabilize after the rapid CO_2-induced acidification. As illustrated in Fig. 2D, this occurs when the efflux of HCO_3^- is balanced by the extrusion of acid from the cell. Of course, this balance is also achieved when HCO_3^--exit and acid-extrusion rates are both zero. The active extrusion of acid from the cell can be mediated by any of several transport processes and is key to the regulation of pH_i. This subject is discussed in more detail in the next section.

The third possible outcome for pH_i during the plateau phase of a CO_2/HCO_3^- exposure is pH_i recovery (i.e., alkalinization). This occurs, as schematized in Fig. 2E, as long as acid extrusion exceeds the HCO_3^- efflux. Such a pH_i recovery is a metabolic compensation to the initial respiratory acidosis

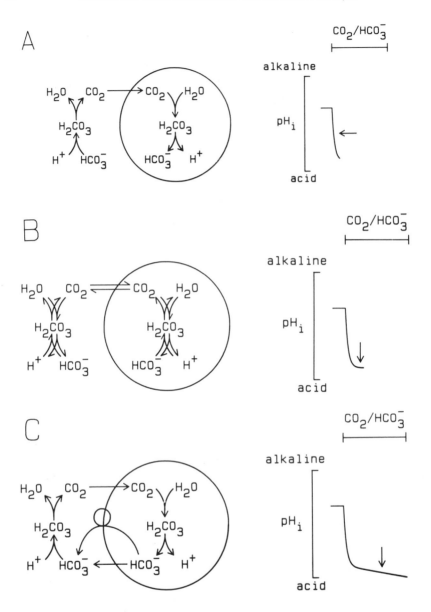

FIG. 2. Effect of CO_2/HCO_3^- on intracellular pH. **A:** The initial phase of an exposure to a solution containing CO_2/HCO_3^- is dominated by the influx of the highly permeant CO_2. On entering, the CO_2 combines with H_2O to form H_2CO_3, which then dissociates into H^+ and HCO_3^-. Alternately, carbonic anhydrase may catalyze the reaction: $CO_2 + OH^- \rightarrow HCO_3^-$. The net effect is a rapid fall in pH_i. **B:** The second phase of the exposure is characterized by the equilibration of CO_2 across the cell membrane. At this point, there is no net flux of CO_2 nor any change in pH_i. **C:** During the third, or plateau, phase of a CO_2/HCO_3^- exposure, pH_i can decline, stabilize, or recover. A continuing decline of pH_i is produced if HCO_3^- efflux dominates. The HCO_3^- efflux could be a purely passive process or could be carrier mediated.

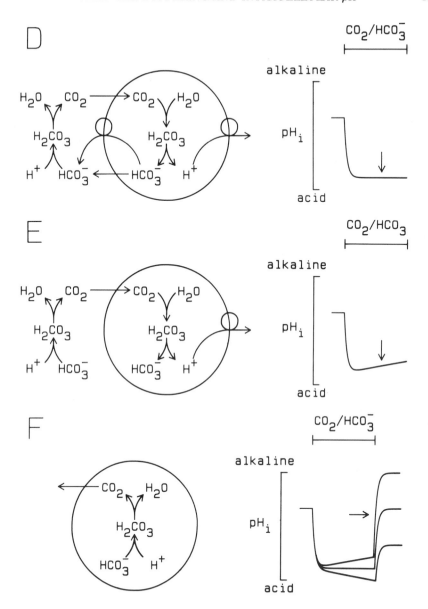

FIG. 2. (*Continued.*) **D:** A stabilization of pH_i during the plateau phase results if the active extrusion of H^+ (or uptake of base) exactly balances the efflux of HCO_3^-. **E:** A recovery of pH_i during the plateau phase occurs if active extrusion of acid dominates the transmembrane traffic of acid-base. **F:** The washout of intracellular HCO_3^- is initiated by the removal of extracellular CO_2/HCO_3^-. Because the cell membrane is far more permeable to CO_2 than to HCO_3^-, virtually all intracellular HCO_3^- combines with H^+ and ultimately exits as CO_2. The net effect is a rapid rise in pH_i. If pH_i fell during the plateau phase, the final pH_i will fall short of the initial value. For the case in which pH_i was stable during the plateau phase, pH_i will return to its initial level. Finally, if pH_i recovered during the plateau phase, the final pH_i will overshoot the initial one.

and can be analyzed in the same way as similar acid-base disturbances in the blood plasma. Whether or not the pH_i recovery returns pH_i to its initial value depends on the kinetics of acid-extruding and HCO_3^--efflux pathways. In some cases, the plateau phase recovery drives pH_i to values far higher than those prevailing in the absence of CO_2/HCO_3^-. This occurs when a potent acid-extruding process is HCO_3^- dependent.

When the external CO_2/HCO_3^- finally is removed from the external solution, practically all intracellular HCO_3^- combines with H^+ to form H_2CO_3, which in turn dissociates into H_2O and CO_2, which exit from the cell. Thus, CO_2 removal produces a rapid pH_i increase (Fig. 2F). If pH_i had fallen during the preceding plateau phase (Fig. 2C), the final pH_i after CO_2 removal will be below the initial one, reflecting the net depletion of base during the plateau phase. If pH_i had been stable during the plateau phase (Fig. 2D), the final pH_i after CO_2 removal will equal the initial one, reflecting no net flux of acid-base equivalents during the plateau phase. Finally, if pH_i had recovered during the plateau phase (Fig. 2E), the final pH_i will exceed the initial one, reflecting the net accumulation of HCO_3^- during the plateau phase.

pH_i-REGULATING MECHANISMS (18-21)

Historically, the problem of pH_i regulation generally has been regarded as one of preventing intracellular acidification. Indeed, for all known animal cells other than erythrocytes and possibly hepatocytes, the electrochemical gradient governing the passive movement of H^+ across the cell membrane favors the inward movement of this ion. Thus, there is a tendency for the cell to acidify as a result of the passive influx of H^+ (Fig. 3). The size of this H^+ influx, however, depends not only on the magnitude of the inward H^+ gradient but also on the membrane's permeability to H^+, as well as on $[H^+]$. Although the gradient and permeability may be high, $[H^+]_o$ is so low (less than one-millionth the value of $[Na^+]_o$), that the absolute net influx of H^+ is expected to be very low. However, this same gradient that affects H^+ also affects cationic weak acids (BH^+ in Fig. 3, an example of which is NH_4^+) and anionic weak bases (A^- in Fig. 3, an example of which is acetate), provided the neutral form of the buffer (B or HA) is equilibrated across the cell membrane. This gradient drives cationic acids into the cell and anionic bases outward, both processes tending to acidify the cell. These other ionized weak acids and bases generally are present at far higher concentrations than is H^+. Thus, even though the membrane may be less permeable to them than to H^+, their fluxes may have a significant effect on pH_i.

It is generally thought that cellular metabolism also contributes to intracellular acid loading, at least under certain conditions. Thus, it appears that the cell is faced with two inescapable sources of internal acidification: passive fluxes of ions and metabolism. In addition to these, many cells possess transport systems that normally mediate HCO_3^- efflux, thereby providing yet a

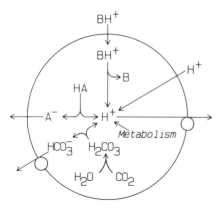

FIG. 3. Factors affecting intracellular acid-base balance. The fundamental problem facing cells *vis-a-vis* acid-base balance is that acid tends to accumulate as the result of the passive influx of H^+, the influx of cationic weak acids BH^+ (e.g., NH_4^+), the efflux of anionic weak bases A^- (e.g., lactate), the efflux of HCO_3^-, and metabolism. In order for the cell to maintain a stable pH_i, these acid-loading processes must be balanced by acid-extruding processes (here stylized as an H^+ pump).

third source of intracellular acid loading. If pH_i is to be stabilized in the face of these acidifying tendencies, acid must be extruded actively from the cell. It has now become clear that there are several systems capable of actively extruding acid from the cell. At least two of these have kinetic properties that are ideally suited for pH_i regulation. Such acid extruders thus defend the cell against intracellular acid loads. In the first of the following two sections, we examine these acid-extruding transport systems. In the second, we examine transporters that normally mediate HCO_3^- efflux and thereby impose an intracellular acid load. These may have evolved to help defend cells against intracellular alkali loads.

Transport Systems that Normally Extrude Acid (1–3,6,7,9–16)

Acid-extruding transporters can be divided into three groups based on their energy source: primary, secondary, and tertiary active transporters. A primary active transport mechanism derives its energy from electron transport or, in the case of the transporters we consider (i.e., the H^+ pump and K-H exchange pump), from the hydrolysis of ATP. A secondary active transport system (e.g., the Na-dependent Cl-HCO_3 exchanger and Na-H exchanger) derives its energy from the electrochemical gradient of an ion (i.e., Na^+ in these cases), the gradient for which is in turn established by a primary active transporter (i.e., the Na-K pump). Finally, a tertiary active transporter (e.g., the monocarboxylate system considered below) is driven by an ion gradient established by a secondary active transporter.

H^+ Pump

Present in the distal nephron of the kidney as well as in the urinary bladder of the reptile is an electrogenic H^+ pump (Fig. 4A, left). Similar H^+ pumps are present in organellar membranes, such as those of endosomes and

A. Primary

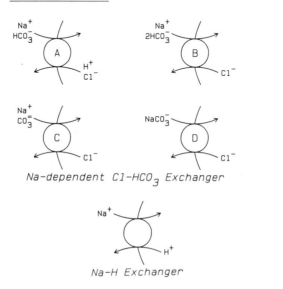

H⁺ Pump   K-H Pump

B. Secondary

Na-dependent Cl-HCO₃ Exchanger

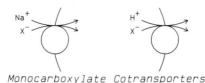

Na-H Exchanger

C. Tertiary

Monocarboxylate Cotransporters

FIG. 4. Acid-extruding transporters. **A:** Primary active transports, which derive their energy from the hydrolysis of ATP. The electrogenic H^+ pump has been identified in specialized cells of the distal nephron and in the reptile bladder. The electroneutral K-H pump is responsible for gastric acid secretion. **B:** Secondary active transporters, which derive their energy from the Na^+ gradient, which is in turn established by the Na-K pump. The thermodynamic characteristics of the Na^+-dependent Cl-HCO₃ exchanger can be accounted for by any of the four models (A,B,C,D). The Na-H exchanger is widely distributed in animal cells. Both exchangers are relatively inactive at alkaline pH_i values and are gradually activated as pH_i falls below a threshold. **C:** Tertiary active transport. The Na-K pump establishes a Na^+ gradient, which in turn energizes Na/monocarboxylate uptake (secondary active transport). Finally, the resulting monocarboxylate gradient drives H^+/monocarboxylate exit (tertiary active transport).

lysosomes. Inasmuch as the extrusion of H^+ by this primary active transport system is not coupled directly to the movements of other ions, the extrusion of each H^+ is associated with the extrusion of one positive charge. Thus, this pump is electrogenic. Because the H^+ pump is driven by the hydrolysis of ATP, which provides a substantial amount of energy, it is capable of generating a large H^+ gradient across the cell membrane. For example, if the voltage across the membrane is approximately zero, the H^+ pump can establish a pH difference of about three pH units. On the other hand, when compared to other H^+ transporters, the H^+ pump is relatively slow. Thus, the H^+ pump is found in epithelia with a requirement for a high-gradient and low-capacity H^+ transporter. The role of the H^+ pump in pH_i regulation has not been studied extensively. Work on cultured cells indicates that, in acid loaded cells, the H^+ pump contributes to the recovery of pH_i toward a normal (i.e., more alkaline) value.

K-H Exchange Pump

Present in the parietal cells of the stomach is an ATP-driven pump that extrudes H^+ from the cell and mediates the uptake of K^+. This K-H exchange pump (Fig. 4A, right) is capable of establishing extremely large pH gradients across the cell membrane and is responsible for producing gastric secretions having pH values as low as 1. The role of this primary active-transport system in pH_i regulation has not been studied extensively.

Na-Dependent Cl-HCO₃ Exchanger

Present in the cell membranes of numerous invertebrate and vertebrate animal cells, this secondary active transport system exchanges extracellular Na^+ and HCO_3^- (or a related species) for intracellular Cl^-. The precise acid-base species transported are unknown, though any of the four models (A, B, C, D) in Fig. 4B are consistent with the data. If external Na^+ or external HCO_3^- or internal Cl^- is absent, transport is blocked completely. Transport is inhibited also by disulfonic stilbene derivatives. Two such compounds, SITS and DIDS, irreversibly and completely block transport. Notably, transport is not affected by amiloride derivatives. This pH_i-regulating system, which was the first to be studied in depth, is nearly inactive at pH_i values above 7.3 to 7.4 (the threshold pH) and is gradually activated as pH_i falls below this threshold. The transporter is thus ideally suited as a feedback-control system for protecting the cell against acid loads. Another feature of the transporter, crucial for the interaction between the intracellular and extracellular environments, is its inhibition at low values of extracellular pH.

Na-H Exchanger

Present in a wide variety of animal cells is a secondary active transport system that exchanges extracellular Na^+ for intracellular H^+. This Na-H exchanger (Fig. 4B, bottom) is unaffected by the removal of HCO_3^- or of Cl^- and is not inhibited by the disulfonic stilbene derivatives. Its distinguishing characteristic is its inhibition by amiloride and certain highly potent amiloride analogs. The inhibition by amiloride appears to be due to a simple competition with Na^+. Like the Na-dependent Cl-HCO_3 exchanger, the Na-H exchanger is inhibited at low external pH and displays pH_i threshold behavior (i.e., inactivity at pH_i values above the threshold and gradual activation by reductions in pH_i below the threshold).

Because the Na-H exchanger is energized by the Na^+ gradient, the maximum transmembrane pH gradient that it can develop is the inverse of the Na^+ gradient. Thus, if $[Na^+]_i$ is 14 mM and $[Na^+]_o$ is 140 mM, the exchanger can develop at most a tenfold out–in H^+ gradient. However, the exchanger's limitation in establishing steep H^+ gradients is offset by its high transporting capacity. Thus, the Na-H exchanger is present in epithelia (e.g., the renal proximal tubule), which must secrete large amounts of acid against a low gradient.

Monocarboxylic Acid Transport

Renal proximal tubule cells of the amphibian and mammal possess two monocarboxylate transporters that, acting in concert, have the capacity to extrude substantial amounts of acid. The process, involving separate Na/monocarboxylate and H/monocarboxylate transport processes, is summarized in Fig. 4C. The first step is the entry of Na^+ and a monocarboxylate across the cell's luminal membrane via a Na/monocarboxylate cotransporter. This process is an example of secondary active transport, inasmuch as the Na^+ gradient (established by the Na-K pump) energizes the influx of monocarboxylate. This transporter is rather nonspecific, capable of transporting D- and L-lactate, pyruvate, acetate, and other monocarboxylates. Studies on membranes isolated from mammalian kidneys indicate that the Na/monocarboxylate cotransporter is electrogenic, moving more Na^+ ions than monocarboxylate ions. Thus, Na/monocarboxylate influx would cause the voltage to become more positive inside the cell. On the other hand, in amphibian renal tubules, evidence indicates that Na/monocarboxylate cotransport is electroneutral and thus has a stoichiometry of 1:1.

Monocarboxylate entry via the Na/monocarboxylate cotransporter, by itself, can have very little effect on pH_i. This is because the pK' governing monocarboxylic acid dissociation ($HA \rightleftharpoons H^+ + A^-$) generally is below 4, whereas pH_i is generally above 7. Thus, fewer than 1 entering monocarboxylate (A^-) in 1,000 is expected to combine with a proton to form the conjugate weak acid (HA). However, in renal proximal tubule cells, the monocarboxylate entering via luminal Na/monocarboxylate cotransport is rapidly lost from the cell along with H^+, with a stoichiometry of 1:1. This can produce a substantial intracellular alkalinization. In the amphibian renal proximal tubule, the coupled exit of H^+ and monocarboxylate is mediated by an H/monocarboxylate cotransporter (or the equivalent, a monocarboxylate-base exchanger) that is confined exclusively to the basolateral (i.e., blood-side) membrane. If the rate of this monocarboxylate exit step is equal to that of the entry step, the net effects are (1) the uptake of luminal Na^+, (2) the basolateral extrusion of H^+, and (3) the reabsorption of monocarboxylate (i.e., from lumen to blood). As far as pH_i regulation is concerned, together the two processes masquerade as an amiloride-insensitive, monocarboxylate-dependent Na-H exchanger. Basolateral H/monocarboxylate cotransport is an example of tertiary active transport because the extrusion of H^+ is driven by a monocarboxylate gradient that is, in turn, established by a secondary active transporter. The proximal tubule H/monocarboxylate cotransporter and similar systems in other cells have a broad specificity for monocarboxylates and are inhibited by certain cinnamate derivatives that are competitive with respect to the monocarboxylate.

In mammalian proximal tubule cells, the role of monocarboxylates in pH_i regulation has been examined only for acetate. These cells possess a Na/acetate cotransporter at the luminal membrane as well as pathways for acetic acid transport at both luminal and basolateral membranes. It is not clear whether the acetic acid flux is mediated by H/acetate cotransporters (as for the amphibian) or by the nonionic diffusion of acetic acid. To the extent that entering acetate exits across the luminal membrane, the net effect is luminal Na-H exchange with no net acetate flux. To the extent that entering acetate exits across the basolateral membrane, the net effect is equivalent to that outlined previously for the amphibian proximal tubule: luminal Na^+ uptake, basolateral acid extrusion, and the transepithelial movement of acetate from lumen to blood.

Transporters that Normally Load the Cell with Acid (4,8,17)

Passive fluxes of H^+, monovalent cationic acids (e.g., NH_4^+), and monovalent anionic bases (e.g., HCO_3^-) are governed by the electrochemical gradient for the ion in question and normally tend to acidify the cell. In principle, such passive transport processes could be exploited for protecting the cell against alkaline loads. In response to a sudden increase in pH_i, the cell could

increase the passive influx of acid or passive efflux of base. In practice, however, such passive acid-base transport processes have not been found to have
a substantial impact on pH_i. Instead, the major acid-loading transport pathways that have been identified involve carrier-mediated transport. Both
Cl-HCO$_3$ exchange and Na/HCO$_3$ are two that cotransport.

Cl-HCO$_3$ Exchanger

Present in a wide variety of animal cell membranes is a transporter that
exchanges external Cl$^-$ for internal HCO$_3^-$. A Cl-HCO$_3$ exchanger is the
major protein in the membrane of the erythrocyte, where it plays a crucial
role in the carriage of CO_2 between the systemic tissues and the lung. The
gene for this particular Cl-HCO$_3$ exchanger, also known as "band 3 protein"
because of its position on SDS-polyacrylamide gels, has been cloned and
sequenced. Because the Cl$^-$:HCO$_3^-$ stoichiometry is 1:1, the transporter is
electroneutral, and the direction of net transport is determined by the size of
the inwardly directed gradient for Cl$^-$ (i.e., $[Cl^-]_o/[Cl^-]_i$) relative to that
for HCO$_3^-$ (i.e., $[HCO_3^-]_o/[HCO_3^-]_i$). Because the inward Cl$^-$ gradient is generally greater than the inward HCO$_3^-$ gradient, the former dominates and
HCO$_3^-$ is driven out of the cell. The transporter is easily reversed, however,
by inverting the sum of the Cl$^-$ and HCO$_3^-$ chemical gradients. The Cl-HCO$_3$
exchanger is blocked by stilbene derivatives, such as DIDS and SITS.

Na/HCO$_3$ Cotransport

Present in the basolateral membrane of several epithelia, including the
renal proximal tubule, this transporter mediates the isodirectional flux of one
Na$^+$ and at least two (and probably three) HCO$_3^-$ ions. If the HCO$_3^-$:Na$^+$
stoichiometry is 3:1, this transporter carries a net charge of -2 in the same
direction as the Na$^+$ and HCO$_3^-$ ions and is, therefore, electrogenic. The
direction of net transport is determined by the sum of electrochemical gradients for one Na$^+$ and three HCO$_3^-$ ions. For renal tubule cells, the overall
driving force favors the efflux of Na$^+$ and HCO$_3^-$. This transporter is the
major pathway for HCO$_3^-$ reabsorption across the early renal proximal tubule
and is predicted to make a contribution of Na$^+$ reabsorption as well. Like the
Na-dependent Cl-HCO$_3$ exchanger and the simple Cl-HCO$_3$ exchanger, the
electrogenic Na/HCO$_3$ cotransporter is strongly inhibited by stilbene derivatives. The cotransporter's dependence on pH_i has not been determined.

In terms of the classification of active transporters as primary, secondary,
and tertiary, the Na/HCO$_3$ cotransporter occupies an unusual niche. The
Na-K pump directly or indirectly establishes the voltage gradient across the
cell membrane. The Na-K pump also sets up the Na$^+$ gradient that energizes
the Na-H exchanger, which in turn generates the transmembrane pH (i.e.,

HCO_3^-) gradient. These voltage and HCO_3^- gradients, directly or indirectly established by the Na-K pump, dictate that the Na-HCO$_3$ cotransporter must operate in the direction of net Na$^+$ efflux. This extrusion of Na$^+$, mediated by the electrogenic Na/HCO$_3$ cotransporter, can therefore be viewed as a secondary-tertiary active transport process. It is secondary in view of its dependence on the voltage gradient and tertiary in view of its dependence on the pH/HCO_3^- gradient.

INTERACTION BETWEEN ACID-LOADING AND ACID-EXTRUDING PROCESSES

What determines whether pH$_i$ rises or falls and, more precisely, the rate at which pH$_i$ changes? The rate of pH$_i$ change (dpH$_i$/dt) must be proportional to the difference between the rate of acid extrusion (J_E) and the rate of acid loading (J_L). The proportionality constant is the reciprocal of the buffering power. This law can be restated mathematically.

$$\frac{dpH_i}{dt} = \frac{(J_E - J_L)}{\beta} \qquad [5]$$

Equation 5 makes good intuitive sense. For example, if the rate of acid extrusion exceeds that of acid loading, pH$_i$ must increase (i.e., dpH$_i$/dt > 0). Furthermore, the rate of this alkalinization is expected to increase as the discrepancy between the acid-extrusion and acid-loading rates increases. Buffering power also is an important determinant of the rate of pH$_i$ change. If β were infinite, pH$_i$ would be fixed regardless of the rates of acid extrusion and acid loading. Conversely, if β approached zero, even a small difference between J_E and J_L would cause pH$_i$ to change very rapidly.

Figure 5 is a plot of acid-extruding and acid-loading rates as a function of pH$_i$ for a hypothetical cell. For the sake of simplicity, we assume that the only transporter contributing to acid extrusion is a Na-H exchanger. As discussed previously, the Na-H exchanger is practically inactive at pH$_i$ values above a certain pH$_i$ threshold (pH$'$) but gradually activates as pH$_i$ falls below this threshold. This is depicted in Fig. 5 as the linear J_E versus pH$_i$ relationship. The dependence of total acid-loading rate on pH$_i$ is depicted by the upward-sloping curve in Fig. 5. Although the shape of this J_L versus pH$_i$ curve is arbitrary, it is reasonable to expect such intracellular acid loading processes as passive H$^+$ influx, carrier-mediated HCO_3^- efflux, and metabolism to increase with increasing pH$_i$. It is obvious from Eq. 5 that in order for the cell to be in a steady state with respect to pH$_i$ (i.e., dpH$_i$/dt = 0), J_E and J_L must be equal. Thus, the steady state pH$_i$ has the value determined by the intersection of the J_E and J_L curves in Fig. 5 (point A). The model of Fig. 5 can be used to analyze a wide variety of intracellular acid-base disturbances; we discuss three: (1) acute intracellular acid load, (2) chronic inhibition of acid extrusion, and (3) chronic reduction in the intracellular acid load.

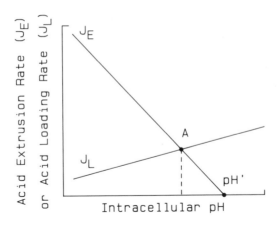

FIG. 5. Model of intracellular pH regulation. The acid-extrusion rate (J_E) is virtually zero at pH_i values above the threshold (pH') and increases as pH_i falls below this threshold. Conversely, the acid-loading rate (J_L) rises with increasing pH_i. By definition, the cell is in a steady state with respect to pH_i when $J_L = J_E$.

Acute Intracellular Acid Load

In Fig. 6A are plots of J_E versus pH_i and J_L versus pH_i for the same hypothetical cell as in Fig. 5. Figure 6B depicts the time course of pH_i after the injection of acid into this cell. The initial steady state pH_i, represented by point a in Fig. 6A, B, is determined by the intersection of the J_E and J_L curves. The injection of acid causes pH_i to fall from point a to b, the magnitude of the pH_i decrease being dictated by the amount of acid injected and the intracellular buffering power. Note, however, that this decline in pH_i stimulates acid extrusion (see b on J_E curve in Fig. 6A) and reduces the rate of acid loading (see b on J_L curve), so that J_E now exceeds J_L. Because ($J_E - J_L$)/β is now greater than zero, pH_i must increase (Eq. 5). As the pH_i recovery proceeds (bcd in Fig. 6B), the acid-extrusion rate gradually falls and the acid-loading rate gradually rises. Eventually, J_E and J_L come into balance at d, which is identical to a. Thus, as long as an acute intracellular acid load does not produce fundamental changes in the kinetics of either acid extrusion or acid loading, the effect on pH_i is only transient. Stated differently, if the J_E versus pH_i and J_L versus pH_i curves in Fig. 6A are unchanged, the steady state pH_i is unchanged. The speed of the pH_i recovery from the acute acid load is determined by β and the slopes of the J_E versus pH_i and J_L versus pH_i relationships. A pure acute alkaline load will have the opposite effects on pH_i, and can be analyzed in an analogous way.

Chronic Inhibition of Acid Extrusion

Imagine that our hypothetical cell, initially in a steady state described by point a in Fig. 6C, D, is treated with sufficient amiloride to reduce Na-H

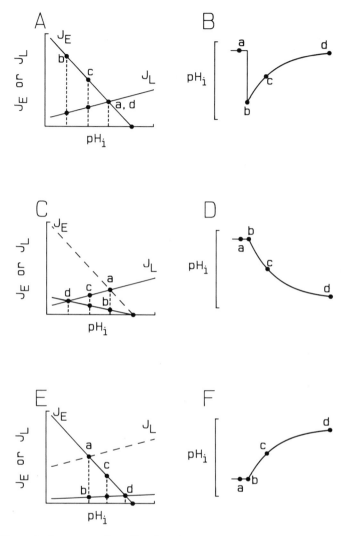

FIG. 6. Theoretical response of a cell to three intracellular acid-base disturbances. **A** and **B:** Response to a sudden intracellular injection of acid. Although $J_E = J_L$ in the initial steady state (a), the injection of acid causes a rapid fall in pH_i (b). Because at this point $J_E \gg J_L$, pH_i begins to recover. However, as the pH_i recovery proceeds, the discrepancy between J_E and J_L declines, so that the rate of recovery also declines (c). Eventually, pH_i returns to its initial value (d). **C** and **D:** Response to a decrease in J_E. The broken J_E line represents the normal, high rate of acid extrusion and point a is the normal pH_i. Suddenly inhibiting acid extrusion causes the slope of the J_E versus pH_i curve to decrease (unlabeled solid line), so that J_L is described by a and J_E by b. Because $J_L \gg J_E$, pH_i falls rapidly at first. As the discrepancy between J_E and J_L lessens, the acidification slows (c) and eventually halts when J_E and J_L come into balance (d). **E** and **F:** Response to a reduction in J_E. The broken line represents the normal, high rate of acid loading. The sudden inhibition of acid loading is represented by the downward displacement of the J_L versus pH_i curve (solid, unlabeled line), so that J_E is described by a and J_L by b. Because $J_E \gg J_L$, pH_i rises rapidly at first. As the discrepancy between J_E and J_L lessens, the pH_i increase slows (c) and eventually halts as J_E comes into balance with J_L (d).

exchange activity by 80%. This is represented in Fig. 6C by reducing the slope of the J_E versus pH_i relationship to one fifth of its original value. Thus, immediately after this reduction in Na-H exchange rate, J_L is unchanged (b on J_L versus pH_i curve of Fig. 6C), and J_E is greatly reduced (b on J_E curve). Because J_L now exceeds the reduced J_E, pH_i must slowly fall (bcd in Fig. 6D). However, the pH_i decline is accompanied necessarily by a rise in J_E and a fall in J_L (Fig. 6C). Eventually J_E and J_L come into balance at d, where pH_i now stabilizes. The rate of pH_i decline during bcd is expected to be greatest at point b, at the instant the inhibition takes effect (i.e., when the discrepancy between J_E and J_L is greatest).

Chronic Inhibition of Acid Loading

Imagine that our hypothetical cell, initially in a steady state described by point a in Fig. 6E, F, suddenly experiences a sustained decrease in the rate of acid loading. This could be produced, for example, by an inhibition of HCO_3^- efflux. In Fig. 6E, the reduction in acid loading is represented by a downward shift in the J_L versus pH_i curve. Thus, immediately after this inhibition of acid loading, J_E is unchanged (b on J_E versus pH_i curve of Fig. 6E), and J_L is substantially reduced (b on J_L curve). Because J_L is now less than the unchanged J_E, pH_i must slowly rise (bcd in Fig. 6F). However, this increase in pH_i is accompanied by a fall in J_E and a rise in J_L. Eventually J_E and J_L come into balance at d, where pH_i stabilizes. According to this model, an inhibition of acid loading could never cause the steady state pH_i to increase beyond the threshold for activation of the acid-extrusion mechanism.

Conclusions

The preceding examples illustrate the dynamic interactions among the processes involved in pH_i regulation. Nevertheless, actual acid-base disturbances are expected to be far more complex. For example, changes in extracellular pH are expected to influence pH_i by affecting both acid-loading and acid-extruding processes.

Extracellular metabolic acidosis (i.e., decreased $[HCO_3^-]$ at constant P_{CO_2}) is expected to decrease acid extrusion by directly inhibiting acid-extruding processes (e.g., Na-H exchange) and to increase acid loading by enhancing HCO_3^- efflux (e.g., via Cl-HCO_3 exchange). Both effects would be predicted to lower steady state pH_i by producing a net transfer of alkali from the intracellular to the extracellular space. A side effect of this alkali transfer would be to ameliorate the extracellular metabolic acidosis.

Extracellular metabolic alkalosis is expected to have the opposite effects, producing an increase in steady state pH_i and a net transfer to acid out of the cell. Thus, the model of Fig. 6 predicts that certain disturbances of extracellular acid-base balance are reflected by changes in steady state pH_i. This interaction between intracellular and extracellular pH is probably the main reason why it is clinically useful to monitor the pH of the blood plasma as an index of whole-body acid-base status.

ACKNOWLEDGMENT

I thank Eleanor Savage for her secretarial assistance.

REFERENCES

1. Aickin, C. C., and Thomas, R. C. (1977): An investigation of the ionic mechanism of intracellular pH regulation in mouse soleus muscle fibres. *J. Physiol*, 273:295–316.
2. Aronson, P. S., Nee, J., and Suhm, A. (1982): Modifier role of internal H^+ in activating the $Na^+ - H^+$ exchanger in renal microvillus membrane vesicles. *Nature*, 299:161–163.
3. Boron, W. F., and Boulpaep, E. L. (1983): Intracellular pH regulation in the renal proximal tubule of the salamander. Na-H exchange. *J. Gen. Physiol.*, 81:29–52.
4. Boron, W. F., and Boulpaep, E. L. (1983): Intracellular pH regulation in the renal proximal tubule of the salamander: Basolateral HCO_3^- transport. *J. Gen. Physiol.*, 81:53–94.
5. Boron, W. F., and De Weer, P. (1976): Intracellular pH transients in squid giant axons caused by CO_2, NH_3 and metabolic inhibitors. *J. Gen. Physiol.*, 67:91–112.
6. Boron, W. F., and De Weer, P. (1976): Active proton transport stimulated by CO_2/HCO_3^- blocked by cyanide. *Nature*, 259:240–241.
7. Boron, W. F., and Russell, J. M. (1983): Stoichiometry and ion dependencies of the intracellular pH-regulating mechanism in squid giant axons. *J. Gen. Physiol.*, 81:373–399.
8. Chaillet, J. R., Amsler, K., and Boron, W. F. (1986): Optical measurement of intracellular pH in single LLC-PK1 cells: Demonstration of Cl/HCO_3^- exchange. *Proc. Natl. Acad. Sci. USA*, 83:522–526.
9. Grinstein, S., Clarke, C. A., and Rothstein, A. (1983): Activation of Na^+/H^+ exchange in lymphocytes by osmotically induced volume changes and by cytoplasmic acidification. *J. Gen. Physiol.*, 82:619–638.
10. Lazdunski, J., Frelin, C., and Vigne, P. (1985): The sodium/hydrogen exchange system in cardiac cells: Its biochemical and pharmacological properties and its role in regulating internal concentrations of sodium and internal pH. *J. Mol. Cell. Cardiol.*, 17:1029–1042.
11. Moolenaar, W. H., Tsien, R. Y., van der Saag, P. T., and de Laat, S. W. (1983): Na^+/H^+ exchange and cytoplasmic pH in the action of growth factors in human fibroblasts. *Nature*, 304:645–648.
12. Pouyssegur, J., Sardet, C., Franchi, A., L'Allemain, G., and Paris, S. (1984): A specific mutation abolishing Na^+/H^+ antiport activity in hamster fibroblasts precludes growth at neutral and acidic pH. *Proc. Natl. Acad. Sci. USA*, 81:4833–4837.
13. Russell, J.M., and Boron, W. F. (1976): Role of chloride transport in regulation of intracellular pH. *Nature*, 264:73–74.
14. Siebens, A. W., and Boron W. F. (1987): Effect of electroneutral luminal and basolateral lactate transport on intracellular pH in salamander proximal tubules. *J. Gen. Physiol.* (in press)
15. Thomas, R. C. (1976): Ionic mechanism of the H^+ pump in a snail neuron. *Nature*, 262: 54–55.
16. Thomas, R. C. (1977): The role of bicarbonate, chloride and sodium ions in the regulation of intracellular pH in snail neurones. *J. Physiol*, 273:317–338.
17. Vaughan-Jones, R. D. (1979): Regulation of chloride in quiescent sheep-heart Purkinje fibres

studied using intracellular chloride and pH-sensitive micro-electrodes. *J. Phyisol.*, 295: 111–137.

General Review Articles

18. Moolenaar, W. H. (1986): Effects of growth factors on intracellular pH regulation. *Annu. Rev. Physiol.*, 48:363–376.
19. Roos, A., and Boron, W. F. (1981): Intracellular pH. *Physiol. Rev.*, 61:296–434.
20. Siesjo, B. K. (1973): Metabolic control of intracellular pH. *Scand. J. Clin. Lab. Invest.*, 32:97–104.
21. Thomas, R. C. (1984): Experimental displacement of intracellular pH and the mechanism of its subsequent recovery. *J. Physiol. (Lond.)*, 354:3P–22P.

The Regulation of Acid–Base Balance, edited
by Donald W. Seldin and Gerhard Giebisch,
Raven Press, Ltd., New York © 1989.

3

Buffer Equilibria in Red Blood Cells

R.B. Gunn

*Department of Physiology, Emory University School of Medicine,
Atlanta, Georgia 30322*

Time Course of Buffering
Equilibrium of Protons and Chloride
Titration of Whole Blood
**Mechanisms for the Transport of Acid and Base Equivalence Across the
    Erythrocyte Membrane**
The Role of H^+ and Cl^- Cotransport on Band 3
The Bohr Effect
**How Large is the Proton Load on Hemoglobin Resulting from Carbon
    Dioxide Transport**
References

When discussing buffer equilibria, we must consider red blood cells separately from other cells and tissues for three reasons. Red blood cells are the
only human cells known to be at pH equilibrium with their extracellular fluid,
the plasma. Red blood cells have a high buffer capacity, which is rapidly
available to the extracellular fluid through the exchange of chloride and bicarbonate anions on the intrinsic membrane protein transporter, band 3.
Hemoglobin is the major buffer for the 15 to 20 moles of protons produced
and consumed in carbon dioxide reactions each day in both the peripheral and
pulmonary capillaries.

TIME COURSE OF BUFFERING (12,14)

Since the majority of blood buffering occurs within the red cell and since
proton equilibration within both the plasma compartment and red cell cytoplasmic compartment is very rapid, the time course of buffering by the blood
depends on the rate of transport of protons or their functional equivalents
(OH^-, HCO_3^-) across the red cell membrane. As has been pointed out in

Chapters 1 and 2, there are several ways to move titrating units across a cell membrane that separates the two compartments. The movement of H^+ (H_3^+O) or OH^- directly changes the pH on both sides of the membrane, but the movement of HCO_3^- in exchange for Cl^- is principally responsible for the transport of titrating units across red cell membranes. Bicarbonate and protons almost instantaneously combine to form carbonic acid (HCO_3^- + H^+ = H_2CO_3) so that for our purposes this reaction can always be considered at equilibrium. The dehydration of carbonic acid (H_2CO_3) to CO_2 and H_2O is moderately slow in the absence of any enzyme, but carbonic anhydrase (EC 4.2.1.1) is the fastest known enzyme ($\sim 5 \times 10^5\ s^{-1}$ at 37°C) and is present in abundance in red cells, so that this reaction is 90% complete in 15 to 30 msec. These reactions between CO_2 and water and the exchange of Cl and bicarbonate are the principal mechanism for equilibrating intracellular and extracellular pH values when fixed base or acid is added to blood.

EQUILIBRIUM OF PROTONS AND CHLORIDE (3,5,9)

In theory, protons must be at equilibrium across the red cell membrane when their concentration is constant (steady state) in the plasma because of three facts: protons permeate the red cell membrane, there is no known active transport across the red cell membrane, and the rates at which protons are produced and consumed by red cell metabolism are negligible (4–8 mmoles/kg hemoglobin/hr) compared with their transport rates (mmoles/kg hemoglobin/min). Similarly, chloride ions that rapidly permeate the red cell membrane, that are not actively transported, and that are not consumed by metabolism, must be at equilibrium across the red cell membrane in the steady state. Experimentally, this also appears to be true, at least as a first approximation. Careful measurements by Funder and Wieth of proton and chloride distributions across the erythrocyte membrane show a slight discrepancy between the ratio of proton activities aH_o/aH_i and the chloride concentration ratio $[Cl_i]/[Cl_o]$.[1]

Erythrocytes have a low membrane potential of about -9 mV ($V_{in} - V_{out}$) in plasma at 37°C and pH 7.4. From thermodynamics, we know that each ion at equilibrium across the cell membrane must be distributed in accordance with that potential. The Nernst equation

---

[1]The reason for the discrepancy is unknown, but there are four possibilities. First, errors in the measurements due to asymmetric liquid junction potentials seem to be in the wrong direction. Second, there is a difference in ionic strength between plasma (≈ 0.15 M) and cytoplasm (≈ 0.20 M), which might make the activity coefficients asymmetric and thus the ratio of chloride concentrations unequal to the ratio of chloride activities. Third, there is recent evidence for a Na_o^+/H_i exchanger in red cells, but any secondary active transport by this mechanism would be too small and would be in the opposite direction to cause the discrepancy. Fourth, the measurement of Cl_i may have been falsely elevated due to the coulometric titration of glutathione as if it were chloride in red cell acid extracts.

$$V_{in} - V_{out} = (RT/F)\ln_e(X_o/X_i)^z$$

is true at equilibrium, where RT/F is about 26 mV and X_o and X_i are the activities of the ion outside and inside the cell respectively and z is the ion's valence (sign and magnitude). Thus, for Cl ($z = -1$) and H^+ (H_3^+O, $z = v1$), aCl_i/aCl_o equals aH_o/aH_i at equilibrium; and, by taking the $\log_{10}$ of both sides and rearranging, we obtain

$$pH_i = pH_o + \log_{10}([Cl_i]/[Cl_o])$$

if we assume that the internal and external activity coefficients for chloride are equal and thus cancel in the ratio. One can, therefore, calculate internal pH at equilibrium from plasma pH and the chloride concentration ratio. The chloride concentration ratio is about 0.70 in normal cells and thus in plasma with a chloride concentration of 103 mM the intraerythrocyte water has 72 mM chloride. Using the equation above, we can calculate that intraerythrocyte pH is 0.155 pH units lower than the plasma pH at proton equilibrium and under normal conditions. This difference between intraerythrocyte and plasma pH can be altered in experimental and pathologic conditions. Clearly, any perturbation of the $[Cl_i]/[Cl_o]$ ratio will have its corresponding effect on the pH difference.

TITRATION OF WHOLE BLOOD

One way to change $[Cl_i]$ is to titrate the intracellular buffers (Table 1). Consider what happens to a liter of packed erythrocytes if their extracellular fluid is titrated one pH unit from pH 7.4 to pH 6.4. A good rule of thumb is that 60 mEq of protons are required to lower the pH one unit for each liter of packed erythrocytes. From the requirement of intracellular electroneutrality, we know that 60 mEq of chloride must enter the cell with 60 mEq of protons. Parenthetically, the number of anionic charges exceeds the total number of cationic charges (5×10^9) in the cell by only 8×10^4 fewer monovalent cations than anions from a total of 5×10^9 when the membrane potential is -9 mV. The addition of these 60 mEq of chloride raises the intracellular chloride concentration from 72 mM at $pH_o = 7.4$ to ~126 mM at $pH_o = 6.4$. (Note that 60 mEq added to the 0.64 liters of cell water/liter of packed cells should raise cell chloride by 94 mM if the cell did not swell. But erythrocytes swell at low pH in response to the entering osmoles of chloride.) This increases the chloride ratio to 1.22, the membrane potential becomes $+5$ mV, and pH_i becomes 6.48 when pH_o is 6.40. This is an extreme case for an *in vitro* experiment. But *in vivo*, the same principles apply, namely, that the chloride ratio, which is less than unity, increases during acidemia and the pH difference between inside and outside diminishes with the absolute value of

TABLE 1. *Theoretical changes in equilibrium values of erythrocytes due to titration of the plasma from pH 7.4 to pH 6.4 in the absence and presence of CO_2*

P_{CO_2}, torr	0	40	0	40
pH_o	7.4	7.4	6.4	6.4
pH_i	7.245	7.245	6.48	6.51
Cl_o, mmoles/liter	103	103	103	103
Cl_i, mmoles/liter cell H_2O	72	72	126	134
r_{Cl}, r_{HCO_3}	0.70	0.70	1.22	1.22
V_m, mV	−9	−9	+5	+7
$HCO_{3\text{-}o}$, mmoles//liter plasma	0	24	0	2.4
$HCO_{3\text{-}i}$, mmoles/liter cell H_2O	0	16.8	0	3.1
Liter cell H_2O/liter packed cells	0.64	0.64	0.70	0.70
Osmolality, mOsm	300	300[a]	300	300[a]

[a]The added bicarbonate has replaced an isosmolal amount of plasma and cytoplasmic protein.

the membrane potential, and the cells swell as HCl enters the cells. These calculations, however, have neglected bicarbonate ions, which are certainly present *in vivo*. The bicarbonate ratio ($HCO_{3\text{-}i}/HCO_{3\text{-}o}$) equals the chloride ratio ($r_{Cl} = 0.7$ at $pH_o = 7.4$) at equilibrium. So when $P_{CO_2} = 40$ torr (mm Hg) and plasma pH $= 7.4$, the plasma HCO_3 is 24 mM and intraerythrocyte $HCO_{3\text{-}i}$ is 16.8 mM. If the plasma pH decreased one pH unit and P_{CO_2} remained constant, $HCO_{3\text{-}o}$ could decrease to 2.4 mM and intraerythrocyte bicarbonate would decrease to 3.1 mM ($r_{HCO_3} = r_{Cl} \approx 1.22$). The 13.7 mM loss of intracellular HCO_3 is replaced by Cl_i, so intraerythrocyte chloride concentration would increase to 134 mM, and red cell chloride content would actually increase more than the 60 mEq required to titrate the cells and change the extracellular pH by one unit.

Erythrocytes are a mobile intracellular space that contains hemoglobin (Hgb), a major buffer of blood. A standard 70 kg man with 1.83 m^2 surface area has approximately 900 g of circulating Hgb in 3.1×10^{13} red cells with 1 kg of dry cell solids and 1.8 kg of cell water. Recall that the rule of thumb is that a liter of red cells requires 60 mEq of acid or base to change the extracellular pH one unit. Since the density of red cells is 1.12 kg/liter, the rule of thumb converts into 167 mEq of acid or base per kg Hgb per pH unit. By using 16,700 as the molecular weight of an α or β chain monomer, one calculates 2.8 theoretical buffer sites per monomer per pH unit.

$$[60 \text{ mEq/(1 cell)}] \times [1.12 \text{ kg cells/(1 cell)}]^{-1} \times [2.8 \text{ kg cells/0.9 kg Hgb}] \times [16.7 \times 10^{-3} \text{ kg/mmole monomer}] = 2.8$$

This rough calculation, of course, assumes that 100% of the buffering within red cells is by Hgb molecules. This is nearly true in a system without CO_2 and bicarbonate or in a closed system where the total amount of CO_2, carbonic acid, and HCO_3 is constant (Table 2). However, *in vivo* where the P_{CO_2} is either tightly regulated by the ventilation rate if one is considering

TABLE 2. *Blood buffering*[a]

	In vivo, P_{CO_2} = 40 torr hematocrit = 45%		*In vitro*, closed system: constant total CO_2 + H_2CO_3 + HCO_3^- = 25.2 mM		*In vitro*, open to air: P_{CO_2} = 0	
	β	%	β	%	β	%
Plasma pH 7.4						
$\quad$ CO_2-carbonic acid-HCO_3^- (25.2 mM)	30.4	42%	1.4	4%	0	
$\quad$ Proteins (7 g/dl plasma)	3.9	5%	3.9	12%	3.9	13%
Red blood cells						
$\quad$ Intracellular CO_2-carbonic acid-HCO_3^-	10.4	15%	0.5	2%	0	
$\quad$ Hemoglobin (15 g/dl whole blood)	27.0	38%	27.0	82%	27.0	87%
Total	71.7	100%	32.8	100%	30.9	100%

[a]Buffer value, β, mEq of H^+ or OH^-/(liter whole blood • pH unit).

the blood as a whole or loosely regulated by the tissues (P_{CO_2} 40–47 torr) if one is considering only capillary blood, only 72% of the buffering within red cells is by Hgb molecules, and the remainder is by the CO_2-carbonic acid-bicarbonate system. The buffer value, β, of intracellular phosphate is less than 0.1 mEq/(liter whole blood • pH unit) and, together with other proteins and organic phosphates in the cytoplasm, may be neglected.

The total body Hgb can be estimated from standard clinical parameters. The mean corpuscular Hgb concentration is about 33 g% (33 g Hgb/100 ml of packed cells or 330 g/liter cells). With 6 liters of blood volume and a hematocrit of 45%, there are 2.7 liters of packed red cells and thus 2.7 times 330 or 890 ≈ 900 g of Hgb in a standard person. This hemoglobin is 38% of the total blood buffer *in vivo*. The total buffer value of 71.7 mEq/(liter whole blood • pH unit) in Table 2 means that as long as ventilation clamps the P_{CO_2} at 40 torr, a liter of blood will take about 7 mEq of nonvolatile acid, such as HCl or H_2SO_4, to lower its pH 0.1 unit. Table 2 lists the contributions of other blood components to the total buffer value.

MECHANISMS FOR THE TRANSPORT OF ACID AND BASE EQUIVALENTS ACROSS THE ERYTHROCYTE MEMBRANE (2,4–6,10,11)

For the purposes of acid-base transport, each red cell membrane may be viewed as a phospholipid bilayer with 10^6 monomers of band 3 protein embedded in the membrane and spanning through the membrane. The transport of acid and base appears to involve (a) band 3-mediated exchange of chloride and bicarbonate, (b) band 3-mediated cotransport of protons with chloride and other small inorganic anions, and (c) a baseline phospholipid bilayer permeability to (i) protons of 10^{-4} cm/sec, such as that found in protein-free vesicles and planar bilayers, (ii) undissociated acids, such as H_2CO_3, and (iii) undissociated bases, such as NH_3. All three are important physiologic pathways. Although Cl-HCO_3 exchange is most familiar (Hamburger shift) and most studied, this pathway probably does not dissipate the proton gradient produced when blood takes up CO_2 in the peripheral tissues or releases it in the lung. Surprisingly, either HCl cotransport or diffusion of H_2CO_3 or NH_3 must equilibrate the plasma with the red cell cytoplasm.

Chloride and bicarbonate ions on both sides of the membrane compete for a single binding and transport site on each band 3 protein monomer. This site when complexed with either anion has alternate access to the cytoplasm and plasma at a rate of 50,000 times per sec, and the total body erythrocytes (3.1 × 10^{13} cells) can optimally exchange 150 moles/min. These rates of tracer exchange are never achieved for net chloride-bicarbonate exchange because most of the swaps are chloride for chloride or bicarbonate for bicarbonate, which have no net physiologic effect. Even under maximal physiologic perturbations from equilibrium where the gradient changes by 2 mM HCO_3 (as when erythrocytes transit pulmonary or tissue capillaries), the exchanger can only briefly operate at 1% of optimum rate before the gradients of HCO_3 and chloride are dissipated and their equilibrium is achieved. At proton, chloride, and bicarbonate equilibrium, of course, band 3 exchange has no net physiologic or transport effect, although the exchange of isotopes (e.g., ^{36}Cl exchange for ^{35}Cl) remains very rapid.

The uptake of CO_2 by the blood is the most important process in blood buffering. It has several steps that must be described here in order to follow the gradients of protons that are developed. Tissue CO_2 equilibrates by diffusion with the incoming capillary blood within 3 to 5 msec, so that the P_{CO_2} of the tissue, plasma, and intraerythrocyte cytoplasm is almost exactly equal. In the plasma, the hydration of CO_2 is slow, whereas in the red cell cytoplasm, it is catalyzed rapidly by carbonic anhydrase within 15 to 30 msec to H_2CO_3, which dissociates to equilibrium with H^+ and HCO_3 within the cytoplasm within microseconds. In parallel, but somewhat slower (250 msec), some CO_2 reacts with Hgb to form carbamino groups with the N-terminal valines of the α and β chains. The transport equilibrium across the red cell membrane between chloride and bicarbonate ions is 90% complete in 400 to 500 msec at body temperature but, nevertheless, is the slowest step in the transfer of CO_2 from the tissues to plasma bicarbonate.

Of the total CO_2 transported by the blood to the lungs, only 8% is transported as dissolved CO_2, 11% is transported as carbamino groups on hemoglobin, and 81% is transported as bicarbonate (Fig. 1). Of the bicarbonate,

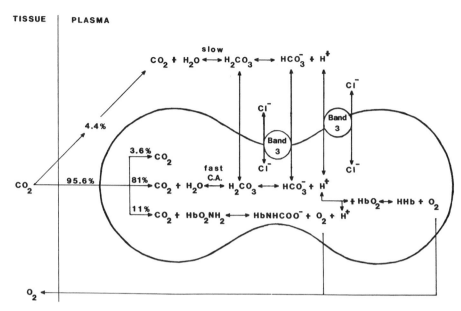

FIG. 1. Carbon dioxide transport and acidification of red cell cytoplasm and plasma in tissue capillaries. CO_2 produced in the tissues is transported in venous blood to the lungs as dissolved CO_2, bicarbonate, and carbamino groups on hemoglobin, $HbNHCOO^-$. The more rapid hydration of CO_2 within the erythrocyte cytoplasm by carbonic anhydrases (C.A.) assures that the cytoplasm becomes transiently more acid than capillary plasma. This proton gradient is not dissipated by the HCO_3-Cl exchange on band 3 but by H/Cl cotransport on band 3 and by diffusion of carbonic acid (H_2CO_3) and other undissociated acids (not indicated). The percentages shown are for the distribution of CO_2 transport in its several chemical forms.

30% (24% of total CO_2 transported) remains inside the red cell cytoplasm, where 70% (57% of total CO_2 transported) is exchanged for extracellular chloride during the equilibration and is thus transported into the lungs in the plasma. With each bicarbonate and carbamino group produced within the erythrocyte, a proton also is produced. These protons are mostly buffered by Hgb, but some remain free in the cytoplasm to increase its acidity over that of extracellular plasma.

How this disequilibrium of protons resolves itself is not readily apparent. CO_2 enters the red cell and forms H_2CO_{3-i}, H_i^+, and HCO_3^-. The same reaction occurs more slowly in the capillary plasma. If the extent of CO_2 conversion to H_2CO_3, H^+, and HCO_3 in the plasma and cytoplasm is proportional to the nonbicarbonate buffer capacities of the plasma and cytoplasm, respectively, no pH disequilibrium will develop. In such a case, the rate of CO_2 hydration within the cell must almost match the ability of Hgb to take up protons, and a lower rate of extracellular hydration must almost match the plasma buffer's ability to take up protons. The result would be that proton concentrations rise slightly but in synchrony on the two sides of the red cell membrane, and the pH difference would remain constant and equal to log r_{Cl}. This does not appear to happen in the circulation, since the hydration rates in the cell are 1,000 to 10,000 times that in the plasma, and the buffer value of red cells (Table 2; 27 mEq/(liter whole blood • pH unit); hematocrit 45%) is only seven times that of the accompanying plasma (3.9 mEq/(liter whole blood • pH unit). The relative extents of CO_2 hydration in plasma and erythrocytes are not known but probably vary among different capillary beds as the amounts of bound endothelial carbonic anhydrases vary. The treatment of patients with those inhibitors of carbonic anhydrase that are impermeable to erythrocyte membranes would produce the greatest disparity in CO_2 hydration rates inside and outside of the cells in all capillary beds. In most normal capillary beds, however, we expect the development of a proton disequilibrium across the red cell membrane favoring proton efflux.

This disequilibrium is propagated by the concurrent $[HCO_3]_i$-$[Cl]_o$ exchange that allows the continued intracellular hydration of CO_2 and its dissociation by removing an intracellular product $[HCO_3]_i$ and provides a sink for extracellular protons and perhaps reversal of extracellular hydration of CO_2. In either case, the band 3-mediated HCO_3-Cl exchange exacerbates the erythrocyte transmembrane disequilibrium of proton activities. The other factor besides activity differences in ion equilibrium is the membrane potential difference. But since the conductances of chloride and bicarbonate are both large and probably equal, the exchange of chloride for bicarbonate and the attendant concentration changes in these ions will not change V_m. Intracellular bicarbonate exchange for extracellular chloride will continue as long as bicarbonate continues to be produced and until r_{HCO_3} ($[HCO_3^-]_i/[HCO_3^-]_o$) decreases and r_{Cl} ($[Cl]_i/[Cl]_o$) increases to the point where they are equal.

THE ROLE OF H^+ AND Cl^- COTRANSPORT ON BAND 3 (4,8)

The proton disequilibrium produced by CO_2 loading of the blood is probably discharged by two mechanisms: the cotransport of protons with chloride on band 3 and the diffusion of H_2CO_3 through the lipid bilayer out of the red cell. Band 3 has at least one proton binding and transport site that appears to cross the erythrocyte membrane, provided a transportable anion, such as chloride is present. There is known to be cotransport of protons with sulfate on band 3, and recently chloride and other monovalent anions have been shown to activate net proton fluxes down a gradient of proton concentration. This cotransport mode of band 3 is 90% inhibitable by salicylates, furosemide (Lasix), bumetanide, and probably other diuretics. The significance of this mode of net proton transport compared with the net transport of H_2CO_3 across the lipid membrane is unknown, but a rough calculation indicates that the band 3-mediated proton flux is about 10 times the diffusive flux H_2CO_3 and comparable to the NH_3 (100 μM) flux. In summary, during transit of a tissue capillary, both intracellular chloride and intracellular protons are above their external electrochemical potentials just after the $[Cl]_o - [HCO_3]_i$ exchange has balanced the chloride and bicarbonate ratios. A net driving force then favors the net efflux of both H^+ and Cl^-. These net effluxes are probably mediated by band 3.

THE BOHR EFFECT (1,7,13)

Protons are released on oxygenation of Hgb above pH 6.3 (alkaline Bohr effect), and protons are taken up on oxygenation of Hgb below pH 6.3 (acid Bohr effect). The alkaline Bohr effect, which is operative at physiologic pH values, is due to pK changes of specific ionizable groups, the most important of which are the imidazole groups of 146 βHis and 122 αHis and the oxygen-linked chloride binding to 1 αVal, 1 βHis, and 143 βHis, which releases protons. Oxygenation lowers the effective pK of Hgb (above pH 6.3) and releases approximately 2.4 protons/Hgb tetramer. The converse is that on deoxygenation Hgb takes up about 2.4 protons/Hgb tetramer. The quantitative analysis of these effects is a result of the theoretical work of Whyman and careful measurements of the titration curve of Hgb at different degrees of O_2 saturation. The Bohr coefficient is the increase in the number of protons bound per heme upon full oxygenation. It is quantitatively expressed by the linkage equation of Wyman as

$$(\Delta H^+ / \Delta Y)_{pH} = (\Delta \log p / \Delta pH)_Y$$

where Y is the fractional saturation of hemoglobin with oxygen and p is oxygen tension. The maximal absolute value of the Bohr coefficient and the pH at which it occurs is a function of the anions present. Chloride and organic phosphates, particularly 2,3-diphosphoglycerate (2,3-DPG), enhance the alkaline Bohr effect (make ΔH^+ more negative). Under physiologic conditions of Cl, 2,3-DPG, and pH, the Bohr coefficient is about -0.6, so that the dissociation of 4 moles of O_2 from the four heme groups results in the uptake of $4 \times 0.6 = 2.4$ protons per Hgb tetramer, or 36 μEq/g Hgb.

The titration curve of deoxyhemoglobin is shifted to the right compared to the curve for oxyhemoglobin. That is, deoxyhemoglobin is a weaker acid or has a higher affinity for protons than oxyhemoglobin. The slope of the titration curve at a particular pH is the buffer value, β (β = d(acid equivalents)/dpH) which is measured in mEq/(liter • pH). The buffer value for an equal concentration of deoxyhemoglobin is slightly greater than for oxyhemoglobin. Since the buffer value is proportional to the concentration of the buffering molecules, it is often expressed as the molar buffer value. For Hgb under physiologic conditions β = 3 Eq/mole of monomer/pH unit or expressed per g (16,700 dalton/monomer) is 0.18 mEq/(g Hgb • pH unit). Assuming a mean corpuscular Hgb concentration (MCHC) of 33 g/dl, this value is 59.4 mEq/(liter packed cells • pH unit), which is the basis for the rule of thumb.

HOW LARGE IS THE PROTON LOAD ON HEMOGLOBIN RESULTING FROM CARBON DIOXIDE TRANSPORT?

In a 70 kg individual at rest, 13 to 20 moles of CO_2 are produced each day by oxidative metabolism. With a cardiac output of 5 liters/min, a production rate of 15 moles of CO_2 per day means 2 mmoles of CO_2 per liter must be carried to the lungs. Since only the 8% carried as dissolved CO_2 gas does not result in the generation of a proton within the red cells, 1.9 mmoles of H^+ are added per liter of whole blood for 13 µEq of protons are generated per gram of Hgb. From our previous calculations, we know that full deoxygenation consumes 36 µEq of protons/g Hgb. Since the mixed venous blood has a Po_2 of 40 torr and is 75% saturated with O_2, Hgb only consumes about 25% of the maximum number of protons or 9 µEq of protons/g Hgb. The difference between 13 and 9, that is, 4 µEq/g Hgb, actually goes toward lowering the pH_i and adding further protons to Hgb and other intracellular buffers. These 4 µEq/g Hgb will lower pH_i by 0.02 units (4/[180 µEq/(g Hgb • pH unit)] = 0.02), whereas without the Bohr effect, the pH_i would decrease 0.07 units (13/180 = 0.07).

Consider for a moment what happens in the capillaries upon exercise: O_2 demands increase, and cardiac output increases. The Po_2 of mixed venous blood declines as it delivers the additional required O_2. CO_2 production increases (as does the respiratory quotient) nearly proportionately, but its effect on venous blood pH is minimized, since more Hgb is available per unit time, and more protons can be bound at the same pH_i, since the venous Hgb is more deoxygenated. This mechanism works well until a theoretical limit is met in some capillary bed where the transit time of the red cells becomes too rapid for the $[HCO_3]_i$-$[Cl]_o$ exchange to be complete (400–500 msec). Then the capillary blood would deliver more O_2 than remove CO_2. Tissue Pco_2 would increase steeply, and tissue acidosis would become severe.

ACKNOWLEDGMENTS

I am grateful for the support and criticisms of Dr. Patricia A. King and Dr. David G. Shoemaker. This work was supported in part by USPHS-NIH grants RO1 HL28674 and RO1 GM30754.

REFERENCES

1. Bohr, C., Hasselbalch, K., and Krogh, A. (1904): Ueber einen in biologischer Beziehung wichtigen Einfluss, den die Kohlensaurespannung des Blutes auf dessen Sauerstoffbindung ubt. *Scand. Arch. Physiol.*, 16:402–412.
2. Deamer, D. W. (1987): Proton permeation of lipid bilayers. *J. Bioenerg. Biomembr.*, 19:457–479.
3. Funder, J., and Wieth, J. O., (1966): Chloride and hydrogen ion distribution between human red cells and plasma. *Acta Physiol. Scand.*, 68:234–245.
4. Gunn, R. B. (1986): H^+ (or OH^-) fluxes activated by inorganic ions on the anion exchanger (band 3) of human red cells. *Biophys. J.*, 49:579a.
5. Gunn, R. B., Dalmark, M., Tosteson, D. C., and Wieth, J. O. (1973): Characteristics of chloride transport in human red blood cells. *J. Gen. Physiol.*, 61:185–206.
6. Gunn, R. B., and Fröhlich, O. (1979): Asymmetry in the mechanism for anion exchange in human red cell membranes: Evidence for reciprocating sites that react with one transported anion at a time. *J. Gen. Physiol.*, 74:351–374.
7. Imai, K. (1982): *Allosteric Effects in Haemoglobin.* Cambridge University Press, Cambridge.
8. Jennings, M. A. (1976): Proton fluxes associated with erythrocyte membrane anion exchange. *J. Membr. Biol.*, 28:187–205.
9. Milanick, M. A., Dissing, S. D., and Hoffman, J. F. (1985): Na/H exchange in human red blood cells: A coupled transport process. *Biophys. J.*, 47:490a.
10. Rossi-Bernardi, L., Roughton, F. J. W., Pace, M., and Coven, E. (1972): The effects of organic phosphates on the binding of CO_2 to human hemoglobin and on CO_2 transport in the circulating blood. In: *Oxygen Affinity of Hemoglobin and Red Cell Acid Base Status*, edited by M. Rørth and P. Astrup, pp. 224–235. Munksgaard, Copenhagen.
11. Wieth, J. O., Andersen, O. S., Brahm, J., Bjerrum, P. J., and Borders, C. L. (1982): Chloride-bicarbonate exchange in red blood cells: Physiology of transport and chemical modification of binding sites. *Philos. Trans. R. Soc. Lond.*, B299:383–399.
12. Wistrand, P. S. (1981): The importance of carbonic anhydrase B and C for the unloading of CO_2 by the human erythrocyte. *Acta Physiol. Scand.*, 113:417–426.
13. Wyman, J. (1964): Linked functions and reciprocal effects in hemoglobin: A second look. *Adv. Protein Chem.*, 19:223.

General Review Articles

14. Brahm, J. (1986): The physiology of anion transport in red cells. *Prog. Hematol.*, 14:1–21.
15. Bunn, H. F., and Forget, B. G. (1986): *Hemoglobin: Molecular Genetic and Clinical Aspects.* Saunders, Philadelphia.
16. Cohen, J. J., and Kassirer, J. P. (1982): *Acid-Base.* Little, Brown & Co., Boston.
17. Forster, R. E. (1985): Buffering in blood with emphasis on kinetics. In: *The Kidney: Physiology and Pathophysiology*, edited by D. W. Seldin and G. Giebisch, pp. 133–148. Raven Press, New York.
18. Gunn, R. B., Fröhlich, O., King, P. A., and Shoemaker, D. G. (1989): Anion transport. In: *The Red Cell Membrane: Structure, Function, and Clinical Implications*, edited by J. C. Parker and P. Agre. Marcel Dekker, New York.

The Regulation of Acid–Base Balance, edited by Donald W. Seldin and Gerhard Giebisch, Raven Press, Ltd., New York © 1989.

4

Internal Exchanges of Hydrogen Ions: Bone

David A. Bushinsky

Department of Medicine, Pritzker School of Medicine, University of Chicago, Chicago, Illinois 60637

The skeleton not only provides the physical structure for the body but also is actively involved in maintaining stable systemic acid-base balance. The fall in extracellular fluid pH from an acute infusion of acid is mitigated by the buffering response of bone mineral mediated through an exchange of hydrogen ions for sodium and potassium and consumption of the hydrogen ion buffer, carbonate. When renal acid excretion fails to balance the sum of hydrogen ion intake and endogenous acid production, as in distal renal tubular acidosis, the bone mineral provides a sink for the excess hydrogen ions, protecting against potentially life-threatening acidemia. With the progressive hydrogen ion retention of chronic renal failure, systemic pH stabilizes as bone mineral is resorbed, providing the hydrogen ion buffers phosphate and carbonate. With normal renal function, the imposition of these acute and chronic acid loads leads to an increase in renal calcium excretion derived in large part from the breakdown of bone mineral. At the cellular level, in response to increases in parathyroid hormone (PTH) and 1,25-dihydroxyvitamin D_3 [$1,25(OH)_2D_3$], hydrogen ions appear to be secreted by osteoclasts, causing local bone resorption. Thus, hydrogen ions are buffered by and cause the dissolution of bone mineral. Although at times hydrogen ion buffering by bone is linked to mineral dissolution, often it is not; the two processes benefit from separate analysis.

COMPOSITION OF BONE (4,20,35)

In humans, bone consists of dense cortical bone found on the outer surface of the long bones and spongy cancellous bone present at the ends of the long bones and in the axial skeleton. Bone is made up of both an inorganic, or mineral, phase and an organic phase. The inorganic or mineral phase, which makes up approximately two thirds of the weight of mature bone, contains small crystals that have an X-ray diffraction pattern most consistent with hydroxyapatite $[Ca_{10}(PO_4)_6(OH)_2]$. However, it is widely recognized that bone apatite is also associated with anions other than the hydroxyl group and that various cations, such as fluoride and magnesium, can be found within the crystal lattice. There are several other phases of bone mineral, including brushite $(CaHPO_4)$, which may be a precursor of apatite, and carbonate (CO_3^{2-}), associated with calcium, potassium, and/or sodium, which has an important role in maintaining acid-base balance.

The organic phase of bone consists of collagen, ground substance, and bone cells. Collagen is a 1.5×300 nm rigid rod formed from three polypeptide (alpha) chains that are linked both end to end and side to side to form fibrils that are several collagen molecules thick. Fibrils are then arranged in bundles or fibers that can be seen on light microscopy. The ground substance, which contains glycoproteins and mucopolysaccharides, permeates the collagen bundles before mineralization. There are three principal cells found in bone: osteoblasts, osteoclasts, and osteocytes. The osteoblasts are bone-forming cells that secrete organic material and form a continuous cuboidal layer on the unmineralized collagen matrix. The osteocytes are the most numerous of the bone cells in mature bone and appear to be resting osteoblasts surrounded by mineralized bone. The osteoclasts, the bone-resorbing cells, are large, multinucleated cells apparently derived from circulating monocytes that have a ruffled border in contact with the bone surface during demineralization. Actual bone elongation and modeling occur into the teens in humans, and after the completion of elongation, bone remodeling continues throughout life. Remodeling consists of the slow resorption and deposition of mineralized bone by the osteoclasts and osteoblasts, respectively, and is thought to involve about 10% of the adult skeleton on a yearly basis.

PTH, $1,25(OH)_2D_3$, and hydrogen ions have important roles in regulating bone formation and dissolution (Fig. 1). PTH is secreted in response to a fall in blood ionized calcium and is responsible for release of calcium from the bone mineral in addition to conservation of calcium by the renal tubule. With

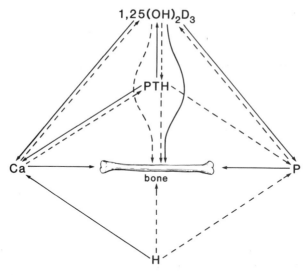

FIG. 1. Schematic diagram of the regulation of calcium (Ca), phosphorus (P), hydrogen ions (H), parathyroid hormone (PTH), and 1,25-dihydroxyvitamin D_3 [1,25 $(OH)_2D_3$] in relation to bone. Solid arrows indicate up regulation, or bone formation and dashed lines indicate down regulation or bone dissolution. (Modified from ref. 20.)

continued secretion of PTH, there is a proliferation of osteoclasts, which promotes further bone dissolution. 25-Hydroxyvitamin D_3 is converted to $1,25(OH)_2D_3$ by the 1-alpha-hydroxylase in the mitochondria of renal proximal tubule cells. The conversion is stimulated by increased serum PTH, a decrease in phosphate intake, and a fall in the ionized component of blood calcium. Along with promoting mineral absorption from the gastrointestinal tract, $1,25(OH)_2D_3$ stimulates osteoclastic bone resorption and/or formation depending upon the ionic environment. As detailed later in this chapter, an increase in hydrogen ion concentration promotes bone mineral dissolution through direct noncell-mediated and perhaps cell-mediated mechanisms.

ROLE OF BONE MINERAL IN SYSTEMIC HYDROGEN ION BUFFERING

Metabolic Acidosis (1,3,5,7–9,11,13,14,16–18,21,24,29,31,34,35,38)

Acute

Bone is involved in buffering the additional hydrogen ions administered during an acute acid load. From the reduction of pH and extracellular fluid bicarbonate observed during the infusion of an acute acid load and the volume of the extracellular fluid, Swann and Pitts first demonstrated that approximately 60% of administered hydrogen ions are buffered outside of the extracellular fluid (ECF) by soft tissues and by bone. The *in vivo* evidence that bone acutely buffers hydrogen ions derives principally from the loss of bone sodium and the depletion of bone carbonate after an acute acid load. Sodium loss from bone implies hydrogen for sodium exchange, and the carbonate loss suggests consumption of this buffer by the administered protons. *In vitro*, when neonatal mouse calvariae (frontal and parietal bones of the skull) are cultured in acidic medium, there is a net influx of protons into the bone, decreasing the hydrogen ion concentration of the medium, indicating that the additional hydrogen ions are being buffered by bone.

Proton for sodium exchange

Bone is a large reservoir for sodium and potassium. The bone surface is coated with fixed negative sites that normally are bonded with sodium, potassium, and protons; the sodium exchanges freely with the surrounding fluid. A decrease in systemic pH is thought to cause the additional protons to displace sodium and potassium from the mineral, resulting in an egress of sodium and potassium and a buffering of systemic acidity. *In vivo* studies by Bergstrom and Ruva support this hypothesis. They demonstrated that 4 hr after the intraperitoneal injection of ammonium chloride into rats, bone sodium falls by approximately 28%. Bettice and Gamble confirmed this observation by the finding that rat bones lose approximately 7 mEq/kg of exchangeable bone sodium after 5 hr of metabolic acidosis.

The indirect evidence that bone is a hydrogen ion buffer, based on the loss of bone sodium, is confirmed *in vitro* by our observation that there is a net influx of protons from an acidic culture medium into neonatal mouse calvariae, thereby buffering the culture medium and increasing its pH (Fig. 2). Examination of calvariae with a high resolution scanning ion microprobe demonstrates that the surface of the bone is rich in sodium and potassium relative to calcium. After incubation in a physiologically acidic medium (pH 7.21), there is loss of bone surface sodium and potassium relative to calcium in conjunction with hydrogen ion buffering, suggesting sodium and potassium for proton exchange on the bone surface (Fig. 3).

Fall in bone carbonate

Bone appears to contain approximately 80% of the total carbon dioxide (including CO_3^{2-}, HCO_3^- and CO_2) in the body. About two thirds of this carbon dioxide is in the form of carbonate (CO_3^{2-}) complexed with calcium, sodium, and other cations and is located in the lattice of the bone crystals. The other third consists of bicarbonate (HCO_3^-) and appears to be located in the hydration shell of the hydroxyapatite.

Acute metabolic acidosis decreases bone total carbon dioxide. Bettice deter-

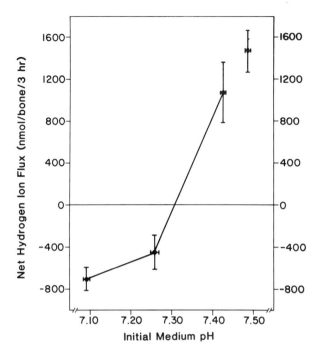

FIG. 2. Effect of initial medium pH on net hydrogen ion flux from neonatal mouse calvariae in 3 hr cultures. Values are mean ± SE. Medium pH was lowered by decreasing the bicarbonate concentration with concentrated HCl (closed circles, n = 8-28) from control (x, n = 15). A positive flux indicates net hydrogen ion movement from the calvariae into the medium, a negative flux the opposite. (From ref. 13.)

mined bone carbon dioxide 24 hr after the initiation of acid loading or the onset of diabetic ketoacidosis in rats (Fig. 4). He found that bone total carbon dioxide fell with acidosis and that the fall was directly proportional to the decline in the ECF pH and bicarbonate concentration. The loss of bone carbon dioxide suggests that bone is actively buffering the increased hydrogen ion concentration. In recent studies, we found that the medium used to culture neonatal mouse calvariae is in equilibrium with the calcium carbonate phase of the bone mineral and not the brushite or hydroxyapatite phase. A reduction of incubation medium pH liberated calcium carbonate from the bone, suggesting that it is the mineral species affected by alterations in proton concentration.

Our *in vitro* studies, in conjunction with the *in vivo* studies described previously, strongly suggest that bone is a hydrogen ion buffer capable of maintaining the extracellular fluid pH near the physiologic normal of 7.40. The loss of both bone sodium and carbon dioxide, possibly from the bicarbonate pool, suggests that in addition to sodium for hydrogen exchange and calcium carbonate dissolution there may be hydrogen ion-mediated loss of sodium bicarbonate from bone mineral. The extent to which sodium bicarbon-

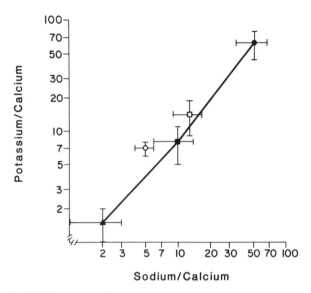

FIG. 3. Relationship between sodium/calcium (x-axis) and potassium/calcium (y-axis) for cultured neonatal mouse calvariae. All values are means ± SE for the ratio of counts per second of detected secondary ions corrected for species-dependent ionization probabilities as measured using a scanning ion microprobe. Closed circle, analysis of most superficial layer of calvariae in control (pH 7.40 ± 0.01) media for 3 hr (n = 10); closed square, analysis of exposed surface of control calvariae after erosion to a depth of ~15 nm by the gallium beam (n = 4); closed triangle, analysis of cross section exposed after fracturing frontal bones of calvariae in half (n = 5); open circle, analysis of surface of the calvariae after incubation in media of reduced pH (pH 7.21 ± 0.01; n = 5) for 3 hr; open square, culture as in reduced pH followed by erosion (n = 7). (From ref. 18.)

ate is present in bone mineral has not been determined, nor is it clear if this compound is directly liberated by an increase in hydrogen ion concentration.

Role of parathyroid hormone

PTH promotes cell-mediated resorption of bone mineral. In conjunction with calcium efflux, there is release of anionic hydrogen ion buffers, such as phosphate and carbonate, which are bound to calcium on the bone mineral. It has been suggested that a fundamental role of PTH is to augment extrarenal hydrogen ion buffering. This hypothesis was first tested by comparing the response of nephrectomized and thyroparathyroidectomized (TPTX) rats and dogs to an acute acid load in the presence or absence of replacement PTH. Without replacement PTH, the acid load was uniformly fatal to both species, whereas those animals receiving PTH all survived. Without added PTH, ECF bicarbonate buffered more of the hydrogen ions, suggesting that PTH augmented the ability of non-ECF bicarbonate buffers, such as bone, to lessen the fall in pH. In a second study, nephrectomized TPTX rats buffered an acid load as well as nephrectomized rats with intact parathyroid glands,

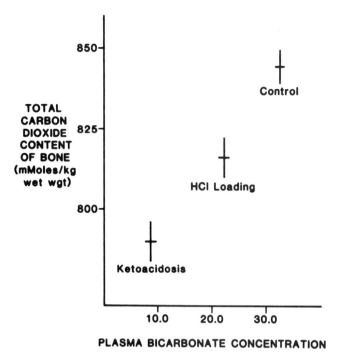

FIG. 4. Total skeletal carbon dioxide (mmoles/kg of wet weight) as a function of plasma bicarbonate concentration (mmoles/liter) for control animals, animals receiving an HCl load, and animals with diabetic ketoacidosis. Values are mean ± SE. (From ref. 8.)

although the former had a higher mortality rate. However, in a third study, nephrectomized TPTX rats buffered and survived an acid load as well as nephrectomized sham TPTX rats. Given these discrepant results, it is not clear if PTH augments systemic buffering of an acute acid load *in vivo.*

In vitro studies fail to support the hypothesis that PTH augments the buffering of an acid load. When neonatal mouse calvariae are cultured for 3 hr in a physiologically acid medium (pH 7.23), they buffer hydrogen ions and return the pH toward the physiologic normal of 7.40. The addition of PTH to the culture medium decreases the influx of protons into the bone, indicating that PTH actually inhibits the hydrogen ion buffering of an acidic medium by neonatal mouse bone (Fig. 5). A presumed mechanism by which PTH promotes the resorption of bone mineral is by the secretion of organic acids and hydrogen ions by osteoclasts into the microenvironment between these resorbing cells and the bone mineral. Only when these acids are able to solubilize the bone mineral are calcium and its accompanying anionic proton buffers released. Thus, it is not surprising that over a few hours, before there is substantial bone resorption and buffer release, PTH may actually retard hydrogen ion buffering by bone.

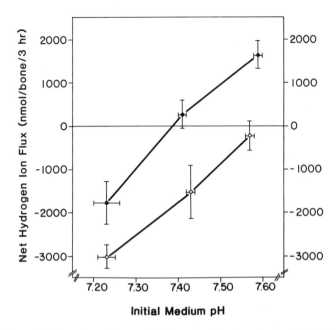

FIG. 5. Effect of initial medium pH on net hydrogen ion flux (nmoles/bone/3 hr) from neonatal mouse calvariae in 3 hr cultures. Values are mean ± SE. Parathyroid hormone (1 × 10⁻⁸ M bovine PTH 1-34) was (solid circles, n = 6-31) or was not (open circles, n = 5-25) added at the beginning of the experiment. Medium pH was lowered with HCl. A positive flux indicates net hydrogen ion movement from the calvariae into the medium; a negative flux indicates the opposite. (From ref. 14.)

Chronic

Stabilization of extracellular fluid pH

On a daily basis, metabolism of dietary foodstuffs generates nonvolatile acids that must be excreted quantitatively by the kidneys to maintain neutral systemic acid-base balance. In patients with renal failure, there is a decrease in acid excretion, leading to unremitting positive acid balance. Were ECF bicarbonate the only hydrogen ion buffer, it would become progressively depleted, and the serum bicarbonate concentration, and thus pH, would progressively fall to levels incompatible with life. However, Schwartz et al. demonstrated that ECF bicarbonate and pH remain stable, though reduced, for long periods of time, suggesting that in patients with chronic renal failure either nonbicarbonate buffers neutralize the retained hydrogen ions or acid production decreases. Goodman et al. demonstrated not only that acid production is maintained but that these patients excrete only approximately two thirds of their daily hydrogen ion production, suggesting substantial buffering of the retained hydrogen ions. Because of its mass and potential buffering capacity, bone was thought to be a likely site for the hydrogen ion buffering.

The notion that bone is involved in the response to excess hydrogen ions in chronic renal failure was supported when Pellegrino and Biltz found that bone calcium and carbonate were significantly decreased in patients with uremia in proportion to the duration of the renal disease.

Bone appears to buffer protons in acidemic, nonuremic patients as well. Patients with normal renal function were fed a chronic acid load and, through the use of balance techniques, were found to be in positive acid balance. These patients did not excrete their acid production quantitatively, yet their serum bicarbonate concentration stabilized. Since bone is a predominant source of buffer in the body, this observation suggested that it was the likely hydrogen ion buffer. As is the case with acute acidosis, the imposition of a chronic acid load appears to decrease bone carbonate. Other investigators fed rats an acid diet and found a marked loss of bone carbonate. Burnell demonstrated that after 5 to 10 days of acidosis, there was a fall in bone carbonate and sodium, suggesting that bone carbonate may be a proton acceptor.

Respiratory Acidosis (13,22,30,33,36,37)

An increase in the partial pressure of carbon dioxide lowers systemic pH and is termed "respiratory acidosis." The additional hydrogen ions are derived from the hydration of carbon dioxide, leading to an increase in carbonic acid, which dissociates to a hydrogen ion and bicarbonate. Were the additional hydrogen ions not buffered, ECF bicarbonate would not increase by a measurable amount. That ECF bicarbonate does increase by a predictable and easily measured amount implies that the excess hydrogen ions are buffered by nonbicarbonate buffers that allow continued formation of new bicarbonate. Giebisch et al. determined that approximately 97% of the hydrogen ion buffering during acute respiratory acidosis takes place outside of the extracellular space. Other than buffering by red cell hemoglobin and serum proteins, the location of the hydrogen ion buffering during respiratory acidosis is not clear.

Poyart et al. postulated that during respiratory acidosis the increased carbon dioxide is hydrated with water present on the surface of bone to form carbonic acid, which then dissociates into bicarbonate and a proton. Bone bicarbonate should then increase, as has been reported by Pasquale et al., who found that a 1 hr exposure of rats to CO_2 concentrations ranging from 1% to 15% resulted in a direct linear relationship between arterial CO_2 and bone carbonate and bicarbonate. When guinea pigs were exposed to 1% CO_2 for up to 8 weeks, there was an initial rise of bone bicarbonate and fall of bone carbonate (at 2 weeks), followed by an increase in both bicarbonate and carbonate. Thus, instead of buffering the increased proton concentration, bone might contribute protons to the ECF through hydration of CO_2 to carbonic acid, increasing the severity of the acidemia. Indeed, *in vitro* we found that neonatal mouse calvariae cultured in an environment of increased P_{CO_2} did

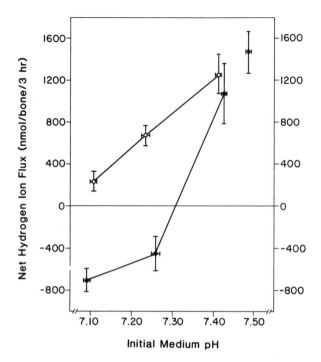

FIG. 6. Effect of initial medium pH on net hydrogen ion flux (nmoles/bone/3/hr) from neonatal mouse calvariae in 3 hr cultures. Values are mean ± SE. pH was lowered from control (x, *n* = 15) either by increasing the partial pressure of carbon dioxide (respiratory acidosis, open circles, *n* =11-43) or by lowering the bicarbonate concentration (metabolic acidosis, closed circles, *n* = 8-28). A positive flux value indicates net hydrogen ion movement from the bone into the medium; a negative flux indicates the opposite. (From ref. 13.)

not buffer hydrogen ions to the same extent as did calvariae cultured in medium acidified to the same degree by lowering the medium bicarbonate concentration. Although there was a net influx of protons from the medium into calvariae during metabolic acidosis, there was no net flux during respiratory acidosis at a similar pH (Fig. 6). Thus, although there is substantial evidence that bone buffers hydrogen ions during metabolic acidosis there is little evidence that it performs the same function during respiratory acidosis. The mechanism for this difference is unclear at present.

ROLE OF HYDROGEN IONS IN BONE CALCIUM DISSOLUTION

Metabolic Acidosis (2,6,10,12,15–17,19,23,25,26,28,29,32)

Acute

The acute infusion of mineral acid into nephrectomized animals leads to an increase in total serum calcium. Since bone contains the vast majority of total body calcium, this implies at least a component of mineral dissolution. To determine if an acute fall in pH causes bone mineral dissolution, we cultured neonatal mouse calvariae for 3 hr in physiologically acid, neutral, or alkaline medium. There was calcium dissolution from the bone mineral into the acidic medium, no change in medium calcium in neutral medium, and an influx of calcium into the bone during culture in alkaline medium (Fig. 7). These findings demonstrate that bone calcium homeostasis is affected by alterations in medium pH within the physiologic range. The mechanism by which hydrogen ions cause dissolution of the bone mineral during these acute incubations could be either direct physicochemical noncell-mediated calcium release or an increase in the activity of the bone-resorbing cells, the osteoclasts. To determine the role of cellular activity in hydrogen ion-mediated bone resorption, we cultured the calvariae with agents that would stimulate [PTH and $1,25(OH)_2D_3$] or suppress (sodium azide and successive freeze–thaw cycles) bone cell activity but not affect the bone mineral directly. We found that bone cell function contributed a constant, pH-independent efflux of calcium from the mineral (Fig. 8). The pH dependency of calcium flux in relation to bone, over a 3 hr period, appears to be caused by alterations in the physicochemical factors that govern the deposition and dissolution of the bone mineral and not alterations in bone cell function.

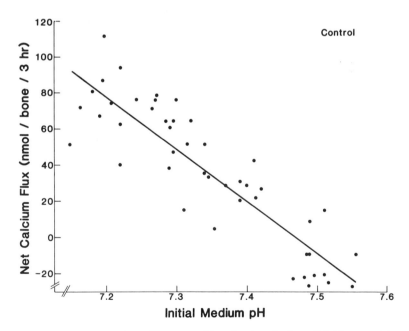

FIG. 7. Effect of initial medium pH on net calcium flux (nmoles/bone/3 hr) in neonatal mouse calvariae cultured for 3 hr. Each point represents data from a single pair of cultured calvariae. A positive flux indicates net calcium movement from calvariae into the medium. Medium pH was adjusted before incubation with concentrated HCl or NaOH. Calvariae were preincubated for 24 hr before this 3 hr incubation. (From ref. 15.)

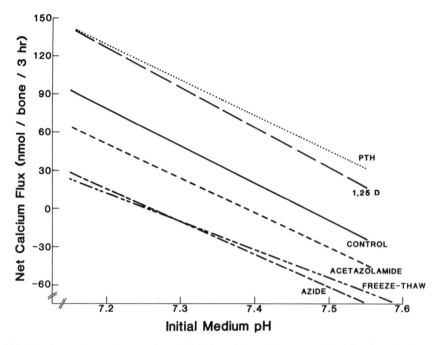

FIG. 8. Comparison of regressions of initial medium pH on net calcium flux (nmoles/bone/3 hr) for six different groups of calvariae. Calvariae were preincubated for 24 hr in similar medium at pH $\cong$ 7.54 before this 3 hr incubation. Medium pH was adjusted with concentrated HCl or NaOH for the 3 hr incubation. A positive flux indicates net calcium movement from calvariae into the medium; a negative flux indicates the opposite. Control, calvariae incubated in unaltered medium (n = 46); PTH, calvariae incubated with 1×10^{-8} M bovine parathyroid hormone 1-34 (n = 19); 1,25 D, calvariae incubated with 1×10^{-8} M 1,25-$(OH)_2D_3$ (n = 19); acetazolamide, calvariae incubated with 4×10^{-4} M acetazolamide (n = 31); freeze–thaw, calvariae subjected to three freeze–thaw cycles before incubation in control medium (n = 22); azide, calvariae incubated with 0.1% sodium azide (n = 29). Regressions are each significant (all $p < 0.001$) and are different due to a difference in intercepts of all groups except PTH and 1,25$(OH)_2D_3$, which are similar, and azide and freeze–thaw, which are similar. (From ref. 15.)

To determine which phase of the bone mineral, calcium carbonate, hydroxyapatite, or brushite, is in equilibrium with the medium and, therefore, affected by the hydrogen ions to cause calcium release, we cultured calvariae in medium in which the driving forces for crystallization with respect to the solid phase of the bone mineral were altered by changing medium pH. With respect to calcium carbonate, but not brushite or hydroxyapatite, there was bone formation from a supersaturated medium, no change in the bone mineral when cultured in a saturated medium, and bone dissolution into an unsaturated medium. The evidence that bone calcium carbonate is in equilibrium with the culture medium and solubilizes during a reduction in medium pH is consistent with the *in vivo* observation that bone total carbon dioxide, of which carbonate is a part, is depleted during metabolic acidosis.

In addition to a direct noncell-mediated affect of hydrogen ions on the bone mineral, studies by Martin et al. suggest that there is a cell-mediated component of calcium release during acute acidosis as well. Using an isolated perfused bone preparation, they demonstrated that acute acidosis increases PTH uptake and cyclic AMP production by the bone cells. Since PTH will increase bone resorption through cellular mechanisms, the possibility exists that in addition to direct effects on the bone mineral, acute acidosis may stimulate cell-mediated bone resorption as well.

Chronic

In humans, chronic metabolic acidosis increases urinary calcium excretion by reducing renal tubule calcium reabsorption without substantially altering intestinal calcium absorption; negative calcium balance ensues. Since over 99% of the body calcium is located within the bone, it is a logical source of the additional urinary calcium excreted during chronic metabolic acidosis. Barzel fed rats NH_4Cl for almost 1 year; when compared to controls, the bones from acid-fed rats were equal in length but were deficient in calcium. Dietary protein increases endogenous acid production by increasing the formation of organic acids and by the metabolism of sulfur-containing amino acids to inorganic sulfate. In a series of studies, Lemann et al. fed normal subjects protein, NH_4Cl and $NaHCO_3$ and measured urine calcium excretion. The oral ingestion of protein and NH_4Cl led to a marked increase in urinary calcium, whereas $NaHCO_3$ led to a decrease in calcium excretion (Fig. 9). There

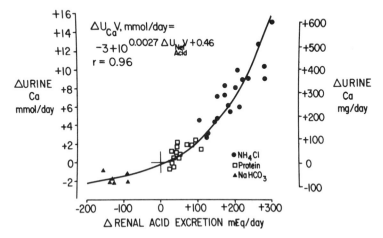

FIG. 9. Changes in urinary calcium excretion in healthy adults when acid production was increased by ammonium chloride (NH_4Cl) loading or dietary protein or reduced by administration of sodium bicarbonate ($NaHCO_3$). The solid line represents the rise in urinary calcium excretion as acid production and, thus, net renal acid excretion was increased. (From ref. 28.)

was no change in intestinal calcium absorption. Balance studies performed on patients given NH_4Cl demonstrated that much of the acid was retained, resulting in a fall in serum bicarbonate. At the conclusion of the NH_4Cl ingestion, the balance study was continued. Twelve days later, an average of 192 mEq of acid had been retained and 185 mEq of calcium excreted. The equivalence of the hydrogen ions retained to calcium excreted strongly suggested that bone is the sink for the hydrogen ions, buffering the ECF bicarbonate, and the source of the additional urinary calcium.

Role of the bone cell

The mechanism by which chronic metabolic acidosis causes dissolution of the bone mineral may be a combination of a direct effect of hydrogen ions on the bone mineral, as in acute acidosis, and cell-mediated bone resorption. Kraut et al. suggested that there is a component of cell-mediated calcium dissolution during prolonged acidosis in whole rat studies. The infusion of hydrogen ions resulted in an increase in serum calcium concentration that appeared to be independent of an increase in gastrointestinal calcium absorption. When cell-mediated calcium release from bone was inhibited with colchicine or calcitonin, there was little change in serum calcium in response to a 16 hr acid infusion, suggesting an abolition of cell-mediated bone resorption. Since these rats were not nephrectomized, however, an alteration in renal calcium handling could not be excluded completely. They then studied the effect of metabolic acidosis on bone formation and resorption in the rat. In TPTX acidotic rats, they found evidence for decreased bone formation at several different sites and enhanced cell-mediated bone resorption in epiphyseal but not in cortical or metaphyseal bone. The interpretation of the enhanced cell-mediated bone resorption in acidosis is difficult because the acidotic rats were hypophosphatemic compared to controls, and hypophosphatemia alone can cause bone resorption.

Arnett and Dempster studied the effects of alterations in pH on cell-mediated bone dissolution. They isolated rat osteoclasts from bone and cultured them on polished bovine femurs in an acidic medium. They found increased, presumably cell-mediated resorption in the acidic cultures. However, they could not completely exclude the possibility that the acid medium simply made the bone mineral more soluble, resulting in more bone dissolution with a constant degree of cellular activity. Goldhaber and Rabadjija recently provided evidence for cell-mediated bone resorption when calvariae are cultured in acidic medium. Our preliminary studies using mouse calvariae indicate that there may be enhanced cell-mediated calcium dissolution after 99 hr of culture in acidic medium produced by a decrease in bicarbonate concentration but not by an increase in P_{CO_2}. Thus, it appears that augmentation of cell-mediated bone resorption may have a role in the hypercalciuria of chronic metabolic acidosis.

Renal tubular acidosis

Renal tubular defects that decrease the excretion of hydrogen ions often are associated with bone disease. As in NH_4Cl-induced metabolic acidosis, urine calcium excretion is increased with both distal (Type I) and proximal (Type II) renal tubular acidosis (RTA). Intestinal calcium absorption does not appear to increase with RTA, and patients are in negative calcium balance. The source of the additional urinary calcium is thought to be bone. Both osteopenia (decreased bone mineral) and osteomalacia, or rickets (defective mineralization of the bone organic matrix), in adults and children, respectively, have been described in patients with RTA. Brenner et al. found that 63% of patients with distal RTA had nephrocalcinosis or nephrolithiasis, but few had radiographic evidence of skeletal abnormalities. The etiology of the renal calcification appears to be multifactorial and related to (1) the increased urine calcium and phosphorus excretion, presumably originating from bone, which raises supersaturation with respect to calcium phosphate crystals, (2) the alkaline pH in the renal tubules, which decreases the solubility of calcium phosphate crystals, and (3) the decreased excretion of citrate during acidosis, which increases the available tubular calcium for binding with phosphate.

In contrast to distal RTA, with the proximal disorder, the occurrence of nephrocalcinosis or nephrolithiasis is rare. However, 67% of the patients described by Brenner et al. had radiographic skeletal abnormalities, which consisted of rickets (widened and irregular epiphyseal–metaphyseal junction or evidence of bowing deformities) in all of the children and osteopenia in many of the adults. The etiology of the bone abnormalities in proximal RTA is complex and not well understood. The acidemia may cause bone mineral dissolution directly. A defect in the conversion of 25-hydroxyvitamin D_3 to $1,25(OH)_2D_3$ by the proximal tubules of the kidney has been described during metabolic acidosis, especially with a low calcium diet or vitamin D deficiency. $1,25(OH)_2D_3$ is necessary for calcium absorption and proper bone mineralization. The absence of nephrocalcinosis and nephrolithiasis may be attributable, in part, to the common association of proximal RTA with the Fanconi syndrome and the concomitant increased excretion of citrate, a potent inhibitor of calcium phosphate crystallization, and to the acidic tubular fluid that retards the calcium phosphate crystallization. Alkali therapy appears to decrease the calcium excretion and to increase bone mineralization in many adults with RTA, and it also appears to increase the depressed growth rate of children with RTA.

Respiratory Acidosis (12,13,27,33,37,39)

In contrast to chronic metabolic acidosis, chronic respiratory acidosis does not appear to be associated with increased urinary calcium excretion. How-

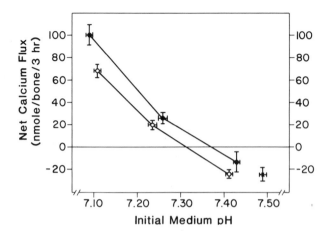

FIG. 10. Effect of initial medium pH on net calcium flux (nmoles/bone/3hr) from neonatal mouse calvariae in 3 hr cultures. Values are mean ± SE. pH was lowered from control (x, $n = 15$) either by increasing the partial pressure of carbon dioxide (respiratory acidosis, open circles, $n = 11$-43) or by lowering the bicarbonate concentration (metabolic acidosis, closed circles, $n = 8$-28). A positive flux value indicates net calcium movement from the bone into the medium; a negative flux indicates the opposite. (From ref. 13.)

ever, there is a greater increase in serum calcium with respiratory than with metabolic acidosis. This suggests that there is at least some hydrogen ion-induced bone calcium dissolution with respiratory acidosis but that the failure to increase urine calcium excretion may be due to a difference in effect on the renal tubule. *In vitro* we found that calvariae cultured in medium acidified by increasing the partial pressure of carbon dioxide had hydrogen ion-induced net calcium efflux. However, at the lowest pH studied (pH ≅ 7.10), there was greater calcium efflux from calvariae cultured in lowered bicarbonate medium than from those cultured in hypercarbic medium (Fig. 10). In chronic 99 hr cultures of neonatal mouse calvariae, there did not appear to be calcium efflux into medium acidified by increasing the partial pressure of carbon dioxide as there was into medium acidified by lowering the bicarbonate concentration. The mechanism of decreased calcium efflux with models of acute and chronic respiratory acidosis is not clear but may relate to the increased formation of calcium carbonate, with utilization of medium calcium or to decreased bone mineral dissolution.

Hormone-Induced Bone Resorption (1,5,14,41)

Parathyroid Hormone

PTH-induced bone dissolution appears to involve hydrogen ion secretion by the bone-resorbing osteoclasts. Evidence for this assertion is based on three important findings. First, carbonic anhydrase is necessary for appreciable production of protons from carbon dioxide and water. Inhibition of carbonic anhydrase with acetazolamide decreases PTH-induced calcium efflux from bone, implying the necessity for proton secretion in hormone-induced bone resorption. Second, the pH at the junction of the resorbing osteoclast and the bone mineral appears to be lower than that of the surrounding medium, again implying hydrogen ion secretion by the osteoclast. Third, there is a greater net hydrogen ion efflux from neonatal mouse calvariae cultured with PTH than from calvariae cultured without the hormone. Whether the enhanced hydrogen ion secretion induced by PTH is in the form of excess organic acids, such as lactic or citric acid, or secreted by a proton pump similar to the proton translocating ATPase found in the renal tubule is not clear at this time.

LINKAGE BETWEEN HYDROGEN ION BUFFERING AND CALCIUM DISSOLUTION

Stoichiometry: Hydrogen Ion and Calcium Fluxes (16,18,29)

During metabolic acidosis, the bone mineral buffers protons and releases calcium. Were all buffering the result of mineral dissolution, there should be one nanoequivalent of hydrogen ion buffered for every nanoequivalent of calcium released by the mineral in the case of calcium carbonate; for apatite, the ratio would be 5:3, and for brushite, the ratio would be 1:1. Using neonatal mouse calvariae in short-term culture (3 hr), we demonstrated that the ratio of hydrogen ions buffered to calcium released was 16–21:1, indicating that hydrogen ion buffering could not be due simply to mineral dissolution but must also involve cation exchanges, that is, hydrogen ions for sodium or potassium (Fig. 11). Using a scanning ion microprobe, we confirmed the marked loss of sodium and potassium from the bone surface, far in excess of the loss of bone calcium (Fig. 3). However, in a chronic *in vivo* balance study, Lemann et al. demonstrated an equivalence between proton retention and calcium excretion 12 days after the discontinuation of oral NH_4Cl, suggesting a marked difference between the acute and chronic response to acidosis.

Considered together, these studies suggest that hydrogen ions are buffered and that calcium is released by bone during both acute and chronic metabolic acidosis. However, during acute metabolic acidosis, it appears that most of the protons are exchanged on the bone surface for sodium and potassium through a direct physicochemical noncell-mediated process. Although there is calcium release during acute metabolic acidosis, simultaneous calcium and proton flux studies suggest that there is little, if any, linkage between the extent of proton-induced calcium release and proton buffering. On a chronic basis, *in vivo* studies suggest that buffering of the additional hydrogen ions

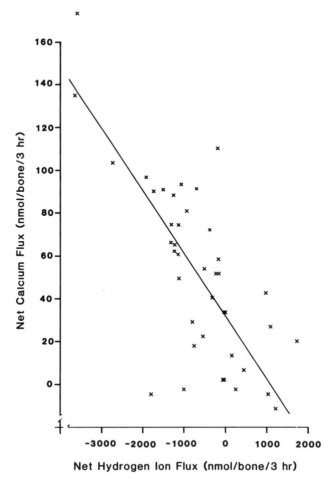

FIG. 11. Correlation of hydrogen ion and calcium fluxes for 3 hr cultures of neonatal mouse calvariae. Each point represents data from a single pair of cultured calvariae. Proton concentration was adjusted with concentrated HCl. For both hydrogen and calcium, a positive flux value indicates net ion movement from bone into the medium; a negative flux value indicates the opposite. Slope of best-fit regression: net calcium flux (nmoles/bone/3 hr) = -0.0279 (net hydrogen ion flux) + 34.831; $r = -0.713$, $n = 41$, $p < 0.001$. (From ref. 16.)

by bone is due to bone mineral dissolution, perhaps through cell-mediated processes. Chronic *in vitro* studies comparing hydrogen ion and calcium fluxes are not yet available.

ACKNOWLEDGMENTS

This work was supported by grant AM 33949 and AR 39906 from the National Institutes of Health and by grant-in-aid No. 87-1061 from the American Heart Association.

I would like to thank Fredric L. Coe for helpful discussions and Nancy S. Krieger for review of the manuscript.

REFERENCES

1. Anderson, R. E., Woodbury, D. M., and Jee, W. S. S. (1986): Humoral and ionic regulation of osteoclast acidity. *Calcif. Tissue Int.*, 39:252–258.
2. Arnett, T. R., and Dempster, D. W. (1986): Effect of pH on bone resorption by rat osteoclasts *in vitro. Endocrinology*, 119:119–124.
3. Arruda, J. A. L., Alla, V., Rubinstein, H., et al. (1980): Parathyroid hormone and extrarenal acid buffering. *Am. J. Physiol.*, 239:F533–F538.
4. Aurbach, G. D., Marx, S. J., and Spiegel, A. M. (1985): Metabolic bone disease. In: *Textbook of Endocrinology*, edited by J. D. Wilson and D. W. Foster, pp. 1218–1255. W. B. Saunders Co., Philadelphia.
5. Baron, R., Neff, L., Louvard, D., and Courtoy, P. J. (1985): Cell-mediated extracellular acidification and bone resorption: Evidence for a low pH in resorbing lacunae and localization of a 100-kD lysosomal membrane protein at the osteoclast ruffled border. *J. Cell. Biol.*, 101:2210–2222.
6. Barzel, U. S. (1969): The effect of excessive acid feeding on bone. *Calcif. Tissue Res.*, 4:94–100.
7. Bergstrom, W. H., and Ruva, F. D. (1960): Changes in bone sodium during acute acidosis in the rat. *Am. J. Physiol.*, 198:1126–1128.
8. Bettice, J. A. (1984): Skeletal carbon dioxide stores during metabolic acidosis. *Am. J. Physiol.*, 247:F326–F330.
9. Bettice, J. A., and Gamble, J. L. Jr. (1975): Skeletal buffering of acute metabolic acidosis. *Am. J. Physiol.*, 229:1618–1624.
10. Brenner, R. J., Spring, D. B., Sebastian, A., et al. (1982): Incidence of radiographically evident bone disease, nephrocalcinosis, and nephrolithiasis in various types of renal tubular acidosis. *N. Engl. J. Med.*, 307:217–221.
11. Burnell, J. M. (1971): Changes in bone sodium and carbonate in metabolic acidosis and alkalosis in the dog. *J. Clin. Invest.*, 50:327–331.
12. Bushinsky, D. A. (1988): Chronic metabolic, but not respiratory, acidosis induces cell-mediated calcium efflux from bone in vitro (Abstr.). *J. Bone Min. Res.*, 3:S205.
13. Bushinsky, D. A. (1988): Net proton influx into bone during metabolic, but not respiratory, acidosis. *Am. J. Physiol.*, 254:F306–F310.
14. Bushinsky, D. A. (1987): Effects of parathyroid hormone on net proton flux from neonatal mouse calvariae. *Am. J. Physiol.*, 252:F585–F589.
15. Bushinsky, D. A., Goldring, J. M., and Coe, F. L. (1985): Cellular contribution to pH-mediated calcium flux in neonatal mouse calvariae. *Am. J. Physiol.*, 248:F785–F789.
16. Bushinsky, D. A., Krieger, N. S., Geisser, D. I., Grossman, E. B., and Coe, F. L. (1983): Effects of pH on bone calcium and proton fluxes *in vitro. Am. J. Physiol.*, 245:F204–F209.
17. Bushinsky, D. A., and Lechleider, R. (1987): Mechanism of proton-induced bone calcium release: Calcium carbonate dissolution. *Am. J. Physiol.*, 253:F998–F1005.
18. Bushinsky, D. A., Levi-Setti, R., and Coe, F. L. (1986): Ion microprobe determination of bone surface elements: Effects of reduced medium pH. *Am. J. Physiol.*, 250:F1090–F1097.
19. Bushinsky, D. A., Riera, G. S., Favus, M. J., and Coe, F. L. (1985): Response of serum $1,25(OH)_2D_3$ to variation of ionized calcium during chronic acidosis. *Am. J. Physiol.*, 249:F361–F365.
20. Coe, F. L., and Bushinsky, D. A. (1984): Pathophysiology of hypercalciuria. *Am. J. Physiol.*, 247:F1–F3.
21. Fraley, D.S., and Adler, S. (1979): An extrarenal role for parathyroid hormone in the disposal of acute acid loads in rats and dogs. *J. Clin. Invest.*, 63:985–997.
22. Giebisch, G., Berger, L., and Pitts, R. F. (1955): The extrarenal response to acute acid-base disturbances of respiratory origin. *J. Clin. Invest.*, 34:231–245.
23. Goldhaber, P., and Rabadjija L. (1987): H^+ stimulation of cell-mediated bone resorption in issue culture. *Am. J. Physiol.*, 253:E90–E98.

24. Goodman, A. D., Lemann, J. Jr., Lennon, E. J., and Relman, A. S. (1965): Production, excretion, and net balance of fixed acid in patients with renal acidosis. *J. Clin. Invest.*, 44:495–506.
25. Kraut, J. A., Mishler, D. R., and Kurokawa, K. (1984): Effect of colchicine and calcitonin on calcemic response to metabolic acidosis. *Kidney Int.*, 25:608–612.
26. Kraut, J. A., Mishler, D. R., Singer, F. R., and Goodman, W. G. (1986): The effects of metabolic acidosis on bone formation and bone resorption in the rat. *Kidney Int.*, 30:694–700.
27. Lau, K., Rodriguez Nichols, F., and Tannen, R. L. (1987): Renal excretion of divalent ions in response to chronic acidosis: Evidence that systemic pH is not the controlling variable. *J. Lab. Clin. Med.*, 109:27–33.
28. Lemann, J. Jr., Adams, N. D., and Gray, R. W. (1979): Urinary calcium excretion in human beings. *N. Engl. J. Med.*, 301:535–541.
29. Lemann, J. Jr., Litzow, J. R., and Lennon, E. J. (1966): The effects of chronic acid loads in normal man: Further evidence for the participation of bone mineral in the defense against chronic metabolic acidosis. *J. Clin. Invest.*, 45:1608–1614.
30. Madias, N. E., and Cohen, J. J. (1982): Respiratory acidosis. In: *Acid-Base*, edited by J. J. Cohen and J. P. Kassirer, pp. 307–348. Little, Brown and Company, Boston.
31. Madias, N. E., Johns, C. A., and Homer, S. M. (1982): Independence of the acute acid-buffering response from endogenous parathyroid hormone. *Am. J. Physiol.*, 243:F141–F149.
32. Martin, K. J., Freitag, J. J., Bellorin-Font, E., Conrades, M.B., Klahr, S., and Slatopolsky, E. (1980): The effect of acute acidosis on the uptake of parathyroid hormone and the production of adenosine 3',5'-monophosphate by isolated perfused bone. *Endocrinology*, 106:1607–1611.
33. Pasquale, S. M., Messier, A. A., Shea, M. L., and Schaefer, K. E. (1980): Bone CO_2-titration curves in acute hypercapnia obtained with a modified titration technique. *J. Appl. Physiol.*, 48:197–201.
34. Pellegrino, E. D., and Biltz, R. M. (1965): The composition of human bone in uremia. Observations on the reservoir functions of bone and demonstration of a labile fraction of bone carbonate. *Medicine*, 44:397–418.
35. Posner, A. S. (1985): The mineral of bone. *Clin. Orthop.*, 200:87–99.
36. Poyart, C. F., Bursaux, E., and Freminet, A. (1975): The bone CO_2 compartment: Evidence for a bicarbonate pool. *Respir. Physiol.*, 25:89–99.
37. Schaefer, K. E., Pasquale, S., Messier, A. A., and Shea, M. (1980): Phasic changes in bone CO_2 fractions, calcium, and phosphorus during chronic hypercapnia. *J. Appl. Physiol.*, 48:802–811.
38. Schwartz, W. B., Hall, P. W. III, Hays, R. M., and Relman, A. S. (1959): On the mechanism of acidosis in chronic renal disease. *J. Clin. Invest.*, 38:39–52.
39. Sutton, R. A. L., Wong, N. L. M., and Dirks, J. H. (1979): Effects of metabolic acidosis and alkalosis on sodium and calcium transport in the dog kidney. *Kidney Int.*, 15:520–533.
40. Swan, R. C., and Pitts, R. F. (1955): Neutralization of infused acid by nephrectomized dogs. *J. Clin. Invest.*, 34:205–212.
41. Vaes, G. (1968): On the mechanisms of bone resorption. The action of parathyroid hormone on the excretion and synthesis of lysosomal enzymes and on the extracellular release of acid by bone cells. *J. Cell Biol.*, 39:676–697.

The Regulation of Acid–Base Balance, edited
by Donald W. Seldin and Gerhard Giebisch,
Raven Press, Ltd., New York © 1989.

5

Internal Exchanges of Hydrogen Ions: Gastrointestinal Tract

Alan N. Charney and *George M. Feldman

*Department of Medicine, New York University School of Medicine, New York,
New York 10010, and *University of Pennsylvania School of Medicine,
Philadelphia, Pennsylvania 19104*

The gastrointestinal tract plays a pivotal role in overall acid-base balance because it is the ultimate source of the substrates from which all acids, volatile and nonvolatile, are produced by the body. The dietary intake of carbohydrates, fats, and proteins and the intestinal excretion of organic anions and bicarbonate are important determinants of the acid load that must be excreted each day if acid-base balance is to be maintained. This gastrointestinal contribution to acid-base balance may be considered at three levels: first, the entire gastrointestinal tract may be considered as an organ that contributes acids and bases to the body in various proportions, second, individual segments of the gastrointestinal tract may be considered as specialized organs that contribute to overall acid-base balance when a particular segment is diseased or malfunctioning (as in vomiting) or when a drug disrupts or augments the function of that segment (as in H_2-receptor antagonist administration), and third, the movement of acids and bases across the cell membranes of individual cells determines the character of each region of the gastrointestinal tract and its physiologic and pathologic response to diet, drugs, and luminal and systemic influences. This chapter focuses on each of these levels to elucidate the important role of the gastrointestinal tract in systemic acid-base balance.

OVERALL GASTROINTESTINAL CONTRIBUTION TO ACID-BASE BALANCE (3,11–14,25)

Components of Fixed Acid Production

The acids in need of renal excretion are commonly referred to as "fixed acids." These acids are nonvolatile as compared to carbonic acid, an acid that can be excreted as carbon dioxide gas by the lungs. There are several means by which fixed acids are produced, and these are summarized in Table 1. The best-known source of fixed acid production is intermediary metabolism. The acids generated by these various catabolic processes include sulfuric acid and the organic acids, lactic acid, acetic acid, and uric acid. Sulfuric acid is generated by the oxidation of the sulfur-containing amino acids methionine and cysteine. These amino acids are contained in the proteins of egg white, meats, milk, and cereals, as well as in tissue proteins. Approximately 70% of dietary organic sulfur is absorbed and metabolized to produce acid, and this accounts for essentially all the sulfuric acid produced in a healthy, fed individual. Sulfuric acid production may be quantitated by measuring urinary sulfate. Each milliequivalent (mEq) of urinary sulfate represents 1 mEq of fixed acid contributed by organic sulfur oxidation. An average diet yields about 0.5 mEq/kg body weight per day of sulfuric acid.

Organic acids generated by the metabolism of glucose (lactic acid), triglycerides (acetoacetic acid), and nucleoproteins (uric acid) yield hydrogen ions when they are not completely metabolized to CO_2 and water. This occurs when the acid cannot be further metabolized (e.g., uric acid) or when the acid anions (e.g., lactate, citrate, acetoacetate) are excreted by the kidney as the sodium or potassium salt. In either case, each milliequivalent of urinary or-

TABLE 1. *Factors affecting net fixed acid production*

Acid production by intermediary metabolism
Dietary potential acids and bases
Bacterial metabolism of unabsorbed carbohydrates, fats, and proteins
Intestinal absorption and secretion of HCO_3^-
Intestinal absorption of organic cations and anions
Metabolic conversion of absorbed organic anions to HCO_3^-

ganic anion represents 1 mEq of fixed acid contributed by organic acid synthesis. In the absence of illness, these organic acids contribute approximately 0.5 mEq of hydrogen ions/kg body weight per day to body fluids.

The diet also contains organic cationic and anionic salts that may be metabolized to yield fixed acids and bases (bicarbonate). This supply of potential acid and base contributes to or detracts from the fixed acid load generated by intermediary metabolism. The quantity of potential acid and base contained in the diet may be estimated conveniently by measuring the milliequivalents of the inorganic salts in the diet rather than the organic cations (ammonium) and anions (citrate and lactate) with which they are associated. The balance of dietary potential acid and base may be calculated by the formula:

$$(Na^+ + K^+ + Ca^{2+} + Mg^{2+}) - (Cl^- + P^{-1.8})$$

where the inorganic cations represent organic anions and inorganic anions represent organic cations, and all measurements are in milliequivalents except phosphorous, which is in millimoles. As indicated, the same valence for phosphorous of 1.8 is assigned in the diet as in body fluids (at 7.40). In general, dietary organic cations and anions total several hundred milliequivalents each and, depending on the particular foods ingested, yield net acid or base to body fluids. Dietary sources of potential acids include meats, fish, rice, wheat and oat products, and eggs (especially egg yolk); dietary sources of potential bases include fruits, vegetables (except corn), milk and milk products, nuts (except peanuts), raisins, and prunes.

Intestinal bacteria also contribute to the potential acids and bases absorbed by the gastrointestinal tract. For example, bacteria may metabolize an organic cation and make it available for absorption. Thus, the bacterial conversion of dietary choline to trimethylamine increases the absorption of this potential acid. More importantly, bacteria themselves generate potential acids and bases from unabsorbed dietary carbohydrates, fats, and proteins. Carbohydrates and fats are metabolized by bacteria to lactate, acetate, proprionate, and other short-chain fatty acid anions, potential bases, and unabsorbed proteins and urea secreted into the intestinal lumen are metabolized to ammonium, a potential acid. However, not all of the approximately 500 mEq of potential acids and bases generated daily are absorbed. The stools contain organic cations and anions of dietary and bacterial origin and bicarbonate that was secreted by the ileum and colon but not subsequently reabsorbed. Obviously, unequal absorption or stool losses of organic cations and anions will affect the quantity of fixed acids in body fluids. For example, stool losses of potential base (including bicarbonate) may total several hundred milliequivalents in certain diarrheal diseases. Indeed, even in the absence of diarrhea, the passage of stools usually results in the net loss of potential base rather than acid. In addition, there are differences among species in the efficiency of metabolism of absorbed organic anions. In species other than humans, as little as 33% and as much as 75% of absorbed potential base actually may be converted to bicarbonate and serve to buffer fixed acids.

The relative importance of the metabolic production of sulfuric and organic acids (measured in the urine as sulfate and organic anions), the dietary contribution and stool losses of actual and potential base, and the net fixed acid in need of renal excretion each day are depicted in Fig. 1. The values are for an average American diet consumed by a healthy adult. The bars indicate that the quantitative contribution of potential base in the diet is very large and approximately equal to the acid produced by intermediary metabolism. Figure 1 also shows that both intermediary metabolism and stool losses of base increase fixed acids in body fluids and that net dietary base offsets to a great extent this quantity of fixed acid. If the net fixed acid requiring renal excretion is quantitatively excreted by the kidney, the person is in acid-base

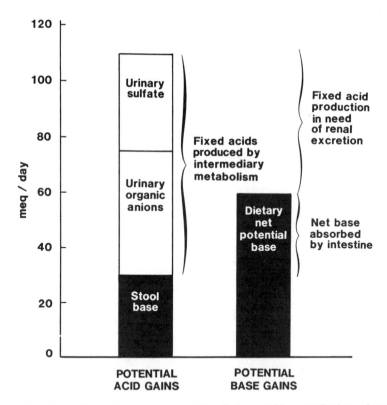

FIG. 1. Potential acids and bases in normal diet. Daily quantitive contributions of potential acids and bases to body fluids of a healthy adult consuming an average American diet are shown. The difference between potential acid gains and potential base gains must be excreted by the kidney to maintain acid-base balance. (Modified from ref. 25.)

balance. The relation of these variables also can be formulated as follows:

$$\text{Renal net acid excretion (urinary titratable acid} + NH_4^+ - HCO_3^-) =$$
$$\text{(urinary } SO_4^{2-} + \text{organic anions)} - [(\text{dietary } Na^+ + K^+ + Ca^{2+} +$$
$$Mg^{2+} - Cl^- - P^{-1.8}) - (\text{stool } Na^+ + K^+ + Ca^{2+} + Mg^{2+} -$$
$$Cl^- - P^{-1.8})]$$

where all variables are expressed in milliequivalents per unit time except P, which is measured in millimoles per unit time.

Effects of Altering Diet

The great difference in the content of potential acids and bases in various foods suggests that dietary preferences can have a profound effect on net fixed acid production. As shown in Table 2, the dietary contribution to overall acid-base balance can provide as much as 60 mEq additional acid to the daily fixed acid load, or as much as 130 mEq base. The average American diet contributes approximately 30 mEq base (also shown in Fig. 1). Table 2 indicates that the intestinal absorption of organic cations and anions varies to some extent with the dietary load but assumes that there is complete metabolic conversion of the absorbed species. In people in acid-base balance, the effect of diet on net fixed acid production is reflected also in their daily urinary net acid excretion. In studies of this relationship with diets similar to those presented in Table 2, urinary net acid excretion varied directly with net fixed acid production. External hydrogen ion balance was zero (acid-base balance was achieved) in these people up to fixed acid production rates of 70 mEq per day. At greater levels of net fixed acid production (>1 mEq/kg per day), positive hydrogen ion balance and mild metabolic acidosis were evident.

As suggested by these findings, the acid-base composition of blood (and extracellular fluid) also varies with the changes in net fixed acid production caused by diet. In another study in which diets were altered to yield urinary net acid excretion rates of 0.3 to 2 mEq/kg per day, there was a linear corre-

TABLE 2. *Effect of diet composition on intestinal contribution to acid-base balance*

Type of diet	Net potential acid or base (mEq)			
	Present in diet	Absorbed by intestine	Lost in stool	Contribution to acid-base balance
Meat	40 acid	40 acid	20 base	60 acid
Average	60 base	30 base	30 base	30 base
Vegetarian	200 base	130 base	70 base	130 base

lation between urinary net acid excretion and the plasma hydrogen ion concentration:

$$\text{Plasma hydrogen ion concentration (mEq/liter)} = +0.01 \text{ (urinary net acid excretion)} + 38.4$$

This relationship was accompanied by a negative, linear correlation between urinary net acid excretion and the plasma bicarbonate concentration; at a blood P_{CO_2} level of 41 mm Hg, the plasma bicarbonate concentration (mEq/liter) = -0.01 (urinary net acid excretion) + 25.5. Since in people in acid-base balance, urinary net acid excretion equals net fixed acid production, the relationships described suggest that diet affects the normal values for blood pH and plasma bicarbonate concentration through its contribution to fixed acid production. Although this effect is relatively small (-0.01 pH unit and -0.01 mEq/liter of HCO_3^- per 1 mEq increase in net acid production), it may be important in patients with a decreased ability to excrete acid. Indeed, the prescription of a low-protein diet for patients with chronic renal failure is based in part on this effect of diet.

Altering the Absorption of Potential Acids and Bases

The intestinal contribution to net fixed acid production may be affected by factors other than diet. The most important of these involve changes in the intestinal luminal concentration and solubility of organic anions. For example, the intestinal bacterial metabolism of organic acids may be reduced by eliminating dietary precursors (carbohydrates and fats), and in this case, stool anion decreases more than 70%. This suggests that the diet is the major source of fecal anion. Nevertheless, even under these circumstances, the stool contains significant quantities of organic anion. Clearly, endogenous substrates may become organic anion precursors. In this regard, it should be recalled that the stool contains potential base even during the ingestion of diets yielding net potential acid (Table 2). Intestinal antibiotic administration also might be expected to reduce stool losses of potential base. However, total stool organic anion content is not decreased and acid-base balance is not affected by antibiotic ingestion, although the proportions of the various anions are altered. Thus, all organic anions except formate are reduced during antibiotic therapy, and succinate concentration increases tenfold. The basis for this change is unknown. Interestingly, a similar increase in succinate at the expense of other stool organic anions is found in patients with chronic renal failure. Possibly, uremia has a similar effect on the intestinal bacterial flora as does antibiotic administration.

The continued stool loss of potential base in patients with chronic renal failure is of particular interest because these patients generally have metabolic acidosis. In fact, metabolic acidosis induced by the administration of ammonium chloride only results in a transient, although marked, reduction in stool potential base. Stool organic anion content soon returns to preacidosis levels, and the kidney alone must excrete the administered acid for acid-base balance to be restored. As much as 6% of the administered acid load can be accounted for by this transient decrease in stool losses of potential base. The mechanism of this intestinal response to acute acidosis is unknown. It may be because of a decrease in the absorption of organic cations or in the net secretion of bicarbonate. However, such transport changes are not sustained beyond several days. If the intestinal response is due to a pH-induced change in the intestinal bacterial flora, the increase in stool succinate concentration (described previously) may result from the growth of resistant bacteria or to metabolic processes in the intestinal mucosa itself. In either case, the intestine does not participate in the body's response to chronic acidosis by decreasing stool losses of potential base.

Another way whereby the absorption of potential acids and bases may be altered is to change their solubility in the intestinal lumen. For example, the alkaline secretions of the upper gastrointestinal tract may become insoluble after the ingestion of calcium chloride. The ingested calcium chloride forms insoluble calcium carbonate that is almost entirely excreted in the stool. This increases the net loss of stool base and thereby increases net fixed acid production and the acidity of body fluids. Approximately 10% of the ingested calcium forms calcium phosphate, and to the extent that this insoluble salt is lost in the stool, it will contribute to the acidifying effects of calcium chloride. Calcium carbonate formation also may be increased by the intake of a polystyrene sulfonate cation exchange resin (e.g., Kayexalate). In the calcium cycle, this resin releases calcium, and the subsequent formation and excretion of calcium carbonate increases net fixed acid production as described previously. In the sodium cycle, this exchange resin releases sodium and chelates dietary calcium, which reduces calcium carbonate losses that would ordinarily accompany dietary calcium ingestion. After ingestion of the exchange resin in the sodium cycle, urinary net acid excretion falls, urine pH rises, and mild metabolic alkalosis may develop. The importance of the intestinal mechanism of action of this effect is suggested by the absence of an effect of potassium balance, sodium chloride intake, or mineralocorticoid levels on the production of the alkalosis. Other substances that affect intestinal calcium absorption, such as ingestion of oxalate-rich foods and aluminum-containing antacids, also may affect the solubility of potential bases in the intestine and the contribution of the intestine to net fixed acid production and overall acid-base balance.

CONTRIBUTION OF GASTROINTESTINAL SEGMENTS TO ACID-BASE BALANCE (1,2,4–10,15–24,26)

Integration of Gastrointestinal Function

By absorbing dietary base, the gastrointestinal tract participates in acid-base homeostasis. On an average diet (Table 2), this contribution amounts to conserving 30 mEq of ingested base daily. However, as in the kidney, this net absorptive process is accomplished by the transport of much larger quantities of H^+, OH^- or HCO_3^-, and other potential acids and bases, such as ammonium and short-chain fatty acid anions. Each segment of the gastrointestinal tract shares in this task by sequentially preparing ingested food for digestion and absorption. During this process, large nonabsorbable substances are catabolized into smaller absorbable compounds that, on absorption, are metabolized to H^+ or HCO_3^-. The abnormal function of any one intestinal segment affects segments distal to it in a cascading fashion.

In the normal adult, the stomach secretes approximately 400 mEq of H^+ daily, and the pancreas, biliary system, and duodenum secrete bicarbonate that titrates this H^+ load. Although the amount of bicarbonate secreted by the duodenum is unknown, it is estimated that the pancreas secretes 250 mEq daily, and free flowing bile contributes an additional 60 mEq. Furthermore, it is clear that intestinal contents entering the jejunal segment of the upper small intestine are either neutral or frankly alkaline and that this intestinal segment absorbs bicarbonate. As the digesta passes to the lower small intestine, ileal secretions add bicarbonate. This alkaline secretion continues in the large intestine at a rate of 250 mEq daily, where the continual supply of base to colonic contents maintains a neutral pH, permitting bacterial growth and metabolism to occur. This fermentation process generates organic acids and amines that are largely absorbed. Together, these intestinal segments transport in excess of 1,000 mEq of H^+ and OH^- (or HCO_3^-) and 500 mEq of organic cations and anions. The character and cellular mechanism of each intestinal segment's contribution are described in the following sections.

Stomach

Organ Physiology

The stomach, like the kidney, is a major acid-secretory organ. Its acid-secretory rate varies greatly and displays a diurnal rhythm, with highest rates observed in the late afternoon and evening. Meals are the most important modulators of acid secretion; basal gastric acid secretion of 10 mmoles/hr may increase to levels as high as 50 mmoles/hr (reducing luminal pH to approximately 1.5). The stimuli involved include efferent vagal signals, gastric distention by food, and the presence of peptides and amino acids (especially phenylalanine and tryptophan) in the stomach lumen. All three stimuli release gastrin from the G cells of the gastric glands located in the antrum and pylorus, and this hormone apparently mediates the increase in acid secretion.

Decreases in luminal pH in the gastric antrum and duodenum suppress gastrin and acid secretion. Bicarbonate secretion by the gastric mucosa also can be demonstrated when acid secretion is inhibited (as by H_2-receptor antagonists). Under basal conditions, the P_{CO_2} of gastric juice may reach 150 mm Hg as a consequence of the neutralization of acid by secreted bicarbonate ions. Acid-secretory stimuli, however, do not stimulate bicarbonate secretion, and gastric fluid pH and P_{CO_2} decrease concomitantly after a meal. Nevertheless, bicarbonate secretion protects the gastric mucosa by generating a pH gradient between the superficial mucous cells (pH approximately 7) and the gastric fluid (pH as low as 1.5). The gradient is maintained by an unstirred mucous gel lining the gastric mucosa.

Cell Physiology

The oxyntic or parietal cells in the gastric glands of the fundus are the source of gastric acid secretion. As depicted in Fig. 2, the cellular mechanism is believed to involve a H^+, K^+-ATPase and depends on intracellular K^+. This enzyme system has been localized to a cytoplasmic tubulovesicular membrane system that appears to fuse with the apical (luminal) cell membrane after stimulation of acid secretion. Transcellular H^+ transport is achieved by the carbonic anhydrase-catalyzed conversion of hydroxyl ions to bicarbonate ions, which then exit the basolateral membrane via a chloride-bicarbonate exchange process. A marked increase in gastric acid secretion, therefore, generates a bicarbonate-rich gastric venous effluent, which when excreted by the kidney is referred to as an "alkaline tide." Alteration of intracellular K^+ concentration influences H^+ secretion, and in this way inhibition of Na^+, K^+-ATPase slows H^+ secretion.

Biliary Tract

Organ Physiology

Originating in hepatic canaliculae, bile has a bicarbonate concentration that ranges from 50 to 100 mEq/liter. Although the mechanism of hepatic bile

LUMEN   BLOOD

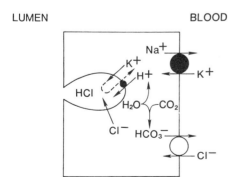

FIG. 2. Acid secretion by stomach parietal cell. H^+ secretion is dependent on a H^+,K^+-ATPase (small solid circle) located on vesicular membranes. These membranes fuse with the apical membrane during secretion. H^+ secretion requires intracellular K^+, which is supplied by Na^+,K^+-ATPase (large solid circle). Balancing the H^+ movement across the apical membrane, HCO_3^- exits across the basolateral membrane via a Cl^--HCO_3^- antiport (open circle).

production is poorly understood, it is affected by hormones, including secretin, cholecystokinin, and gastrin. The gallbaladder serves to concentrate bile, reducing volume by 90% in 4 hr and causing the bicarbonate concentration to fall to less than 10 mEq/liter. The absorptive function of the gallbladder follows a diurnal pattern and is influenced by neurohumoral factors, including vasoactive intestinal polypeptide (VIP) and α-adrenergic receptors. The former induces secretion, whereas the latter enhances absorption.

Cell Physiology

The mechanism of hepatic bile formation is poorly understood because of the difficulty of studying this function at the cellular and canalicular levels. However, it is of interest that remarkably high bicarbonate concentrations are generated by this system. In addition, as in the renal cortex, hepatic CO_2 tension has been observed to be greater than 60 mm Hg. Bicarbonate secretion depends on Na^+, K^+-ATPase activity, located on the basolateral (noncanalicular) membrane, and on the concentration of blood bicarbonate.

Ion flux in the gallbladder has been examined in more detail, but the results conflict and depend on the species studied. Some studies suggest that the mechanism of NaCl absorption is parallel exchanges of Na^+ for H^+ and Cl^- for HCO_3^-, whereas others suggest that neutral NaCl entry across the apical cell membrane is responsible. Neither mechanism accounts for net bicarbonate absorption unless the dual antiporters operate at dissimilar rates; that is, Na^+-H^+ exceeds the anion exchange. Although the paracellular pathway is permeable to cations, it is significantly less permeable to anions, suggesting that HCO_3^- is unlikely to move between cells.

Pancreas

Organ Physiology

Aside from producing insulin, glucagon, and digestive enzymes, the pancreas generates and secretes 200 to 250 mEq of bicarbonate daily. The rate of bicarbonate secretion and its concentration in pancreatic fluid is under hormonal control. Basal secretions contain HCO_3^- at a concentration similar to that in plasma, whereas stimulated pancreatic secretion contains concentrations approaching 150 mEq/liter. Effective secretagogues include secretin and cholecystokinin. In isolation, the former effectively increases HCO_3^- generation, whereas the latter generates fluid low in volume and HCO_3^- concentration but high in enzyme concentration. Together these hormones potentiate one another, with the highest bicarbonate outputs occurring when both hormones are present. VIP has a structural similarity to secretin and also stimulates pancreatic HCO_3^- output. In addition, neural (vagal) stimulation causes increases in HCO_3^- output, which, although not inhibited by atropine, is thought to represent neural VIP release and action. Other humoral agents inhibit pancreatic bicarbonate output, for example, somatostatin, glucagon, pancreatic polypeptide, and antidiuretic hormone.

Ingestion of food is a potent stimulus of pancreatic bicarbonate secretion. Between meals, basal bicarbonate secretion idles at 2% of its stimulated rate. Although sight and smell of food (cephalic phase) stimulate pancreatic secretion, this fluid is low in bicarbonate content. Similarly, gastric distention (gastric phase) stimulates a bicarbonate-poor pancreatic secretion. However, entry of food into the upper small intestine markedly stimulates the pancreas. The nature of the ingested food alters the type of pancreatic secretion, with acid contents stimulating bicarbonate secretion, protein and amino acids reducing bicarbonate secretion, and fatty acids, depending on chain length, stimulating bicarbonate secretion.

Cell Physiology

Two basic cell populations are responsible for isotonic pancreatic secretions: acinar cells generate chloride-rich fluid, and ductular cells produce bicarbonate. The ductular cells secrete bicarbonate into an electronegative lumen. Ductular bicarbonate secretion depends on Na^+, K^+-ATPase activity, and the rate of secretion is significantly influenced by the blood bicarbonate concentration. Some studies suggest that Na^+-H^+ exchange occurs along the basolateral cell membranes, and HCO_3^- or OH^- exits across the apical membrane. Other investigations suggest that the HCO_3^- ion crosses both the basolateral and apical cell membrane, since acetate readily substitutes for HCO_3^- as the transported species.

Duodenum

Organ Physiology

The duodenum secretes bicarbonate in order to neutralize acid stomach drainage. As may be expected by anatomic location, the more proximal portion of the duodenum secretes more bicarbonate than does the more distal portion. Under basal conditions, the proximal 5 cm secretes approximately 1 mmole/hr, whereas the 5 cm just distal to the pancreatic duct secretes at 10% that rate. Besides neutralizing luminal contents for later digestion, bicarbonate secretion functions to protect the muscosal lining.

The primary stimulus for duodenal bicarbonate secretion is the acidity of entering fluid. The proximal segment attains a bicarbonate secretory rate of 3 mmoles/hr. Neural (vagal) pathways and α-1-adrenergic agonists stimulate bicarbonate secretion, whereas α-2-adrenergic agonists inhibit secretion. VIP, released by the duodenum when the mucosa is bathed with acid, is a powerful stimulant of duodenal bicarbonate secretion. Opiates and opioid peptides stimulate bicarbonate secretion as do prostaglandins ($E_2 > F_{2a}$) and gastrin.

Cell Physiology

It appears likely that duodenal surface cells rather than those located in Brunner's glands secrete bicarbonate. Cyclic AMP stimulates bicarbonate secretion, and the motive power for flux is linked to Na^+ movement through Na^+, K^+-ATPase. HCO_3^- appears to enter the basolateral side of the cell linked to Na^+ and exits across the apical cell membrane in exchange for Cl^-. Experimentally, HCO_3^- secretion varies with the blood bicarbonate concentration.

Jejunum

Organ Physiology

The jejunum reabsorbs bicarbonate secreted by the duodenum, biliary tract, and pancreas, keeping luminal pH in the neutral range. The rate of bicarbonate absorption varies with the concentrations of luminal HCO_3^- and Na^+. Unlike bicarbonate flux in other intestinal segments, jejunal bicarbonate absorption is not influenced markedly by systemic acid-base alterations. The role of neurohumoral control of jejunal bicarbonate absorption has not been examined.

Cell Physiology

It is believed that the jejunum absorbs bicarbonate by secreting H^+ into the lumen, elevating luminal CO_2 tension. H^+ may exit the apical cell membrane via a Na^+-H^+ antiporter as documented by studies of membrane vesicles. Nevertheless, the bulk of the experimental evidence suggests that jejunal bicarbonate transport also may involve direct HCO_3^- absorption. In addition, pH measurements reveal an acid microclimate overlying the the apical cell surface. Interestingly, this acid microclimate can be physically stripped away and is intrinsic to the removed mucous material.

Ileum

Organ Physiology

In contrast to the jejunum, the ileum secretes HCO_3^-, and approximately 70 mEq of HCO_3^- leave the ileum and enter the colon daily. *In vivo*, HCO_3^-

secretion is stimulated by cholera toxin and cyclic AMP, accounting at least in part for the metabolic acidosis observed in diarrheal diseases. On the other hand, catecholamines reduce net HCO_3^- secretion. Alterations of blood HCO_3^- concentration also influence ileal HCO_3^- secretion, with higher levels enhancing and lower levels diminishing secretion.

Cell Physiology

The mechanism of HCO_3^- secretion is thought to represent $Cl^- - HCO_3^-$ exchange, since luminal chloride is required for secretion to occur. In support of this exchange, apical brush border vesicles have been found to exhibit a Cl^--HCO_3^- antiport. It also has been proposed that OH^- rather than HCO_3^- may be the secreted ion, since luminal CO_2 tension is decreased as HCO_3^- secretion is stimulated. In addition, Na^+-H^+ exchange also occurs along the apical cell membrane. The disparity in rates between these simultaneous exchanges accounts for net HCO_3^- secretion. Epinephrine inhibits HCO_3^- secretion and increases serosal alkalinization, suggesting that catecholamines stimulate Na^+-H^+ exchange. Interestingly, a $Na^+/K^+/2\ Cl^-$ symport also may exist in the ileum and influence the rate of HCO_3^- secretion. The overall driving force for HCO_3^- secretion comes from Na^+,K^+ ATPase, since ouabain effectively inhibits secretion.

Colon

Organ Physiology

The colon normally conserves salt and water, excreting about 100 ml/day. As a part of this conserving function, the colon secretes more than 200 mEq of bicarbonate daily. However, this quantity of secreted bicarbonate does not normally appear in stool, since the majority is titrated by luminal H^+ generated by bacterial metabolism. The rate of bicarbonate secretion is influenced by the blood HCO_3^- concentration, increasing as the blood level rises and decreasing as the blood level falls. Like the ileum, colonic bicarbonate secretion is dependent on luminal chloride and is stimulated by many diarrheal diseases. In addition, the presence of organic anions (short-chain fatty acid anions) in the lumen stimulate colonic bicarbonate secretion.

Cell Physiology

As depicted in Fig. 3, colonic bicarbonate secretion is thought to occur by Cl^--HCO_3^- exchange at the apical membrane, since Cl^- is required for HCO_3^- secretion. Indeed, inhibitors of this exchanger prevent the appropri-

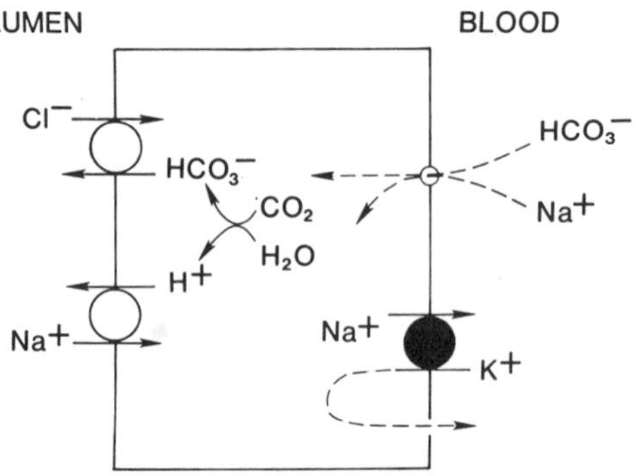

FIG. 3. Acid-base transport in colon epithelial cell. HCO_3^- exits the apical membrane via a Cl^--HCO_3^- exchange mechanism. The sources of secreted HCO_3^- include ambient CO_2 and HCO_3^- entry across the basolateral membrane. The latter process requires Na^+ and may be a Na^+/HCO_3^- cotransport system. Na^+,K^+-ATPase (solid circle) generates the Na^+ gradient that drives HCO_3^- into the cell. In addition, the colon secretes H^+ in exchange for Na^+, titrating a portion of secreted HCO_3^-. This CO_2-dependent event facilitates NaCl absorption in the colon.

ate fluxes in membrane vesicle studies. As in the ileum, apical Na^+-H^+ exchange also exists in the colon, and these exchange mechanisms operate at unequal rates in order to account for net HCO_3^- secretion. For example, inhibition of the H^+ secretory process results in increased net HCO_3^- secretion. However, the operating rates of Na^+-H^+ and Cl^--HCO_3^- exchanges are influenced by the ambient CO_2 tension. As a supplier of intracellular H^+ and HCO_3^-, increased CO_2 tension enhances colonic NaCl absorption, increasing Na^+-H^+ and Cl^--HCO_3^- simultaneously. Importantly, CO_2 tension does not affect net HCO_3^- secretion, thus demonstrating that other transport steps contribute to and modulate net HCO_3^- secretion.

Measurements of intracellular pH suggest that the intracellular bicarbonate concentration is sufficient to drive a HCO_3^- secretory process across the apical membrane. Apparently, the power that causes HCO_3^- secretion comes from the Na^+ pump, since ouabain inhibition of Na^+,K^+-ATPase effectively stops secretion. The rate of HCO_3^- secretion is dependent on basolateral Na^+, suggesting that HCO_3^- entry into the cell across the basolateral membrane is linked to Na^+ and its favorable electrochemical gradient. Since in the proximal tubule, this form of HCO_3^- movement is conductive, perhaps this explains why imposed transepithelial voltage gradients alter net HCO_3^- secretion in the colon. As yet, there is no direct demonstration of neurohumoral control of colonic HCO_3^- secretion, but dietary manipulations do alter the secretory rate; ingesting an acidifying diet decreases the rate of HCO_3^- secretion. An acidifying diet alters the cellular process of HCO_3^- secretion by changing the apparent mechanism of basolateral HCO_3^- entry.

The absorption of organic cations and anions is linked to colonic HCO_3^- secretion. As is true for chloride, organic anion absorption occurs largely via an anionic exchange for bicarbonate. Organic anions, especially short-chain fatty acid anions, also may be absorbed by diffusion of the highly permeable acid form. In the latter scheme, environmental CO_2, that is, carbonic acid, would supply H^+ to convert the organic anion to the acid form in the lumen, simultaneously generating intraluminal HCO_3^-. In a similar way, the organic cation ammonium may be absorbed by diffusion of its nonpolar form (ammonia). In this scheme, bicarbonate secretion continually generates nonpolar ammonia from metabolically produced ammonium. This system adds an element of saturation kinetics, since the titration rate of ammonium to ammonia is limited by the rate of bicarbonate secretion. Such a mechanism may account for the fecal losses of ammonium in congenital and acquired chloride diarrhea.

ELECTROLYTE PROFILES DURING GASTROINTESTINAL DERANGEMENTS

As described previously, the contribution of the gastrointestinal tract to overall acid-base balance depends on dietary intake, the volume and character of the fluid secreted and absorbed by the intestine, and coordination among the various intestinal segments. Systemic acid-base abnormalities may be generated, worsened, or improved by alterations in any one of these three elements. The most serious acid-base disorders of gastrointestinal origin are caused by fluid losses from the intestine. These losses are usually manifest as vomiting, diarrhea, or enterocutaneous fistulas or ostomies.

The volume and electrolyte composition of the fluid lost from the gastrointestinal tract determines the nature of the resulting acid-base disorder. Table 3 shows the electrolyte concentrations of fluids that may be lost from various

TABLE 3. *Electrolyte concentrations of gastrointestinal drainage*

Drainage site	Na^+	K^-	Cl^- (mEq/liter)	HCO_3^-
Saliva	40–80	20	10–40	20–50
Gastric				
Normal	20–100	5–10	30–90	0
Achlorhydria	50–120	5–10	100	20
Bile	135–155	5–10	85–110	40
Pancreas	115–155	3–7	55–95	95–110
Jejunum	75–120	4–7	70–125	30
Ileum				
Fresh ostomy	115–140	5–15	95–125	30
Adapted ostomy	50	5	20	15–30
Cecostomy	50–115	10–30	35–70	15–25

TABLE 4. *Electrolyte concentrations of diarrheal fluid*

Condition	Na^+	K^+	Cl^-	HCO_3^-
			(mEq/liter)	
Normal feces	<10	<10	<15	<15
Secretory (e.g., cholera)	75–140	15–40	75–105	40–70
Inflammatory (e.g., colitis)	50–100	15–20		
Osmotic	5–20	20–30		
Chloride diarrhea				
Congenital	30–80	15–60	120–150	<5
Acquired	80–120	15–30	85–110	pH<7.1

regions of the intestine. Table 4 shows the electrolyte concentrations of diarrheal fluids lost during several different causes of clinical diarrhea. Note that the composition varies greatly, as may the diarrheal volume.

REFERENCES

1. Bieberdorf, F. A., Gorden, P., and Fordtran, J. S. (1972): Pathogenesis of congenital alkalosis with diarrhea. Implications for the physiology of normal ileal electrolyte absorption and secretion. *J. Clin. Invest.*, 51:1958–1968.
2. Charney, A. N., and Feldman, G. M. (1984): Systemic acid-base disorders and intestinal electrolyte transport. *Am. J. Physiol.*, 247:G1–G12.
3. Cohen, J. J., and Kassirer, J. (1982): *Acid-Base*, 1st ed. Little Brown & Co., Boston, pp. 57–59.
4. Cummings, J. H. (1984): Colonic absorption: The importance of short chain fatty acids in man. *Scand. J. Gastroenterol.*, 93S:89–99.
5. Davis, G. R., Morawski, S. G., Santa Ana, C. A., and Fordtran, J. S. (1983): Evaluation of chloride/bicarbonate exchange in the human colon *in vivo. J. Clin. Invest.*, 71:201-207.
6. Feldman, G. M., Arnold, M. A., and Charney, A. N. (1984): On the mechanism of luminal CO_2 generation during jejunal bicarbonate absorption. *Am. J. Physiol.*, 246:G687–G694.
7. Flemstrom, G., and Garner, A. (1982): Gastroduodenal HCO_3^{2-} transport: Characteristics and proposed role in acidity regulation and mucosal protection. *Am. J. Physiol.*, 242:G183–G193.
8. Garcia-Marin, J. J., Dumont, M., Corbic, M., de Couet, G., and Erlinger, S. (1985): Effect of acid-base balance and acetazolamide on ursodeoxycholate-induced biliary bicarbonate secretion. *Am. J. Physiol.*, 248:G20–G27.
9. Hubel, K. A. (1985): Intestinal nerves and ion transport: Stimuli, reflexes, and responses. *Am. J. Physiol.*, 248:G261–G271.
10. Hubel, K. A. (1974): The mechanism of bicarbonate secretion in rabbit ileum exposed to choleragen. *J. Clin. Invest.*, 53:964–970.
11. Kleinman, J. G., and Lemann J. Jr. (1988): Acid production in clinical disorders. *In: Clinical Disorders of Fluid and Electrolyte Metabolism*, edited by M. Maxwell, C. Kleeman, and R. Narins. McGraw Hill, New York.
12. Kurtz, I., Maher, T., Hulter, H. N., Schambelan, M., and Sebastian, A. (1983): Effect of diet on plasma acid-base composition in normal humans. *Kidney Int.*, 24:670–680.
13. Lemann, J. Jr., and Lennon, E. J. (1972): Role of diet, gastrointestinal tract and bone in acid-base homeostasis. *Kidney Int.*, 1:275–279.

14. Lennon, E. J., Lemann, J. Jr., and Litzow, J. R. (1966): The effects of diet and stool composition on the net external acid balance of normal subjects. J. Clin. Invest. 45:1601–1607.
15. Moran, W. M., Hudson, R. L., and Schultz, S. G. (1986): Transcellular sodium transport and intracellular sodium activities in rabbit gallbladder. *Am. J. Physiol.*, 251:G155–G159.
16. Powell, D. W. (1987): Intestinal water and electrolyte transport. *In: Physiology of the Gastrointestinal Tract*, edited by L. R. Johnson, pp. 1267–1305. Raven Press. New York.
17. Powell, D. W., Berschneider, H. M., Lawson, L. D., and Martens, H. (1985): Regulation of water and ion movement in intestine. *Ciba Found. Symp.*, 112:14–33.
18. Reenstra, W. W., Bettencourt, J. D., and Forte, J. G. (1986): Active K^+ absorption by the gastric mucosa: Inhibition by omeprazole. *Am. J. Physiol.*, 250:G455–G460.
19. Rubinstein, R., Howard, A. V., and Wrong, O. M. (1969): *In vivo* dialysis of feces as a method of stool analysis. IV. The organic anion component. *Clin. Sci.*, 37:549–564.
20. Schulz, I. (1987): Electrolyte and fluid secretion in the exocrine pancreas. In: *Physiology of the Gastrointestinal Tract*, edited by L. R. Johnson, pp. 1147–1171. Raven Press, New York.
21. Sheerin, H. E., and Field, M. (1975): Ileal HCO_3^- secretion: Relationship to Na^+ and Cl^- transport and effect of theophylline. *Am. J. Physiol.*, 228:1065–1074.
22. Turnberg, L. A., Bieberdorf, F. A., Morawski, S. G., and Fordtran, J. S. (1970): Interrelationships of chloride, bicarbonate, sodium, and hydrogen transport in the human ileum. *J. Clin. Invest.*, 49:557–567.
23. Turnberg, L. A., Fordtran, J. S., Carter, N. W., and Rector, F. C. Jr. (1970): Mechanism of bicarbonate absorption and its relationship to sodium transport in the human jejunum. *J. Clin. Invest.*, 49:548–556.
24. Van Dyke, R. W., Stephens, J. E., and Scharschmidt, B. F. (1982): Effects of ion substitution on bile acid-dependent and -independent bile formation by rat liver. *J. Clin. Invest.*, 70:505–517.
25. Van Ypersele de Strihou, C. (1980): Importance of endogenous acid production in the regulation of acid-base equilibrium: The role of the digestive tract. *In: Advances in Nephrology, Vol. 9*, edited by M. H. Maxwell. Year Book, Chicago.
26. Winfield, J. M., and Mersheimer, W. L. (1958): Intestinal obstruction. Physiological and pathological alterations. *Surg. Clin. North Am.*, 38.

The Regulation of Acid–Base Balance, edited
by Donald W. Seldin and Gerhard Giebisch,
Raven Press, Ltd., New York © 1989.

6

Acid-Base Balance in Specialized Tissues: Central Nervous System

Allen I. Arieff

Geriatrics Research, Veterans Administration Medical Center, San Francisco, California 94121

ACID-BASE STATUS OF BRAIN AND CEREBROSPINAL FLUID (1–10,14,21,24–29)

The central nervous system (CNS) consists of the brain and cerebrospinal fluid (CSF), and the regulation of acid-base balance in this compartment is distinctly different from that of the rest of the body. There have been a substantial number of studies dealing with the acid-base status of brain and CSF. Those dealing with the CSF are generally reasonably straightforward and less controversial because of the ready applicability of commonly used techniques for measurement of blood gases for direct measurement of gases in CSF. By contrast, the techniques for evaluation of intracellular pH (pH_i) in brain involve the use of indirect measurements (generally, the creatine phosphate equilibrium or isotope techniques, such as ^{14}C-labeled dimethadione), and intracellular P_{CO_2} in brain is generally assumed to be represented by the P_{CO_2} in cortical CSF. Such measurements, by their indirect nature, are subject to more controversy. There is a feeling in the medical profession that the pH of CSF reflects the pH_i of brain better than does arterial pH. In fact, this simply is not true. The CSF is more of a passive sink for both blood and brain. In many clinical circumstances, brain pH_i often is closer to arterial pH than to that of CSF.

There are three separate compartments in the central nervous system— blood, brain, and CSF—that are separated by the blood–brain and blood– CSF barriers (Fig. 1). A discussion of the general status of acid-base equilibrium among brain, CSF, and arterial blood follows.

The steady state relationships between acid-base components in arterial blood versus cisternal CSF in humans are shown in Fig. 2. In general, the bicarbonate concentration is similar in blood and CSF (about 24 mmoles/liter). The arterial pH (about 7.40) is higher than that of CSF (about 7.32) because the Pco_2 is about 48 mm Hg in CSF and about 40 mm Hg in arterial blood. The buffering capacity of CSF is substantially less than that in blood. Much of this difference is because the CSF protein concentration (about 4×10^{-2} g/dl) is minute compared to that in plasma (about 7 g/dl). However, despite this apparent inferior buffering capacity, the pH of CSF remains remarkably constant despite substantial changes in arterial pH. In those conditions characterized by acute alterations in systemic Pco_2 (respiratory alkalosis and acidosis), there are acute alterations in pH and Pco_2 of CSF that are directionally similar to those in arterial blood. However, the changes in CSF pH initially are less than those observed in arterial blood, and within 1 hr, efficient compensatory mechanisms have been initiated. In certain unique clini-

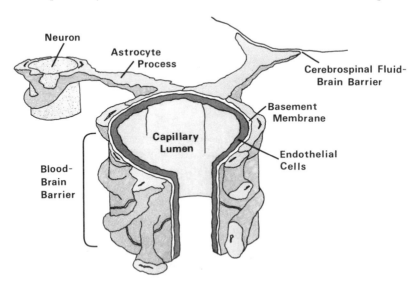

Fig. 1. This is a diagrammatic rendition of the blood–brain barrier. The principal components are the astrocytic foot processes, endothelial cells with tight junctions, and thick capillary basement membranes. The brain–CSF barrier consists primarily of choroid plexus and ependyma. (From ref. 24.)

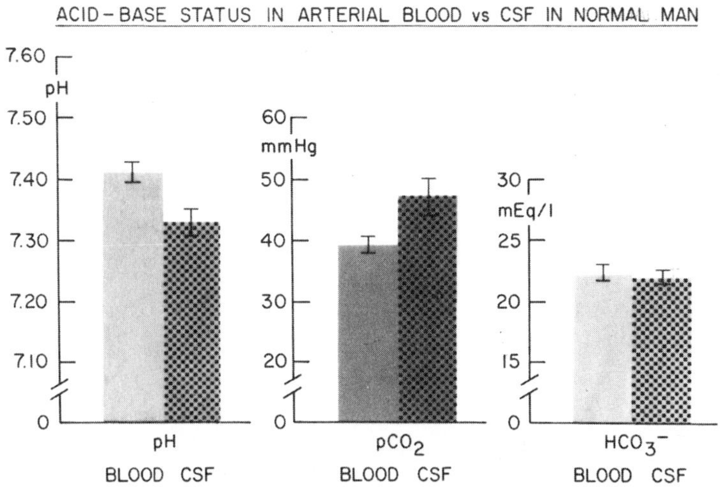

ACID–BASE STATUS IN ARTERIAL BLOOD vs CSF IN NORMAL MAN

Fig. 2. Comparison of the relationship between pH, Pco_2, and bicarbonate (HCO_3^-) in arterial blood versus cortical CSF. (Data from ref. 26.)

cal situations, such as the treatment of uremic patients with hemodialysis (Fig.3) or therapy of patients with metabolic acidosis with $NaHCO_3$ infusion, the pH of CSF moves in a direction that is opposite to that of blood.

RESPIRATORY ACID-BASE ABNORMALITIES

Respiratory Acidosis

In experimental acute respiratory acidosis (arterial Pco_2 above 80 mm Hg), there is an initial decline in the pH of CSF. Within 1 to 2 hr, the bicarbonate

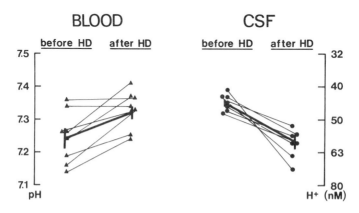

Fig. 3. Comparison of the pH in arterial blood and CSF before and after rapid hemodialysis (HD) of dogs with acute renal failure (BUN = 75 mmoles/liter). As the arterial pH rises, that of CSF falls. (From ref. 2.)

concentration in CSF begins to rise. However, the compensatory increase in pH of CSF is only minimal after 4 to 6 hr. The compensation in brain is much more rapid. After 1 hr of hypercapnia, brain pH_i has declined by about 0.2 pH units (from 7.1 to 6.9). However, if the arterial PCO_2 is maintained above 80 mm Hg for 3 hr, brain pH_i has returned to normal despite the sustained hypercapnia.

In clinical situations, respiratory acidosis usually is observed in patients with pulmonary insufficiency. Severe respiratory acidosis frequently is associated with depression of sensorium, as manifested by lethargy, stupor, or obtundation. Coma may supervene with substantial degrees of CO_2 retention (arterial PCO_2 above 60 mm Hg). It is difficult to identify which specific symptoms are caused by CO_2 retention because it is rare to have hypercapnia without some degree of concomitant hypoxemia. Clinically, patients who have chronic obstructive pulmonary disease or bronchial asthma virtually always have some degree of hypoxia when they have hypercapnia. However, by examining separately the CNS effects of both hypoxia and hypercapnia, it is possible to ascertain some of the effects of each.

The effects of hypercapnia versus hypoxia have been studied in laboratory animals. When acute hypercapnia is induced in laboratory animals (PCO_2 = 80–90 mm Hg) in the absence of hypoxia (arterial PO_2 above 70 mm Hg), there are acute decrements in pH of both arterial blood and CSF. There is thus no apparent barrier to the penetration of CO_2 into the CSF. However, largely because of an increase in cerebral blood flow, the PCO_2 in CSF will rise relatively less than arterial PCO_2, resulting in a smaller decline of pH in CSF. Within 1 hr after the PCO_2 is elevated, there is a gradual rise in the bicarbonate concentration in CSF, such that pH of CSF begins to rise toward normal values. These changes precede any alterations in arterial bicarbonate concentration.

After 3 hr with arterial PCO_2 maintained at 80 to 90 mm Hg, the CSF bicarbonate has risen (in the dog) from 20 to 25 mmoles/liter. However, if the hypercapnia is maintained for 6 hr, the pH of CSF is still significantly below normal values. After 1 day of hypercapnia, pH in CSF has returned to normal, whereas CSF bicarbonate is 35 mmoles/liter, significantly above normal. However, arterial pH is still acidotic, demonstrating the lag between systemic compensation by the kidneys versus CSF compensation via transport of bicarbonate into the central nervous system. The increased bicarbonate concentration in CSF is secreted mainly by the choroid plexus. Although it is not entirely clear whether hypercapnia or CSF acidemia is the stimulus for increased secretion of bicarbonate, it is clear that bicarbonate is formed at the choroid plexus and transported against a concentration gradient into the CSF. The process is carbonic anhydrase-dependent and can be largely blocked by the action of acetazolamide.

The compensatory mechanisms for pH regulation in the brain of animals with acute respiratory acidosis are more rapid than those in either blood or

CSF. With acute hypercapnia (P_{CO_2} = 80–90 mm Hg) in the dog, arterial pH falls from 7.4 to 7.1 in 1 hr, whereas the simultaneously measured intracellular pH (pH_i) in brain (cerebral cortex) is 6.90 (normal value = 7.06). However, after only 30 to 60 min of hypercapnia, the calculated cerebral cortex bicarbonate concentration has increased to 57% above the normal value. After 3 hr of hypercapnia, with no change whatsoever in arterial pH, brain pH_i has returned to normal values (about 7.06). The brain bicarbonate is now 24.4 mmoles/kg H_2O (normal value = 11.3 mmoles/kg H_2O). Thus, with both the arterial and CSF P_{CO_2} maintained at about 85 mm Hg, the brain is able to normalize its pH_i within 3 hr.

The means by which the brain restores its pH_i to normal during respiratory acidosis are probably complex. There appears to be a fixed amount of nonbicarbonate buffer in brain, which is equivalent to about 33 mmoles of buffer/kg of brain tissue. In addition, during respiratory acid-base disorders, there is a substantial generation of bicarbonate by brain. Most of the generation of bicarbonate by brain appears to take place within 30 min of the initial stimulus for increased bicarbonate generation. The mechanisms by which the brain generates the bicarbonate are unclear, although they are probably not entirely secondary to the action of carbonic anhydrase. Acetazolamide, an inhibitor of the action of carbonic anhydrase, does not completely block brain bicarbonate generation.

There are several other biochemical means by which the brain might also generate bicarbonate. Numerous reactions in the brain produce CO_2, particularly those that involve decarboxylation. There could be direct hydroxylation of gaseous CO_2 to bicarbonate, as occurs in some elasmobranch fish. Other CO_2-producing reactions in brain include either metabolism of glucose via the Krebs (tricarboxylic acid) cycle or conversion of glutamic acid to γ-aminobutyric acid. In the later instance, CO_2 in brain may be in the form of either carbonic acid or bicarbonate. Most of these reactions are intimately linked to glucose metabolism, since glutamic acid is produced via the Krebs cycle, and pyruvate, a product of the metabolism of glucose via the Embden-Meyerhof pathway (glycolysis), is a precursor of most amino acids found in the brain. Several steps in the metabolism of glucose are pH-dependent, and it is possible that intracellular acidosis might shift some equilibrium reactions to favor certain CO_2-producing components.

During respiratory acidosis, in the initial 2 to 3 hr of hypercapnia, there is a marked upward shift in the brain CO_2 dissociation curve. Thus, brain buffering capacity actually increases with the presence of chronic hypercapnia. There is also probably increased conversion of glutamic acid to α-ketoglutamic acid, with liberation of NH_3. The metabolism of glutamic acid could remove a potential source of H^+ ion, whereas increased production of NH_3 could buffer additional H^+ ion by conversion to NH_4^+. Thus, buffering by the brain in respiratory acidosis probably occurs by a combination of several different interacting factors.

Although cerebral compensation of the acidosis of acute hypercapnia is apparently complete within 4 hr, the same is not true of other tissues. In skeletal muscle, for instance, after 1 hr of respiratory acidosis, the pH_i has declined from 6.85 to 6.53. After 3 hr of hypercapnia, however, muscle pH_i and bicarbonate concentration are unaltered, whereas brain pH_i has returned to normal.

Respiratory Alkalosis

In acute respiratory alkalosis in experimental animals, there is an increase in the CSF concentrations of both lactate and other, as yet unidentified, organic acids, which results in a decrease of CSF pH toward normal. In experimental animals, this process is nearly complete after 4 to 6 hr. Similar alterations are observed when comparing arterial pH with the brain pH_i. When hypercapnia is induced by hyperventilation (arterial P_{CO_2} of 15 mm Hg), the arterial pH is about 7.6 to 7.7. After 1 hr under such conditions, the simultaneously determined pH_i of brain has risen by about 0.2 pH units (from 7.0 to 7.2), but after 2 hr, it has returned to normal values.

Respiratory alkalosis in humans frequently is observed during the course of several systemic disease states, which include bronchial asthma, hepatic cirrhosis, salicylate intoxication, hypoxia, sepsis, and certain lesions of the brain. In these conditions, the related symptoms usually are those of the underlying disorder rather than the alkalosis *per se*. Modest acute respiratory alkalosis may be accompanied by only mild symptoms (paresthesias, dizziness). However, more severe alkalosis (pH 7.5 – 7.7) in patients with respiratory insufficiency and hypoxia can result in a symptom complex of hypotension, seizures, asterixis, myoclonus, and coma, with a mortality exceeding 75%.

The arterial P_{CO_2} is an important regulator of cerebral blood flow, but there is also an effect of both arterial and CSF pHs. Hypocapnia is a potent cerebral vasoconstrictor. This effect is used clinically during anesthesia, when hyperventilation (to induce hypocapnia) can effectively decrease intracranial volume and relieve cerebral swelling. By contrast, both hypercapnia and hypoxia are potent cerebral vasodilators.

With acute hypocapnia in experimental animals, there is an initial rise in the brain pH_i. Almost immediately, there is a decline in brain bicarbonate concentration with a rise in brain concentration of lactate. Within 2 hr, with arterial P_{CO_2} maintained below 20 mm Hg, brain pH_i has returned to control values. The return of brain pH_i to normal occurs concomitant with the fall of brain bicarbonate, which has an almost stoichiometric relationship with the increase in lactate. There also is a rise of lactate and fall in bicarbonate in CSF, but the CSF lactate is not high enough to account for all of the observed decline in CSF bicarbonate.

In addition to the rise in brain lactate, there is also a change in the brain

CO_2 dissociation curve, such that brain buffering capacity is decreased. There is no associated change in brain concentration of adenosine triphosphate (ATP), adenosine diphosphate (ADP), phosphocreatine, or creatine. The decrease in brain buffering capacity did not correlate with the finding that there were no alterations in brain concentration of glutamic acid, glutamine, or NH_3. Thus, although brain buffering capacity is decreased during hypocapnia, the biochemical mechanisms whereby such a phenomenon occurs are not known.

In patients with acute respiratory alkalosis, there is a significant decline in cerebral blood flow that correlates well with marked slowing of the electroencephalogram (EEG). There also is an increase in jugular venous $[K+]$ and a decline in $[Na+]$. Thus, within 2 hr of the onset of respiratory alkalosis, the brain, after an initial rise in pH_i, has restored its pH_i to normal. This is accomplished primarily by cerebral vasoconstriction, leading to a reduction in cerebral blood flow and increased anaerobic metabolism. Although high-energy phosphate compounds are not affected, there is an increase in brain lactate, leading to a fall in brain bicarbonate. This sequence appears to represent the brain's primary response to acute respiratory alkalosis.

EFFECTS OF METABOLIC ACID-BASE DISTURBANCES ON BRAIN (1,4,5,9)

In contrast to the investigation of respiratory abnormalities, relatively little investigation has been carried out on the effects of metabolic disorders of acid-base metabolism on the CNS. During acute metabolic disturbances of acid-base balance, the effects on pH in CSF are only minimal.

Metabolic Acidosis

Metabolic acidosis has been induced in laboratory animals by means of HCl or NH_4Cl infusion. When arterial pH was lowered from 7.4 to 7.2 by infusion of HCl, there was no significant alteration in pH of CSF. Similarly, when $NaHCO_3$ was infused so that arterial pH was increased from 7.4 to 7.5, the pH of CSF was unaltered. It appears that the blood–CSF barrier is readily permeable to CO_2, but neither bicarbonate nor hydrogen ion can cross this barrier easily into the brain.

In some animals when HCl was infused to produce an arterial pH of 7.06 with plasma bicarbonate of 6 mmoles/liter, the brain pH_i fell by 0.3 pH units, with no change in the brain extracellular space. In other studies, however, metabolic acidosis in rats (NH_4Cl injection, arterial pH = 7.31) had no effect on brain pH_i or bicarbonate concentration.

In rabbits with experimental hypoxic lactic acidosis (arterial pH = 7.1), brain pH_i was not measured directly, but there was a significant increase in brain lactate concentration (from 3.9 to 18.1 mmoles/kg), so that brain pH$_i$ probably fell. In rats with diabetic ketoacidosis (plasma ketones = 9.5 mmoles/liter), there was no change in brain pH$_i$. Thus, it appears that, as a general rule, metabolic acidosis has only small and inconsistent effects on brain pH$_i$.

Metabolic Alkalosis

Metabolic alkalosis has been produced in hypocapnic rats and dogs by infusing NaHCO$_3$. In rats with arterial pH of 7.8 (Pco_2 = 16 mm Hg, bicarbonate = 25 mmoles/liter), there were increases in brain lactate and pyruvate concentrations, with an increase in the lactate/pyruvate ratio from 16 to 24. There was no significant change in brain pH$_i$ when compared to normal values (7.05). In normocapnic dogs or rats, when arterial pH was raised to 7.5 to 7.7 by NaHCO$_3$ infusion (plasma bicarbonate above 34 mmoles/liter), there was also no significant change in brain pH$_i$. In brain of the alkalotic rats, there was no change in brain concentration of ATP, ADP, AMP, or phosphocreatine. Therefore, in experimental animals, metabolic alkalosis (arterial pH of 7.5 – 7.8) has essentially no effect on brain pH$_i$, there is only a minimal rise in brain lactate concentration, and there is no change in brain bicarbonate.

CENTRAL NERVOUS SYSTEM ACID-BASE STATUS IN UREMIA (6,7,11–13,15)

Intracellular acid-base status has been evaluated extensively in both uremic humans and various animal models of acute or chronic renal failure. In animals who have acute renal failure and metabolic acidosis, the pH$_i$ in brain and skeletal muscle is normal (Fig. 4). In patients with chronic renal failure, pH$_i$ has been reported to be normal in both skeletal muscle and leukocytes, as well as in the whole body. In dogs with chronic renal failure, despite a metabolic acidosis, the pH$_i$ is normal in several different parts of the brain, in liver, and in skeletal muscle (Fig. 5). The pH$_i$ of brain has not yet been evaluated in uremic humans, although newer techniques, such as magnetic resonance spectroscopy, may soon permit such parameters to be measured *in vivo*. The pH of CSF has been shown to be normal in both patients and laboratory animals with renal failure. Thus, in uremic animals and humans, despite the presence of extracellular metabolic acidosis, the brain intracellular buffering capacity is capable of maintaining pH$_i$ in the normal range. A similar effect is observed in muscle, white blood cells, and most other tissues as well in both humans and laboratory animals.

BUFFERING CAPACITY OF BRAIN VERSUS OTHER TISSUES (1,5,6,9,16,17,25,29)

Studies have been carried out in order to evaluate the acute buffering capacity of liver, brain, skeletal muscle, and cardiac muscle. In liver, despite a

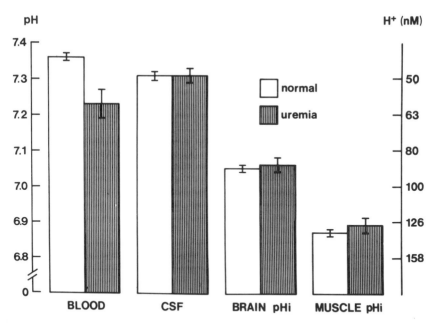

Fig. 4. The arterial pH, pH of cerebrospinal fluid (CSF), and the intracellular pH (pH$_i$) of brain (cerebral cortex) and skeletal muscle in dogs with acute renal failure (BUN = 75 mmoles/liter). Despite a metabolic acidosis, the pH of CSF and pH$_i$ of brain and muscle are normal. (From ref. 1.)

range of extracellular pH from 7.1 to 7.6 induced by either respiratory or metabolic means, the pH$_i$ of the liver did not vary from normal (normal hepatic pH$_i$ = 7.0 ± 0.03). This was largely accomplished by acute alterations of hepatic intracellular bicarbonate. Over the aforementioned range of extracellular pH, the liver intracellular bicarbonate varied from 5.4 to 21.6 mmoles/liter of cell H$_2$O (normal value = 10.4 mmoles/liter of cell H$_2$O).

Tissue buffering capacity can be calculated when the change in intracellular pH for a known change in Pco$_2$ is known. The formula, as described by Kjallquist et al., is

$$\text{Buffering capacity} = \Delta \log \text{Pco}_2 / \Delta \text{ pH}_i$$

Using this formula, one can calculate the relative buffering capacities of different tissues subjected to the same acute acid-base disturbance. When the extracellular pH was over the same range of extracellular pH (7.1 – 7.6), brain pH$_i$ was more subject to fluctuation than was that of liver. The control brain (cerebral cortex) pH$_i$ is 7.05 ± 0.02, and after 1 hr of hypercapnia (Pco$_2$ = 80 – 90 mm Hg), brain pH$_i$ was 6.93 ± 0.04, with buffering capacity of 13.9. Muscle and liver had pH$_i$ of 6.53 and 6.98, respectively (Fig. 6).

With acute respiratory alkalosis (arterial pH = 7.55, Pco$_2$ = 15 mm Hg), buffering capacities of liver, skeletal muscle, and brain (cerebral cortex) were

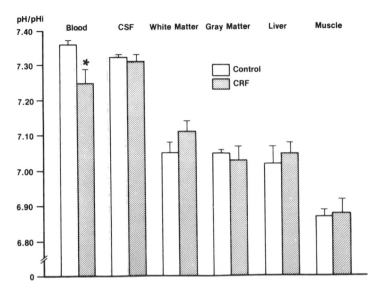

Fig. 5. The pH of arterial blood and CSF and the intracellular pH (pH$_i$) of brain (white and gray matter), liver, and skeletal muscle in dogs with chronic renal failure (glomerular filtration rate less than 10 ml/min for 4 months). Despite a metabolic acidosis, the pH of CSF and pH$_i$ of brain and liver are normal. (From ref. 11.)

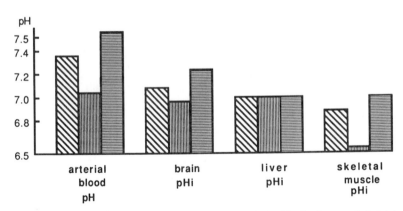

Fig. 6. Comparison of arterial pH with intracellular pH (pH$_i$) of brain, liver, and skeletal muscle in normal dogs (diagonal hatching) and dogs with either respiratory acidosis (vertical hatching) or respiratory alkalosis (horizontal hatching). (Data from refs. 1,25.)

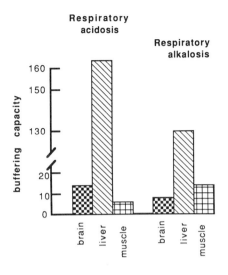

Fig. 7. Comparison of the intracellular buffering capacity of brain (cerebral cortex), liver, and skeletal muscle in dogs with either respiratory acidosis or respiratory alkalosis. (Data from refs. 1,14,25.)

130, 13, and 7.2, respectively. With acute respiratory acidosis, (arterial pH = 7.07, P_{CO_2} = 80 mm Hg), buffering capacities of liver, skeletal muscle, and brain (cerebral cortex) were 164, 4.9, and 13.9, respectively. Thus, in acute respiratory disturbances, the liver has the most efficient buffering capacity, with brain being somewhat more efficient than skeletal muscle. These data are shown graphically in Fig. 7.

METABOLIC ACIDOSIS AND SENSORIUM (2,3,8,10,19,24)

Patients with metabolic acidosis from a variety of causes often have depression of sensorium, and the question arises about the relationship between metabolic acidosis and coma. Metabolic acidosis probably is not an important cause of coma in such patients. Acidosis *per se* usually is not associated with coma in patients with a variety of systemic diseases, such as uremia, cholera, or hypercapnia. Furthermore, infusion or ingestion of acid (HCl or NH_4Cl) to induce acute metabolic acidemia does not cause coma in laboratory animals or humans.

There has been some evidence suggesting that depression of sensorium in patients with metabolic acidosis correlates not with arterial pH but rather with the pH of CSF, although subsequent investigation has failed to confirm these impressions. There was no apparent relationship between depression of sensorium and pH of CSF in patients with nonketotic coma, in subjects with cholera who were treated with $NaHCO_3$, or in patients with ketoacidosis who received intravenous $NaHCO_3$. In the latter two groups of patients, despite the fact that the pH of CSF fell after administration of intravenous $NaHCO_3$, there was actually an improvement in sensorium. It is thus most likely that pH$_i$ in brain, rather than pH of CSF, actually correlates with depression of sensorium. Since there is a generally poor correlation between pH of CSF versus brain pH$_i$, especially in metabolic disorders, it may be that in the earlier studies, conditions were such that brain pH$_i$ and pH in CSF had undergone similar changes.

CENTRAL NERVOUS SYSTEM ACID-BASE STATUS IN DIABETIC COMA (2,3,8,13,20,22,24)

Diabetic ketoacidosis is a metabolic abnormality that is characterized by hyperglycemia (blood glucose above 14 mmoles/liter) and metabolic acidosis (arterial pH below 7.25 and/or plasma bicarbonate less than 16 mmoles/liter due to hyperketonemia [plasma acetoacetate + β-hydroxybutyrate above 7 mmoles/liter (plasma acetest greater than 2+ at a 1:1 dilution)], with depression of sensorium to at least a state of obtundation. This disorder is most common among juvenile or growth-onset diabetic patients.

In patients with diabetic ketoacidosis, the extracellular (arterial) pH demonstrates a metabolic acidosis because of high levels of ketoacids (acetoacetic and β-hydroxybutyric) in blood. There is essentially no available information on the pH$_i$ of brain or any other tissue in patients with diabetic coma. However, there are substantial data on the acid-base status of CSF in patients with diabetic ketoacidosis. In nine patients with diabetic ketoacidosis, the arterial pH was 7.06, bicarbonate was 5.6 mM, and PCO_2 was 12 mm Hg. Despite the metabolic acidosis, the pH of CSF was normal (7.27). This was accomplished despite the fact that CSF bicarbonate was 10 mM (normal, 22 – 26 mM) because the PCO_2 of CSF was only 24 mm Hg (normal, 42 – 54 mm Hg) Similar results in patients with diabetic ketoacidosis have been reported by other workers.

There is a substantial amount of data on the acid-base status of the CNS in various animal models of diabetic ketoacidosis. In rats with experimental diabetic ketoacidosis, brain pH$_i$ is normal, as is lactate concentration. Since the pH of CSF is usually also normal in patients with ketoacidosis, it is unlikely that brain pH$_i$ is depressed in such subjects. However, in patients with severe acidemia (pH less than 7.00), there may be a decrement in brain pH$_i$. More recent experimental evidence suggests that when hyperglycemia is combined with some degree of cerebral ischemia, such as might occur during therapy of hyperglycemia, there is an initial decrement of brain intracellular pH. Such an intracerebral acidemia may be a factor in brain damage associated with therapy of hyperglycemia. Additionally, the presence of cerebral intracellular acidosis could impair the conversion of glucose-6-phosphate to pyruvate by inhibition of phosphofructokinase in brain. Subsequent inhibition of the Krebs cycle could be an important factor in the pathogenesis of coma in patients with diabetic ketoacidosis.

Cerebral edema is an uncommon complication of the correction of diabetic coma and has been reported in patients with either diabetic ketoacidosis or nonketotic hyperosmolar coma. In patients with uncomplicated ketoacidosis, cerebral edema usually occurs during otherwise successful correction of systemic metabolic abnormalities. In the clinical setting, elevation of CSF pressure has been observed to occur in most patients who are being treated for ketoacidosis. It is probable that most patients with either diabetic ketoacidosis or nonketotic hyperosmolar coma (nonketotic coma) develop subclinical brain edema during therapy, which usually resolves spontaneously. In a small minority of subjects, the brain edema progresses until it reaches clinical significance. When this happens, survival is infrequent. The reasons why such a minority of patients develop clinically important brain edema are not entirely clear but may involve transient intracellular acidemia.

The sudden loss of consciousness and increased CSF pressure that accompany substantial brain swelling during treatment of ketoacidosis or nonketotic coma may be related to the administration of large amounts of bicarbonate to correct systemic acidosis. Although phosphate depletion in ketoacidosis may result in a decrease in the concentration of 2,3-diphosphoglycerate in red blood cells and subsequently decrease tissue oxygen delivery, the oxygen-hemoglobin dissociation curve in diabetic coma is most likely normal because of the low arterial blood pH, so that oxygen delivery to tissues probably is normal. The administration of bicarbonate to restore a normal blood pH, then, might further reduce oxygen delivery to tissues by reversing the compensatory effect of metabolic acidemia. This mechanism could explain the similarity between some of the neuropathologic changes of ketoacidosis and those of cerebral hypoxia.

Administration of bicarbonate to patients with ketoacidosis may induce a paradoxical fall in the pH of CSF because of the rapid equilibration of CO_2 between blood and CSF and poor diffusion of bicarbonate from blood to CSF. The pH of CSF in uncomplicated ketoacidosis is usually normal. During treatment of ketoacidosis, even without administration of alkali, a significant fall in CSF pH generally has been observed. Any further reduction in CSF pH by the administration of bicarbonate could be significant in the production of severe obtundation or coma in some patients. Recent reports have demonstrated that although there is generally a secondary development of CSF acidosis when bicarbonate is administered to patients with ketoacidosis, there are no apparent clinical sequelae. When patients with metabolic acidosis from other causes (such as cholera) are treated with bicarbonate, the pH of CSF falls slightly as arterial pH rises (from 7.1 to 7.5). However, there are no clinical sequelae observed. Thus, the secondary decline of CSF pH is more a laboratory curiosity than an important pathophysiologic event. No focal neurologic signs, increased CSF pressure, or other evidence of cerebral edema have been observed after bicarbonate administration despite a significant fall in CSF pH from 7.3 to 7.1. It has now been shown, however, that bicarbonate administration to patients with ketoacidosis has no effect on the rate of rise in arterial pH. Several recent studies document the fact that arterial pH in patients with ketoacidosis rises at a similar rate with or without the administration of bicarbonate. Furthermore, rapid correction of metabolic acidosis with bicarbonate in patients with cholera did not induce either significant changes in neurologic status or significant CSF acidosis.

It would appear that, despite earlier claims of correlation between CSF acidosis and CNS symptoms, severe CSF acidosis may exist without evidence of cerebral edema, worsening level of consciousness, or other neurologic changes.

REFERENCES

1. Arieff, A. I., Guisado, R., Massry, S. G., and Lazarowitz, V. C. (1976): Central nervous system pH in uremia and the effects of hemodialysis. *J. Clin. Invest.*, 58:306–311.
2. Arieff, A. I., Massry, S. G., Barrientos, A., and Kleeman, C. (1973): Brain water and electrolyte metabolism in uremia: Effects of slow and rapid hemodialysis. *Kidney Int.*, 4:177–187.
3. Assal, J. P., Aoki, T. T., Manzano, F. M., and Kozak, G. P. (1974): Metabolic effects of sodium bicarbonate in management of diabetic ketoacidosis. *Diabetes*, 23:405–411.
4. Chopp, M., Frinak, S., Walton, D. R., Smith, M. B., and Welch, K. M. (1987): Intracellular acidosis during and after cerebral ischemia: *In vivo* nuclear magnetic resonance study of hyperglycemia in cats. *Stroke*, 18:919–923.
5. Cooper, J. D., Lazarowitz, V. C., and Arieff, A. I. (1978): Neurodiagnostic abnormalities in patients with acute renal failure. *J. Clin. Invest.*, 61:1448–1455.
6. Cowie, A., Lambie, A. T., and Robson, J. S. (1962): The influence of extracorporeal dialysis on the acid-base composition of blood and cerebrospinal fluid. *Clin Sci.*, 23:397–404.
7. Granholm, L., and Siesjo, B. K. (1971): The effect of combined respiratory and nonrespiratory alkalosis on energy metabolics and acid-base parameters in the rat brain. *Acta Physiol. Scand.*, 81:307–314.
8. Guisado, R., and Arieff, A. I. (1975): Neurological manifestations of diabetic comas: Correlation with biochemical alterations in the brain. *Metabolism*, 24:665–679.
9. Kjallquist, M., Nardini, M., and Siesjo, B. K. (1969): The effect of acetazolamide upon tissue concentrations of bicarbonate, lactate, and pyruvate in the rat brain. *Acta Physiol. Scand.*, 77:241–251.
10. Lai, Y. L., Attenbery, B. A., and Brown, E. B. (1973): Intracellular adjustments of skeletal muscle, heart and brain to prolonged hypercapnia. *Respir. Physiol.*, 19:115–122.
11. Mahoney, C. A., and Arieff, A. I. (1983): Central and peripheral nervous system effects of chronic renal failure. *Kidney Int.*, 24:170–177.
12. Maschio, G., Bazzato, G., Bertaglia, E., Sardini, D., and Mioni, G. (1970): Intracellular pH and electrolyte content of skeletal muscle in patients with chronic renal acidosis. *Nephron*, 7:481–487.
13. Morris, L. R., Murphy, M. B., and Kitabachi, A. E. (1986): Bicarbonate therapy in severe diabetic ketoacidosis. *Ann. Intern. Med.*, 105:836–840.
14. Park, R., Leach, W. J., and Arieff, A. I. (1979): Determination of liver intracellular pH *in vivo* and its homeostasis in acute acidosis and alkalosis. *Am. J. Physiol.*, 236:F240–F245.
15. Pauli, H. G., Vorburger, C., and Reubi, F. (1962): Chronic derangements of cerebrospinal fluid acid-base components in man. *J. Appl. Physiol.*, 17:993–998.
16. Pavlin, E. G., and Hornbein, T. F. (1975): Distribution of H^+ and HCO_3 between CSF and blood during metabolic acidosis in dogs. *Am. J. Physiol.*, 228:1134–1140.
17. Pierce, N. F., Fedson, D. S., Brigham, K. L., Permutt, S., and Mondal, A. (1971): Relation of ventilation during base deficit to acid-base values in blood and spinal fluid. *J. Appl. Physiol.*, 30:677–683.

18. Ponten, U. (1966): Consecutive acid-base changes in blood, brain tissue and cerebrospinal fluid during respiratory acidosis and baseosis. *Acta Neurol. Scand.*, 42:455–471.
19. Posner, J. B., and Plum, F. (1967): Spinal fluid pH and neurologic symptoms in systemic acidosis. *N. Engl. J. Med.*, 277:605–613.
20. Refsum, H. E. (1963): Relationship between state of consciousness and arterial hypoxemia and hypercapnia in patients with pulmonary insufficiency breathing air. *Clin. Sci.*, 25:361–367.
21. Relman, A. S. (1972): Metabolic consequences of acid-base disorders. *Kidney Int.*, 1:347–349.
22. Seisjo, B. K., and Ponten, U. (1966): Acid-base changes in the brain in nonrespiratory acidosis and alkalosis, *Exp. Brain Res.*, 2:176–190.
23. Tizianello, A., De Ferrari, G., Gurreri, G., and Acquarone, N. (1977): Effects of metabolic alkalosis, metabolic acidosis and uremia on whole-body intracellular pH in man. *Clin. Sci.*, 52:125–135.

General Review Articles

24. Arieff, A. I. (1985): Central nervous system effects of water, electrolyte and acid-base disorders. In: *Fluid, Electrolyte and Acid-Base Disorders*, edited by A. I. Arieff, and R. A. DeFronzo, Chap. 21, pp. 969–1040, Churchill Livingstone, New York, London.
25. Arieff, A. I., Kerian, A., Massry, S. G., and DeLima, (1976): Intracellular pH of brain: Alterations in acute respiratory acidosis and alkalosis. *Am. J. Physiol.*, 230:804–812.
26. Katzman, R., and Pappius, H. M. (1973): Acid-base balance in the cerebrospinal fluid. In: *Brain Electrolytes and Fluid Metabolism*, pp. 224–245, Williams & Wilkins, Baltimore.
27. Maren, T. H. (1972): Bicarbonate formation in cerebrospinal fluid: Role in sodium transport and pH regulation. *Am. J. Physiol.*, 222:885–899.
28. Pollay, M. (1974): Transport mechanisms in the choroid plexus. *Fed. Proc.*, 33:2064.
29. Waddell, W. J., and Butler, T. C. (1969): Intracellular pH. *Physiol. Rev.*, 49:285–329.

The Regulation of Acid–Base Balance, edited
by Donald W. Seldin and Gerhard Giebisch,
Raven Press, Ltd., New York © 1989.

7

Buffer Equilibria in Specialized Tissues: Lungs

Alan H. Morris and Robert O. Crapo

*Department of Medicine, University of Utah School of Medicine and LDS Hospital,
Salt Lake City, Utah 84143*

Metabolism: The Fire of Life
  Carbon Dioxide Transport • Matching Organ Function to Metabolic
  Rate • Matching $PaCO_2$ and $[HCO_3^-]$ • Influence of Low Cardiac Output
Buffering: Open Versus Closed Systems
Interactions of Heart and Lung
  Alveolar and Dead Space Ventilation • Evaluating Hypercapnea
Identifying Abnormal Responses
  Acid Base Maps and Interpretative Equations • Acute Versus Chronic
  Changes • Distinction Between Normal and Abnormal
References

METABOLISM: THE FIRE OF LIFE (9)

The term "respiration" has been used in a number of different ways. In the past "external respiration" was used to denote the movement of air in and out of the lungs during breathing, and "internal respiration" was used to denote the mitochondrial oxidation of foods with the capture of some of their chemical energy in the form of high-energy phosphate bonds of ATP, the energy currency of the body. Although this distinction is still made occasionally today, it is, in our opinion, not the best way to approach the problems raised by patients in most clinical settings. Respiration is best defined as the cellular (mitochondrial) process associated with the transfer of the chemical energy of foods to high energy intermediates (i.e., ATP) that sustain cellular activity and life. Respiration (metabolism is a synonym) is a fire, consuming both food

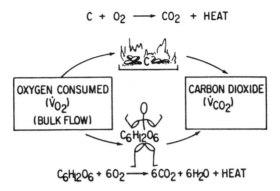

FIG. 1. The body (stick figure) and a charcoal grill both are sites of fire. Fuel is represented by glucose ($C_6H_{12}O_6$) in the body and carbon (charcoal) (C) in the grill. Both fires consume O_2 (bulk flow = $\dot{V}O_2$, the O_2 consumption) and produce CO_2 (bulk flow = $\dot{V}CO_2$, the CO_2 production). The equation below the stick figure represents cellular respiration.

(fuel) and oxygen and generating both CO_2 and heat. That respiration (metabolism) is a fire was recognized in the 18th century by Lavoisier and is indicated by Fig. 1 and its equation.

It is useful to compare this cellular process with a charcoal fire with which one might cook a steak. Both processes consume fuel, the fuel being carbon (C) in the form of charcoal briquettes in the brazier or glucose ($C_6H_{12}O_6$) within the body, represented by the stick figure in Fig. 1. A continuous supply of both fuel and oxygen is necessary to maintain the fire, which continuously produces CO_2 and heat. The rate at which this fire of life burns is commonly referred to as the "metabolic rate" and can be quantified by the consumption or production of any of the variables in the equation in Fig. 1. The quantitative expressions most commonly used for the metabolic rate are oxygen consumption ($\dot{V}O_2$) and carbon dioxide production ($\dot{V}CO_2$) (Table 1). Fuel consumption is used as a measure of metabolic rate in some clinical research units where research dietitians are employed. One least commonly finds the heat production used to define metabolic rate, since this requires the presence of a human calorimeter, which is not commonly available. Any of these measures of metabolic rate can be converted to any other using the stoichiometry of the equation in Fig. 1 if the composition of the fuel consumed is known (e.g., glucose, fats, proteins).

Carbon dioxide (CO_2), a volatile acid, is produced at the rate of about 14,000 mmoles/day. Even in normal people at rest, the production of this very volatile acid presents a major challenge to the body, which must keep [H^+] in body fluids within a narrow range in order to maintain acid-base homeostasis. The basal rate of CO_2 production ($\dot{V}CO_2$) (the metabolic rate) can increase by an order of magnitude as body activity changes, for example, with exercise. The heart and lung provide immediate responses to changing $\dot{V}CO_2$ in order to maintain [H^+] within its narrow homeostatic range.

TABLE 1. *Abbreviations and terms*

Symbol	Term	Units
V̇E	Minute ventilation	Liter/min
V̇A	Alveolar ventilation	Liter/min
V̇D	Dead space ventilation	Liter/min
f	Ventilatory rate	1/min
V̇o$_2$	Oxygen consumption	Liter/min
V̇co$_2$	Carbon dioxide production	Liter/min
Q̇t	Cardiac output	Liter/min
Cao$_2$	Arterial oxygen content	ml/dl
Cv̄o$_2$	Mixed venous (pulmonary artery) oxygen content	ml/dl
C(a − v̄)o$_2$	Arterial − mixed venous oxygen content difference	ml/dl
Caco$_2$	Arterial carbon dioxide content	ml/dl
Cv̄co$_2$	Mixed venous (pulmonary artery) carbon dioxide content	ml/dl
C(v̄ − a)co$_2$	Mixed venous − arterial carbon dioxide content difference	ml/dl
Paco$_2$	Arterial carbon dioxide	mm Hg
[Ha$^+$]	Arterial hydrogen ion concentration	nmole/liter
pHa	Arterial pH	—

Carbon Dioxide Transport (3,4,14)

CO_2 is the end product of aerobic metabolism in the mitochondria, where its pressure (Pco_2) is highest. Like all fluids in the universe, CO_2 flows from high pressure to low pressure. As CO_2 dissolved in water passes from the mitochondria to the atmosphere (the point of lowest Pco_2), the pressure difference from one compartment to the next determines the rate at which CO_2 flows. Most of this CO_2 enters and leaves the blood as molecular CO_2.

Only about 5% of the total CO_2 content of blood, however, is present as dissolved molecular CO_2. Another 5% is present as carbarmino CO_2, attached to the terminal amino groups of Hgb within the red blood cell. The rest of the CO_2 in blood is present as HCO_3^- (about one third in red blood cells and two thirds in plasma). The formation of carbarmino CO_2 is very rapid and does not require the hydration of CO_2. In contrast, the formation of HCO_3^- requires the hydration of CO_2 to form H_2CO_3 (Eq. 1).

$$CO_2 + H_2O \leftrightarrow H_2CO_3 \tag{1}$$

This is a slow reaction that is strikingly accelerated (more than 1,000-fold) in the body by the enzyme carbonic anhydrase, present in red blood cells. The H^+ that dissociates from H_2CO_3 (Eq. 2) primarily exchanges with K^+ of the Hgb salt (Eq. 3).

$$H_2CO_3 \leftrightarrow H^+ + HCO_3^- \tag{2}$$

$$H^+ + HCO_3^- + K^+ + Hgb^- \leftrightarrow HHgb + K^+ + HCO_3^- \tag{3}$$

The imidazole groups of the histidine residues of Hgb buffer the $[H^+]$ from H_2CO_3. The newly formed HCO_3^- within the red blood cell exchanges with Cl^- from the plasma, thereby rapidly augmenting plasma $[HCO_3^-]$, according to the Gibbs-Donnan effect. This important mechanism of exchange of HCO_3^- between red blood cells and plasma is termed "the chloride shift."

Matching Organ Function to Metabolic Rate (10)

The flow of CO_2 from the body's cells to the atmosphere depends on adequate heart, lung, and blood function. Whenever disruptions of this flow occur or when cellular respiration is threatened or impaired, the first question that must be answered is, "Which organ is responsible for the threat to respiration?" If more than one organ is involved, the question is, "Which organ bears the major responsibility?" This question is answered, not by identifying whether heart and lung function is normal, high, or low but rather by identifying whether heart and lung function are meeting the demand placed on them by the metabolic rate of the aggregate cellular mass of the body. The assessment of the adequacy of heart or lung function is best carried out by examining the matching of their outputs to metabolic rate. With respect to oxygen flow through the body, this is commonly done by using the mass balance equation that bears the name of Dr. Adolph Fick (Eq. 4).

$$\dot{V}_{O_2} = \dot{Q}t \times C(a-\bar{v})_{O_2} \qquad [4]$$

The oxygen consumption ($\dot{V}_{O_2}$) is here expressed as the product of the cardiac output ($\dot{Q}t$, the flow of blood pumped by the heart) and the oxygen extraction by the body [$C(a-\bar{v})_{O_2}$, the difference between the content of oxygen in the blood entering the body's cellular mass and the content of the oxygen in the blood leaving the body's cellular mass]. This is a particular application of the general principles of mass balance that are operative in assessing the adequacy not only of heart function but of lung function as well (Table 2).

Solving for the difference between the inlet and outlet concentration reveals that the difference between the concentration in and the concentration out is uniquely determined by the matching of organ output to metabolic

TABLE 2. *Mass balance considerations*

Organ	Fluid	Concentration In $-$ Out		Fluid flow (organ output) =	Measure of metabolic rate	
						[5]
Heart	Blood	Ca_{O_2}	$C\bar{v}_{O_2}$	$\dot{Q}t$	$\dot{V}_{O_2}$	[6]
Lung	Air	$F_I{_{CO_2}}$	$F_A{_{CO_2}}$	$\dot{V}A$	$\dot{V}_{CO_2}$	[7]

TABLE 3. *Matching of organ output to metabolic rate*

Organ	Concentration in	−	Concentration out	=	Metabolic rate/organ output	[8]
Heart	Ca_{O_2}	−	$C\bar{v}_{O_2}$	=	$\dot{V}_{O_2}/\dot{Q}t$	[9]
Lung	$F_A{CO_2}$	−	$F_I{CO_2}$	=	$\dot{V}_{CO_2}/\dot{V}A$	[10]

rate, according to the equations in Table 3. Since there is essentially no CO_2 in inspired air ($F_I{CO_2} \cong 0$), the difference in CO_2 concentration between the inlet and the outlet of the system becomes nothing more than the alveolar CO_2 fraction ($F_A{CO_2}$), according to

$$F_A{CO_2} = \dot{V}{CO_2}/\dot{V}A \qquad [11]$$

With conversion of $F_A{CO_2}$ to $Pa{CO_2}$, this simplifies to

$$Pa{CO_2} = (\dot{V}{CO_2}\ k)/\dot{V}A \qquad [12]$$

Since under usual circumstances, the arterial (a) and alveolar (A) $P{CO_2}$ are almost identical, this becomes

$$Pa{CO_2} = (\dot{V}{CO_2}\ k)/\dot{V}A \qquad [13]$$

It is clear from Eq. 13 that the $Pa{CO_2}$ is determined neither by alveolar ventilation ($\dot{V}A$) nor by CO_2 production ($\dot{V}{CO_2}$) but uniquely by the matching of alveolar ventilation to CO_2 production. In the same way, $C(a-\bar{v}){O_2}$ is uniquely determined by the matching of cardiac output to oxygen consumption (Eq. 9). These variables ($Pa{CO_2}$ for lung and $C(a-\bar{v}){O_2}$ for heart) provide the most specific indicators of the adequacy of lung and heart output relative to the metabolic demand placed on these organs by the body. An elevated $Pa{CO_2}$ indicates alveolar underventilation (hypoventilation) relative to the metabolic rate ($\dot{V}{CO_2}$). A depressed $Pa{CO_2}$ indicates overventilation (hyperventilation) relative to metabolic rate ($\dot{V}{CO_2}$).

Matching $Pa{CO_2}$ and $[HCO_3^-]$ (3,4,10,14)

Although the $Pa{CO_2}$ is the definitive estimator of the adequacy of alveolar ventilation ($\dot{V}A$), it provides no information about the cause of alterations of $\dot{V}A$ and usually provides no specific stimulus for therapy. A more important therapeutic stimulus is provided by the hydrogen ion concentration in arterial blood ($[Ha^+]$ or pHa), since the hydrogen ion concentration is a more important homeostatic variable for the maintenance of cellular function than is the Pa_{CO_2}. For example, the tertiary configuration and, therefore, function of many cellular enzymes are likely to be much more influenced by the $[Ha^+]$ than by the Pa_{CO_2}. The $[Ha^+]$ is determined, not by the Pa_{CO_2} level (a lung function) nor by the $[HCO_3^-]$ level (a kidney function) but by the matching of the two according to

$$[Ha^+] = 24 \times (Pa_{CO_2}/[HCO_3^-]) \qquad [14]$$

Equations 13 and 14 provide the basis for evaluating both the adequacy of alveolar ventilation and the matching of Pa_{CO_2} and $[HCO_3^-]$, which determines the arterial hydrogen ion concentration. The hydrogen ion concentration in the arterial blood usually is a reasonable indicator of the hydrogen ion concentration within cells and thus is quite useful in making decisions about acid-base therapy.

Influence of Low Cardiac Output (10)

Caution is advised, however, in those states associated with low cardiac output $(\dot{Q}t)$ because of the relationship that follows from expanding Table 2 using blood CO_2 contents (Tables 4 and 5).

The $C(\bar{v}-a)_{CO_2}$ is uniquely determined by the matching of cardiac output $(\dot{Q}t)$ to metabolic rate $(\dot{V}_{CO_2})$, just as is the $C(a-\bar{v})_{O_2}$ when metabolic rate is expressed as $\dot{V}_{O_2}$. If the $\dot{Q}t$ is very low relative to metabolic rate, the $C(\bar{v}-a)_{CO_2}$ becomes very large, and the assessment of arterial CO_2 (whether Ca_{CO_2} or Pa_{CO_2}) becomes a very poor reflection of the CO_2 in the mixed venous blood $(C\bar{v}_{CO_2}$ or $P\bar{v}_{CO_2})$ or in the body tissues. Under conditions of low cardiac output, therefore, Pa_{CO_2} may provide no indication of a very profound intracellular and mixed venous hypercapnia (and acidosis). The data in Table 6 were obtained from a 29-year-old man with cardiomyopathy during an evaluation for cardiac transplantation.

During exercise, this patient was unable to increase cardiac output ($\dot{Q}t$ only 5.5. liters/min) and was forced to increase the $C(\bar{v}-a)_{CO_2}$ (to 15 ml/dl), leading to a much higher $P\bar{v}_{O_2}$ (63 mm Hg) and a much lower $pH\bar{v}$ (7.26) than would have been suggested by the arterial values (37 and 7.38, respectively).

TABLE 4. *Mass balance considerations: CO_2 and heart*

Organ	Fluid	Concentration In − Out		× Fluid flow (organ output)	= Measure of metabolic rate	
Heart	Blood	$C\bar{v}_{CO_2}$	Ca_{CO_2}	$\dot{Q}t$	$\dot{V}_{CO_2}$	[15]

TABLE 5. *Matching of organ output to metabolic rate: CO_2 and heart*

Concentration in	−	Concentration out	=	Metabolic rate/organ output	[8]

$C\bar{v}_{CO_2}$	−	Ca_{CO_2}	=	$\dot{V}_{CO_2}/\dot{Q}t$	[16]

Solving for the difference in CO_2 contents:

$$C(\bar{v} - a)_{CO_2} = \dot{V}_{CO_2}/\dot{Q}t \qquad [16]$$

TABLE 6. *Rest and exercise data in a 29-year-old man with cardiomyopathy*

	pH	P_{CO_2} (mm Hg)	CO_2 content (ml/dl)	$C(\bar{v} - a)_{CO_2}$ (ml/dl)	$\dot{Q}t$ (liter/min)
Rest					
Arterial	7.45	36			
Mixed venous	7.43	41			
Exercise					
Arterial	7.38	37	47	15	5.5
Mixed venous	7.26	63	62		

For these reasons, even the simplest interpretation of acid-base state requires consideration of both lung and heart function.

BUFFERING: OPEN VERSUS CLOSED SYSTEMS (3,4,14)

The response of acid-base systems to sudden perturbations because of addition or removal of acid or base depends on the characteristics of the system, specifically whether it is open and capable of equilibrating with the atmosphere and losing volatile acid, or closed and therefore unable to exchange volatile acid with the environment (atmosphere). Under normal circumstances, the lung and heart are efficient enough to assure that the body acts as if it were an open system, with achievement of a new steady state after induction of an acid-base perturbation through modification of the rate of elimination of CO_2 from the body through the lung to the atmosphere. This, however, is not the case when alveolar ventilation ($\dot{V}A$) is either fixed or dramatically limited because of disease (such as in patients with severe airway obstruction or neuromuscular dysfunction disorders) or because of mechanical limitations when alveolar ventilation is provided by a mechanical ventilator. Under these circumstances, changing acid loads (e.g., that due to an increase in metabolic rate, $\dot{V}_{CO_2}$) cannot be accommodated rapidly through the usual alterations in the rate at which CO_2 passes through the lung to the atmo-

sphere. Such restrictions on alveolar ventilation convert the normal open behavior of the heart and lung to a partially closed behavior and significantly
change the body's acid-base response. Since the lung eliminates about 250
times as much acid in the form of CO_2 as does the kidney (in the form of fixed
acids), it is imperative that the lung and the heart be able to respond rapidly
to variations in $\dot{V}CO_2$. Responses must be effected within seconds or minutes.
In contrast, renal responses to the accumulation of fixed acids need be applied
over periods of hours to days. Restrictions placed on $\dot{V}A$, making the lung a
partially closed system, therefore, make the body extremely susceptible to
rapid accumulation of volatile acid and rapid development of acidemia as metabolic rate ($\dot{V}CO_2$) increases. The development of respiratory acidosis with severe acidemia may occur in a period of minutes.

INTERACTIONS OF HEART AND LUNG (4,10)

Alveolar and Dead Space Ventilation

The purpose of alveolar ventilation, the first step in the system that results
in gas exchange between the atmosphere and the body's cells, is the maintenance of normal PCO_2 and PO_2 in the alveolar air space. This can be achieved
only by the addition of fresh air that is rich in oxygen but contains no CO_2.
The addition of fresh air counterbalances both the reduction in alveolar oxygen due to oxygen uptake by the pulmonary capillary blood and the increase
in the alveolar CO_2 due to evolution of CO_2 into the alveolar air from the
pulmonary capillary blood. Fresh air, however, constitutes only part of the
tidal breath that is inhaled with each inspiration. The initial parts of the tidal
volume contain alveolar air from the previous expiration from which oxygen
had already been extracted and to which CO_2 had already been added. This
initial part of the tidal volume (the alveolar air from the previous breath) has a
composition essentially equal to that of alveolar air and, therefore, does not
alter alveolar gas composition, failing both to increase the alveolar PO_2 and to
decrease the alveolar PCO_2. This part of the tidal volume, which contains alveolar (and not fresh) air and does not contribute to the maintenance of normal gas concentrations in alveoli, constitutes dead space ventilation, although
it is in fact inhaled and is part of the measured change in volume of the chest
and alveoli during inspiration. That fraction of the tidal volume that consists of
fresh air does increase alveolar PO_2 and decrease alveolar PCO_2 and is called
the "alveolar volume" (alveolar volume per breath $\times$ f = $\dot{V}A$).

Alveolar ventilation ($\dot{V}A$) is the difference between minute ventilation ($\dot{V}E$)
and dead space ventilation $\dot{V}D$) (Eq. 18).

$$\dot{V}A = \dot{V}E - \dot{V}D \qquad [18]$$

Equation 13 can, therefore, be rewritten as

$$\text{Paco}_2 = (\dot{V}\text{co}_2\, k)/(\dot{V}\text{E} - \dot{V}\text{D}) \qquad [19]$$

Evaluating Hypercapnea

Increased Metabolic Rate

Equation 19 provides a conceptual framework for exploring the causes of an elevated Paco_2. Increases in $\dot{V}\text{co}_2$ may result from a process stimulating metabolism (stoking the fire of life), such as muscular activity (exercise or shivering), fever, hyperthyroidism, stress, or overfeeding. CO_2 production also may be increased by HCO_3^- buffering of an ongoing metabolic acidosis. Changes in CO_2 production usually can be discovered simply by examining the patient and evaluating the clinical situation, although it may be necessary to actually to measure $\dot{V}\text{co}_2$.

Decreased Alveolar Ventilation

Minute and dead space ventilation

Decreased $\dot{V}\text{A}$ may simply be the consequence of decreased minute ventilation ($\dot{V}\text{E}$) as a result of a neuro-muscular problem, severe airway obstruction, drug overdose, or other situation. When the Paco_2 is increased but $\dot{V}\text{E}$ is not reduced and $\dot{V}\text{co}_2$ is not increased, the problem must be associated with an increased dead space ventilation ($\dot{V}\text{D}$), and consideration of anatomic, physiologic, and instrument (or machine) contributions to dead space becomes important. Respiratory therapy devices may allow excessive instrument dead space to be created. In some ventilator circuits, the entire tubing column from the ventilator to the exhalation valve is potential dead space. Since anatomic dead space ordinarily changes little with changes in tidal volume, a change in the patient's ventilatory pattern may significantly alter $\dot{V}\text{D}$. For example, if a patient with an anatomic dead space of 0.15 liter changes from a ventilatory pattern of breathing ten 1-liter breaths/min ($\dot{V}\text{E}$ = 10 liters/min) to one of breathing forty 0.25-liter breaths/min ($\dot{V}\text{E}$ = 10 liters/min), $\dot{V}\text{D}$ increases from about 1.5 liters/min to about 6.0 liters/min, and $\dot{V}\text{A}$ decreases from about 8.5 to 4 liters/min. Parenchymal lung diseases may be associated with increases in physiologic or alveolar dead space. Changes in cardiac output (pulmonary blood flow) also may be associated with changes in physiologic dead space. In low cardiac output ($\dot{Q}t$) states, the region of the lung (zone I) within which alveolar pressure exceeds both pulmonary artery and pulmonary venous pressure enlarges. In this region, all blood vessels are collapsed, and ventilation is unassociated with any blood flow. Zone I constitutes dead space and frequently increases as cardiac output decreases.

Ventilatory pattern (tidal volume, frequency)

Since minute ventilation ($\dot{V}E$) is the product of tidal volume (V_T) and ventilatory rate (f), Eq. 19 becomes

$$PaCO_2 = (\dot{V}CO_2\ k)/([V_T \times f] - \dot{V}D) \qquad [20]$$

V_T is the product of the transpulmonary pressure change generated by respiratory muscular effort and the lung compliance. V_T will change as the lung becomes more stiff, as in pulmonary congestion due to heart failure. As the lung compliance decreases, tidal volume may decrease, and ventilatory rate may become greater. Because the anatomic dead space changes little with decreasing V_T, this changed pattern of ventilation with more rapid shallow breaths due to increased lung stiffness may, in itself, increase $\dot{V}D$ and, therefore, reduce $\dot{V}A$ for any given $\dot{V}E$ (*see* Chapter 19). In addition to the transpulmonary pressure necessary to stretch the lung (a function of compliance), more pressure must be applied across the lung in order to overcome the flow resistance of the airways and lung tissue.

Heart failure, airway obstruction, and expiratory time

Left atrial hypertension, induced by either heart failure or other causes, raises pulmonary vascular pressures and produces an increase in transudation of fluid into lung tissue. This increased fluid, during the genesis of lung edema, first accumulates in the loose perivascular and peribronchial interstitium and causes a decrease in bronchial diameter and an increase in airway resistance. In patients with normal lungs, pulmonary congestion produces only mild airway obstruction as a result of the increase in airway resistance due to peribronchial edema. However, in patients with well-established airway obstruction, such as patients with chronic obstructive pulmonary disease or asthma, airway resistance may increase enough to produce a significant decrease in expiratory air flow. Such a decrease in expiratory airflow may make the patient incapable of adequately deflating the lung during the expiratory time available. Since conditions that produce peribronchial edema usually increase ventilatory rate (f) and airway resistance, expiratory time frequently is shortened. This leads to a further mismatch between the time available during expiration and the time necessary for lung deflation (or decompression) during expiration. This may lead to overinflation of the lung (other terms used to describe this phenomenon are "breath-stacking" and "auto-PEEP").

This pulmonary overinflation, resulting from an inadequate expiratory time relative to the expiratory air flow, is analogous to the left atrial overdistention that can occur in patients with mitral stenosis when tachycardia produces a short diastolic atrial emptying time (more commonly referred to as a "shortened diastolic ventricular filling time"). The appropriate matching of fluid flow (air in the lung and blood in the heart) across the obstruction (expiratory obstruction in the lung and atrial outlet obstruction in mitral stenosis) to the

TABLE 7. *Importance of decompression time in the presence of obstruction to flow in both the lung and heart*

Structure to be emptied (decompressed)	Fluid	Obstruction limiting fluid flow	Time period for flow	Consequences of inadequate decompression time	Secondary effects
Lung	Air	Airway	Expiration	Overinflation (breath stacking, Auto-PEEP)	Zone I VD compliance Work
Left atrium	Blood	Mitral stenosis	Diastole	Left atrial overdistention	Left atrial pressure Pulmonary micro-vascular pressure Lung edema

time available for decompression can be disrupted both by changes in resistance across the obstruction and by changes in decompression time induced by tachypnea for the lung or tachycardia for the heart (Table 7). In addition, a decrease in compliance (increase in lung stiffness) or an increase in airway resistance may produce a significant increase in work of breathing and, therefore, may increase metabolic rate ($\dot{V}CO_2$).

The preceding comments reflect only some of the interactions between heart and lung but should suffice to indicate that the evaluation of lung function, through examination of $PaCO_2$, in the absence of consideration of cardiac function may be quite misleading. Attention must be given to cardiac and other nonpulmonary factors that may change $\dot{V}D$ and, thereby, $\dot{V}A$ (for any given $\dot{V}E$) to assess the effectiveness of overall ventilation.

Summary

The schema in Fig. 2 has provided a useful framework for integrating information about metabolism, lung function, heart function, and renal function as

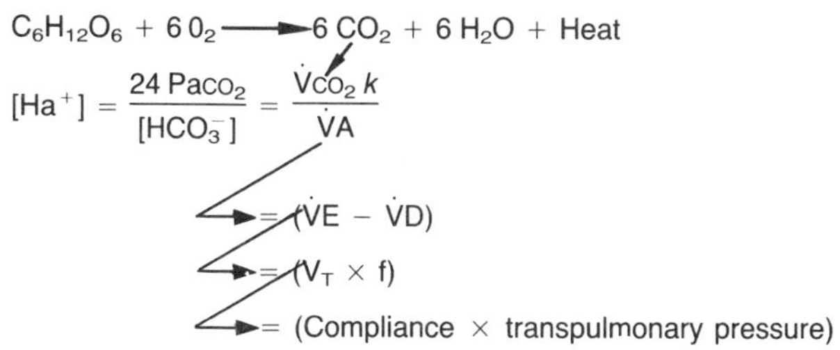

$$C_6H_{12}O_6 + 6 O_2 \longrightarrow 6 CO_2 + 6 H_2O + Heat$$

$$[Ha^+] = \frac{24\, PaCO_2}{[HCO_3^-]} = \frac{\dot{V}CO_2\, k}{\dot{V}A}$$

$$= (\dot{V}E - \dot{V}D)$$
$$= (V_T \times f)$$
$$= (Compliance \times transpulmonary\ pressure)$$

FIG. 2. CO_2 elimination scheme for integrating lung, heart, and renal function with metabolic activity.

they relate to elimination of the volatile acid (CO_2) from the body and the maintenance of hydrogen ion homeostasis ([Ha^+]).

IDENTIFYING ABNORMAL RESPONSES (7,8,12,14)

Acid-Base Maps and Interpretative Equations (1,2,5,6,11,13)

Data from which most acid-base maps (Fig. 3) or interpretative equations were derived were obtained from humans and animals. The data for both acute and chronic acid-base disturbances were acquired from subjects in whom a single, identifiable acid-base perturbation had occurred. For animals and

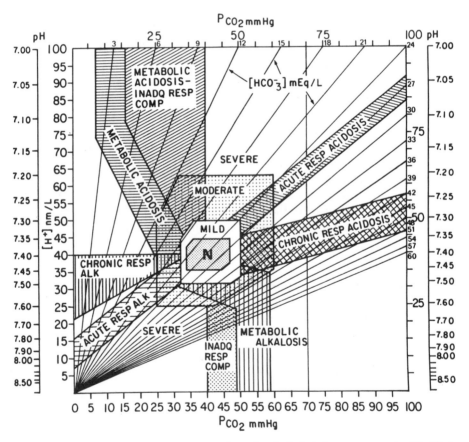

FIG. 3. Acid-base map. The 70 mm Hg P_{CO_2} line is included as an example. (Modified from refs. 5,6,11.)

humans subjected to an acid or base load, this involved administration of the appropriate material to a previously normal subject and measurement of the response. For humans subjected to chronic acid-base abnormalities, such as chronic respiratory acidosis, this involved identifying patients for whom the respiratory acidosis was the only discernible abnormality. For all of these data sources, it is apparent that two conditions were met.

1. The subject was previously normal.
2. The subject sustained a single acid-base perturbation.

Application of the acid-base maps or the acid-base interpretation equations derived from such data bases assumes both that the patient was previously normal and that the patient has sustained a single acid base perturbation. When these assumptions are satisfied, the confidence bands outlining specific acid-base derangements can be used for acid-base diagnoses with reasonable accuracy. If these conditions are met, an acid-base map may be read as follows (Fig. 3). If previously normal people suddenly experience an increase in $PaCO_2$ from 40 to 70, 95% of them will have a pHa that lies within that portion of the band called "acute respiratory acidosis" on the $PaCO_2 = 70$ line. If enough time is allowed to pass, at $PaCO_2 = 70$ for maximum renal compensation to occur, 95% of these subjects will have a pHa value within that portion of the band called "chronic respiratory acidosis" on the $PaCO_2 = 70$ line.

However, in both outpatients and the hospitalized critically ill, clinical circumstances are encountered in which the patient was either not initially normal or has sustained more than one (frequently multiple) acid-base perturbation, or both. In such situations, the interpretations obtained from acid-base maps or from acid-base interpretation equations are unreliable and cannot be used confidently for diagnostic purposes. The commonly expressed caveat at the bottom of blood gas laboratory reports (e.g., "preliminary interpretation only, final diagnosis requires clinical correlation") is a direction to the physician interpreter to ask whether the two conditions listed above have, in fact, been met.

Acute Versus Chronic Changes (1,2,13)

The distinction between acute and chronic respiratory acid-base derangements rests upon the presence or absence of renal compensation. Since significant renal compensation does not begin for a period of a few to 12 hours, generation of a chronic acid-base derangement usually requires that the condition be present for many hours to a day. Acute changes, present for minutes to a few hours, are usually unassociated with renal compensation and, therefore, produce more dramatic changes in $[Ha^+]$ and pHa than would occur with chronic changes. Since the regeneration and reabsorption of $[HCO_3^-]$ is directly linked to the P_{CO_2} in the renal tubular cell, there is an automatic feedback system that increases or decreases the regeneration of $[HCO_3^-]$ as P_{CO_2} increases or decreases, respectively, in blood and other body fluids.

Distinction Between Normal and Abnormal (1,2,5,6,11,13)

This distinction can be made in a number of ways, each with its own virtues and disadvantages. We have chosen the 95% confidence interval (CI) as the means of separating those values that fall within from those that fall without the predicted normal range. The 95% CI assumes a Gaussian (normal) distribution of values around the predicted value, an assumption that may be wrong. The 95% CI approach does, however, allow statistical analysis of much data in the literature and, until the availability of further information indicating a more favorable approach, is our choice for the distinction between normal and abnormal. This approach has been used in generating Tables 8 and 9

TABLE 8. *Room air CO_2 values at sea level*

Age (yr)	Predicted P_{CO_2} (mm Hg)	Lower limit P_{CO_2} (mm Hg)	Upper limit P_{CO_2} (mm Hg)
20	40	33	47
30	40	34	47
40	40	34	47
50	40	34	47
60	40	34	47
70	41	34	47
80	41	34	47

Modified from ref. 11.

TABLE 9. *Arterial pH, P_{CO_2}, $[HCO_3^-]$ at sea level*

Measurement	Normal range (room air)	Degree of abnormality		
		Mild	Moderate	Severe
pH	7.35–7.45	<7.35–7.30 7.46–7.49	<7.30–7.20 7.50–7.59	<7.20 ≥7.60
P_{CO_2}, mm Hg	33–47	<33–32 >47–50	<32–25 >50–60	<25 ≥60
$[H_2CO_3^-]$ mEq/liter	19–30	<19–17 >30–37	<17–13 >37–41	<13 ≥41

Modified from ref. 11.

and Fig. 3. Even though Fig. 3 uses confidence bands with a *P* value of 0.05, interpretations of pHa and $PaCO_2$ measurements will lead to both false positive and false negative interpretations. Minimizing the number of these false positive and false negative errors requires that interpretation of blood gas values always be made with full knowledge of the clinical circumstances and after an attempt has been made to establish the likelihood or prior probabilities of the hypotheses being tested. These concepts are developed further in Chapter 19.

REFERENCES

1. Arbus, G. S., Hebert, L. A., Levesque, P. R., Etsten, B. E., and Schwartz, W. B. (1969): Characterization and clinical application of the "significance band" for acute respiratory alkalosis. *N. Engl. J. Med.*, 280:117–123.
2. Brackett, N. C., Cohen, J. J., and Schwartz, W. B. (1965): Carbon dioxide titration curve of normal man: Effect of increasing degrees of acute hypercapnia on acid-base equilibrium. *N. Engl. J. Med.*, 272:6–12.
3. Davenport, H. W. (1974): *The ABC of Acid-Base Chemistry: The Elements of Physiological Blood-Gas Chemistry for Medical Students and Physicians*, 6th ed., rev. University of Chicago Press, Chicago.
4. Forster, R. E., DuBois, A. B., Briscoe, W. A., and Fisher, A. B. (1986): *The Lung: Physiologic Basis of Pulmonary Function Tests*, Year Book, Chicago.
5. Gardner, R. M., Crapo, R. O., Morris, A. H., and Beus, M. L. (1982): Computerized decision-making in the pulmonary function laboratory. *Resp. Care*, 27:799–808.
6. Goldberg, M., Green, S. B., Moss, M. L., et al. (1973): Computer-based instruction and diagnosis of acid-base disorders. *JAMA*, 223:269–275.
7. Howorth, P. J. N. (1975): Review article: The physiological assessment of acid-base balance. *Br. J. Dis. Chest.*, 69:75–97.
8. Jones, N. L. (1980): *Blood Gases and Acid-Base Physiology*. B. C. Decker Co, New York.
9. Kleiber, M. (1975): *The Fire of Life: An Introduction to Animal Energetics*. Kreiger Publishing Company, Huntington, NY.
10. Morris, A. H. (1987): Acute respiratory failure: Therapeutic strategies. In: *Current Therapy in Critical Care Medicine*, edited by J.E. Parrillo. B.C. Decker, Philadelphia.
11. Morris, A. H., Kanner, R. E., Crapo, R., O., and Gardner, R. M. (1984): *Clinical Pulmonary Function Testing: A Manual of Uniform Laboratory Procedures*. 2nd Ed. Intermountain Thoracic Society, Salt Lake City, UT.
12. Narins, R. G., and Emmett, M. (1980): Simple and mixed acid-base disorders: A practical approach. *Medicine*, 59:161–187.
13. Schwartz, W. B., Brackett, N. C., and Cohen, J. J. (1965): The response of extracellular hydrogen ion concentration to graded degrees of chronic hypercapnia: The physiologic limits of the defense of pH. *J. Clin. Invest.*, 44:291–301.
14. Winters, R. W., Engel, K., and Dell, R. B. (1969): *Acid-Base Physiology in Medicine: A Self-Instruction Program*, 2nd ed. The London Company, Cleveland and Radiometer A/S, Copenhagen.

The Regulation of Acid–Base Balance, edited
by Donald W. Seldin and Gerhard Giebisch,
Raven Press, Ltd., New York © 1989.

8

Segmental Hydrogen Ion Transport

Bruce M. Koeppen and *Gerhard Giebisch

*Departments of Medicine and Physiology, University of Connecticut Health Center,
Farmington, Connecticut 06032,* Department of Cellular and Molecular Physiology,
Yale University School of Medicine, New Haven, Connecticut 06510*

The role of the kidneys in systemic acid-base balance is to excrete the salts
of nonvolatile acids produced each day by cellular metabolism and, in the
process, produce HCO_3^-, which is returned to the blood. In addition, the kidney also must reabsorb the filtered load of HCO_3^- ($\approx 4,500$ mEq/day). Both of
these processes result from the secretion of H^+ into the urine by the cells of
the renal tubule. In this chapter, we review the current understanding
of the mechanisms of urine acidification. Emphasis is placed on describing
the molecular mechanisms of H^+ and HCO_3^- movement across the apical
(luminal) and basolateral (peritubular) membranes of the renal tubular cell.
Also considered here are the mechanisms by which various physiologic and
pharmacologic factors act to modulate transport at the cellular and membrane
levels.

TECHNIQUES FOR STUDYING RENAL TUBULAR
H^+ AND HCO_3^- TRANSPORT (7)

To understand the renal mechanisms of urine acidification, measurements of H^+ and HCO_3^- movement across the tubule epithelium, as well as across the individual membranes of the renal tubule cell, must be obtained. In this section the techniques used to study H^+ and HCO_3^- at the tubular, cellular, and membrane levels are reviewed.

Transepithelial Transport (7)

Although the process of urine acidification involves the secretion of H^+ by cells of the renal tubule, determinations of net H^+ transport rates usually are made by measuring the reabsorption of HCO_3^- from the lumen of the tubule. Such measurements have been made *in vivo* using micropuncture techniques, as well as in single nephron segments perfused *in vitro*.

HCO_3^- transport can be quantitated by measuring the pH of the tubular fluid, assuming a value for or measuring its Pco_2, and then calculating the $[HCO_3^-]$ using the Henderson-Hasselbalch equation. Several different types of pH electrodes have been used for this purpose, including quinhydrone, antimony, and glass membrane. Although difficult to construct at the dimensions required for the study of single renal tubules, the glass membrane electrodes have become the most popular of the three electrode types. Its popularity stems primarily from the fact that the pH-sensitive glass responds only to the H^+ activity of the solution, whereas other ions may interfere with the response of both the quinhydrone and antimony electrodes.

The determination of HCO_3^- transport rates from measurements of intratubular pH is, however, associated with several problems. The first is that in order to apply the Henderson-Hasselbalch equation, the CO_2/HCO_3^- system must be in equilibrium. In many parts of the nephron, however, equilibrium is not achieved. Second, the Pco_2 of the tubular fluid must be known. Early studies assumed Pco_2 values equal to arterial blood. However, direct measurements have found that the Pco_2 of the renal cortex is elevated above that of arterial blood by approximately 20 mm Hg. Third, given the nature of the Henderson-Hasselbalch equation, measuring pH is a very insensitive way of determining the $[HCO_3^-]$ except when its concentration is low.

The development of the picapnotherm has provided a convenient and accurate means for measuring $[HCO_3^-]$ in nanoliter volumes of tubular fluid. In this technique, a sample of tubular fluid is placed in acid, which converts the HCO_3^- to CO_2. The CO_2 is delivered to a LiOH crystal, where it reacts exothermically. The heat released by this reaction is measured by sensitive thermistors that provide a signal proportional to the total amount of CO_2 present in the sample. At the pH, Pco_2, and $[HCO_3^-]$ found in tubular fluid, the measured total CO_2 provides a good estimate of the $[HCO_3^-]$. For example, at a pH of 7.4, a P_{CO_2} of 40 mm Hg, and a $[HCO_3^-]$ of 24 mEq/liter, the total CO_2 measured by the picapnotherm is 25.2 mEq/liter. The determination of total CO_2 by the picapnotherm has become the method of choice for measuring net rates of HCO_3^- transport in renal tubules.

Intracellular pH (7)

To determine the electrochemical driving force for H^+ and HCO_3^- movement across apical and basolateral membranes of the cell, it is necessary to measure intracellular pH. Several methods have been applied to the study of renal tissue.

Nuclear magnetic resonance (NMR) spectroscopy measures pH from the shift in the ^{31}P signal of inorganic phosphate. Although the peak for $H_2PO_4^-$ is shifted with respect to that for HPO_4^{2-}, the interconversion between these two forms is so rapid that only a single peak actually is seen. Its position, though, is dependent on the $[H_2PO_4^-]/[HPO_4^{2-}]$ ratio. Since this ratio is pH dependent, quantitation of the shift in the inorganic phosphate peak provides a measure of intracellular pH. The major disadvantage of NMR is the requirement for large amounts of tissue. Its use is limited, therefore, to studies of tubular suspensions and whole kidneys.

pH-Sensitive microelectrodes also have been used to measure intracellular pH of single renal tubule cells. Two general types of electrodes have been used, those made of pH-sensitive glass, and those using a liquid neutral H^+ ligand. The glass membrane electrodes are difficult to manufacture, and the relatively large tip size (≈ 1 μm) has limited their use to nonmammalian tissues, where the cells are relatively large. The neural H^+ ligand electrodes consist of a conventional intracellular microelectrode into which a drop of liquid neural H^+ ligand is introduced into the tip. These electrodes have the advantage that the tip diameter is less than 1 μm and thus can be used to study the small cells of the mammalian nephron.

The newest approach for measuring intracellular pH involves the use of pH-sensitive fluorescent dyes. Once these dyes are introduced into the cell, pH-dependent changes in the absorbance, excitation, or emission spectra can be used to measure intracellular pH. In order to load dyes into the cell, a neutral lipid-soluble form is used. This lipid-soluble form contains multiple ester linkages, which are cleaved off inside the cell by cytoplasmic esterases. In the absence of these ester linkages, the dye is highly charged and, therefore, effectively trapped within the cell. The use of fluorescent dyes has several advantages over the other techniques described thus far. First, it is nontraumatic to the cell. Second, it can be used on any cell, regardless of size. Third, the response of the dye to changes in pH is extremely rapid, thus allowing the study of transient changes in intracellular pH. These advantages must be balanced, however, by difficulties in calibration of the dye spectrum *in vivo*, the possible effects of the dye on cell function, and binding and sequestration of the dye in subcellular compartments.

Membrane Vesicles (7)

Membrane vesicles can be prepared from either the apical or basolateral membranes of the cell. The first step in preparing the vesicles is disruption of the cell, which is usually done mechanically. During the process of cell disruption, the various membrane compartments spontaneously form vesicles (1 μm or less in diameter). These vesicles are then separated and purified to obtain a relatively homogeneous population. A number of different techniques are used in this step (e.g., electrophoresis, differential centrifugation, precipitation), each of which yields a particular membrane fraction. The purity of the vesicle preparation is determined by the presence or absence of specific marker enzymes. Once it is purified, the transport of ions into and out of the vesicles is measured. For studies of H^+ transport, intravesicular pH is measured spectrofluorometrically using fluorescent amine dyes. These dyes (e.g., acridine orange) are lipophilic weak bases and rapidly distribute across the vesicle membrane in accordance with the pH. When the intravesicular pH is more acidic than the bathing medium, the dye will accumulate within the vesicle. This accumulation results in quenching of the fluorescent signal, and with appropriate calibration, this can be correlated with pH and H^+ flux.

The study of membrane vesicles has provided much of our current understanding of the types of acid-base transport systems present in the membranes of renal tubule cells. In addition to identification of specific transporters, information has been obtained on their stoichiometry, kinetics, inhibitor specificity, and whether the transporter is electrogenic or electroneutral.

OVERVIEW OF RENAL H^+ TRANSPORT (1,5,7)

Before considering the cellular mechanisms of H^+ and HCO_3^- transport in the different segments of the nephron, the general features of renal acid-base handling are reviewed.

HCO_3^- Reabsorption (1,5,7)

HCO_3^- is filtered freely at the glomerulus, and its concentration in the glomerular filtrate is similar to that of plasma. Accordingly, with a plasma concentration of 24 mEq/liter, the filtered load of HCO_3^- in a normal adult, in whom the glomerular filtration rate (GFR) is 180 liters/day, would be 4,320 mEq/day. Of this, normally less than 1% is excreted in the final urine. Figure

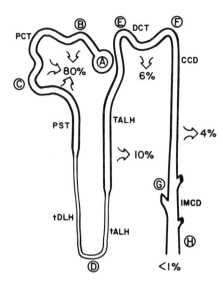

	[HCO₃⁻], mEq/l	pH	Pco₂, mmHg
A Plasma	24	7.4	40
B Early PCT	18	7.1	65
C Late PCT	8	6.7	65
D Loop of Henle	21	7.4	35
E Early DCT	8	6.7	65
F Late DCT	7	6.6	65
G IMCD	1	6.1	35
H Urine	<1	<6.0	35

FIG. 1. Reabsorption of HCO₃⁻ along the nephron. Indicated are the percentages of the filtered load of HCO₃⁻ reabsorbed in the various regions of the nephron. The composition of the luminal fluid at various points along the nephron also is summarized. (PCT) proximal convoluted tubule; (PST) proximal straight tubule: (tDLH) thin descending limb of Henle's loop; (tALH) thin ascending limb of Henle's loop; (TALH) thick ascending limb of Henle's loop; (DCT) distal convoluted tubule; (CCD) cortical collecting duct; (IMCD) inner medullary collecting duct.

1 summarizes the contribution of each nephron segment to the reabsorption of the filtered load of HCO₃⁻.

The major fraction of the filtered load of HCO₃⁻ is reabsorbed by the proximal tubule (approximately 80%). In the superficial nephron of the rat, the rate of HCO₃⁻ reabsorption under free-flow conditions is greater in the early portion (S1) and decreases progressively in later portions (S2 and S3). This axial distribution of transport rates reflects both a progressive fall in luminal [HCO₃⁻] (Fig. 1) and intrinsic differences in these regions of the nephron.

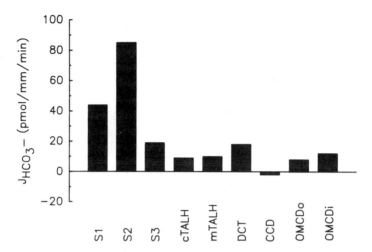

FIG. 2. Net HCO_3^- fluxes measured in various regions of the nephron. Positive values of HCO_3^- flux indicate net reabsorption, and negative values indicate net secretion. All tubules, except the distal convoluted tubule (DCT), were isolated and perfused *in vitro*. Data for the cTALH, mTALH, and DCT were obtained in the rat. All other data were obtained in the rabbit.

Axial heterogeneity in HCO_3^- transport has been observed in segments of the rabbit proximal tubule isolated and perfused *in vitro* (Fig. 2). With this technique, each tubule can be studied under identical conditions. Thus, observed differences in HCO_3^- reabsorptive flux reflect only intrinsic differences in transport capacity of the tubule segments. As can be seen in Fig. 2, the S2 segment of the proximal tubule has the largest transport capacity, whereas the S3 segment has the least. The reasons for the different pattern of HCO_3^- reabsorption in the rabbit (S2>S1>S3) compared to that in the rat (S1>S2>S3) are not known. Possible explanations include species differences and differences between the *in vitro* and *in vivo* conditions.

It also has been shown recently that the HCO_3^- reabsorptive capacity of the proximal tubule differs between superficial and juxtamedullary nephron populations. Specifically, HCO_3^- reabsorptive rates in juxtamedullary proximal tubules exceed those found in the corresponding regions of superficial nephrons. Despite these differences in absolute reabsorptive rates between superficial and juxtamedullary proximal tubules, fractional reabsorption of HCO_3^- is equivalent, since the later nephrons receive a larger filtered load.

As tubule fluid flows down the descending limb of Henle's loop, both the $[HCO_3^-]$ and the pH rise. This results from the reabsorption of water along the length of the thin descending limb. As the $[HCO_3^-]$ increases, back-titration will occur

$$HCO_3^- + H^+ \rightarrow CO_2 + H_2O$$

and net HCO_3^- reabsorption will result. Additional HCO_3^- reabsorption occurs in the thick ascending limb of some species (e.g., rat) but not in others (e.g., rabbit). In the rat, the thick ascending limb reabsorbs approximately 10% of the filtered load of HCO_3^-.

The $[HCO_3^-]$ and pH do not change appreciably along the length of the distal convoluted tubule (DCT). This does not mean, however, that this segment does not reabsorb HCO_3^-; rather it simply reflects the fact that the reabsorptive rates for HCO_3^- and fluid are roughly equal in magnitude. Indeed, the DCT reabsorbs approximately 6% of the filtered load of HCO_3^-. This portion of the nephron also has been found to have the capacity to secrete HCO_3^- into the tubule lumen under some conditions.

Important segmental differences exist along the collecting duct with regard to HCO_3^- transport. The cortical collecting duct is capable of either net HCO_3^- reabsorption or net HCO_3^- secretion, the direction and magnitude of net transport being dependent on the acid-base status of the animal. In particular, net HCO_3^- reabsorption occurs during chronic acidosis, and net HCO_3^- secretion occurs during chronic alkalosis. In the outer medullary and inner medullary portions, only HCO_3^- reabsorption occurs, even in animals with chronic alkalosis.

Figure 2 summarizes data comparing the rates of net HCO_3^- transport in different segments of the nephron under conditions where the luminal and peritubular HCO_3^- concentrations are identical. Under these conditions, HCO_3^- transport occurs against an electrochemical gradient and, therefore, is the result of active transport processes. Because each tubule segment is studied under identical conditions, the measured HCO_3^- fluxes also provide a measure of the maximal transport capacity. As indicated, the proximal tubule segments have the largest capacity for HCO_3^- transport. All segments normally reabsorb HCO_3^- except for the cortical collecting duct, which, under conditions of normal acid-base balance, secretes HCO_3^- to a small degree.

Titratable Acid and Ammonium Excretion (1,5,7)

In addition to reabsorbing the filtered load of HCO_3^-, the kidney also must excrete H^+ equivalent to the amount of nonvolatile acid produced by metabolism. This is accomplished by the excretion of titratable acid[1] and NH_4^+.

The amount of H^+ that can be excreted as titratable acid is fixed by the filtered load of the various buffer species (primarily phosphate). Micropuncture studies of superficial nephrons have identified the proximal tubule as the major nephron site where titratable acid is generated. As fluid moves down the loop of Henle, however, the concentration of titratable acid in the luminal fluid decreases. This probably reflects the fact that phosphate is reabsorbed

---

[1]Titratable acid is determined by measuring the amount of OH^- required to titrate an acid tubular fluid sample back to the pH of blood. Under most conditions, phosphate accounts for the major portion of what is termed "titratable acid." Additional buffer species that may contribute to titratable acid are uric acid, creatinine, and β-hydroxybutyrate.

by this portion of the nephron. Additional titratable acid is generated along the collecting duct, since this is the portion of the nephron where the urine is maximally acidified.

NH_4^+ is produced by the cells of the renal tubule. Its production and, therefore, its excretion are regulated by the acid-base status of the animal, with chronic acidosis leading to an increase in NH_4^+ excretion. Thus, the NH_4^+ system allows the excretion of net acid to be adjusted to match the daily production of nonvolatile acid.

The proximal tubule is the major nephron site of NH_4^+ production. Quantitatively, the amount of NH_4^+ added to the luminal fluid by the proximal tubule is equal to the amount excreted in the final urine. This NH_4^+, however, does not remain in the tubule lumen. As illustrated in Fig. 3, NH_3 and NH_4^+ are reabsorbed by the loop of Henle. This reabsorption occurs by two mechanisms. The first involves the backtitration of NH_4^+. As indicated previously, fluid flowing down the descending limb of Henle's loop is concentrated by the process of water abstraction. Consequently, the following reaction takes place

$$NH_4^+ + HCO_3^- \rightarrow NH_3 + H_2O + CO_2$$

and both HCO_3^- and NH_4^+ are reabsorbed. The second mechanism involves the direct transport of NH_4^+ by the thick ascending limb. As a result of these

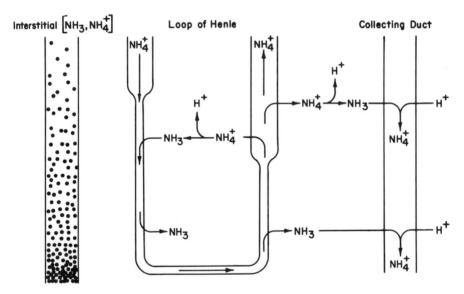

FIG. 3. Ammonia handling in the inner medulla. NH_4^+ is added to the luminal fluid in the proximal tubule. In the inner medulla, this is converted to NH_3 by the abstraction of H_2O and backtitration of NH_4^+ by HCO_3^-. The NH_3 then diffuses into the medullary interstitium across the thin limbs of Henle. NH_4^+ is also reabsorbed from the thick ascending limb. As a result of these two processes, NH_3 and NH_4^+ accumulate in the interstitial fluid. NH_3 enters the final urine by diffusing into the collecting duct, where it is protonated and trapped as NH_4^+.

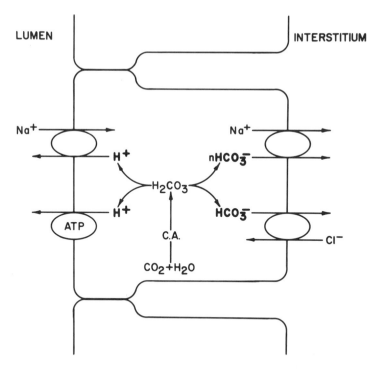

FIG. 4. General mechanisms for H^+ and HCO_3^- transport across the apical and basolateral membranes of a renal tubule cell.

processes, the concentrations of NH_3 and NH_4^+ in the medullary interstitium are elevated. Because the collecting duct fluid is acidic, NH_4^+ will accumulate in the lumen by the process of nonionic diffusion. Although the major portion of NH_4^+ enters the final urine by medullary shunting, both the distal convoluted tubule and the cortical collecting duct also contribute to the titration and excretion of NH_4^+.

BASIC MECHANISMS OF CELLULAR H^+ TRANSPORT (1,5,7,15)

Both the reabsorption of the filtered load of HCO_3^- and the excretion of titratable acid and NH_4^+ result from the secretion of H^+ by the cells of the renal tubule. At the cellular level, this requires that H^+ is extruded from the cell across the apical membrane and that HCO_3^- exits the cell across the basolateral membrane. Figure 4 summarizes the basic mechanisms involved in this process.

Apical Membrane

Measurements of apical membrane voltages and intracellular pH have shown that H^+ is below electrochemical equilibrium across this membrane.

Consequently, the transport of H^+ from the cell into the tubule lumen is active and requires the expenditure of energy. The two major mechanisms for this active transport of H^+ are a H^+-ATPase and a Na/H antiporter.

The H^+-ATPase has been identified immunocytochemically in virtually all cells of the nephron. However, its role in urine acidification is best understood in terms of collecting duct function. The H^+-ATPase is composed of a catalytic subunit located on the cytoplasmic side of the membrane, which hydrolyzes ATP, and a membrane-spanning channel. Biochemical studies have shown this H^+-ATPase to be distinct from that of mitochondria and similar to that found in endosomal membranes. This later observation may explain why immunocytochemical studies have found widespread distribution of this enzyme through the nephron. Although the stoichiometry of the H^+-ATPase is not known with certainty, it has been estimated that 3 H^+ are pumped for each ATP hydrolyzed. Given this stoichiometry, the H^+-ATPase is electrogenic.

The Na/H antiporter is the major mechanism for H^+ secretion in the proximal tubule and thick ascending limb of Henle's loop. The secretion of H^+ by this antiporter is termed "secondary active" because the energy is derived from the lumen-to-cell Na^+ gradient and not directly from the hydrolysis of ATP. The Na^+ gradient is generated and maintained by the Na,K-ATPase located in the basolateral membrane of the cell. Thus, H^+ secretion will be influenced by factors that alter the activity of the Na,K-ATPase (e.g., ouabain). The Na/H antiporter exchanges 1 Na^+ for 1 H^+ and is, therefore, electroneutral. NH_4^+ can substitute for H^+, thus providing a mechanism for NH_4^+ addition to the tubule lumen. Kinetic studies of the antiporter have shown that acidification of the intracellular fluid stimulates and alkalinization inhibits the rate of transport. It also has been reported that cyclic AMP may act to inhibit the antiporter, perhaps via protein kinase and phosphorylation of the protein. The K^+-sparing diuretic amiloride will, at high doses, inhibit the antiporter.

Basolateral Membrane

Measurements of basolateral membrane voltage and intracellular $[HCO_3^-]$ have shown that HCO_3^- is above electrochemical equilibrium across this membrane. Thus, HCO_3^- exit from the cell is passive. Because of this favorable gradient, it would be possible for HCO_3^- to exit the cell through a simple conductive pathway. However, there is at present no evidence for such a pathway. All HCO_3^- movement across the basolateral membrane appears to be coupled to other ions.

An important HCO_3^- transport system is the Na/HCO_3 symporter found in the proximal tubule. Electrophysiologic studies have determined that this symporter is electrogenic and carries net negative charge out of the cell. Thus, at least two HCO_3^- must be transported for each Na^+. Measurements of intracellular Na^+ and HCO_3^- concentration and the basolateral membrane voltage would require that the stoichiometry be 3 HCO_3^-:1 Na^+. The disulfonic stilbenes (e.g., SITS and DIDS), which are potent inhibitors of the red blood cell band 3 anion transport system, also inhibit this symporter.

The other major mechanism for HCO_3^- exit from the cell is a Cl/HCO_3 antiporter. This antiporter is electroneutral and has a stoichiometry of 1 Cl^-: 1 HCO_3^-. Like the 3 HCO_3^-:1 Na^+ symporter, it too is inhibited by the disulfonic stilbenes.

Carbonic Anhydrase

Carbonic anhydrase catalyzes the hydration of CO_2 and, thus, accelerates the interconversion of CO_2 and H_2O to H^+ and HCO_3^-. It plays an important role in urine acidification, and it is found in all renal tubule cells involved in acid-base transport. Indeed, its localization to a particular nephron segment or cell type often is used as evidence for a role in urine acidification, even when direct transport data are not available.

The kidney contains two isoenzymes of carbonic anhydrase. The major form is the type II isoenzyme. It is a cytoplasmic enzyme and is found in several cell types of the nephron (e.g., proximal tubule and intercalated cell of the collecting duct). The other isoenzyme is membrane bound, and termed type IV. In addition to differences in location (i.e., cytoplasmic and membrane bound) these isoenzymes also can be distinguished by their kinetic properties. Type II is characterized by a high V_{max}, and is very sensitive to inhibition by sulfonamide derivatives. Type IV has both a lower V_{max} and a lower sensitivity to sulfonamides.

The role of carbonic anhydrase in urine acidification is illustrated in Fig. 4. Intracellular carbonic anhydrase catalyzes the formation of H^+ and HCO_3^- from CO_2 and H_2O.[2] By this action, it provides H^+ for excretion into the tubule lumen and the return of HCO_3^- to the blood. In certain portions of the nephron (e.g., proximal convoluted tubule), membrane-bound enzyme is in contact with the luminal fluid. In this location, it serves to convert luminal H_2CO_3, which is formed from the reaction of filtered HCO_3^- and secreted H^+, to CO_2 and H_2O. As a result, the associated fall in luminal fluid pH is ameliorated, and a more favorable cell-to-lumen H^+ gradient is maintained. Thus, H^+ secretion can continue at a high rate.

It should be noted that the reaction catalyzed by carbonic anhydrase will occur in the absence of the enzyme, although the rate of the reaction is

---

[2]Detailed studies of the enzyme indicate that the catalytic site binds anions. Thus, the precise step in the reaction catalyzed by the enzyme is thought to be

$$OH^- + CO_2 \rightarrow HCO_3^-$$

markedly slowed. Consequently, inhibition of renal carbonic anhydrase will impair but not completely block the process of urine acidification.

CELLULAR MECHANISMS OF H⁺ AND HCO₃⁻ TRANSPORT

In the following sections, the cellular mechanisms of H^+ and HCO_3^- transport in the various portions of the nephron are reviewed. In addition, the mechanisms by which the transport of these ions is regulated at the cellular level are considered.

Proximal Tubule (3,6,11,13)

As noted earlier, the proximal tubule reabsorbs approximately 80% of the filtered load of HCO_3^-. In addition, NH_4^+ is added to the luminal fluid, and titratable acid is formed. The fundamental process underlying these transport events is the secretion of H^+ across the apical membrane of the cell. During this process, a HCO_3^- is generated in the cell and returned to the blood. Figure 5 summarizes the general features of proximal tubule H^+ and HCO_3^- transport.

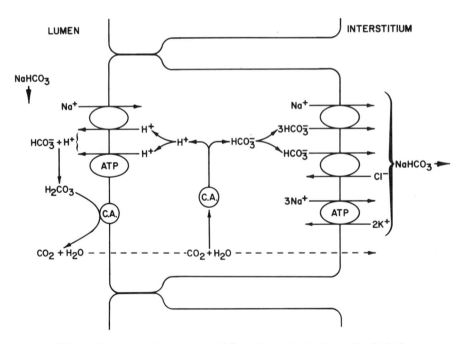

FIG. 5. Cellular mechanisms for HCO_3^- reabsorption by the proximal tubule.

Apical Membrane

The secretion of H^+ by cells of the proximal tubule occurs primarily by a Na/H antiporter. An additional component of H^+ secretion is Na^+ independent, and this is thought to be the result of the activity of a H^+-ATPase. Recent studies have estimated that the Na/H antiporter accounts for approximately 65% of total H^+ secretion, and the remaining 35% is presumed to be mediated by the H^+-ATPase.

The secretion of H^+ by the Na/H antiporter is driven by the lumen-to-cell Na^+ gradient, which in turn is dependent on the activity of the Na,K-ATPase located in the basolateral membrane of the cell. Intracellular pH has been shown to be an important regulator of Na/H antiporter activity. As intracellular pH falls, the rate of H^+ transport by the antiporter increases. Conversely, as intracellular pH rises, H^+ transport decreases. There is also some evidence that cyclic AMP, perhaps via protein kinases and phosphorylation of the transport protein, can inhibit the activity of the Na/H antiporter.

The role of the H^+-ATPase in proximal tubule H^+ secretion is less well understood. The existence of H^+-ATPase in the apical membrane has, however, been demonstrated unequivocally both by immunocytochemistry and by transport studies of apical membrane vesicles. Since the cells of the proximal tubule have a well-developed endocytic and membrane-recycling system and since the intracellular membrane compartments associated with this process (e.g., endosomes, clathrin-coated vesicles) are rich in H^+-ATPase, it may be that H^+ secretion into the lumen is simply a reflection of this process.

As H^+ are extruded from the cell into the tubule lumen, they combine with HCO_3^- to form H_2CO_3, and luminal pH falls. Because the apical membrane contains carbonic anhydrase, which is in functional contact with the luminal fluid, the H_2CO_3 is quickly converted to CO_2 and H_2O, and the fall in luminal pH is ameliorated. Since the proximal tubule is highly permeable to CO_2 and H_2O, they are rapidly reabsorbed. The importance of this membrane-bound carbonic anhydrase in the process of HCO_3^- reabsorption is evidenced by the fact that inhibition of this enzyme reduces net transport by 80 to 90%.

An anion antiporter, which exchanges 1 Cl^- for 1 HCO_3^- has been localized to the apical membrane. Given the existing transmembrane gradients for these ions, this antiporter would normally secrete HCO_3^- into the tubule lumen. Its role in acid-base excretion is not yet understood, but it is believed to be important in the reabsorption of NaCl.

Basolateral Membrane

Within the cytoplasm of the cell, H^+ and HCO_3^- are produced by a carbonic anhydrase-catalyzed reaction. As indicated previously, the H^+ is transported into the lumen of the tubule. In order to affect net HCO_3^- reabsorption, the HCO_3^- ion produced in this reaction must exit the cell across the basolateral membrane and be returned to the blood.

HCO_3^- is transported across the basolateral membrane by at least two mechanisms. The major mechanism involves a Na/HCO_3 symporter. This symporter is electrogenic and normally operates to carry net negative charge out of the cell. Thus, at least 2 HCO_3^- must be transported together with 1 Na^+. Studies in the amphibian proximal tubule are consistent with a 2 HCO_3^-:1 Na^+ stoichiometry. However, in the rat, such a stoichiometry would result in the net uptake of HCO_3^- into the cell. Consequently, in this latter species, a 3 HCO_3^-:1 Na^+ stoichiometry is assumed. The symporter is inhibited by disulfonic stilbenes, a group of compounds that inhibit anion transport systems in a number of cells. It has been estimated that 90% of all HCO_3^- movement across the basolateral membrane occurs via this symporter.

Studies of HCO_3^- transport by vesicles prepared from the basolateral membrane have provided strong evidence for the existence of a Cl/HCO_3 antiporter. This antiporter would operate under normal conditions to carry HCO_3^- out of the cell. This antiporter also is inhibited by disulfonic stilbenes.

In addition to these two mechanisms, which operate to carry HCO_3^- out of the cell, other mechanisms for H^+ and HCO_3^- transport across the basolateral membrane have been identified. For example, in some species, this membrane contains a Na/H antiporter, which is important in the regulation of intracellular pH. Because this antiporter would transport H^+ from cell to interstitium, it does not contribute to the reabsorption of the filtered load of HCO_3^-. A 1 Na^+:2 HCO_3^-:1 Cl^- antiporter also has been described. This antiporter is electroneutral and transports Na^+ and HCO_3^- into the cell in exchange for Cl^-. Thus, this transporter also cannot contribute to the process of net reabsorption of HCO_3^- but is probably important for the reabsorption of Cl^-.

Passive Transport of H^+ and HCO_3^-

When considering the transport properties of the proximal tubule, it must always be recognized that this epithelium is characterized by having large passive permeabilities to many ions. This is certainly the case for both H^+ and HCO_3^-. Although the H^+ permeability is quite large, the $[H^+]$ of either the luminal or interstitial fluid is so small that passive transport rates are negligible and usually are ignored. The HCO_3^- permeability is smaller than that for H^+, but because the concentration of HCO_3^- is much larger, passive HCO_3^- movement can influence net transport significantly. When the luminal $[HCO_3^-]$ is below that of the interstitial fluid, HCO_3^- will leak back into the tubule lumen and thus reduce the overall rate of net HCO_3^- reabsorption. When the luminal $[HCO_3^-]$ exceeds that of the interstitial fluid, passive reabsorption will occur, and the rate of net HCO_3^- reabsorption is increased.

Regulation of H^+ Transport

A number of factors have been identified that play an important role in regulating the secretion of H^+ by the cells of the proximal tubule and thus determine the amount of the filtered load of HCO_3^- that is reabsorbed in this segment (Table 1).

Reabsorption of HCO_3^- by the proximal tubule is inhibited by acidification of the luminal fluid (reduced $[HCO_3^-]$) and stimulated by alkalinization (increased $[HCO_3^-]$). This relationship is illustrated in Fig. 6. At least two mechanisms account for this phenomenon. The first relates to the secretion of H^+ from cell to lumen. As luminal pH is altered, the gradient against which H^+ must be transported out of the cell also will change. Accordingly, as luminal pH is decreased, the cell-to-lumen H^+ gradient in increased, and H^+ secretion by both the Na/H antiporter and the H^+-ATPase will be reduced. Consequently, at a more alkaline luminal pH, this gradient is reduced, and H^+ secretion is increased. Because of the passive permeability properties of the proximal tubule, changes in the luminal $[HCO_3^-]$ will effect the rate of net HCO_3^- reabsorption. As noted previously, when the luminal $[HCO_3^-]$ falls below that of the interstitial fluid, HCO_3^- will leak passively into the lumen and decrease the rate of net reabsorption. As luminal $[HCO_3^-]$ is increased, the backleak of HCO_3^- is reduced, and at even higher concentrations (i.e., luminal $[HCO_3^-]$ > interstitial $[HCO_3^-]$), passive HCO_3^- reabsorption occurs. Thus, under this latter condition, net HCO_3^- reabsorption exceeds the rate of H^+ secretion by the cells. The contribution of passive HCO_3^- movement to net reabsorption by the proximal tubule also is illustrated in Fig. 6.

Changes in luminal flow rate lead to parallel changes in HCO_3^- reabsorption (Fig. 7). This flow effect is due, at least in part, to flow-related changes in luminal fluid $[HCO_3^-]$. For example, as HCO_3^- is reabsorbed along the proximal

TABLE 1. *Factors regulating H^+ secretion (HCO_3^- reabsorption) by the proximal tubule*

Increased H^+ secretion
  Increased lumen pH or $[HCO_3^-]$
  Increased luminal fluid flow rate
  Decreased peritubular pH or $[HCO_3^-]$
  Elevated P_{CO_2}
  Decreased extracellular fluid volume
  Chronic K^+ depletion

Decreased H^+ secretion
  Decreased lumen pH or $[HCO_3^-]$
  Decreased luminal fluid flow rate
  Increased peritubular pH or $[HCO_3^-]$
  Decreased P_{CO_2}
  Increased extracellular fluid volume
  Parathyroid hormone (PTH)

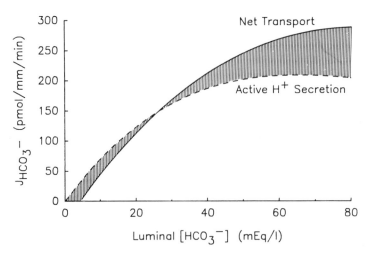

FIG. 6. The relationship between proximal tubule HCO_3^- transport and the luminal $[HCO_3^-]$. Passive HCO_3^- flux is indicated by the shaded area between the two curves. Note that when the luminal $[HCO_3^-]$ is less than that of plasma (i.e., 24 mEq/liter), net transport is less than active H^+ secretion, with the difference representing passive backleak of HCO_3^-. The opposite is observed at luminal $[HCO_3^-]$ above that of plasma. (Redrawn from ref. 3.)

tubule, the $[HCO_3^-]$ falls, and the cells in downstream portions must then secrete H^+ against a steeper gradient. As luminal flow rate is increased, the $[HCO_3^-]$ in these downstream segments is increased to values that approach those of the glomerular filtrate. As a result, a more favorable gradient for cell-to-lumen H^+ secretion exists, and HCO_3^- reabsorption is stimulated. An additional mechanism thought to be important in determining the flow de-

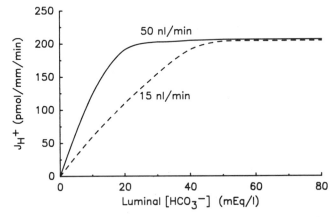

FIG. 7. Effect of luminal flow rate on H^+ secretion by the proximal tubule. At luminal $[HCO_3^-]$ below 40 mEq/liter, changes in luminal flow rate have a marked effect on H^+ secretion. Above a luminal $[HCO_3^-]$ of 40 mEq/liter, no flow dependency is observed. (Redrawn from ref. 3.)

pendency of HCO_3^- reabsorption is the existence of radial concentration gradients within the tubule lumen. According to this mechanism, the $[HCO_3^-]$ and pH near the apical membrane of the cell are lower than in the bulk-phase luminal fluid. Increased flow within the lumen of the tubule would be expected to dissipate this gradient, thus raising the $[HCO_3^-]$ and pH near the membrane. As a result, a more favorable cell-to-lumen gradient would exist for H^+ secretion, and the rate of net HCO_3^- reabsorption would be increased. Finally, chronic elevation of the luminal flow rate, as occurs with reduced nephron mass, for example, has been shown to increase the activity of the Na/H antiporter. The mechanism for this increased activity is unknown but is not related to the changes in cell-to-lumen H^+ and HCO_3^- gradients described previously. One possibility is that the number of Na/H antiporters in the apical membrane is increased in this situation.

Changes in the peritubular acid-base environment also modulate HCO_3^- reabsorption by the proximal tubule. Decreases in peritubular $[HCO_3^-]$ and pH stimulate and increases in peritubular $[HCO_3^-]$ and pH inhibit net HCO_3^- reabsorption (Fig. 8). Several factors account for this response. Changes in the peritubular $[HCO_3^-]$ and pH, by altering the cell-to-interstitium gradients for these ions, will directly influence the rate of HCO_3^- exit from the cell across the basolateral membrane. As a result, decreasing the peritubular $[HCO_3^-]$ will accelerate exit of HCO_3^- from the cell, whereas increasing the peritubular $[HCO_3^-]$ will have the opposite effect. Associated with these changes in peritubular $[HCO_3^-]$ and pH will be parallel changes in the intracellular pH. These changes in intracellular pH, in turn, will lead to alterations in the secretion of H^+ across the apical membrane by several mechanisms. First, the cell-to-lumen H^+ gradient will be altered. For example, as this gradient is made more favorable (e.g., decreased intracellular pH),

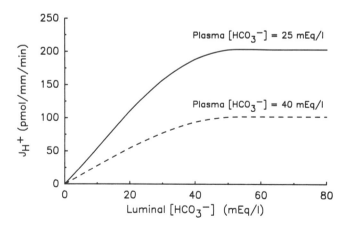

FIG. 8. Effect of plasma $[HCO_3^-]$ on H^+ secretion by the proximal tubule. H^+ secretion is decreased when the plasma $[HCO_3^-]$ is increased to 40 mEq/liter regardless of the luminal $[HCO_3^-]$. (Redrawn from ref. 3.)

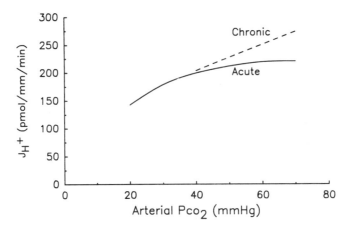

FIG. 9. Effect of arterial P_{CO_2} on H^+ secretion by the proximal tubule. The effect of acute and chronic changes in the P_{CO_2} is illustrated. (Redrawn from ref. 3.)

H^+ secretion will be stimulated. Second, intracellular pH directly regulates the activity of the Na/H antiporter independent of the transmembrane H^+ gradient. Thus, the Na/H antiporter is stimulated by decreased intracellular pH and inhibited by increased intracellular pH. Changes in intracellular pH may result in the insertion and retrieval of transporters (e.g., Na/H antiporter and H^+-ATPase) into and out of the apical membrane. Accordingly, with a decrease in intracellular pH, the number of transporters in the apical membrane would be increased, and the number would be decreased with an increase in pH.

Changes in the peritubular P_{CO_2} also modulate proximal tubule HCO_3^- reabsorption. Decreases on P_{CO_2} inhibit and increases stimulate reabsorption (Fig. 9). Since the membranes of the proximal tubule cell are highly permeable to CO_2, changes in peritubular P_{CO_2} directly alter intracellular pH. Thus, intracellular pH falls as the P_{CO_2} is increased and rises as it is decreased. These changes in pH will then alter HCO_3^- reabsorption by the mechanisms outlined (above). Since CO_2 is critically important for the generation of intracellular H^+ and HCO_3^- (Fig. 5), regulation of transport could also occur at this step.

Changes in the volume of the extracellular fluid compartment influence proximal tubule reabsorption, with volume expansion inhibiting and volume contraction stimulating transport. This response is related to the changes in proximal tubule Na^+ and fluid transport induced by these maneuvers. Since H^+ secretion is coupled to Na^+ reabsorption via the Na/H exchanger, changes in HCO_3^- resorption will parallel changes in Na^+ reabsorption. In addition, it has been found that changes in extracellular fluid volume alter the permeability of the paracellular pathway. Specifically, volume expansion increases the HCO_3^- permeability. Thus, under this condition the passive backleak of HCO_3^- into the tubule lumen will be increased, with the result that net reabsorption is decreased.

Chronic K^+ depletion stimulates HCO_3^- reabsorption by the proximal tubule. Although the mechanisms underlying this response are poorly understood, two possibilities have been proposed. First, NMR measurements of intracellular pH show that K^+ depletion leads to intracellular acidification. This will stimulate H^+ secretion across the apical membrane. Second, the voltage across the basolateral membrane is hyperpolarized during K^+ depletion. Since a portion of HCO_3^- exit from the cell across this membrane is electrogenic (Fig. 5), this will result in an increase in the cell-to-interstitium electrochemical gradient for HCO_3^- efflux. As a result of these two processes, net HCO_3^- reabsorption would be expected to be increased.

Parathyroid hormone (PTH) inhibits HCO_3^- reabsorption by the proximal tubule. Studies of apical membrane vesicles have shown that the activity of the Na/H antiporter is inhibited by increased levels of intracellular cyclic AMP. Since PTH acts via adenylate cyclase and its actions on the tubule are mimicked by cyclic AMP, it seems likely that the reduction in HCO_3^- reabsorption seen with PTH is a result of cyclic AMP-dependent inhibition of the Na/H antiporter.

Loop of Henle (1,4,7)

The loop of Henle reabsorbs approximately 10% of the filtered load of HCO_3^-. A portion of this occurs in the thin limbs and is related to the back titration of HCO_3^-. In addition, the thick ascending limb of some species actively reabsorbs HCO_3^- from the tubule lumen.

Histochemical studies of several species have localized carbonic anhydrase to the cells of the thick ascending limb, although species differences do exist. For example, the thick ascending limb of the rabbit does not contain the enzyme, whereas those of the rat, mouse, and human kidneys do.

Studies of the rabbit thick ascending limb have shown that this segment does not transport HCO_3^-. In contrast, significant HCO_3^- reabsorption is found in both the cortical and medullary portions of the rat thick ascending limb. Although the thick ascending limb of the mouse contains carbonic anhydrase, no significant HCO_3^- has been measured. The reason for this is not known but may reflect differences in specific transport systems or differences in technical aspects of the study. The fact that the thick ascending limb of the human kidney contains carbonic anhydrase would suggest that this segment may be involved in the transport of HCO_3^-.

The cellular mechanism for HCO_3^- reabsorption by the cells of the thick ascending limb is incompletely understood. Studies in isolated perfused segments of the rat cortical and medullary thick ascending limb have demonstrated that HCO_3^- reabsorption is inhibited by acetazolamide. It is coupled to Na^+, since removal of luminal Na^+ or inhibition of the Na,K-ATPase in the basolateral membrane inhibits HCO_3^- reabsorption. Because addition of amiloride to the luminal fluid also inhibits HCO_3^- reabsorption, it is likely that H^+ secretion across the apical membrane occurs by a Na/H antiporter. Immunocytochemical studies also have localized a H^+-ATPase to the apical membrane of these cells. However, the contribution of this H^+-ATPase to the process of HCO_3^- reabsorption has not been defined. The mechanism by which HCO_3^- exits the cell across the basolateral membrane also has not been defined.

Regulation of H^+ Transport

Regulation of HCO_3^- reabsorption by the loop of Henle has not been studied extensively. Because Na^+ reabsorption and HCO_3^- are coupled in the thick ascending limb, it is likely that factors that regulate Na^+ reabsorption (e.g., delivery of solute, vasopressin, β-adrenergic agonists) may also affect HCO_3^- transport. However, data directly examining the actions of these maneuvers on HCO_3^- transport have not been reported. Aldosterone has been shown to stimulate the Na/H antiporter in the apical membrane of the early distal tubule of the amphibian kidney. Since this segment is homologous to the thick ascending limb of the mammalian kidney, it may be that aldosterone plays a role in regulating HCO_3^- reabsorption by the thick ascending limb.

As noted previously, HCO_3^- reabsorption is inhibited by the carbonic anhydrase inhibitor acetazolamide and the K^+-sparing diuretic amiloride. In contrast to these agents, the loop diuretics (e.g., furosemide) stimulate HCO_3^- reabsorption. The mechanism for this stimulation is thought to be related to a reduction in intracellular $[Na^+]$ secondary to the inhibition of the 1 Na^+:1 K^+:2 Cl^- symporter in the apical membrane of these cells. As a result of this reduction in intracellular $[Na^+]$, the energy in the lumen-to-cell Na^+ gradient is increased, and secondary active H^+ secretion by the Na/H antiporter is increased.

Distal Convoluted Tubule (1,2,7–9,15)

The distal convoluted tubule traditionally has been defined as extending from the macula densa to the confluence of tubules at the collecting duct. It is now recognized that this portion of the nephron is composed of three distinct segments: the distal convoluted tubule proper (DCT), the connecting tubule (CNT), and the initial collecting tubule (ICT). Measurements of HCO_3^- transport, however, have not distinguished among these segments. Combined, they reabsorb approximately 6% of the filtered load of HCO_3^-.

The cellular mechanisms of H^+ and HCO_3^- transport by the DCT have not yet been defined. The DCT segment is composed of a single cell type, and a

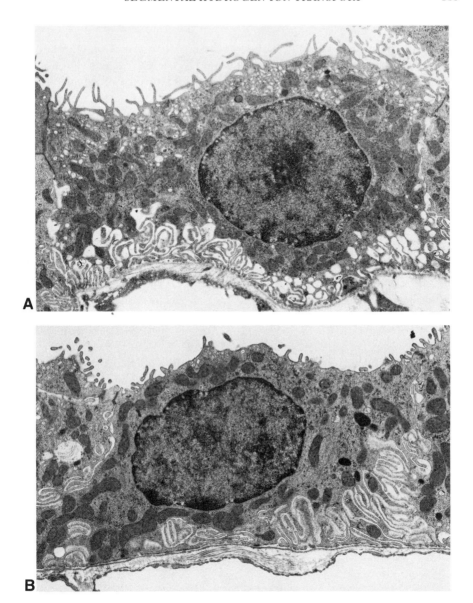

FIG. 10. Transmission electron micrographs of an intercalated cell **(A)** and a principal cell **(B)** in the initial collecting tubule of the rat. ×15,000. (Courtesy of B. Stanton and D. Biemesderfer.)

H^+-ATPase has been localized to the apical membrane. Beyond this, however, little is known about the ability of this segment to reabsorb HCO_3^- or the cellular mechanisms involved. In the CNT and ICT, two cell types are found. Figure 10 illustrates the differences between these cell types. The majority cell type is the principal cell (termed connecting tubule cell in the CNT). It is thought that this cell is involved in the transport of Na^+. The other cell type is the intercalated cell. It contains carbonic anhydrase and is, therefore, thought to be involved in acid-base transport. The intercalated cell also is found in the collecting duct, and its function is discussed in relation to this latter segment.

Regulation of H^+ Transport

The reabsorption of HCO_3^- by the DCT varies in proportion to the delivered load. Thus, when delivery is increased, the HCO_3^- reabsorptive rate is increased. The opposite occurs when delivery is reduced. The mechanism responsible for this load dependency is not known but probably is related to the H^+ electrochemical gradient across the apical membrane, as described for the proximal tubule.

It has been possible in some studies to demonstrate both HCO_3^- reabsorption and HCO_3^- secretion in the DCT. Since the cortical portion of the collecting duct also has the capacity for HCO_3^- reabsorption and secretion, these processes are considered in detail in the subsequent section. ·

HCO_3^- transport by the cortical portion of the collecting duct is modulated by aldosterone, β-adrenergic agonists, and cyclic AMP. Because of the structural and functional similarities between the cortical collecting duct and the ICT, similar effects would be expected in this latter segment. However, this has not been examined directly.

Collecting Duct (1,7,9,10,12,14)

The collecting duct exhibits considerable structural and functional heterogeneity. Based on the general morphologic landmarks of the kidney, the collecting duct is divided into three portions: the cortical collecting duct (CCD), the outer medullary collecting duct (OMCD), and the inner medullary collecting duct (IMCD). In the following sections, H^+ and HCO_3^- in these three regions are reviewed.

Cortical Collecting Duct

The CCD has the capacity to both reabsorb and secrete HCO_3^-. Both processes are Na^+-independent and facilitated by carbonic anhydrase. There is recent morphologic evidence that HCO_3^- reabsorption and HCO_3^- secretion occur by two distinct cell types of the intercalated cell. Figure 11 summarizes the transport features of these two cells.

HCO_3^- reabsorption occurs by the process of H^+ secretion. In the H^+-secreting intercalated cell subtype, this is accomplished by an electrogenic H^+-ATPase located in the apical membrane. The HCO_3^- generated by the

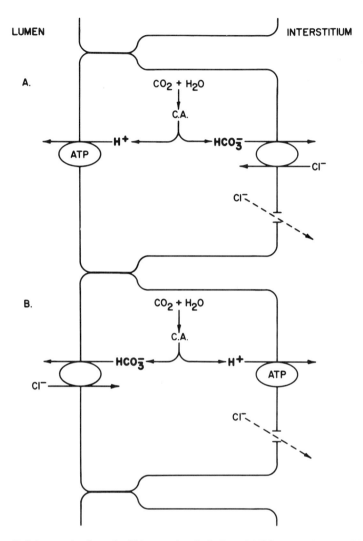

FIG. 11. Cellular mechanisms for H^+ secretion (cell A) and HCO_3^- secretion (cell B) by the intercalated cells of the collecting duct.

intracellular hydration of CO_2 exits the cell across the basolateral membrane by an electroneutral Cl/HCO_3 antiporter. The basolateral membrane also contains a Cl^- conductive pathway, which provides a pathway for Cl^- recycling. The features of this model have been confirmed by microelectrode studies of single intercalated cell and by immunocytochemical localization of the H^+-ATPase to the apical membrane and the Cl/HCO_3 antiporter to the basolateral membrane.

Overall, the process of H^+ secretion (HCO_3^- reabsorption) is electrogenic and results in the generation of a lumen-positive transepithelial voltage. Normally, however, the transepithelial voltage in the CCD is oriented lumen negative, reflecting the electrogenic reabsorption of Na^+ by the principal cell. Thus, in the steady state, the transepithelial voltage of the CCD represents the sum of two electrogenic processes: one for Na^+ reabsorption and one for H^+ secretion. Although the secretion of H^+ is independent of Na^+, changes in the transepithelial voltage, secondary to alterations in Na^+ transport, can have an important effect on H^+ secretion. This is discussed in detail in a later section.

The process of H^+ secretion is critically dependent on carbonic anhydrase, and inhibition of this enzyme, by acetazolamide, for example, virtually abolishes transport. Inhibition of the Cl/HCO_3 antiporter, either by treatment with disulfonic stilbenes (e.g., SITS) or by removing Cl^- from the peritubular bathing medium, also abolishes transport.

HCO_3^- secretion also is driven by a H^+-ATPase. In the HCO_3^--secreting intercalated cell subtype, this H^+-ATPase is located in the basolateral membrane rather than the apical membrane. HCO_3^- is secreted into the tubule lumen in exchange for Cl^-; the Cl^- then exits the cell across the basolateral membrane via a Cl^- conductive pathway. As can be seen from the model, the transcellular secretion of HCO_3^- is electroneutral and, therefore, does not contribute to the transepithelial voltage.

Like the process of H^+ secretion, HCO_3^- secretion is dependent on the activity of cytoplasmic carbonic anhydrase, and treatment with acetazolamide markedly inhibits transport. Given the presence of a Cl/HCO_3 antiporter in the apical membrane, it would be expected that disulfonic stilbenes added to the luminal fluid would inhibit HCO_3^- secretion. This, however, is not the case. The absence of an effect of disulfonic stilbenes suggests that the Cl/HCO_3 antiporter in the apical membrane of the HCO_3^--secreting intercalated cell differs from that in the basolateral membrane of the H^+-secreting intercalated cell. In support of this interpretation is the observation that monoclonal antibodies that react with the basolateral membrane antiporter do not cross react with the apical membrane antiporter. The apical membrane antiporter can, however, be inhibited by removing Cl^- from the luminal fluid. When this is done, HCO_3^- secretion is markedly reduced.

The reason that the cortical collecting duct (also the DCT) has developed two parallel and opposing systems for acid-base transport is not completely understood. Since HCO_3^- secretion is stimulated by systemic alkalosis, it may represent an adaptive response to this condition. However, recent studies of this system have focused on its role in Cl^- reabsorption. The results of these studies indicate that the HCO_3^--secreting intercalated cell subtype may be more important for maintaining Cl^- balance than for acid-base homeostasis.

Outer Medullary Collecting Duct

The outer medullary collecting duct reabsorbs HCO_3^- by an electrogenic process identical to that described for the H^+-secreting cell of the CCD (Fig.

11A). In contrast to the CCD, however, HCO_3^- secretion does not occur in the OMCD.

The outer medullary collecting duct can be subdivided into an outer stripe ($OMCD_o$) and an inner stripe ($OMCD_i$). In the rabbit, these two segments have different transport properties, especially with regard to urine acidification. The $OMCD_o$, like the CCD, reabsorbs Na^+ and secretes H^+. The $OMCD_i$ does not transport Na^+ and appears to be specialized for H^+ secretion.

Inner Medullary Collecting Duct

The inner medullary collecting duct reabsorbs HCO_3^-. HCO_3^- secretion has not been found to occur in this segment. Very little is known of the cellular mechanisms involved in H^+ and HCO_3^- transport by this segment. Except for a small portion near the junction with the outer medulla, the IMCD does not contain intercalated cells, although urine acidification does take place along its entire length. The cells involved in acid-base transport in the terminal portions of the IMCD have not been identified. Studies of single IMCD cells in suspension have provided evidence for both Na^+-dependent and Na^+-independent mechanisms of H^+ transport. However, the cellular mechanisms involved are not known. Since the transepithelial voltage is near 0 mV, the overall process appears to be electroneutral.

Regulation of H^+ and HCO_3^- Transport

A number of factors have been identified that play a role in regulating HCO_3^- transport by the collecting duct. In certain instances, it has been possible to differentiate between effects on the H^+-secreting and HCO_3^--secreting subtypes of the intercalated cell, whereas in other conditions, it has not been possible to make such distinctions. Table 2 summarizes some of the factors that regulate H^+ and HCO_3^- transport by the collecting duct. Where data are available, effects on specific cell types are indicated.

Alterations in the peritubular acid-base environment lead to both acute and chronic changes in collecting duct H^+ and HCO_3^- transport. When the peritubular pH is acutely reduced by decreasing the $[HCO_3^-]$, H^+ secretion (HCO_3^- reabsorption) is increased. Conversely, when the pH and $[HCO_3^-]$ are increased, H^+ secretion is reduced. As noted earlier, the CCD has the capacity to both reabsorb and secrete HCO_3^-. When animals are chronically made either acidotic or alkalotic, the direction and magnitude of HCO_3^- transport is altered, even when the tubule is studied under conditions simulating normal acid-base balance. For example, when animals are made acidotic for several days, the CCD reabsorbs HCO_3^-. On the other hand, when animals are made chronically alkalotic, the CCD secretes HCO_3^-.

TABLE 2. *Factors regulating H^+ and HCO_3^- Transport*
by the collecting duct

Increased H^+ secretion
  Decreased peritubular pH or [HCO_3^-]
  Increased P_{CO_2}
  Increased magnitude of lumen-negative transepithelial
    voltage
  Aldosterone
  cAMP

Decreased H^+ secretion
  Increased peritubular pH or [HCO_3^-]
  Decreased P_{CO_2}
  Decreased magnitude of lumen-negative transepithelial
    voltage
  Adrenalectomy
  Prostaglandin E_2

Increased [HCO_3^-] secretion
  Increased peritubular pH or [HCO_3^-]
  β-Adrenergic agonists (e.g., isoproterenol)
  cAMP

At least two mechanisms appear to be responsible for the changes in collecting duct transport determined by the acid-base environment of the peritubular fluid. Considering first the H^+-secreting intercalated cell subtype (Fig. 11A), alterations in the peritubular [HCO_3^-] will alter the exit of HCO_3^- from the cell across the basolateral membrane via the Cl/HCO_3 antiporter. Thus, as peritubular [HCO_3^-] and pH are lowered, HCO_3^- will more easily exit the cell, resulting in a decrease in intracellular pH. The opposite will occur if the peritubular [HCO_3^-] and pH are increased. These changes in intracellular pH will alter the electrochemical gradient for H^+ across the apical membrane, which in turn will alter the rate of H^+ secretion into the lumen. Accordingly, when the intracellular pH is more acid, H^+ secretion will be increased. H^+ secretion will be reduced when the intracellular pH is alkaline. Changes in the intracellular pH also regulate the number of H^+-ATPase units in the apical membrane. When intracellular pH is alkaline, H^+-ATPase is retrieved from the apical membrane by a process of endocytosis. The endocytosed H^+-ATPase remain in vesicles within the apical cytoplasm of the cell. In response to acidification of the cytoplasm, these vesicles fuse with the apical membrane and reinsert the H^+-ATPase by the process of exocytosis. Thus, the rate of H^+ secretion parallels the change in number of H^+-ATPase in the membrane.

The response of the HCO_3^--secreting intercalated cell subtype to changes in the peritubular acid-base environment has been less well characterized. However, simple inspection of the model depicted in Fig. 11B shows that alterations in peritubular pH will directly influence the gradient against which the H^+-ATPase in the basolateral membrane must pump. It is unknown whether changes in the intracellular pH of this cell also lead to the insertion and retrieval of H^+-ATPase into and out of the basolateral membrane.

Recent studies of the CCD have shown that chronic changes in systemic acid-base balance lead to alterations in the proportion of intercalated cells that are of the H^+-secreting or HCO_3^--secreting subtype. Thus, with acidosis, there is a higher percentage of H^+-secreting cells, whereas the HCO_3^--secreting cell predominates in alkalotic animals. It has been postulated that this results from remodeling of the cell, converting one cell type to the other. The mechanisms involved in this process, however, are not known.

Alterations in the PCO_2 of the peritubular environment also lead to changes in collecting duct HCO_3^- transport. This has been clearly shown in the OMCD, where reducing the PCO_2 inhibits H^+ secretion. In contrast to the OMCD, changes in the PCO_2 do not appreciably alter HCO_3^- transport by the CCD. This probably reflects the fact that changes in PCO_2 would be expected to have equivalent effects on both the H^+-secreting and the HCO_3^--secreting intercalated cell subtypes. Thus, net transport by the tubule, which reflects the function of both cell types, would not be altered. The effect of PCO_2 on the cell is mediated through changes in intracellular pH, as described previously.

In the CCD, changes in the transepithelial voltage can influence H^+ secretion. The transepithelial voltage of this segment is normally oriented lumen negative as a result of the electrogenic reabsorption of Na^+ by the principal cell. Since the process of H^+ secretion also is electrogenic, changes in the transepithelial voltage will affect H^+ secretion. In particular, an increase in the lumen-negative transepithelial voltage will stimulate H^+ secretion, whereas a decrease in this voltage will inhibit H^+ secretion. Thus, any maneuver that alters Na^+ reabsorption by the CCD will, through a change in the transepithelial voltage, influence H^+ secretion. For example, when Na^+ reabsorption is inhibited, either by the addition of amiloride to the luminal fluid or by the inhibition of the Na,K-ATPase by ouabain, H^+ secretion also is inhibited. Since the process of HCO_3^- secretion is electroneutral, it is not influenced by changes in the transepithelial voltage.

The mineralocorticoid hormone aldosterone plays an important role in regulating collecting duct HCO_3^- transport. Aldosterone stimulates H^+ secretion by a direct effect on the cell and also indirectly by its effect on Na^+ transport. Aldosterone acts directly on the H^+-secreting intercalated cell subtype and stimulates H^+ secretion. The mechanism responsible for this stimulation has not been elucidated. Aldosterone also acts on the principal cell to stimulate Na^+ reabsorption. Because of this action, the lumen-negative transepithelial voltage (in the CCD) increases in magnitude. As noted previously, this will improve the electrochemical gradient for H^+ secretion across the apical membrane of the cell, and H^+ secretion will be increased. With chronic high-dose aldosterone treatment, a metabolic alkalosis develops. As a result of this alkalosis, there is an adaptive increase in HCO_3^- secretion by the CCD. This effect on the HCO_3^--secreting intercalated cell subtype does not appear to represent a direct action of aldosterone on the cell but rather a response to the systemic alkalosis.

β-Adrenergic agonists (e.g., isoproterenol) also have been shown to regulate HCO_3^- transport by the collecting duct. Specifically, they act on the CCD to stimulate HCO_3^- secretion. Although the cellular mechanism of action of these agonists is not known, it is mediated via the activation of adenylate cyclase. Cyclic AMP also stimulates H^+ secretion, but neither the mechanism of action nor the endogenous activator of the adenylate cyclase is known. Finally, prostaglandin E_2 has been shown to inhibit H^+ secretion.

SUMMARY

In this chapter, the process of urinary acidification has been examined at the cellular level. The reabsorption of the filtered load of HCO_3^- and the titration of urinary buffers (titratable acid and NH_4^+) occurs by the process of H^+ secretion. The precise cellular mechanisms by which this occurs differ among nephron segments. Despite these differences, the cellular process of H^+ secretion can be viewed as the extrusion of H^+ against an electrochemical gradient across the apical membrane and the movement of HCO_3^- across the basolateral membrane.

In the proximal tubule, approximately 80% of the filtered load of HCO_3^- is reabsorbed. This occurs without the development of large transepithelial pH gradients. The secretion of H^+ across the apical membrane occurs primarily via a Na/H antiporter. A H^+-ATPase also contributes to this process, but to a lesser degree.

An additional 10% of the filtered load of HCO_3^- is reabsorbed along the loop of Henle. This reabsorption of HCO_3^- occurs by a passive process of backtitration in the thin limbs and by active transport by the thick ascending limb. This latter process, like that in the proximal tubule, involves a Na/H antiporter in the apical membrane of the cell.

The remainder of the filtered load of HCO_3^- is reabsorbed in the distal convoluted tubule (6%) and the collecting duct (4%). It is these segments, particularly the collecting duct, in which large lumen-to-blood pH gradients are established. The secretion of H^+ in these segments occurs primarily via a H^+-ATPase located in the apical membrane. In addition, the collecting duct has a separate mechanism for the secretion of HCO_3^-.

REFERENCES

1. Alpern, R.J., Warnock, D.G., and Rector, F.C. Jr. (1986): Renal acidification mechanisms. In: *The Kidney*, 3rd ed., edited by B.M. Brenner and F.C. Rector Jr., pp. 206–249. W.B. Saunders, Philadelphia.

2. Capasso, G., Kinne, R., Malnic, G., and Giebisch, G. (1986): Renal bicarbonate reabsorption in the rat. I. Effects of hypokalemia and carbonic anhydrase. *J. Clin. Invest.*, 78: 1558–1567.

3. Cogan, M.G., and Alpern, R.J. (1984): Regulation of proximal bicarbonate reabsorption. *Am. J. Physiol.*, 247:F387–F395.

4. Good, D.W. (1985): Sodium-dependent bicarbonate absorption by cortical thick ascending limb of rat kidney. *Am. J. Physiol.*, 248:F821–F829.

5. Good, D.W., and Knepper, M.A. (1985): Ammonia transport in the mammalian kidney. *Am. J. Physiol.*, 248:F459–F471.

6. Jacobson, H.R. (1987): Ion transport in proximal nephron segments. In: *Contemporary Issues in Nephrology, Vol. 15: Modern Techniques of Ion Transport*, edited by B.M. Brenner and J.H. Stein, pp. 799–836. Churchill-Livingstone, New York.

7. Koeppen, B., Malnic, G., and Giebisch, G. (1985): Mechanism and regulation of renal tubular acidification. In: *The Kidney: Physiology and Pathophysiology*, edited by D.W. Seldin and G. Giebisch, pp. 1491–1525. Raven Press, New York.

8. Kunau, R.T. Jr., and Walker, K.A. (1987): Total CO_2 absorption in the distal tubule of the rat. *Am. J. Physiol.*, 252:F468–F473.

9. Levine, D.Z., and Jacobson, H.R. (1986): The regulation of renal acid secretion: New observations from studies of distal nephron segments. *Kidney Int.*, 29:1099–1109.

10. Lombard, W.E., Kokko, J.P., and Jacobson, H.R. (1983): Bicarbonate transport in cortical and outer medullary collecting tubules. *Am. J. Physiol.*, 244:F289–F296.

11. Maddox, D.A., Deen, W.M., and Gennari, F.J. (1987): Control of bicarbonate and fluid reabsorption in the proximal convoluted tubule. *Semin. Nephrol.*, 7:72–81.

12. Madsen, K.M., and Tisher, C.C. (1986): Structural-functional relationships along the distal nephron. *Am. J. Physiol.*, 250:F1–F15.

13. Rector, F.C. Jr. (1983): Sodium, bicarbonate, and chloride absorption by the proximal tubule. *Am. J. Physiol.*, 244:F461–F471.

14. Schuster, V.L., and Stokes, J.B. (1987): Cl transport by the cortical and outer medullary collecting duct. *Am. J. Physiol.*, 253:F203–F212.

15. Steinmetz, P.R. (1986): Cellular organization of urinary acidification. *Am. J. Physiol.*, 251: F173–F187.

The Regulation of Acid–Base Balance, edited
by Donald W. Seldin and Gerhard Giebisch,
Raven Press, Ltd., New York © 1989.

9

New Concepts in Renal Ammonium Excretion

David W. Good

Division of Nephrology, John Sealy Hospital, University of Texas Medical Branch, Galveston, Texas 77550-2778

Excretion of ammonium[1] by the kidney plays a critical role in the regulation of systemic acid-base balance. Changes in renal net acid excretion in response to both acid and alkali loads are due in large part to controlled changes in the rate of urinary ammonium excretion. Over the past few years, considerable progress has been made in our understanding of the transport processes involved in renal ammonium excretion. A number of new concepts have emerged that differ considerably from previously held views. The purpose of this chapter is to review briefly some of these new concepts and to fit them into an overall model of renal ammonium excretion.

---

[1]The term "total ammonia" is used to indicate the sum of NH_4^+ and NH_3. Because at least 98% of total ammonia in the kidney is in the form of NH_4^+, total ammonia transport is referred to generally as "ammonium transport," and total ammonia excretion is referred to as "ammonium excretion." When mechanisms of transport are discussed, the chemical formula NH_4^+ and NH_3 are used to indicate the specific chemical species that is being transported.

AMMONIUM EXCRETION AND REGULATION
OF ACID-BASE BALANCE 5,19–21

The role of renal ammonium excretion in systemic pH regulation is summarized in Fig. 1. Most of the ammonium excreted in the urine is produced in proximal tubule cells from amino acids, primarily glutamine. Glutamine is metabolized in the proximal tubules to form ammonium ions and bicarbonate. The bicarbonate formed is transported across the basolateral membrane to the extracellular fluid (ECF), where it restores blood bicarbonate that was neutralized by systemic metabolic acid production. The ammonium ions formed are secreted into the luminal fluid and are excreted in the urine. This ammonium excretion is important to acid-base regulation for the following reason. If the ammonium was not excreted and was returned to the ECF, it would be incorporated into urea in the liver according to the net reaction shown in Fig. 1. If this were to occur, the two hydrogen ions liberated during urea synthesis would neutralize the two bicarbonate ions produced from glutamine, and no net gain of bicarbonate would result. Thus, the ability of the kidney to excrete the ammonium ions results in the net addition of bicarbonate to the extracellular fluid. Note that this scheme differs considerably from the traditional view, which states incorrectly that NH_3 is produced and that NH_3 combines with and removes from the body a proton derived from carbonic acid. Instead, the proton is actually produced in the metabolism of glutamine, resulting in the formation of ammonium ions within the proximal tubule cell. Excretion of ammonium by the kidney then eliminates this proton from the body, thus contributing to the overall process of systemic acid-base regulation. Note that the "new bicarbonate" that is added to the ECF in association with ammonium excretion actually is produced in the proximal tubules from the metabolism of α-ketoglutarate formed from glutamine (Fig. 1).

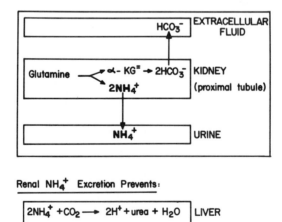

FIG. 1. Role of ammonium excretion by the kidney in regulation of systemic pH. See text for explanation.

The rate of renal ammonium production is regulated in response to changes in systemic acid-base status. Ammonium production by the proximal tubules increases markedly in response to acute and chronic metabolic acidosis and decreases during metabolic alkalosis. These changes in ammonium production contribute in a major way to the changes in urinary ammonium excretion that occur when acid-base balance is altered.

PATHWAYS OF AMMONIUM TRANSFER IN THE KIDNEY (18,20,21)

The general pathway for transfer of ammonium from its site of production in the proximal tubule to the final urine is summarized in Fig. 2. This pathway has been derived from micropuncture and microcatheterization studies in a number of different laboratories (see refs. 18 and 20 for review of these studies). The overall transfer process can be viewed as the net result of several distinct transport steps. First, ammonium is secreted into the lumen of the proximal tubule. Second, the ammonium is carried into the renal medulla in the loop of Henle, from which much of it is reabsorbed. Third, ammonium accumulates in the renal medulla, most likely as a result of loop ammonium absorption. Finally, ammonium is secreted into the collecting ducts for excretion in the final urine.

Traditionally, each of the transport steps listed in Fig. 2 has been explained in terms of the diffusion-trapping model, described for renal ammonium excretion by Pitts in 1948. According to this model, NH_3 diffuses from less acidic to more acidic compartments in the kidney, where it is protonated and trapped in the form of the less permeant ammonium ion. Two of the basic premises of the model are (1) that a state of diffusion equilibrium exists for NH_3, i.e., that diffusion of NH_3 occurs so rapidly that concentration differences between adjacent compartments cannot be present, and (2) that NH_4^+ that is formed in the luminal fluid becomes trapped in the urine because renal epithelia do not transport and are relatively impermeable to ammonium ions. It has now become evident, however, that when ammonium transport is examined at the single nephron level *in vivo* or in isolated tubule segments *in vitro*, the diffusion-trapping model is not adequate as a complete description of renal ammonium transport. In particular, recent studies have revealed that NH_3 concentration gradients do exist between adjacent structures in the kidney and that ammonium ions can be actively transported. These points are

TRANSPORT STEPS IN RENAL AMMONIUM EXCRETION

1. Secretion into proximal tubule lumen
2. Reabsorption from loop of Henle
3. Accumulation in renal medulla
4. Secretion into collecting ducts

FIG. 2. Pathways of ammonium transfer in the kidney.

illustrated in the following sections, which describe transport mechanisms involved in the transfer steps listed in Fig. 2.

Ammonium Secretion by the Proximal Tubule (5,7,11,14,15,18,20)

The first step in the transfer of ammonium to the urine is secretion by the proximal tubule. Based on the observations that all subsegments of the proximal tubule produced ammonium from glutamine *in vitro* and that delivery of ammonium to the end of the proximal convoluted tubule *in vivo* exceeded the filtered load, it had generally been assumed that ammonium secretion occurred uniformly along the proximal tubule. However, recent micropuncture studies have demonstrated that the ammonium transport rate varies considerably as a function of proximal tubule length (Fig. 3).

The panel on the left in Fig. 3 shows luminal total ammonia concentration plotted as a function of length along the proximal convoluted tubule of the rat *in vivo*. In rats with chronic metabolic acidosis as a result of administration of NH$_4$Cl for several days, total ammonia concentration increased along both the early and late segments of the proximal convoluted tubule. In contrast, in control rats, total ammonia concentration increased along the early portion of the proximal convoluted tubule but did not increase farther along the late proximal convoluted tubule. The corresponding total ammonia transport rates are shown on the right in Fig. 3. In the early proximal convoluted tubule, there was net secretion of ammonium in both control and acidotic rats, with

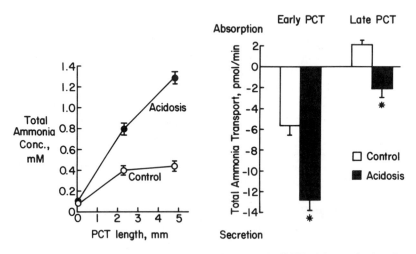

FIG. 3. Ammonium transport by proximal convoluted tubule (PCT) of the rat *in vivo*. Control rats drank tap water; rats with chronic metabolic acidosis drank NH$_4$Cl. **Left:** Total ammonia concentrations in luminal fluid as a function of tubule length. **Right:** Total ammonia transport rates for early and late PCT segments. (From ref. 20, plotted from data in ref. 7.)

the rate of ammonium secretion in the acidotic rats about twice that measured in controls. In contrast, in the late proximal convoluted tubule, there was small net absorption of ammonium in control rats, and this was converted to net ammonium secretion during metabolic acidosis. Note, however, that even in the acidotic rats, the rate of ammonium secretion along the early proximal segment was much greater than that along the late proximal segment. It is evident, therefore, that considerable axial heterogeneity exists for ammonium transport in the proximal convoluted tubule *in vivo*, with most or all of the ammonium secretion occurring along the early proximal segment.

To determine if this pattern of ammonium transport in the proximal convoluted tubule was consistent with the concept of diffusion equilibrium for NH_3 (i.e., if the NH_3 concentration was similar in the different proximal tubule segments), further studies were performed in which luminal pH and total ammonia concentrations were measured to calculate luminal NH_3 concentrations using the Henderson-Hasselbalch equation (Fig. 4).

The most striking finding was that in both control rats and in rats with chronic metabolic acidosis, the luminal NH_3 concentration in the early proximal convoluted tubule was approximately twice that in the late proximal convoluted tubule. This indicates clearly that NH_3 is not in diffusion equilibrium throughout the renal cortex and that the higher rate of ammonium secretion in the early proximal segment was associated with a higher luminal NH_3 concentration. In addition, the NH_3 concentration determined in the early proximal tubule was up to six times higher than the NH_3 concentration in arterial plasma. It was inferred from this finding that the early proximal NH_3 concentration also was above that in renal cortical plasma, indicating that a transepithelial NH_3 concentration gradient was present in the early proximal convoluted tubule. This indicates that ammonium is secreted from

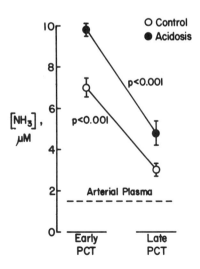

FIG. 4. NH_3 concentrations in early and late proximal convoluted tubule (PCT) of control rats and rats with chronic metabolic acidosis. Broken line is NH_3 concentration in arterial plasma. *p* values compare early versus late PCT. (Plotted from data in ref. 7).

the proximal tubule cell into the lumen at a faster rate than NH_3 can diffuse into the blood and that ammonium accumulates in the luminal fluid to higher concentrations than would be predicted by the diffusion-trapping model. Similar observations were made earlier by Nagami and Kurokawa in mouse proximal tubules *in vitro*. These findings are consistent with the presence of transport processes within the proximal convoluted tubule that preferentially secrete synthesized ammonium across the apical membrane into the tubule lumen rather than into the blood. The exact transport mechanisms involved in this preferential secretion have not yet been identified. One possibility would be direct secretion of NH_4^+ due to substitution of NH_4^+ for protons on the internal binding site of the apical membrane $Na^+ - H^+$ exchanger. The feasibility of sodium-ammonium exchange has been demonstrated by Kinsella and Aronson in brush border membrane vesicles from rabbit renal cortex, and results consistent with ammonium secretion by $Na^+ - NH_4^+$ exchange have been obtained by Nagami in the isolated, perfused proximal tubule of the mouse.

Reabsorption of Ammonium from the Loop of Henle (2–4,8,10,18,20)

Following preferential secretion by the proximal tubule, the next step in the transfer of ammonium to the urine is reabsorption from the loop of Henle. Micropuncture studies in rats have shown that approximately half of the ammonium delivered out of the proximal convoluted tubule subsequently is reabsorbed by the loop segment. Using the isolated, perfused tubule technique, Good et al. demonstrated that cortical and medullary thick ascending limbs from rats reabsorbed ammonium *in vitro* at rates sufficient to account for ammonium reabsorption measured between the late proximal and early distal tubule of superficial nephrons of rats *in vivo*. Ammonium absorption by the thick ascending limbs was due to the direct transport of ammonium ions from lumen to bath. This conclusion was based on the observation that thick ascending limbs absorb ammonium and bicarbonate simultaneously. Because both luminal pH and total ammonia concentration fell below their values in the bath, the ammonium absorption occurred against a large transepithelial concentration gradient for NH_3 and, thus, could not be explained by nonionic diffusion. Two possible mechanisms were proposed to explain the direct NH_4^+ absorption. First, NH_4^+ could be absorbed passively, driven by the lumen-positive transepithelial voltage. Second, the absorption could occur transcellularly by secondary active transport, possibly due to substitution of NH_4^+ for K^+ on the apical membrane sodium/potassium/chloride cotransport system. Recent studies designed to evaluate the relative importance of these two pathways have revealed that active transport of NH_4^+ is the predominant pathway for ammonium absorption in the medullary thick ascending limb (Fig. 5).

In these studies, medullary thick ascending limbs from rats were perfused *in*

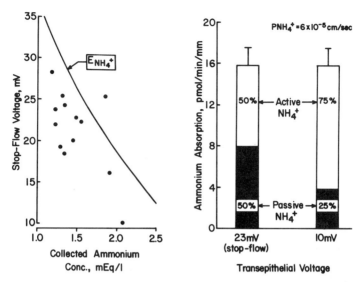

FIG. 5. Evidence for active NH_4^+ absorption in rat medullary thick ascending limb. **Left:** Relation between stop-flow voltage (the maximum transepithelial voltage generated by the tubules) and limiting luminal ammonium concentration (measured in collected luminal fluid at slow flow rates). Filled circles are values for single tubules; bath ammonium concentration was 4.0 mM. Curve for equilibrium voltage (E_{NH4}^+) was calculated from lumen to bath NH_4^+ concentration ratio using the Nernst equation. E_{NH4}^+ exceeded the measured stop-flow voltage, indicating that passive driving forces cannot account for the fall in lumen NH_4^+ concentration. **Right:** Proportion of NH_4^+ absorption accounted for by active and passive transport, assuming two values for transepithelial voltage. Passive NH_4^+ flux was calculated from NH_4^+ permeability ($P_{NH_4^+}$) and transepithelial voltage using the Goldman equation. Active NH_4^+ flux is the difference between measured net absorptive flux (total bar height) and passive NH_4^+ flux. (Plotted from data in ref. 4.)

vitro with 4 mM NH_4Cl in perfusate and peritubular bath. The first method used to test for active transport (Fig. 5, left) was to compare the limiting luminal NH_4^+ concentration with the maximum transepithelial voltage measured under stop-flow conditions. The solid line (labeled $E_{NH_4^+}$) is the theoretical transepithelial voltage, calculated from the Nernst equation, that would be required to account for the collected ammonium concentrations if diffusion was the only mechanism of transport. The results show that, in nearly every case, the measured stop-flow voltage was less lumen-positive than the calculated equilibrium voltage, indicating that the maximum transepithelial voltage generated by the tubules was not sufficient to account for the observed fall in luminal NH_4^+ concentration. It was concluded, therefore, that a portion of the ammonium absorption was transcellular and involved active transport.

To evaluate the relative contributions of active and passive transport to ammonium absorption, a second series of experiments was performed in which the NH_4^+ permeability and the transepithelial voltage were measured to calculate the rate of ammonium absorption that could occur by voltage-

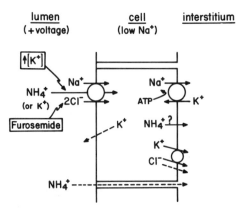

FIG. 6. Mechanisms of NH_4^+ absorption in thick ascending limb. Active absorption occurs by apical membrane $Na^+/NH_4^+/2\ Cl^-$ cotransport that is inhibited directly by luminal furosemide. Passive absorption is paracellular, driven by the lumen-positive transepithelial voltage. The mechanism of basolateral NH_4^+ exit is unknown. (From ref. 4.)

driven diffusion (Fig. 5, right). The total height of the bars indicates the measured rate of ammonium absorption. When the measured NH_4^+ permeability (6×10^{-5}cm/sec) and the stop-flow voltage were used to calculate the maximum possible passive flux, the results showed that, at most, 50% of the ammonium absorption could be accounted for by voltage-driven diffusion. Thus, at least half of the ammonium absorption was due to active transport. If a more reasonable estimate of transepithelial voltage of 10 mV is assumed for perfused tubules, similar calculations indicate that as much as 75% of total ammonia absorption could be accounted for by active transport of NH_4^+.

Ammonium transport pathways in the medullary thick ascending limb are summarized in Fig. 6. Most of the ammonium absorption occurs by active transport of NH_4^+. The observations in our laboratory that the ammonium absorption is inhibited by luminal furosemide and by high concentrations of luminal potassium, and the recent finding of Kinne et al. in rabbit medullary vesicles that ammonium and potassium compete for a common binding site on the furosemide-sensitive cotransport system support the view that the transcellular absorption is secondary active, mediated by apical membrane $Na^+/NH_4^+/2\ Cl^-$ cotransport. In addition to the active transport pathway, a minor fraction of NH_4^+ absorption also occurs by voltage-driven diffusion. This passive absorption most likely occurs via the paracellular pathway. These conclusions have been confirmed and extended by Garvin et al. in the medullary thick ascending limb of the rabbit.

Accumulation of Ammonium in the Renal Medulla: Countercurrent Multiplication (1,6,8,13,16,18,20)

Because the function of the nephron is to excrete ammonium, it is reasonable to ask how active absorption of NH_4^+ from the thick ascending limb could

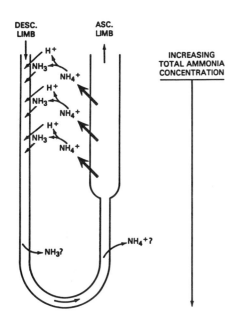

FIG. 7. Countercurrent multiplication of ammonium in the renal medulla. Active absorption of NH_4^+ by the thick ascending limb generates a transepithelial concentration difference that is multiplied by counterflow between the two limbs of the loop of Henle. The ammonium recycling results in a gradient for ammonium along the corticomedullary axis. The ammonium transport properties of the inner medullary loop segments are unknown. (From ref. 18.)

contribute to renal ammonium excretion. A possible answer to this question is illustrated in Fig. 7. Active absorption of NH_4^+ by the thick ascending limb would provide a single effect for countercurrent multiplication of ammonium, analogous to the single effect for sodium, in the renal medulla. The ammonium concentration difference generated across the thick ascending limb would be multiplied by countercurrent flow in the ascending and descending limbs, resulting in a gradient for ammonium along the medullary axis. The cycling pathway would be completed by secretion of ammonium into either the proximal straight tubule or the descending limb. The potential advantage of such a system would be the generation of high concentrations of ammonium in the medullary interstitium that would permit the excretion of high concentrations of ammonium in the final urine.

To assess the actual extent of ammonium accumulation in structures of the renal medulla, we performed experiments to determine NH_3 concentrations *in vivo* in kidneys of control rats and rats with chronic metabolic acidosis (Fig. 8). Total ammonia concentrations and pH values were measured to calculate NH_3 concentrations in arterial plasma, in the proximal convoluted tubule, at the bend of Henle's loop, and in the inner medullary collecting duct. In addition, NH_3 concentrations were determined in vasa recta plasma as an indirect measure of the ammonium content of medullary interstitial fluid. The concentrations of NH_3 in all structures of the medulla, including the vasa recta, were up to two orders of magnitude higher than values determined in arterial plasma and in the cortex in the proximal tubule. It was evident, therefore, that ammonium accumulates to high concentrations not only in the collecting ducts and loops of Henle but also in the medullary interstitium,

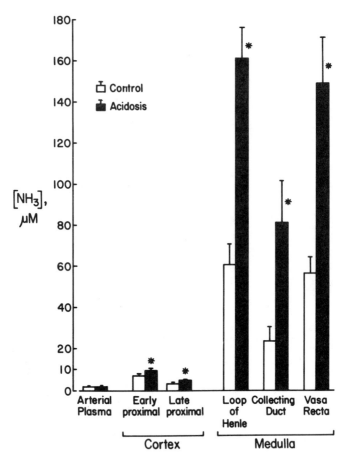

FIG. 8. NH_3 concentrations in cortex and medulla of rat kidney. Asterisks indicate NH_3 concentrations higher in rats with chronic metabolic acidosis than in controls. (Plotted from data in refs. 6,7.)

consistent with countercurrent trapping of ammonium in the renal medulla.

Ammonium Secretion by the Collecting Duct (3,4,6,9,12,17,18,20,22)

The remainder of this chapter addresses two questions: Does the process of medullary ammonium accumulation actually contribute to renal ammonium excretion? Are there conditions that might influence ammonium excretion by affecting the countercurrent process? Both of these issues bear directly on the final step in the ammonium transfer process, namely, secretion of ammonium into the collecting ducts. It had been hypothesized in the late 1960s by Pitts,

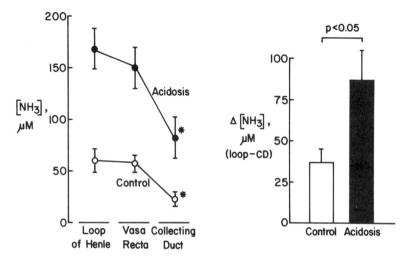

FIG. 9. NH_3 concentration gradients in inner medulla of control rats and rats with chronic metabolic acidosis. **Left:** NH_3 concentrations in loop of Henle, vasa recta, and inner medullary collecting duct. Asterisks indicate NH_3 concentration in collecting duct less than that in loop. **Right:** Mean NH_3 concentration difference between loop of Henle and inner medullary collecting duct. p value indicates that gradient was increased in acidotic rats compared with controls. (Plotted from data in ref. 6.)

Giebisch, Gottschalk, Robinson, and others that ammonium absorbed from the loops of Henle could be transferred directly to the collecting ducts in the renal medulla. Because ammonium secretion by the collecting ducts had been shown to occur predominantly by diffusion of NH_3, we used micropuncture techniques to examine NH_3 concentration gradients within the medulla of the rat (Fig. 9).

Figure 9, left, compares NH_3 concentrations determined in the loop of Henle, the vasa recta, and the inner medullary collecting duct. In both control rats and rats with chronic metabolic acidosis, the NH_3 concentration at the bend of Henle's loop did not differ from that in the vasa recta but was significantly greater than that in the inner medullary collecting duct. Thus, NH_3 was not in diffusion equilibrium, and a concentration gradient favoring diffusion of NH_3 from the loop of Henle to the collecting duct was present in the inner medulla of the rat. The difference in NH_3 concentration between the loop and collecting duct was substantially increased during metabolic acidosis (Fig. 9, right). In addition, we observed, as have other investigators, that the rate of entry of ammonium into the inner medullary collecting duct was increased in the acidotic rats. Thus, the increase in the NH_3 concentration gradient was associated with an increase in collecting duct ammonium secretion.

Of particular interest was the nature of the effect of metabolic acidosis on the NH_3 concentration gradient. According to the traditional view, an increase in ammonium secretion in acidosis was thought to involve a decrease in collecting duct NH_3 concentration because of increased luminal acidification converting NH_3 to NH_4^+. The results in Fig. 9 show, however, that the NH_3 concentration in the inner medullary collecting duct actually was higher in the acidotic rats than in controls. The NH_3 concentration gradient increased because the NH_3 concentration in the loop of Henle and medullary interstitium (i.e., vasa recta) increased more than the NH_3 concentration in the collecting duct. This indicates that the processes involved in countercurrent multiplication of ammonium, which raise interstitial NH_3 concentration above that in the medullary collecting ducts, play an important role in promoting increased ammonium excretion during chronic metabolic acidosis. The high interstitial NH_3 concentrations due to countercurrent multiplication act in conjunction with luminal acidification to generate the transepithelial NH_3 concentration gradient that drives medullary collecting duct ammonium secretion.

In addition to acidosis, another important factor that influences renal ammonium excretion is systemic potassium balance. In general, potassium depletion stimulates renal ammonium excretion, and potassium excess (hyperkalemia) reduces ammonium excretion. Traditionally, these effects have been attributed to the well-known effects of potassium on proximal tubule ammonium production. However, an additional possibility not considered previously is that potassium could influence ammonium excretion by directly affecting renal tubule ammonium transport. Recently, a direct effect of potassium concentration on ammonium transport was demonstrated in the isolated, perfused medullary thick ascending limb of the rat (Fig. 10). The potassium concentrations studied—4 and 24 mM—represent the physiologic range of values expected to surround this segment *in vivo*. The results show that when potassium concentration in the lumen and peritubular bath was increased, the ammonium absorption rate was inhibited by 50%. Further studies revealed

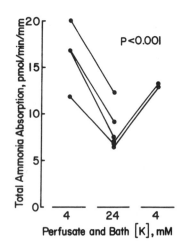

FIG. 10. Effect of increasing potassium concentration on ammonium absorption by the isolated, perfused medullary thick ascending limb of the rat. (From ref. 3.)

that the increase in potassium concentration inhibited specifically the active component of NH_4^+ absorption, most likely because of competition between NH_4^+ and K^+ for a common site on the apical membrane $Na^+/K^+/2\ Cl^-$ cotransport system (Fig. 6). It is possible, therefore, that changes in systemic potassium balance could influence ammonium excretion by directly affecting thick ascending limb ammonium absorption and altering countercurrent multiplication of ammonium in the renal medulla. For example, conditions that increase medullary potassium levels could reduce ammonium excretion by inhibiting thick ascending limb ammonium absorption and impairing the transfer of ammonium from the loops of Henle to the medullary collecting ducts.

SUMMARY

The control of renal ammonium excretion plays a crucial role in the regulation of systemic acid-base balance. Excretion of ammonium is regulated by control of ammonium production in cells of the proximal tubule and by regulation of the tubule transport processes that transfer ammonium from its site of production in the proximal tubule to the final urine. This transfer process can be viewed as the net result of several distinct steps.

1. Ammonium is secreted by the proximal tubule. This secretion occurs predominantly along the early portion of the proximal convoluted tubule and involves specialized mechanisms for preferential secretion of ammonium into the luminal fluid.
2. Ammonium is reabsorbed from the loop of Henle, largely as a result of active absorption of NH_4^+ from the thick ascending limb. The active NH_4^+ absorption is mediated by apical membrane $Na^+/NH_4^+/2\ Cl^-$ cotransport.
3. Thick ascending limb ammonium absorption results in accumulation of ammonium to high concentrations in the renal medulla by countercurrent multiplication.
4. Countercurrent multiplication generates a transepithelial concentration gradient for NH_3 that favors secretion of ammonium into the medullary collecting ducts.

Both metabolic acidosis and changes in systemic potassium balance may influence ammonium excretion by affecting countercurrent multiplication of ammonium and altering transfer of ammonium from the loops of Henle to the medullary collecting ducts.

ACKNOWLEDGMENTS

The laboratory work was supported by grants from the National Institutes of Health and the American Heart Association and by funds contributed in part by the American Heart Association, Texas Affiliate, Inc. D.W. Good is the recipient of a National Institutes of Health Research Career Development Award.

REFERENCES

1. Garvin, J. L., Burg, M. B., and Knepper, M. A. (1987); NH_3 and NH_4^+ transport by rabbit renal proximal straight tubules. *Am. J. Physiol.*, 252:F232–F239.
2. Garvin, J. L., Burg, M. B., and Knepper, M. A. (1988): Active NH_4^+ absorption by the thick ascending limb. *Am. J. Physiol.*, 255:F57–F65.
3. Good, D. W. (1987): Effects of potassium on ammonia transport by medullary thick ascending limb of the rat. *J. Clin. Invest.*, 80:1358–1365.
4. Good, D. W. (1988): Active absorption of NH_4^+ by rat medullary thick ascending limb: Inhibition by potassium. *Am. J. Physiol.*, 255:F78–F87.
5. Good, D. W., and Burg, M. B. (1984): Ammonia production by individual segments of the rat nephron. *J. Clin. Invest.*, 73:602–610.
6. Good, D. W., Caflisch, C. R., and DuBose, Jr., T. D. (1987): Transepithelial ammonia concentration gradients in inner medulla of the rat. *Am. J. Physiol.*, 252:F491–F500.
7. Good, D. W., and DuBose, Jr., T. D., (1987): Ammonia transport by early and late proximal convoluted tubule of the rat. *J. Clin. Invest.*, 79:684–691.
8. Good, D. W., Knepper, M. A., and Burg, M. B. (1984): Ammonia and bicarbonate transport by thick ascending limb of rat kidney. *Am. J. Physiol.*, 247:F35–F44.
9. Hamm, L. L., Trigg, D., Martin, D., Gillespie, C., and Buerkert, J. (1985): Transport of ammonia in the rabbit cortical collecting tubule. *J. Clin. Invest.*, 75:478–485.
10. Kinne, R., Kinne-Saffran, E., Schutz, H., and Scholermann, B. (1986): Ammonium transport in medullary thick ascending limb of rabbit kidney: Involvement of the Na^+,K^+,Cl^--cotransporter *J. Membrane Biol.*, 94:279–284.
11. Kinsella, J. L., Aronson, P. S. (1980): Properties of the $Na^+ - H^+$ exchanger in renal microvillus membrane vesicles. *Am. J. Physiol.*, 238: F461–F469.
12. Knepper, M. A., Good, D. W., and Burg, M. B. (1985): Ammonia and bicarbonate transport by rat cortical collecting ducts perfused *in vitro*. *Am. J. Physiol.*, 249:F870–F877.
13. Kurtz, I., Star, R., Balaban, R. S., Garvin, J. L., and Knepper, M.A. (1986): Spontaneous luminal disequilibrium pH in S_3 proximal tubules. Role in ammonia and bicarbonate transport. *J. Clin. Invest.*, 78:989–996.
14. Nagami, G. T. (1988): Luminal secretion of ammonia in the mouse proximal tubule perfused *in vitro*. J. Clin. Invest., 81:159–164.
15. Nagami, G. T., and Kurokawa, K. (1985): Regulation of ammonia production by mouse proximal tubules perfused *in vitro*. Effect of luminal perfusion. *J. Clin. Invest.*, 75:844–849.
16. Robinson, R. R., and Owen, E. E. (1965): Intrarenal distribution of ammonia during diuresis and antidiuresis. *Am. J. Physiol.*, 208: 1129–1134.
17. Star, R. A., Burg, M. B., and Knepper, M. A. (1987): Luminal disequilibrium pH and ammonia transport in outer medullary collecting duct. *Am. J. Physiol.*, 252:F1148–F1157.

General Review Articles

18. Good, D. W., and Knepper, M. A. (1985): Ammonia transport in the mammalian kidney. *Am. J. Physiol.*, 248:F459–F471.
19. Halperin, M. L., and Jungas, R. L. (1983): Metabolic production and renal disposal of hydrogen ions. *Kidney Int.*, 24:709–713.

20. Knepper, M. A., Packer, R., and Good, D. W. (1988): Ammonium transport in the kidney. *Physiol. Rev. (in press)*.
21. Silbernagl, S., and Scheller, D. (1986): Formation and excretion of NH_3–NH_4^+. New aspects of an old problem. *Klin. Wochenschr.*, 64:862–870.
22. Tannen, R. L. (1987): Effect of potassium on renal acidification and acid-base homeostasis. *Semin. Nephrol.*, 7:263–273.

The Regulation of Acid–Base Balance, edited
by Donald W. Seldin and Gerhard Giebisch,
Raven Press, Ltd., New York © 1989.

10

Overall Acid-Base Regulation by the Kidney

Sandra Sabatini and Neil A. Kurtzman

*Departments of Internal Medicine and Physiology, Texas Tech University
Health Sciences Center, Lubbock, Texas 79430*

STATEMENT OF THE PROBLEM

The regulation of acid-base balance is of critical importance to the overall homeostasis of the organism. The kidney plays the major role in the modulation of acid-base balance. Because of the high acid ash content of virtually all western diets, the kidney is faced with the responsibility of excreting approximately 70 to 100 mEq of nonvolatile acid per day. The problem may be summarized as follows:

$$HR + NaHCO_3 \rightarrow NaR + H_2O + CO_2$$
$$(\simeq 100 \text{ mEq/day}) \qquad (\simeq 100 \text{ mEq/day})$$

TABLE 1. *Sources of nonvolatile acids in humans*

Source	Amount	Nonvolatile acid	Comments
Diet	$\simeq$ 30 mEq/day	Phosphoproteins, sulfur-containing amino acids, chloride salts	∞ to dietary intake ↑ with hyperalimentation
Products of intermediary metabolism	$\simeq$ 30 mEq/day	Ketoacids Lactic acid	↑ in diabetes, alcoholism, starvation ↑ in hepatic failure, shock (tissue under-perfusion)
Stool loss	$\simeq$ 30 mEq/day	Loss of HCO_3 (or base equivalent)	↑ in diarrheal states

The 100 mEq of nonvolatile acid (HR) will be buffered by bicarbonate to form the sodium salt of the acid (NaR) plus CO_2 and water. Thus, 100 mEq of acid production results in the decomposition of 100 mEq of bicarbonate. The kidney must reverse this process daily by excreting precisely 100 mEq of acid, and regenerating exactly 100 mEq of bicarbonate. Failure to perform this task will result in renal acidosis; excretion of too much acid will generate metabolic alkalosis.

Not only must the kidney excrete 100 mEq of acid; it must also reabsorb all the filtered bicarbonate. For example, the excretion of 100 mEq of acid per day and 100 mEq of bicarbonate per day would result in a net acid excretion of zero.

Net acid excretion = Urinary acid excretion − urinary bicarbonate excretion

Thus, the role of the kidney in preserving acid-base homeostasis consists of reclaiming virtually all the filtered bicarbonate while titrating urinary buffers to result in the excretion of precisely the amount of nonvolatile acid liberated into the plasma.

The nonvolatile acids produced daily are derived from three sources and approximate 1 mEq/kg/day: diet, intermediary metabolism, and stool bicarbonate loss (Table 1). Although the example gives $NaHCO_3$ as the only buffer, HR is buffered by a host of extracellular and intracellular buffers, the most important of which are bicarbonate and hemoglobin.

Bicarbonate Reclamation and Bicarbonate Regeneration

The proximal tubule reabsorbs 85 to 90% of the filtered bicarbonate, $\simeq$4,500 mEq/day (Fig. 1). This process, although incompletely understood, is thought to occur primarily via a Na^+/H^+ antiporter located in or at the brush border membrane (Table 2). Na ions are reabsorbed, protons are secreted into the tubular lumen, and bicarbonate is returned to the blood (HCO_3 reclamation,

Proximal Tubule

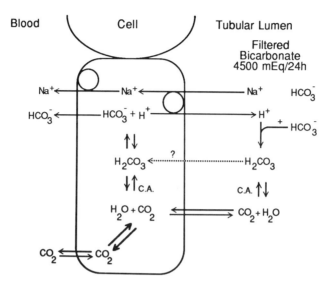

FIG. 1. Hydrogen ion secretion by the proximal tubule. Carbonic anhydrase (CA) is found on the brush border of the proximal tubular cells as well as inside the cell. Not shown is the electrogenic H^+-ATPase, which is probably localized at the brush border membrane (*see Fig. 3*). The pH at the end of the proximal tubule is $\approx$ 6.8 to 7.0.

4,500 mEq/day). This series of events occurs after the hydration of HCO_3 to carbonic acid and CO_2 under the influence of the enzyme carbonic anhydrase (CA). In the proximal tubule, CA is located both on the luminal membrane and inside the cell. It is not yet known if electrogenic proton secretion or reabsorption of the bicarbonate anion *per se* occurs in the proximal tubule. Recent evidence suggests that an electrogenic proton-translocating ATPase is present in the proximal tubule, although its role in urinary acidification at this site is not yet clear.

Figure 2 shows the relationship of the reabsorption of bicarbonate and various solutes as filtrate moves farther away from the glomerulus (0 point). A tubular fluid/plasma concentration (TF/P) ratio of 1 equals isotonicity; TF/P values < 1 indicate reabsorption from the proximal tubule (inulin TF/P is a marker of water reabsorption). At approximately one-fourth the length of the proximal tubule, 50% of the filtered bicarbonate has been reabsorbed. By the end of the proximal tubule, virtually all the filtered bicarbonate has been reabsorbed (80–90%). The proximal tubule is a high capacitance system, capable of moving large quantities of solute, but it generates a small pH gradient (i.e., the pH of the fluid leaving the proximal tubule is $\approx$6.8–7.0, and the osmolality is 300 mOsm/kg). The many factors that control HCO_3 reabsorption by the proximal tubule are discussed in detail in succeeding sections of this chapter.

TABLE 2. *Acid-base function of the nephron and the bladder*

Nephron segment	Primary acid-base transport capability
Proximal tubule	HCO_3 reabsorption[a]; H^+ secretion
Thin limbs	0
Thick ascending limb	
Medullary	HCO_3 reabsorption[b]; H^+ secretion
Cortical	HCO_3 reabsorption[b]; H^+ secretion
Collecting duct	
Cortical	H^+ secretion
Medullary	H^+ secretion
Papillary	(?) H^+ secretion
Bladder	0

[a]HCO_3 reabsorption is thought to occur via a Na^+/H^+ antiporter located at the luminal membrane; H^+ secretion is thought to occur via an electrogenic H^+-ATPase located at the luminal membrane.
[b]Only in some species under carefully controlled circumstances; overall importance not yet known. It is not known if primary HCO_3 reabsorption occurs in the nephron.

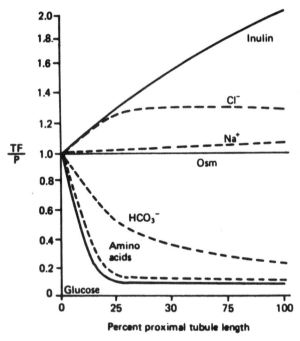

FIG. 2. Solute reabsorption relative to length of the proximal tubule. TF/P (tubular fluid/ plasma concentration ratio) reflects solute concentration relative to water. TF/P < 1 = reabsorption. [From ref. 7.]

It is obvious that bicarbonate reabsorption alone (i.e., HCO_3 reclamation), regardless of how complete, cannot preserve normal acid-base homeostasis. Consequently, the kidney has a second completely separate and continual process for synthesizing new bicarbonate (i.e., HCO_3 regeneration). Bicarbonate regeneration is largely a function of the distal nephron (i.e., the collecting duct). As shown in Fig. 3, the amount of bicarbonate regenerated daily (70–100 mEq) is far less than the amount reclaimed by the proximal tubule (daily filtered HCO_3 ≈4,500 mEq/day). Despite the small absolute amount, the regenerated bicarbonate is the final regulator responsible for perfect acid-base homeostasis.

The mechanisms of distal nephron acidification are quite different from those of the proximal tubule (Table 2). Most of the distal nephron acidification is performed by the collecting duct (in some species, HCO_3 reabsorption has been noted in thick ascending limb, although its physiologic role is unknown). The luminal membrane of the collecting duct epithelium contains an electrogenic proton pump (Fig. 3), a proton-translocating ATPase that is capable of transporting hydrogen from the cell interior against an electrochemical gradient into the tubular lumen. The collecting duct can generate very large pH gradients (≈3 pH units), but it is a low capacitance system. Sodium reabsorp-

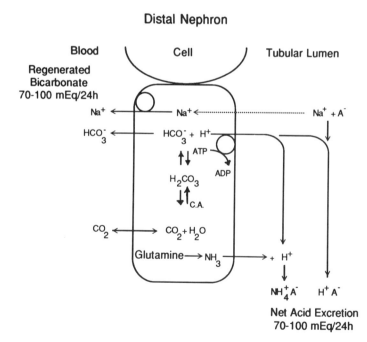

Distal Nephron

FIG. 3. Hydrogen ion secretion by the distal nephron. Carbonic anhydrase (CA) is present only inside the cell. An electrogenic H^+-ATPase is depicted at the luminal membrane. pH of the tubular fluid may be as low as pH 4.5 (A) anion (phosphate, sulfate, urate).

tion, although it occurs, is completely separate from proton secretion in the cortical collecting duct. Sodium reabsorption does not occur in the medullary collecting duct (at least in the best studied animal, the rabbit) but proton secretion does. In collecting duct cells, CA activity can be demonstrated histochemically only inside the cells (cortical > medullary > papillary collecting duct); no enzyme activity appears at the luminal membrane as it does in the proximal tubule.

Cells lining the collecting duct are strikingly different as regards surface morphology (scanning microscopy), intracellular composition (transmission electron microscopy), and biochemistry. Two major cell types are present (Table 3): the principal cell and the intercalated cell. These mammalian cells have exact counterparts in amphibian and reptilian membranes. In turtle bladder, for example, the granular cell is analogous to the principal cell of mammals; the mitochondria-rich cell is equivalent to the mammalian inter-calated cell. These descriptively named cells of turtle bladder membrane subserve quite different cellular functions. The granular cell of turtle bladder contains quantities of Na,K ATPase far in excess of that needed for cell volume regulation. It is thought, although not proven, that the granular cell (and, by inference, the mammalian principal cell) is the sodium-transporting cell. The mitochondria-rich cell of turtle bladder contains a proton pump (H^+-ATPase), numerous mitochondria, abundant CA, and microplicae on its luminal surface. This cell almost certainly is the hydrogen secretory cell of turtle bladder. By analogy, therefore, the intercalated cell of the mammalian collecting duct is probably the proton secretory cell. In turtle bladder, 30% of the surface epithelial cells are mitochondria-rich cells.

In mammalian nephron, the percentage of intercalated cells (the mitochon-dria-rich cell equivalent) varies depending on nephron site (Table 3). In corti-cal collecting duct, a site capable of high rates of acidification, 30% of the cells are intercalated cells; medullary collecting duct has fewer intercalated cells, and papillary collecting duct has virtually none. In isolated collecting tubule segments of rat, H^+-ATPase activity recently has been measured. The corti-cal, medullary, and papillary collecting tubule segments, dissected before entry into the ducts of Bellini, contain H^+-ATPase activity of approximately equivalent proportions; the papillary collecting duct, dissected after entry into the ducts of Bellini, contains very little H^+-ATPase activity. These data provide reasonably good correlative evidence of collecting tubule structure and function. Some discrepancies do exist, however, and these await further elucidation.

Net Acid Excretion

Under normal conditions, urine has the composition shown in Table 4. Urine pH, although variable in humans, generally is acidic. Ammonia and

TABLE 3. *Transport function (Na^+ and H^+), morphology, and enzymatic activity of the mammalian collecting duct*

Anatomic site	Transport function[a]			Morphology		Enzyme activity[b]		
	Na^+ reabsorption	H^+ secretion	HCO_3^- secretion	% Intercalated cells[c]	% Principal cells[d]	Na,K-ATPase	H-ATPase	CA[e]
Cortical collecting duct	+++	+++	++	≈30	70	+++	+++	++
Medullary collecting duct	+/0	++++	?	<10	>90	+++	+++	+
Papillary collecting duct	+++	+	?	0	100	+	+	±

[a]Summarized from micropuncture, microperfusion, and isolated tubule studies.
[b]Summarized from isolated tubule studies.
[c]Intercalated cells are the mammalian equivalent of turtle bladder mitochondrial-rich cells (the proton secretory cell). In general, the turtle bladder membrane transports Na^+ and H^+ in a manner similar to that of the mammalian collecting duct. The turtle bladder generates large mucosal pH gradients in response to aldosterone. The bladder does not respond to arginine vasopressin.
[d]Principal cells are the mammalian equivalent of turtle bladder granular cell (the sodium reabsorptive cell).
[e](CA) carbonic anhydrase enzyme activity found histochemically.

TABLE 4. *Normal acid-base values of blood and urine[a] in humans*

Body fluid	Value
Blood	
Plasma $[HCO_3^-]$	24–26 mEq/liter
Pa_{CO_2}	39–43 mm Hg
Plasma $[H^+]$	39–42 nEq/liter
pH	7.38–7.41
Urine	
FE_{Na}^+	1–2%
$FE_{HCO_3^-}$	0.3%
Pa_{CO_2}	30–40 mm Hg
pH	6.1 (minimum urine pH = 4.5)
Tubular reabsorption of phosphate (TRP)[b]	78–94%
NH_4^+	≈50 mEq/day
Titratable acid[c]	≈ 40 mEq/day
Net acid excretion (NAE)	90–100 mEq/day

[a](FE) fractional excretion.
[b]TRP = 100 − (clearance of phosphate/clearance of creatinine).
[c]Urine phosphate is only one component of titratable acid.

phosphate are the two primary urinary buffers. Other buffers are present in the urine, although they contribute to titratable acid buffering only under special circumstances (e.g., urate, creatinine, sulfate, butyrate). These buffers accept protons varying with their dissociation constant (pK_a), and assume greater (or lesser) roles depending on urine pH. Note that bicarbonate does not appear in the urine in significant quantities; the fractional excretion (FE) of HCO_3^- in humans is often ≈0.3% or less. Net acid excretion (NAE) by the kidney is defined as

$$NAE + \left(\begin{array}{c} \text{ammonium} \\ \text{excretion} \end{array} + \begin{array}{c} \text{titratable acid} \\ \text{excretion} \end{array} \right) - \text{urine } HCO_3 \text{ excretion}$$

To remain in steady state, NAE must be equivalent to daily acid production. If this does not occur, one of the acid-base disorders develops. As stated, the mechanisms for acidification in the proximal and distal nephron are different. The factors controlling acidification in these two parts of the nephron are different as well. If any of the controlling factors of proximal or distal acidification are disrupted, however, an acid-base abnormality occurs. These abnormalities are of renal origin and hence are termed "metabolic" acid-base disorders. For example, proximal renal tubular acidosis is the consequence of a massive bicarbonate leak occurring alone or in combination with glucose or

$$^1 FE_{HCO_3}\% = \frac{\text{Urine } HCO_3/\text{plasma creatinine}}{\text{Plasma } HCO_3/\text{urine creatinine}} \times 100$$

amino acids (Fanconi syndrome). Examination of Fig. 2 predicts the abnormalities expected if proximal tubular function is disrupted. If the abnormality occurs in the distal nephron and new bicarbonate is generated in excess, e.g., metabolic alkalosis occurs. Aldosterone excess, an often seen clinical condition, stimulates proton secretion in the collecting duct, and thus, predisposes to metabolic alkalosis. Aldosterone deficiency, on the other hand, results in metabolic acidosis, and clinically is a variety of the distal renal tubular acidoses.

CONTROL OF BICARBONATE REABSORPTION (MAJOR FACTORS)

A summary of factors that control proximal bicarbonate reabsorption is shown in Table 5.

TABLE 5. *Factors affecting HCO_3 reabsorption by the proximal renal tubular cell*

Maneuver	HCO_3 reabsorption	Mechanism/Comment
Volume contraction	↑ FR[a]	↓ GFR[b], ↓ filtered load[c], direct tubular effect
Potassium depletion	↑	↓ Cell pH, ± volume contraction, ↓ GFR
Hypercapnia (↑ P_{CO_2})	↑	↓ Cell pH, probably direct effect of pH to stimulate Na^+/H^+ antiporter of the brush border membrane, minor effect of ↓ GFR
Carbonic anhydrase inhibition	↓	e.g., acetazolamide, > HCO_3 transport by juxtamedullary nephrons
Glucose loading	↑	?
Parathyroid hormone	↓	? Direct effect on cystosolic Ca^{2+} similar to the Ca^{2+} ionophore; no effect on GFR
Vitamin D	↑	? ↑ Na^+/H^+ antiporter of brush border membrane
Hypercalcemia	↑ FR	Probably solely via ↓ GFR
Phosphate depletion	↓	↑ Cell pH
Chloride depletion	↑ FR	? ↓ GFR, hypokalemia is always present in this model, no effect independent of volume and potassium
Aldosterone	No effect	? Not known if the hormone ↑ H^+-ATPase activity in the proximal tubule
Glucocorticoids	↑ (↔ FR)	↑ Na^+/H^+ antiporter of brush border membrane, ↑ GFR
Chronic Renal Failure	↑ FR	↑ HCO_3 reabsorption per nephron; if nephron loss of sufficient magnitude, metabolic acidosis results

[a](FR) fractional reabsorption.
[b](GFR) glomerular filtration rate.
[c]Filtered load = GFR (ml/min) × plasma concentration of HCO_3 (mEq/liter).

Effective Arterial Blood Volume

The concept of effective arterial blood volume was introduced by Peters et al. to explain why the kidney responds in a similar fashion (by increasing NaCl reabsorption) after the development of a nonedema-forming volume contracted state (i.e., hemorrhagic shock) or an edematous state (i.e., congestive heart failure). The term as used is different from "blood volume," a volume measurable by a variety of techniques. Effective arterial blood volume is not a measurable volume but denotes the effective filling of the arterial circulation; it is equivalent to organ perfusion.

In all species tested, a decrease in arterial volume (either absolute or effective) results in an increase in bicarbonate reabsorption by the proximal renal tubule. Laboratory methods documenting this include classic clearance techniques with bicarbonate titration in humans, dogs, and rats and micropuncture or microperfusion techniques (dogs, rats) in which glass micropipettes are placed in the proximal tubular lumen and associated peritubular capillary.

A representative bicarbonate titration curve is shown in Fig. 4. Note that as the plasma HCO_3 is increased, bicarbonate reabsorption by the kidney is complete (i.e., no bicarbonate appears in the urine) until the plasma concentration is ≈ 26 mEq/liter (normal plasma $HCO_3 \cong 24$ mEq/liter). Thereafter, bicarbonate reabsorption plateaus (HCO_3 Tm). At this point, bicarbonate begins to appear in the urine. If volume is massively expanded (NaCl or $NaHCO_3$ infusion), bicarbonate reabsorption falls markedly (Fig. 4, lower curve). If volume is contracted, either absolutely as in hemorrhagic shock or

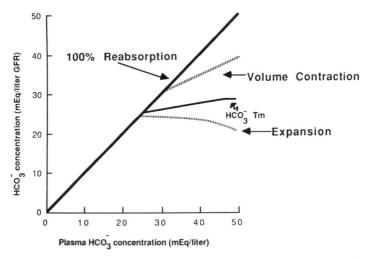

FIG. 4. Theoretical relationship of plasma bicarbonate to bicarbonate reabsorption under normal, contracted, and expanded conditions. (HCO_3^-Tm) tubular maximum for HCO_3 reabsorption. [From ref. 4.]

effectively as in congestive heart failure, bicarbonate reabsorption increases markedly (Fig. 4, upper curve), approaching the line of 100% reabsorption.

Volume is the most potent stimulus regulating bicarbonate reabsorption. In some manner, volume alters the activity of the Na^+/H^+ antiporter located in the brush border of the proximal tubule. It is not known if the activity of the proton-translocating ATPase changes in response to volume.

Plasma Chloride

It is practically impossible to study the role of chloride on bicarbonate reabsorption without inducing a change in the state of arterial volume or the plasma potassium concentration. Chloride is the primary extracellular anion (normal plasma Cl = 100 mEq/liter), and its movement transcellularly can be accounted for completely by the Nernst equation. Therefore, changes in chloride alone must be associated with significant changes in some other ions.

In the whole animal or human, one way the role of chloride can be studied is in the volume contracted state. If animals are placed on a normal diet and volume contracted, bicarbonate reabsorption by the proximal tubule increases, and plasma bicarbonate rises. If chloride is then removed from the diet by peritoneal dialysis, the rise in plasma bicarbonate is sustained. Whole kidney GFR and juxtamedullary single nephron GFR fall markedly. The decrease in GFR after chloride deprivation is greater than is seen in the volume contracted state alone. These observations suggest that chloride affects proximal bicarbonate reabsorption solely by affecting GFR. More recent studies using this model show that if GFR is kept constant, chloride replacement alone corrects the metabolic alkalosis. This was attributed to a distal effect. These animals, however, were hypokalemic, and that influence on proximal bicarbonate reabsorption cannot be ignored. The correction of metabolic alkalosis was associated with an increase in plasma potassium. Removal of chloride from the perfusion solution in rabbit proximal tubule has no effect on acidification as measured by CO_2 flux. Whether chloride directly alters the Na^+/H^+ antiporter of the brush border membrane, the Cl^-/HCO_3^- antiporter of the brush border, membrane CA activity, or H^+-ATPase activity is as yet unknown.

Glomerular Filtration Rate and Filtered Load of Bicarbonate

In 1946, Pitts et al. first demonstrated that bicarbonate reabsorption varied in proportion with changes in GFR. These investigators also noted that when the filtered load of bicarbonate was very low (filtered load = plasma HCO_3 concentration in mEq/liter $\times$ GFR in liters/day), bicarbonate reabsorption was complete, and no bicarbonate appeared in the urine. If plasma bicarbonate was increased to ≈26 mEq/liter, bicarbonate reabsorption reached a plateau, and bicarbonate began to appear in the urine. Pitts et al. called this

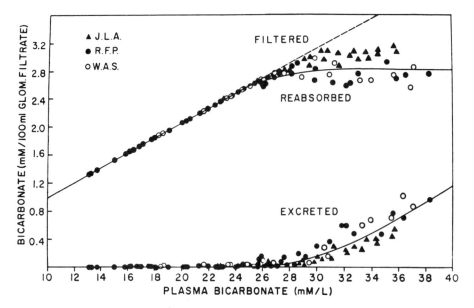

FIG. 5. Filtration, reabsorption, and excretion of bicarbonate as a function of plasma concentration in normal man. [From ref. 11.]

the "Tm for bicarbonate." In their original data (Fig. 5), it is clear that this value (i.e., the plateau) is not a true Tm, because to demonstrate its presence, the data had to be expressed as reabsorption per unit GFR rather than reabsorption per unit of time.

It has been suggested that the filtered load of bicarbonate is the major determinant of bicarbonate excretion; however, several conflicting pieces of information exist. In whole animals using clearance techniques, bicarbonate reabsorption increases as the filtered load increases, but it is affected by plasma bicarbonate, PCO_2, or GFR. In some micropuncture studies, bicarbonate reabsorption increased as filtered load increased in both normal and acidotic rats; moreover, volume expansion had no effect on proximal bicarbonate reabsorption separate from the effect of filtered load. In isolated tubule studies *in vitro*, volume expansion, induced by changes in bath protein concentration, decreased sodium chloride transport but had no effect on bicarbonate transport. This last observation is in sharp contrast to a body of earlier work in whole animals showing that volume expansion corrects metabolic alkalosis when GFR and filtered load are maintained constant by aortic constriction. These markedly contrasting studies await final elucidation.

Arterial Carbon Dioxide Tension, Blood pH, and Cell pH

An abrupt fall in arterial PCO_2 (i.e., hypocapnia) markedly decreases renal bicarbonate reabsorption. A rise in PCO_2 (i.e., hypercapnia) increases proximal bicarbonate reabsorption. Although the mechanisms are incompletely understood, they are probably related to a change in renal hemodynamics and a change in cell pH.

The hemodynamic effects of varying P_{CO_2} are well known. If P_{CO_2} is acutely increased, renal vasodilation results, GFR falls, and bicarbonate reabsorption rises markedly. If one prevents the fall in GFR, hypercapnia *per se* still increases bicarbonate reabsorption; the change, however, is of a much lesser magnitude.

If P_{CO_2} is changed in proportion to the plasma bicarbonate concentration (and arterial pH is constant), proximal renal bicarbonate reabsorption is the same as control. If P_{CO_2} is changed and pH is allowed to change with it, an effect on proximal bicarbonate reabsorption can be uncovered. When pH falls, proximal bicarbonate reabsorption is increased; when pH rises, bicarbonate reabsorption is decreased. These observations suggest that pH is a major determinant of bicarbonate reabsorption.

In all likelihood, it is the intracellular pH, not the extracellular pH, that determines bicarbonate reabsorption. Intracellular pH is ≈ 7.1. Since carbon dioxide is freely diffusible across cell membranes, changing plasma P_{CO_2} would change cell pH dramatically. Increasing P_{CO_2} decreases arterial pH and results in a fall in intracellular pH. Changing the extracellular bicarbonate concentration, by contrast, does not result in a rapid change in intracellular pH because the HCO_3 anion cannot easily enter mammalian cells.

Recent studies in brush border vesicles from proximal tubule show that a decrease in pH stimulates the Na^+/H^+ antiporter. This maneuver alone might be enough to increase proximal bicarbonate reabsorption. A fall in cell pH would also result in a secondary change in renal hemodynamics. Such a change could then affect proximal bicarbonate reabsorption, either through a direct effect on the renal tubule or by changing the filtered load of bicarbonate.

Potassium

It has been known for many years that renal bicarbonate reabsorption is inversely proportional to body potassium stores (Fig. 6). In the chronic potassium-loaded animal, bicarbonate reabsorption is depressed; in the chronic potassium-depleted animal, bicarbonate reabsorption is markedly increased. Potassium probably alters proximal bicarbonate reabsorption by two mechanisms: First, potassium deficiency decreases cell pH. As stated in the previous section, a decrease in cell pH would secondarily increase proximal bicarbonate reabsorption. Second, potassium depletion decreases GFR and secondarily decreases bicarbonate excretion while increasing fractional bicarbonate reabsorption.

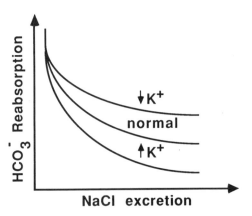

FIG. 6. Theoretical relationship of bicarbonate reabsorption to sodium chloride excretion in potassium depletion (upper curve) and potassium loading (lower curve) as compared to normals. ↑ NaCl excretion is a measure of volume expansion. [Redrawn from ref. 8.]

Carbonic Anhydrase

CA plays a major role in the transport of bicarbonate by the kidney (Figs. 1 and 3). The importance of the enzyme is easily demonstrable following *in vivo* infusion of inhibitors (e.g., acetazolamide). CA inhibitors cause a prompt bicarbonate diuresis; 30% of the filtered bicarbonate appears in the urine. In sharp contrast to these studies, micropuncture studies show that 80% of the filtered bicarbonate is trapped in the proximal tubular lumen after acetazolamide is administered. In isolated perfused proximal tubule of rabbit, acetazolamide inhibits virtually all acidification (i.e., 100% of the bicarbonate is trapped in the lumen). These observations have puzzled renal physiologists for a number of years. The explanation for the apparent discrepancy is as follows. Micropuncture (*in situ*) and microperfusion (*in vivo*) studies examine only the superficial nephrons of the renal cortex. Although these nephrons comprise 70% of the total nephron population, their long loops do not enter the renal medulla. The remaining 30% of the nephrons originate at the juxtamedullary cortex, and their long loops descend deep into the papillary tip. Although the fundamental processes of the superficial and juxtamedullary nephron populations are similar, nephron heterogeneity also exists. The deep nephrons transport bicarbonate at a higher rate than do the superficial nephrons. A large fraction of bicarbonate transported by these nephrons is independent of CA. A concentration gradient for bicarbonate exists in the deep nephrons during CA inhibition; the concentration of bicarbonate is higher in the tubular lumen than in the vasa recta. This gradient causes the passive movement of bicarbonate from the tubular lumen into the peritubular capillaries and, thus, decreases bicarbonate excretion.

MINOR FACTORS REGULATING BICARBONATE REABSORPTION

There are a number of other factors that regulate bicarbonate reabsorption by the proximal renal tubule. These are of less overall significance when compared to those previously discussed. These factors include glucose loading, parathyroid hormone, vitamin D, hypercalcemia, and phosphate depletion.

After prolonged fasting, patients returning to a normal diet commonly develop metabolic alkalosis. Glucose loading to animals on a normal diet clearly increases proximal bicarbonate reabsorption. This increase appears to be the direct effect of glucose, since insulin administration is without effect. In addition to its effect on the proximal tubule, glucose loading in humans also enhances acid excretion. Neither the mechanism for the accelerated proton secretion nor the site of action within the nephron is known. It is possible that, with massive glucose loading, the metabolic machinery of the renal cell (proximal or distal nephron) incompletely oxidizes the hexose, releasing organic acids of intermediary metabolism. In the proximal tubule, the Na^+/H^+ activity would increase secondary to a fall in cell pH. In the distal nephron, the organic anions would be relatively impermeant (much as sulfate) and directly enhance distal hydrogen ion secretion (*see also* section, Nature and Quantity of the Anion, *in this chapter*).

Parathyroid hormone (PTH) in pharmacologic doses enhances urinary bicarbonate excretion. Proximal bicarbonate reabsorption decreases, but the effect of PTH, however, is very small. In humans with chronic renal failure, there is no difference in bicarbonate reabsorption between those subjects having high endogenous PTH levels and those who have had parathyroidectomy. PTH may stimulate distal hydrogen ion secretion, although this effect is probably also a minor one and is likely the result of increased distal phosphate delivery.

The effect of PTH on extrarenal buffering probably is far more important on acid-base homeostasis than is its effect on either proximal tubular bicarbonate reabsorption or distal hydrogen ion secretion. Acute or chronic renal failure anephric animals are capable of buffering an acute acid (HCl) infusion to a greater extent than are intact anephric animals (Fig. 7). This is presumably due to the enhanced extrarenal buffering caused by endogenous PTH, since PTH infusion to normal or thyroparathyroidectomized animals also protects the arterial pH in response to an acute acid infusion. PTH releases bone carbonates and bicarbonate into the extracellular fluid. Although other tissue buffers exist in the body (muscle and liver), bone is probably the most important source. If release of bone buffers is prevented, as with administration of CA inhibitors or diphosphonates, the protective effect of PTH on arterial pH is lost.

Vitamin D stimulates calcium absorption from the gastrointestinal tract and bone osteoclastic and osteoblastic activity. The active form of the hormone (1,25-dihydroxycholecalciferol) is synthesized by the proximal renal tubular

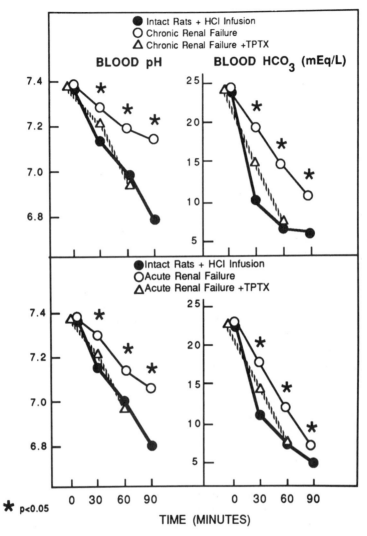

FIG. 7. **Top:** Response of acid-base parameters to acute HCl infusion in intact rats (●), animals with chronic renal failure (CRF) (0), and CRF animals following thyroparathyroidectomy (TPTX) (Δ). Blood pH and HCO₃ concentration at 30, 60, and 90 min are significantly higher in intact CRF animals (0), presumably due to endogenous parathyroid hormone stimulating bone buffer stores. Renal failure was produced by removal of 1 kidney and 7/8 infarction of the other kidney. The remnant kidney was removed just before acute HCl infusion. **Bottom:** Response of acid-base parameters to acute HCl infusion in intact rats (●), animals with acute renal failure (BUL) (0) and BUL animals following thyroparathyroidectomy (TPTX) (Δ). Blood pH and HCO₃ concentration are significantly higher in intact BUL animals (0) as compared to control. Acute renal failure (BUL) was produced by bilateral ureteral obstruction and was of 24 hr duration. Both kidneys were removed just before acute HCl infusion. [From ref. 3.]

cells. Chronic administration of vitamin D in high doses enhances proximal bicarbonate reabsorption. The mechanism is not clearly understood, but the hormone probably stimulates the Na^+/H^+ antiporter of the proximal brush border membrane.

Acute infusion of calcium enhances bicarbonate reabsorption in animals. This can be demonstrated in animals devoid of parathyroid glands. PTH, vitamin D, and calcium infusion all affect calcium transport and theoretically raise cytosolic calcium in the proximal tubular cell. Their mechanisms for altering bicarbonate reabsorption must be different, however, since PTH decreases bicarbonate reabsorption, whereas vitamin D and calcium infusion raise it.

Phosphate depletion, a condition seen commonly in chronic alcoholics and patients with diabetic ketoacidosis, decreases bicarbonate reabsorption by the proximal tubule. Phosphate is the primary intracellular anion, and its absence increases cell pH. The high cell pH of the proximal tubular cell is likely a direct stimulus decreasing bicarbonate reabsorption. It should be noted that in the clinical conditions associated with phosphate depletion, extracellular acid-base homeostasis is virtually normal because of the marked stimulus to extrarenal tissue buffering induced by phosphate depletion.

Aldosterone has no effect on proximal bicarbonate reabsorption as measured using conventional *in vivo* clearance studies. It is not known if the hormone affects proximal H^+-ATPase activity. Aldosterone does stimulate H^+-ATPase in the collecting tubule (medullary, ? cortical). Glucocorticoids increase GFR and stimulate the activity of the proximal Na^+/H^+ antiporter. Thus, bicarbonate reabsorption goes up in parallel with the increase in filtered load such that reabsorption per unit GFR remains unchanged.

In summary, many factors affect proximal bicarbonate reabsorption. Volume contraction, hypercapnia, hypokalemia, glucose loading, and acute hypercalcemia enhance bicarbonate reabsorption. Volume expansion, hypocapnia, hyperkalemia, hyperparathyroidism, and phosphate depletion decrease bicarbonate reabsorption. Of all these factors, the most potent stimulus enhancing proximal bicarbonate reabsorption is that of volume contraction, either absolute volume contraction or effective arterial volume contraction.

URINARY ACID EXCRETION

Net acid excretion (NAE) is the sum of urine titratable acid and ammonium concentrations minus the urine bicarbonate concentration. Under normal conditions, practically no bicarbonate appears in the urine, thus the major components of net acid excretion are urinary titratable acid and ammonium. Both are excreted in humans in approximately equal proportions (Table 4). There are a number of factors, however, that affect urinary acid excretion: distal sodium delivery, aldosterone, nature and quantity of the anion, and ammoniagenesis.

Distal Sodium Delivery

Sodium reabsorption by the distal nephron has a major impact on net acidification. This effect is the result of the negative potential difference generated by the active transport of sodium on the distal nephron. In the collecting duct, sodium reabsorption across the luminal membrane is thought to occur through specific sodium channels. Cell sodium activity normally is very low (10 mEq/liter), and as it begins to rise with sodium entry, activity of the basolateral Na,K-ATPase increases. The Na,K-ATPase enzyme pumps sodium from the cell into the peritubular capillary. Reabsorption of sodium leaves the luminal space with a highly negative charge (-10 to -40 mV). The negative lumen potential difference accelerates the rate at which the positively charged protons are secreted into the urinary space. Proton secretion in the distal tubule occurs by a proton-translocating ATPase (H^+-ATPase), which is electrogenic and not directly dependent on sodium transport. Indirectly, however, sodium transport influences the proton pump by altering the lumen negative potential difference.

The influence of sodium transport on acidification is illustrated by the effect of the diuretic, amiloride, in a membrane very similar to the collecting duct (turtle bladder). The turtle bladder can be voltage clamped (zero potential difference) or allowed to generate a spontaneous negative voltage as would be seen within the renal tubule. Amiloride acts at the luminal membrane to block the sodium entry channels, thus preventing sodium reabsorption. It also changes the potential difference in an unfavorable way. If the effect of potential difference is abolished by voltage clamping, amiloride does not alter proton secretion in the turtle bladder. If, on the other hand, the potential difference is able to change (i.e., the membrane is unclamped), amiloride decreases proton secretion. Thus, there is a component of acidification that is voltage-dependent. Under a variety of normal and abnormal circumstances, this voltage-dependent component may be the critical modulator of net acidification. In other words, the proton pump overall may be relatively constant. The rate of proton transport may be secondarily altered (i.e., decreased), however, as sodium transport changes (i.e., decreased).

Any event that reduces distal sodium delivery or transport in the collecting duct, all other things being equal, results in a reduction of distal urinary acidification. Distal sodium transport may be decreased because of an intrinsic abnormality in the tubule, a decreased availability of sodium, as in congestive heart failure and volume contraction, or a deficiency of aldosterone.

Aldosterone

Aldosterone is a mineralocorticoid hormone produced from cholesterol by the zona glomerulosa of the adrenal glands. It is released in response to angiotensin II and hyperkalemia. Once released, the hormone circulates, and of its many target tissues (kidney, colon, sweat glands), the renal collecting duct is probably the most important. After crossing the cell membrane, aldosterone combines with a cytosolic receptor, forming an active steroid–receptor complex. This complex then enters the nucleus and synthesizes new DNA, new mRNA, and new proteins (aldosterone-induced proteins). The aldosterone-induced proteins stimulate cell metabolism, proton secretion, and membrane sodium permeability. Luminal potassium permeability also increases, but this is independent of aldosterone-induced proteins. In the kidney the effects of aldosterone clearly occur in the collecting duct; the proximal tubule and the thin limbs are unaffected by the hormone. A recent study shows that the thick limb responds to the hormone, but the significance of this finding is as yet unknown. In mammalian medullary collecting duct, aldosterone increases activity of H^+-ATPase. At the present time, we do not know whether this is due to an increase in enzyme V_{max}, K_m, or both. The effect of aldosterone in the cortical collecting duct is controversial. One study shows that the hormone increases H^+-ATPase activity in cortical collecting duct; another does not (in both cortical and medullary collecting ducts, aldosterone stimulates Na, K-ATPase).

The effects of aldosterone on sodium reabsorption and proton secretion occur through separate mechanisms. Aldosterone, however, may modulate distal acidification indirectly by its effect on sodium (i.e., enhanced sodium reabsorption increases the lumen negative potential difference) or directly by stimulating the proton pump. Through its effect on cell metabolism, aldosterone enhances ammoniagenesis; this maneuver further increases acid excretion. It should be noted that the amino acid precursor, glutamine, may be rate limiting for maximal ammoniagenesis in conditions associated with a decrease in renal blood flow.

The overall role of aldosterone in the maintenance of both acid-base and potassium homeostasis can be summarized as follows. The steroid allows the distal nephron to secrete relatively large amounts of both protons and potassium under conditions of decreased distal sodium delivery. When distal sodium delivery is large, sufficient proton and potassium can be secreted by aldosterone-independent mechanisms to preserve acid-base and potassium homeostasis. Clinically, therefore, the deficiency of aldosterone results in hyperkalemia and metabolic acidosis only when distal sodium delivery is low. Similarly, excess of aldosterone results in hypokalemia and metabolic alkalosis only when large amounts of sodium are delivered to the distal nephron.

Nature and Quantity of the Anion

The type of anion delivered to the distal nephron is important in modulating acid secretion. Penicillins, especially carbenicillin, and sulfates ($SO_4^=$) have been noted to cause metabolic alkalosis in humans. Both of these anions are reabsorbed poorly by the kidney and, if presented to the collecting duct as the sodium salt, markedly increase the lumen negative potential difference secondary to sodium reabsorption. The increase in transtubular potential difference creates a favorable gradient for proton secretion, markedly increasing urine acid excretion (and that of potassium). The overall consequence of this is hypokalemic metabolic alkalosis.

Urinary phosphate is the major anion contributing to urine acid excretion. The phosphate buffer pair has a pK_a of 6.8 and, thus, is an ideal urinary buffer. At a blood pH of 7.4, the ratio of Na_2HPO_4/NaH_2PO_4 is 4:1, and at pH 6.8, the ratio is 1:1. Phosphate is filtered by the glomerulus, and $\approx 1/3$ is titrated before urine pH decreases to 6.8. At this point 50% of the phosphate is in the

$$HPO_4^= + H^+ \rightleftarrows H_2PO_4^-$$

monohydrogen form, and 50% is in the dihydrogen form. At very low urine pH, other acids having lower pK become important (urate $pK_a = 5.8$; creatinine $pK_a = 5.0$). None of these other anions, however, appears in the abundant quantity as does phosphate.

Phosphate depletion decreases acid excretion, and it does so by at least four mechanisms. As stated, phosphate depletion decreases proximal bicarbonate reabsorption probably by increasing the pH of the proximal tubular cell. Additionally, the quantity of phosphate in the urine in the distal nephron decreases, since virtually all the filtered phosphate is avidly reabsorbed by the Na^+/phosphate symporter of the proximal tubule brush border membrane. This results in a decrease in titratable acid and net acid excretion. Phosphate depletion also decreases distal urinary acidification. When cellular phosphate stores are severely depleted, the synthesis of ATP may become rate limiting. As a consequence, the active metabolic pumps inside the cell, of which H^+-ATPase is but one, would decrease activity, causing less hydrogen to be secreted into the tubular lumen. The K_m for ATP of the collecting tubule H^+-ATPase makes this a likely explanation for the distal urinary acidification defect consistently observed with phosphate depletion.

Factors Controlling Ammoniagenesis and NH_4^+ Excretion

Ammonia (NH_3) is a weak base with a pK of 9.4 ($NH_3 + H^+ \rightleftarrows NH_4^+$). The nonionized gas is freely diffusible across cell membranes; however, at a pH of ≈ 7.4, it is virtually all in the cationic form. The cationic form is not thought to be diffusible across mammalian cell membranes, although this may not be the case in lower species. Ammonia is synthesized from glutamine in the renal tubular cell. Approximately two thirds of the glutamine comes from the plasma, and the rest is the consequence of renal cell metabolism. Gluta-

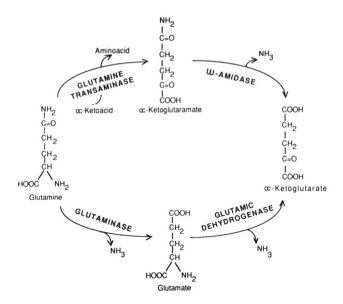

FIG. 8. Metabolic pathways of renal ammonia formation from glutamine. The kidney contains two glutaminase-I isoenzymes: phosphate-independent (mitochondrial, ? microsomal localization) and phosphate-dependent (mitochondrial localization). Glutamine dehydrogenase is located in renal cortex and is probably important, since it controls the level of glutamate in the kidney. Glutamine transaminase (glutaminase-II) activity is cytosolic. Transamination of keto-acids (e.g., pyruvate) yields an amino acid (e.g., alanine) and α-ketoglutaramate, which then may be deaminated (ω-amidase). This is considered to be of minor significance in all but a few species. [From ref. 13.]

mine enters the renal tubular cells from both the peritubular capillary and the luminal membrane. Once inside the cell, most of the glutamine is transported into mitochondria, where the two glutaminase-I isoenzymes are found (Fig. 8). A profile of the two isoenzymes is shown in Fig. 9. The proximal tubular cell contains predominantly phosphate-independent glutaminase-I; the distal tubule contains the phosphate-dependent glutaminase-I isoenzyme. A second metabolic pathway for ammonia production from glutamine exists in the cytosol (glutamine transaminase, glutaminase-II pathway; Fig. 8). This eventually results in ω-deamidation of α-ketoglutaramate to NH_3 and α-ketoglutarate. This second pathway is considered of minor significance in the production of ammonia in many species, including humans. Transamination of other amino acids and activity of glutamate dehydrogenase may be further sources of cell ammonia, although the importance of these pathways remains to be established.

At least five factors influence the amount of ammonia that is produced and secreted into the tubular lumen: the urine pH, flow (capillary and tubular), the degree of acidosis, potassium, and aldosterone.

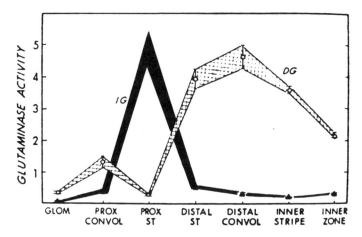

FIG. 9. Distribution of phosphate-independent (IG) and phosphate-dependent (DG) glutamin-ase isoenzymes in rat kidney. Inner stripe and inner zone are deep within the medulla; the rest of the segments are from superficial cortex. [From ref. 5.]

Urine pH

There is an inverse relationship between urine pH and the amount of ammonia excreted in the urine (Fig. 10). The lower the urine pH, the more effective the trapping mechanism for ammonium (NH_4^+) in the tubular lumen. As a result, there is a continuous cell-to-lumen gradient for NH_3. Ammonium is found in the urine in the form of ammonium chloride, ammonium sulfate, and ammonium phosphate. Approximately 30 to 50 mEq/day of acid are excreted as ammonium under normal conditions, and acidemia can augment this to values well over 200 mEq/day (Fig. 11). An intravenous acid infusion results in a rise in ammonium excretion within 15 min. Although the precise stimulus for the immediate increase is not completely known, activity of the proximal tubule phosphate-dependent glutaminase-I increases 20-fold.

Flow

When renal plasma flow decreases, blood flow in the peritubular capillaries falls. This results in a decrease in the amount of substrate (glutamine) available for ammonia formation. As a consequence, urine ammonium excretion decreases. If urinary flow rate increases, more ammonium appears in the tubular lumen. The mechanism for this effect is thought to be caused by the enhanced sodium delivery to the cortical collecting duct secondarily increasing in proton secretion.

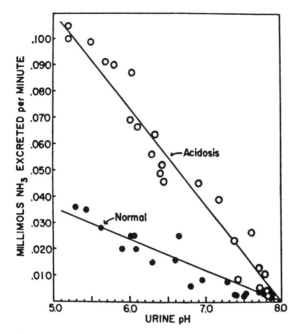

FIG. 10. Effect of decreasing urine pH on ammonia excretion in normal people and during chronic metabolic acidosis. [From ref. 12a.]

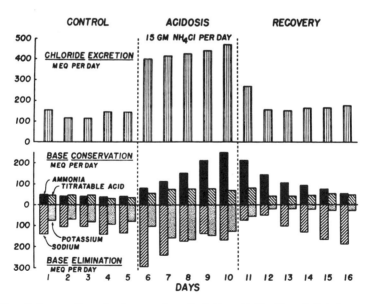

FIG. 11. Daily excretion rate of ammonium, titratable acid, Na, K, and Cl during ammonium chloride loading in a normal subject. Note the marked increase in ammonium excretion (**middle panel,** dark bars) and no change in titratable acid excretion in response to metabolic acidosis. [From ref. 12, with permission of the American Society for Clinical Investigation.]

Degree of Acidosis

Pitts et al. first showed that, at any given urine pH, ammonia excretion is greater in animals with chronic metabolic acidosis than in normal animals (Fig. 10). Since those original observations, many experiments have been performed to elucidate the mechanism for this effect. The effect of chronic metabolic acidosis does not appear to be mediated by systemic pH, since ammonium excretion does not increase to the same degree during respiratory acidosis. It may well be that the reduction in renal blood flow seen in respiratory acidosis is of sufficient degree that glutamine becomes rate limiting.

Potassium

Just as potassium is a regulator of proximal bicarbonate reabsorption, it also is an important regulator of ammonia synthesis. An acute increase in potassium concentration *in vitro* decreases ammonia synthesis in isolated tubule suspensions; whether or not the opposite occurs is controversial. Chronic potassium depletion, both *in vitro* and *in vivo*, stimulates ammonia production. The mechanism for this is thought to be a fall in cell pH. This explanation, however, must be incomplete, since hypokalemia and respiratory acidosis decrease cell pH. Potassium depletion markedly stimulates ammonia synthesis, whereas respiratory acidosis does not.

Glomerular Filtration Rate

A decrease in GFR decreases ammonium secretion. Patients with chronic renal failure have a fall in absolute ammonium excretion. However, when expressed on a per nephron basis, ammonium excretion is either normal or increased. Maneuvers that decrease GFR (nitroprusside, respiratory acidosis) decrease ammonium production. If the fall in GFR is prevented by norepinephrine infusion, ammonium excretion returns to normal or is increased.

In adrenalectomized acidotic rats, ammonium excretion is lower than acidotic controls. Increasing GFR by saline loading increased ammonium excretion to normal even though aldosterone was not provided. These results suggest that GFR plays a major role in modulating ammonium excretion and that aldosterone has a rather minor one.

SUMMARY

Many factors contribute to the overall renal regulation of acid-base balance. Renal bicarbonate reabsorption usually is virtually complete, and little or no bicarbonate appears in the urine. The proximal tubule reclaims most of the filtered bicarbonate. Volume contraction is the most potent stimulus to bicarbonate reabsorption, although many other major factors independently regulate it. The proximal tubule is a high capacitance, low pH gradient system capable of reabsorbing large quantities of bicarbonate. The distal nephron, by contrast, is a low capacitance, high pH gradient system. In the distal nephron, new bicarbonate is regenerated by active proton secretion. Once secreted, protons are excreted into the final urine in the form of titratable acid (predominantly phosphate and ammonium salts). Factors regulating distal urinary acidification are aldosterone, distal sodium delivery, adequate amounts and type of urinary buffer, the nature of the anion, and ammonia production. Overall renal regulation of acid-base balance depends on the precise integration of proximal and distal nephron function.

ACKNOWLEDGMENTS

Dr. Sabatini is the recipient of a National Institutes of Health Research Career Development Award, K04-DK-01527. The authors thank Ms. Sondra Rogers for her excellent typing and artistic assistance.

REFERENCES

1. Adler, S., and Fraley, D. S. (1985): Acid-base regulation: Cellular and whole body. In: *Fluid Electrolyte and Acid-Base Disorders*, edited by A. I. Arieff and R. A. DeFronzo, pp. 221–267. Churchill-Livingstone, New York.
2. Alpern, R. J., Warnock, D. G., and Rector, F. C., Jr. (1986): Renal acidification mechanisms. In: *The Kidney*, 3rd ed., edited by B. M. Brenner and F. C. Rector, Jr., pp. 250–260. Saunders, Philadelphia.
3. Arruda, J. A. L., Alla, V., Rubinstein, H. (1980): Parathyroid hormone and extrarenal acid buffering. *Am. J. Physiol.*, 239:F533–F538.
4. Batlle, D. C., and Kurtzman, N. A. (1985): Renal regulation acid-base homeostasis: Integrated response. In: *The Kidney: Physiology and Pathophysiology*, edited by D. W. Seldin and G. Giebisch, pp. 1539–1566. Raven Press, New York.
4a. Brautbar, N. (1981): Extrarenal factors in the homeostasis of acid-base balance. Semin. Nephrol., 1:232–249.
5. Curthoys, N. P., Lowry, O. H. (1973): *J. Biol. Chem.*, 248:162.
6. Emmett, M., and Seldin, D. W. (1985): Clinical syndromes of metabolic acidosis and metabolic alkalosis. In: *The Kidney: Physiology and Pathophysiology*, edited by D. W. Seldin and G. Giebisch, pp. 1567–1639. Raven Press, New York
7. Ganong, W. F. (1981): *Review of Medical Physiology*, 10th ed., Lange, California.
8. Kurtzman, N. A., White, M. G., and Rogers, P. (1973): Pathophysiology of metabolic alkalosis. *Arch. Intern. Med.*, 131:702.
8a. Jacobson, H. R., and Seldin, D. W. (1983): On the generation, maintenance, and correction of metabolic alkalosis. *Am. J. Physiol.*, 245:F425–F432.
9. Laski, M. E., and Kurtzman, N. A. (1985): Acid-base disturbances in pulmonary medicine. In: *Fluid Electrolyte and Acid-Base Disorders*, edited by A. I. Arieff and R. A. DeFronzo, pp. 385–411. Churchill-Livingstone, New York.
9a. Peters, J. P. (1948): *N. Engl. J. Med.*, 239:353–362.

10. Pitts, R. F. (1963): *Physiology of the Kidney and Body Fluids*, pp. 1–243. Year Book, Chicago

11. Pitts, R. F., Ayer, J. L., and Schiess, W. A. (1949): *J. Clin. Invest.*, 28:35.

12. Pitts, R. F., et al. (1949): *J. Clin. Invest.*, 28:423.

12a. Pitts, R. F. (1948): *Federation Proc.*, 7:418–426.

12b. Sabatini, S., and Kurtzman, N. A. (1984): The maintenance of metabolic alkalosis: Factors which decrease bicarbonate excretion. *Kidney Int.*, 25:357–361.

13. Simpson, D. P. (1971): *Medicine*, 50:503.

Abnormal Acid–Base Balance

The Regulation of Acid–Base Balance, edited
by Donald W. Seldin and Gerhard Giebisch,
Raven Press, Ltd., New York © 1989.

11

Evaluation of Acid–Base
Disorders from Plasma Composition

Michael Emmett and *Donald W. Seldin

*Nephrology/Metabolism Division, Baylor University Medical Center,
Dallas, Texas 75246; and *University of Texas Southwestern Medical Center
at Dallas, Dallas, Texas 75235*

The acid-base status of the body is carefully regulated to maintain the arterial pH in a narrow range between 7.35 and 7.45. The pH is stabilized by multiple buffer systems in extracellular fluid (ECF), within cells, and in the skeleton. Neurorespiratory control of the CO_2 tension and renal regulation of the bicarbonate concentration in serum ($[HCO_3^-]_s$) constitute two of the most important variables in this complex system of buffers.

In this chapter, we first review the determinants of acid-base status: closed buffer systems in the ECF, cells, and bone, the open HCO_3^-/CO_2 buffer system resulting from physiologic regulation of $[HCO_3^-]_s$ by the kidneys and CO_2 by the lungs, and metabolic buffering that is accomplished by accelerating or slowing the production of relatively strong organic acids, such as lactic acid. (An analysis of open and closed buffer systems is presented in Chapters 1 and 2.) The normal range of acid-base parameters is described. Next, the nature and magnitude of compensation for acid-base disturbances is analyzed. Finally, an approach to simple and mixed acid-base disturbances is developed using four diagnostic tools: (1) formulae that predict the range of normal compensation, (2) the acid-base nomogram, (3) the anion gap, and (4) changes in $[Cl^-]_s$ relative to $[Na^+]_s$.

CLOSED AND OPEN BUFFER SYSTEMS AND THEIR PHYSIOLOGIC REGULATION (55,60)

Buffer Chemistry

The Brönsted-Lowry theory defines an acid as any substance that can donate protons (H^+) and a base as any substance that can accept protons. When an acid reversibly releases H^+, the product produced is a base that can accept H^+. In the Brönsted-Lowry system, such an acid and base constitute a conjugate acid-base pair. Their relationship is expressed by the following chemical reaction.

$$HA \leftrightarrows A^- + H^+ \qquad [1]$$
$$\text{Acid} \qquad \text{Base}$$

At equilibrium, the mass action law defines the following arithmetic relationship.

$$[HA] \, \alpha \, [H^+] \, [A^-]$$

so that

$$K'[HA] = [H^+][A^-]$$
$$K' = \frac{[H^+][A^-]}{[HA]} \qquad [2]$$

K' is the equilibrium, or dissociation, constant for this generic acid-base reaction. It reflects the "strength" of the acid. Strong acids have a large K' and readily release H^+. When K' is small, H^+ is more tightly bound. These acids only partially release H^+ and are designated as weak.

When a strong acid releases H^+, it becomes a weak base (i.e., H_2SO_4 is a strong acid and SO_4^{2-} is a very weak base). Conversely, a strong base accepts H^+ to become a weak acid (i.e., NH_3, a strong base, accepts H^+ to become NH_4^+, a weak acid). Relatively weak acids dissociate to become relatively weak conjugate bases. Solutions of relatively weak acids and bases may have good buffering potential. H^+ addition to such a solution increases H^+ binding by the base, which blunts the fall in pH. If H^+ is removed from the solution, relatively weak acids release H^+ to blunt the increase in pH.

The conjugate acid-base equilibrium equation (Eq. 2) may be rearranged and converted to a logarithmic form.

$$\frac{[H^+][A^-]}{[HA]} = K'$$

$$[H^+] = K' \frac{[HA]}{[A^-]}$$

$$\log [H^+] = \log K' + \log \frac{[HA]}{[A^-]}$$

$$-\log(H^+) = -\log K' - \log \frac{[HA]}{[A^-]}$$

$$pH = pK' - \log \frac{[HA]}{[A^-]}$$

$$pH = pK' + \log \frac{[A^-]}{[HA]} \qquad [3]$$

where $pH = -\log_{10}[H^+]$ and $pK' = -\log_{10} K'$

This conjugate acid-base relationship is the Henderson-Hasselbalch equation.

In general, weak acid-base conjugate pairs can buffer pH changes effectively in the range surrounding their pK'. When the $pH = pK'$, the Henderson-Hasselbalch equation simplifies as follows.

$$pH = pK' + \log \frac{[A^-]}{[HA]}$$

$$pH = pH + \log \frac{[A^-]}{[HA]}$$

$$0 = \log \frac{[A^-]}{[HA]}$$

$$\frac{[A^-]}{[HA]} = 1$$

$$[A^-] = [HA]$$

Therefore, when the $pH = pK'$, the weak acid concentration equals the conjugate base concentration. At a 1:1 molar ratio of acid and base, the buffer is best poised to minimize a pH change in either the acid or alkaline direction.

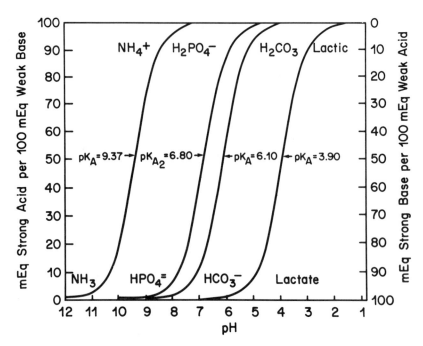

FIG. 1. Buffer mechanisms of tissues and body fluids. The titration curves of several conjugate acid-base pairs present in body fluids are depicted. As the pH decreases because of the addition of strong acid, the buffer base is titrated to its conjugate acid partner. The pK_A of each pair represents the ionization, or dissociation, constant of the acid. When the pH is equal to the pK_A, the buffer distribution is 50% acid and 50% base. In the pH range near the pK_A of a weak acid, the addition of large amounts of strong acid (left vertical axis) or strong base (right vertical axis) produces relatively small pH changes. This is indicated by the steep titration curve in the pH range near the pK_A. When the pH is greater than 1.5 units removed from the pK_A, the buffering potency of that particular weak acid becomes minimal. (Adapted from ref. 60.)

This principle is illustrated in Fig. 1, where the long vertical portions of the titration curves pass through this equivalence point. Note the relatively small pH change despite a large accession of strong acid or strong base.

Closed Buffer Systems

In a closed system, the sum of the concentrations of the conjugate acid-base pair remains fixed. As shown in Eq. 1, acid may be converted to base and vice versa, but no acid or base enters the system from an exogenous source (or is removed from the system). If n moles of HA dissociate, n moles of H^+ and A^- form. $HA + A^-$ is constant.

In an intact organism, a variety of systems can be defined. For purposes of this chapter, the system is the entire organism, and the definition of open or closed will devolve about the issue of whether acid or base is added from, or excreted into, the external environment. However, one could define an acid-base system as the ECF, the blood plasma, or any other body compartment. The movement of acids or bases from the plasma into red cells or parenchymal cells would still be consistent with a closed system, as viewed from the perspective of the intact organism, but an open one, as viewed from the more narrowly defined system of the blood plasma itself.

HCO_3^-/CO_2—An Open Buffer System (25,26,30,39,46,47,49)

The pH of the ECF is buffered primarily by alterations in the concentrations of HCO_3^- and CO_2. The HCO_3^-/CO_2 buffer system is much more complex than the simple two-component closed conjugate acid-base system we discussed previously. First, it includes a series of interrelated molecular species —CO_3^{2-}, HCO_3^-, H_2CO_3, dissolved CO_2, and gaseous CO_2—rather than one acid and its base pair. Furthermore, one component, CO_2, is volatile. It can readily escape from the solution. CO_2 also is generated by metabolic processes and is constantly added to the system. Another component, HCO_3^-, can be added or removed by the kidney. The species in this buffer system have the following interrelationship.

$$\overset{a}{2H^+ + CO_3^{2-} \rightleftharpoons} \overset{b}{HCO_3^- + H^+ \rightleftharpoons} \overset{c}{H_2CO_3 \rightleftharpoons} H_2O + \overset{d}{CO_2 \rightleftharpoons CO_2}$$

$$\text{(dis)} \quad \text{(gas)} \quad [4]$$

Reaction a is unimportant in the physiologic pH range of most body fluids.[1] Reaction b is rapid in either direction and is usually at equilibrium. Reaction c is relatively slow in either direction. However, the enzyme carbonic anhydrase accelerates this reaction by a factor of more than 1,000. At equilibrium, reaction c is poised far to the right producing a CO_2/H_2CO_3 ratio of between 400:1 and 800:1. Reaction d represents the interconversion of dissolved and gaseous CO_2.

Consider reaction b.

$$HCO_3^- + H^+ \rightleftharpoons H_2CO_3$$

At equilibrium

$$\frac{[HCO_3^-][H^+]}{H_2CO_3} = K' \qquad [5]$$

Rearrangement and logarithmic conversion yield

$$pH = pK' + \log\frac{[HCO_3^-]}{[H_2CO_3]} \qquad [6]$$

---

[1]In extremely alkaline urine, produced by urea-splitting bacteria, the formation of CO_3^{2-} becomes important and contributes to the formation of struvite renal stones.

The pK' for this reaction is 3.8, which indicates that H_2CO_3 is a relatively strong acid and is almost entirely dissociated at a pH of 7.4. The buffer system represented by Eq. 5, taken by itself, would have poor buffering effect in the physiologic pH range. However, several factors serve to enhance this system's capacity. First, H_2CO_3, which is generated or consumed, is in equilibrium with dissolved and gaseous CO_2. This helps to stabilize the $[H_2CO_3]$ and the pH. Combining reactions 4b and 4c yields

$$[HCO_3^-] + [H^+] \rightleftarrows [\text{dissolved } CO_2] \qquad [7]$$

From Eq. 4d

$$[\text{Dissolved } CO_2] \propto [\text{gaseous } CO_2]$$

Therefore

$$[\text{Dissolved } CO_2] = K_{CO_{2\cdot 1}} [\text{gaseous } CO_2]$$

Furthermore gas law equations state that

$$[\text{Gaseous } CO_2] \propto P_{CO_2}$$

Therefore

$$K_{CO_{2\cdot 2}} (P_{CO_2}) = [\text{gaseous } CO_2]$$

Combining

$$[\text{Dissolved } CO_2] = (K_{CO_{2\cdot 1}})(K_{CO_{2\cdot 2}})(P_{CO_2})$$

Call

$$(K_{CO_{2\cdot 1}}) (K_{CO_{2\cdot 2}}) = \alpha$$

Then

$$[\text{Dissolved } CO_2] = (\alpha) (P_{CO_2})$$

In plasma at 37°C, a has been measured to be equal to 0.0301, Eq. 7 may be rewritten as

$$[HCO_3^-] + [H^+] \rightleftarrows (0.0301) (P_{CO_2})$$

and

$$[HCO_3^-] [H^+] = K'a (0.0301) (P_{CO_2})$$

Rearrangement and logarithmic conversion yields

$$pH = pK'a + \log \frac{[HCO_3^-]}{(0.0301) (P_{CO_2})} \qquad [8]$$

In plasma at 38°C the pK'a for this composite reaction is 6.1.

Under normal conditions, the $[HCO_3^-]_s$ is about 24 mEq/liter and the P_{CO_2} is about 40 mm Hg. Therefore, the base/acid ratio in Eq. 8 is

$$24/(0.0301)\,(40) = 24/1.2 = 20/1$$

As discussed previously, buffer efficiency is greatest in the pH range near the pK, where the concentrations of each member of the conjugate pair are equal. The HCO_3^-/CO_2 buffer system described has a $pKa = 6.1$ and a base/acid ratio of 20:1 at pH 7.4. Therefore, it would not be expected to function as an effective buffer in the physiologic pH range (albeit better than the system represented by Eq. 6 with a $pK = 3.8$). In fact, the HCO_3^-/CO_2 buffer system is an extremely potent buffer in man.

The potency of the HCO_3^-/CO_2 system is owing to its open characteristics. An open buffer system is one that communicates with its environment so that acid or base may be added to or removed from the system. This characteristic of the HCO_3^-/CO_2 system constitutes a critical component of its buffering response. CO_2 is rapidly and continuously produced, added to the body's fluids, and removed by the lungs. Its concentration in these fluids can be modulated rapidly. When acid is added to a HCO_3^--containing solution, H^+ combines with HCO_3^- to generate H_2CO_3, which then dehydrates to CO_2. If the generated CO_2 can escape from the solution, buffering will be markedly enhanced.

Consider an open beaker containing a HCO_3^- solution at a concentration of 24 mEq/liter and bubbled with CO_2 to maintain a CO_2 tension of 40 mm Hg. This generates a $[H_2CO_3]$ of 1.2 mEq/liter (0.0301×40 mm Hg). If HCl is added to the beaker, HCO_3^- will be titrated to form H_2CO_3, which then dehydrates to CO_2 and escapes from the solution. If NaOH is added to the beaker, H_2CO_3 will be titrated to HCO_3^-. Additional H_2CO_3 is generated by hydration of CO_2, which bubbles continuously into the solution. The $[H_2CO_3]$ is fixed at 1.2 mm/liter because of the particular open design of such a system.

Contrast these results with those that occur in a closed system. In such a system, the sum of the conjugate acid and base concentrations remains constant, although their proportions change. Figure 2 compares such a closed system with two open HCO_3^-/CO_2 systems. The addition of HCl to the closed system generates H_2CO_3 and CO_2, which must remain in the solution. The $[H_2CO_3]$ and P_{CO_2} increase markedly and the pH falls sharply (Panel A). Alternatively, if the CO_2 tension is fixed at 40 mm Hg by bubbling CO_2 into an open beaker as described previously, a smaller decrease in pH occurs (Panel B). This constitutes an open buffer system that is *unregulated*. Panel C illustrates an open buffer system subject to physiologic regulation, simulating the response of an intact subject. Here the CO_2 tension falls in response to the acid challenge (as occurs in a patient whose ventilation increases in response to acidemia). The buffering capacity of the HCO_3^-/CO_2 system is thereby greatly enhanced.

We have described how regulation of the denominator of the Henderson-Hasselbalch equation, the P_{CO_2}, is critical to the function of the HCO_3^-/CO_2 system as a physiologically important buffer. This constitutes one limb of this regulated open buffer system. In addition, the concentration of the numera-

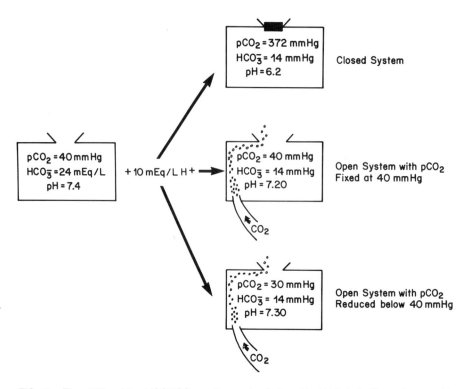

FIG. 2. The ability of the HCO_3^-/CO_2 system, poised at a pH of 7.4, to buffer a strong acid load is demonstrated under three conditions. In a closed system, the addition of strong acid generates CO_2 and H_2CO_3, which cannot escape from the solution. In consequence, the pH falls sharply. If the P_{CO_2} is fixed at 40 mm Hg, the addition of acid decreases $[HCO_3^-]$ but does not increase the $[H_2CO_3]$. The fall in pH is much less than with the closed system. This represents an open and unregulated system. If the system is open, and the CO_2 tension can be reduced in response to the acid load—a situation that most closely simulates physiological conditions—the reduction in $[HCO_3^-]$ is associated with a reduced $[H_2CO_3]$, and the acid load is best buffered. This represents an open and regulated HCO_3^-/CO_2 system. These diagrams illustrate one of the open limbs of the HCO_3^-/CO_2 system. In the intact patient, the $[HCO_3^-]$ also can be regulated independently.

tor, $[HCO_3^-]_s$, also can be regulated independently by the kidneys, which can add or remove HCO_3^- from the blood. This is the other open limb of the HCO_3^-/CO_2 system. To the extent that the kidneys regulate the $[HCO_3^-]_s$ in response to acid-base stresses, the system's buffer capacity will be further amplified.

In summary, the great potency of the HCO_3^-/CO_2 buffer system, despite its relatively low pK′, is a result of its *open* and *regulated* characteristics.

Closed Buffer Systems in the Extracellular Fluid (60)

The HCO_3^-/CO_2 buffer system is the most important ECF buffer. In addition, other buffers contribute to stabilization of the ECF pH. The isohydric principle states that in a solution of multiple buffers each buffer pair is in equilibrium with the same pH of the solution and, in turn, determines that pH. The concentration ratios of each acid and conjugate base pair is determined by the solution's pH and the equilibrium constant for that pair.

$$HA \leftrightharpoons H^+ + B^-$$
$$\text{Acid} \qquad \text{Base}$$

and

$$[H^+] = K_1 \frac{[HA]}{[B^-]}$$

Therefore, the following isohydric equation may be written.

$$H^+ = K_1 \frac{[HA_1]}{[B^-_1]} = K_2 \frac{[HA_2]}{[B^-_2]} = K_3 \frac{[HA_3]}{[B^-_3]} = K'a \frac{[\alpha\, P_{CO_2}]}{[HCO_3^-]} \qquad [9]$$

A change in the $\dfrac{[\alpha P_{CO_2}]}{[HCO_3^-]}$ ratio reflects a pH change and also reflects proportionate changes in every acid-base conjugate ratio that coexists in the solution. The ECF buffers are all in dynamic equilibrium described by the isohydric relationship.

Despite the presence of other buffers in the ECF, the HCO_3^-/CO_2 system is of overwhelming importance in buffering pH changes. As discussed, renal regulation of $[HCO_3^-]_s$ and neurorespiratory regulation of the P_{CO_2} markedly enhance the buffering potency of the HCO_3^-/CO_2 system. If metabolic acidosis depresses the $[HCO_3^-]_s$ from 25 to 5 mEq/liter in an otherwise normal individual, the pH falls only about 0.3 to 0.5 units. This small reduction in pH is the consequence of a major P_{CO_2} reduction. Because the decrease in pH is so small, other buffers, such as proteins and inorganic phosphate, cannot make a major contribution. Although these other buffers are present in significant concentrations and have relatively higher pK's, their contribution remains small.

These concepts are well illustrated by experiments reported by Pitts (60) and depicted in Figs. 3 and 4. A dog is nephrectomized to eliminate renal regulation of $[HCO_3^-]_s$. HCl is then intravenously infused. The majority of the acid load (57%) enters cells (*see* next section). Of the acid that remains in the ECF, 98% is buffered by titration of HCO_3^- to CO_2. Only 2% of the acid remaining in the ECF is buffered by the other ECF buffers, such as phosphate and proteins.

When HCO_3^- is infused intravenously into an anephric dog, 68% of the alkaline load remains in the ECF. Less than 1% of the ECF HCO_3^- is buffered by non-HCO_3^- buffers (Fig. 4). In each case, relatively small pH changes result, owing to the potent HCO_3^-/P_{CO_2} buffer system that precludes major participation by other ECF buffers.

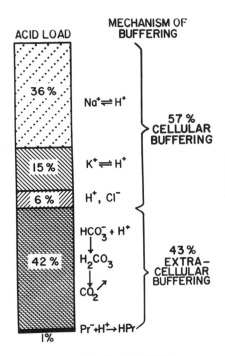

FIG. 3. The buffering distribution of a strong acid (HCl) infused intravenously in a nephrectomized dog. The load primarily enters cells (and to a small extent bone). Of the acid load, 43% is buffered within the ECF; 42 of the 43% is buffered by titration of HCO_3^- to CO_2. (From ref. 60.)

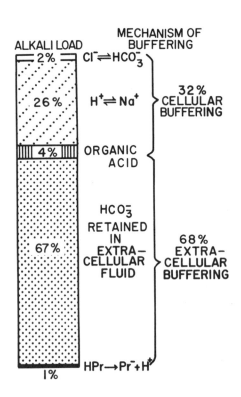

FIG. 4. The buffering distribution of an alkaline load ($NaHCO_3$) infused intravenously into an anephric dog. Of the HCO_3^- load, 68% remains in the ECF; 67 of this 68% remains as HCO_3^-. The other 1% is titrated to CO_2 by protons released from protein and other ECF buffers. About one third of the HCO_3^- load leaves the ECF and is buffered within cells (and possibly the skeleton). (From ref. 60.)

Cell and Skeleton Buffering (6,9,15,29,54)

As shown in Fig. 3, acute HCl loads are buffered primarily outside the ECF. The H^+ enters red blood cells, parenchymal cells, and the skeleton. About 6% of the H^+ load enters red cells together with Cl^-. In the red cell, H^+ combines primarily with hemoglobin. Hemoglobin has a high histidine content, and the imidazole group of histidine can accept or release H^+. A larger portion of the H^+ load enters parenchymal cells. H^+ entering these cells primarily exchanges for intracellular Na^+ or K^+, and a smaller fraction may enter with Cl^-. Within parenchymal cells, H^+ is buffered by proteins, peptides, organic and inorganic phosphates, and intracellular HCO_3^-.

The intracellular concentration of organic acids, such as lactic and citric acid, may also be decreased by the reduction in intracellular pH (and increased when the pH rises). These effects constitute metabolic regulation (*see* next section).

The skeleton becomes a major buffer during chronic metabolic acidosis. Acidemia dissolves bone, releasing alkaline calcium salts, leaches HCO_3^- from the active surface of bone, and drives H^+ into the mineral matrix. Efficient use of skeletal buffers requires the action of parathyroid hormone. Skeletal buffering in acute metabolic acidosis and in acute and chronic metabolic alkalosis is less well characterized than the response to chronic metabolic acidosis.

Physiologic Regulation of Buffers (21,61)

Under normal conditions humans are confronted by an ongoing acid challenge. Thousands of millequivalents of relatively strong organic acids, such as acetate, lactate, citrate, and pyruvate, are generated each day by metabolic reactions. They are removed by other metabolic reactions, principally in the Krebs cycle, where CO_2 is produced (15,000–20,000 mm/day) and then excreted by the lungs. Other acids that are produced require renal excretion. These fixed acids have three sources: (1) organic acids formed in excess of organic bases and not further metabolized, (2) strong acids, such as H_2SO_4, derived from sulfur-containing amino acids, or H_3PO_4, derived from organophosphates, which cannot be metabolically neutralized, and (3) acid generated by the excretion of alkali into the stool.

Physiologic regulation of buffers serves to minimize changes in the HCO_3^-/CO_2 ratio in the face of these acid loads by three mechanisms: metabolic regulation, respiratory regulation, renal regulation.

Metabolic Regulation of Buffers

Metabolic reactions may generate or consume acid. Normally, several thousand milliequivalents per day of relatively strong organic acids (e.g., lactate, pyruvate, citrate) are generated and consumed. The metabolic conversion of an organic acid, such as lactic acid, to a neutral product, such as glucose, consumes both H^+ and lactate$^-$. The conversion of lactic acid to CO_2, which is exhaled, and H_2O also consumes both H^+ and lactate$^-$.

If lactic acid accumulates in blood, the H^+ decomposes HCO_3^-. Lactate$^-$ then replaces HCO_3^- and can be considered to be a form of decomposed and potential HCO_3^-.

$$H\ lactate\ +\ NaHCO_3 \rightarrow Na\ lactate\ +\ H_2CO_3$$
$$\downarrow$$
$$H_2O\ +\ CO_2$$

To the extent that lactic acid accumulates, the lactate concentration increases and $[HCO_3^-]_s$ decreases proportionately. Lactate is a metabolizable anion. If the anion is metabolized, it must be metabolized as lactic acid. This reaction will remove both lactate and H^+ from the solution and regenerate HCO_3^-.

$$Lactate^-\ +\ HOH \rightarrow H\ lactate\ +\ OH^-$$
$$\downarrow \qquad\qquad +$$
$$\qquad\qquad CO_2$$
$$neutral \qquad \downarrow$$
$$product \qquad HCO_3^-$$

This reaction proceeds without the need for renal intervention. Alternatively, if the acid HCl accumulates

$$HCl\ +\ NaHCO_3 \rightarrow NaCl\ +\ H_2CO_3$$
$$\downarrow$$
$$H_2O\ +\ CO_2$$

The Cl^- also represents decomposed HCO_3^-. However, Cl^- cannot be metabolized. Hence, the HCO_3^- can only be regenerated by the kidney, which converts filtered NaCl to HCl or an HCl equivalent, such as NH_4Cl or titratable acid plus Cl^-. Nonphysiologic regeneration of $NaHCO_3$ from NaCl also can be accomplished by the removal of HCl-rich gastric secretions via vomiting or suction.

If Na lactate is infused and the lactate is metabolized to a neutral product or oxidized to CO_2 and H_2O, $NaHCO_3$ is generated. Again the lactate anion is metabolized as lactic acid, which removes H^+ from the solution and generates HCO_3^-.

$$Na\ lactate\ +\ HOH \rightarrow H\ lactate\ +\ NaOH$$
$$\downarrow \qquad\qquad +$$
$$\qquad\qquad CO_2$$
$$\qquad\qquad \downarrow$$
$$neutral \qquad NaHCO_3$$
$$products$$

Metabolic regulation of organic acid concentrations normally maintains a blood lactic acid level of between 1 and 2 mEq/liter. An abnormally acid or alkaline environment can alter cellular metabolism so that it serves a buffering function. Many metabolic reactions that generate or consume organic acids are catalyzed by key regulatory enzymes that are pH sensitive. For example, phosphofructokinase, an important regulatory enzyme in the glycolytic pathway, is activated by an alkaline pH and inhibited by a more acid pH. Therefore, intracellular alkalosis stimulates glycolysis and accelerates pyruvic and lactic acid generation. Intracellular acidosis has the opposite effect. Other enzymes that are also pH sensitive act in concert to increase organic acid levels in response to alkalemia. (The concentrations of most of the intermediates in the Krebs cycle increase in response to alkalemia.) Thus, the concentrations of many organic acids, especially lactic acid, increase during alkalosis and thereby depress the $[HCO_3^-]_s$. This process decreases the severity of alkalosis. Acidosis has opposite effects on organic acid levels.

Respiratory Regulation of Buffers

The oxidation of substrates results in the production of 15,000 to 20,000 mmoles of CO_2 which are excreted by the lungs daily. Normally, CO_2 excretion and production rates are exactly matched to produce a steady state arterial P_{CO_2} of about 40 mm Hg. Relative underexcretion results in hypercarbia, whereas relative overexcretion produces hypocarbia. It should be stressed that the blood P_{CO_2} usually is determined primarily by the neurorespiratory function and not the metabolic CO_2 production rate. (See Chapter 7 for a detailed description of the mechanism of respiratory regulation.[2])

Renal Regulation of Buffers

The kidneys stabilize the $[HCO_3^-]_s$ by two processes. (1) They reclaim filtered HCO_3^- by tubular reabsorption. (2) They regenerate the HCO_3^- that has been decomposed by the addition of acids to the blood or lost from the body via renal, gastrointestinal, or other routes. The kidneys also regulate the steady state $[HCO_3^-]_s$, increasing it in response to respiratory acidosis and decreasing it in response to respiratory alkalosis (*see* Compensation for Primary Acid-base Disturbances).

---

[2]In addition to CO_2, acetone is removed principally via respiration. Acetoacetic acid decomposes nonenzymatically to acetone. The acetone is then metabolically converted to glucose, to other neutral products, or is exhaled. To the extent that acetone, derived from acetoacetic acid, is exhaled, this represents a volatile excretory pathway for that organic acid. Respiratory acetone excretion becomes important during prolonged, severe ketoacidosis.

Below a critical $[HCO_3^-]_s$, which is about 25 mEq/liter in normal individuals, the entire filtered HCO_3^- load is reabsorbed. Above this concentration, called the "bicarbonate threshold," HCO_3^- enters the urine. As $[HCO_3^-]_s$ increases further, HCO_3^- reabsorption is augmented but not in proportion to the increase in $[HCO_3^-]_s$. Above a $[HCO_3^-]_s$ of about 28 mEq/liter in normal individuals, further increases of $[HCO_3^-]_s$ do not elicit a further increase in HCO_3^- reabsorption. At this point, an apparent tubular maximum (apparent T_{max}) for HCO_3^- absorption has been reached.

To maintain normal acid-base balance, the kidney must not only reclaim the filtered HCO_3^- but also regenerate the HCO_3^- that has been decomposed by acid accumulation or lost from the body into stool or urine.

When acids invade the blood they decompose HCO_3^- in the following fashion.

$$HA + NaHCO_3 \rightarrow NaA + H_2CO_3$$
$$\downarrow$$
$$CO_2 + H_2O$$

The NaA that remains represents decomposed $NaHCO_3$. If the A^- can be metabolized to neutral products or CO_2 and H_2O, H^+ also will be consumed, and NaA represents both decomposed and potential $NaHCO_3$. However, if A^- cannot be metabolized (i.e., SO_4^{2-}, $H_2PO_4^-$, Cl^-), the kidney must regenerate the HCO_3^-.[3] If the NaA is filtered at the glomerulus, the tubule can convert the NaA to a form equivalent to HA and simultaneously return $NaHCO_3$ to the blood. This occurs through a process of Na^+ reabsorption and H^+ secretion. The H^+ that enters the urine may be partially titrated by the acid anion A^-. However, the pK of many acids is much lower than the minimal urine pH, and this precludes the formation of significant quantities of HA. Secreted H^+ also may titrate phosphate and other buffers present in urine to form additional titratable acid. Finally, H^+ can titrate NH_3 to NH_4^+. The net effect of these reactions is the return of $NaHCO_3$ to the blood (regeneration) and the urinary excretion of A^- and an equimolar quantity of H^+ in the form of titratable acid and NH_4^+. Net renal acidification is given by the expression

$$NH_4^+ + \text{titratable acid} - HCO_3^- = \text{net acid excretion} \qquad [10]$$

Metabolizable acids can be converted to neutral compounds or to CO_2 and H_2O. They also can be excreted by the kidney via the mechanisms discussed above. Normally, gastrointestinal HCO_3^- losses, organic acid production, and the acid derived from the diet produce 70 to 100 mEq of nonmetabolizable (fixed) acids, which require renal excretion.

---

[3] HCl also can be lost in gastric secretions if patients vomit or require gastric suction. However, this is not a normal physiologic route for removing an acid load.

MEASUREMENTS OF ACID-BASE PARAMETERS AND
THEIR NORMAL RANGE (11,31,39)

Arterial pH usually is measured with an electrode that incorporates a pH-sensitive glass segment. A solution buffered to a stable pH is present on one side of the glass and the unknown solution is placed on the other. An electric potential difference develops across the glass membrane, and this potential difference is proportional to the pH difference between the buffered solution and the unknown specimen. This generated potential difference is compared with the potential difference of a second reference electrode. The final result is converted directly into pH units. The normal arterial pH in the adult is 7.4 ± 0.04 (± 2 SD).

The CO_2 tension of blood is generally also measured with an electrode that is sensitive to Pco_2. Pco_2 electrodes contain a membrane permeable to gaseous CO_2. As CO_2 diffuses into the electrode, the pH of the internal solution, which has a relatively stable $[HCO_3^-]$, changes in proportion to the CO_2 tension. Therefore, the generated potential difference, compared with a reference electrode, is proportional to the unknown Pco_2. The arterial Pco_2 of adults is normally 40 ± 4 (± 2 SD) mm Hg.

$[HCO_3^-]_s$ is difficult to measure directly. Although HCO_3^--sensing electrodes recently have been introduced, they are not yet widely used. Most commonly, determination of the $[HCO_3^-]_s$ is based on a measurement of the total CO_2. Total CO_2 includes HCO_3^-, dissolved CO_2, and CO_2 bound by proteins, such as hemoglobin and albumin. The $[HCO_3^-]_s$ may be approximated by subtracting the dissolved CO_2, which is equal to (0.0301) (Pco_2), from the total CO_2. Normally, the dissolved CO_2 is about 1 mEq/liter $(0.0301 \times 40 = 1.2$ mEq/liter). Therefore, the $[HCO_3^-]_s$ normally represents about 95% of $[$total $CO_2]_s$. Total CO_2 may be measured by anaerobically adding a strong acid to the unknown specimen in order to convert all the HCO_3^- to CO_2. The CO_2 in the specimen is then measured with either a manometric or a colorimetric method. The $[HCO_3^-]_s$ in the normal adult is about 25 ± 1 (± 2 SD) mEq/liter in arterial blood and 27 ± 2 mEq/liter in venous blood.

The Henderson-Hasselbalch equation interrelates these three acid-base measurements: pH, Pco_2, and $[HCO_3^-]_s$. Using this equation and appropriate constants, the measurement of any two of these variables permits calculation of the third. Furthermore, if all three variables are independently measured, they should be interrelated as predicted by the Henderson-Hasselbalch equation. If this expected relationship is not identified, one of these measurements is probably erroneous.

Usually the measured $[HCO_3^-]_s$ is compared with the $[HCO_3^-]_s$ calculated from the measured pH and Pco_2. One should be aware of the method used to measure the $[HCO_3^-]_s$. If it is a total CO_2 method, dissolved CO_2 should be subtracted. Furthermore, if the measured $[HCO_3^-]_s$ is from a venous specimen, it usually will exceed the arterial $[HCO_3^-]_s$ by 1 to 2 mEq/liter. (As CO_2

enters the blood from capillaries and increases the Pco_2, HCO_3^- is formed, primarily in red cells, and increases the $[HCO_3^-]_s$ of blood plasma.)

Random errors often are responsible for large differences between calculated and measured $[HCO_3^-]_s$. However, certain pathologic conditions may introduce systematic measurement errors. Hyperlipidemia has multiple effects on $[HCO_3^-]_s$ measurements. First, the excess lipid will displace plasma water. If a quantitative sample of plasma is analyzed, it will contain less plasma water and therefore less HCO_3^-, which is relatively insoluble in fat. This will produce a form of pseudohypobicarbonatemia. The $[HCO_3^-]$ in plasma water may be normal, but the measured concentration in whole plasma will be reduced. Second, CO_2 is more soluble in fat than in water. Therefore, if total CO_2 is measured in such a specimen, a larger quantity of the CO_2 is derived from dissolved CO_2. This will have the effect of overestimating the $[HCO_3^-]$. The net effect of these relatively offsetting actions is not readily predictable. The lipid effects should not alter the pH and Pco_2 electrode measurements. Therefore, the calculated $[HCO_3^-]$ should remain accurate.

Bicarbonate ion selective electrodes are being used with increasing frequency in clinical laboratories. These electrodes also are calibrated under normal conditions. The effect of extreme abnormalities of ionic strength, plasma composition, hyperlipidemia, etc. on $[HCO_3^-]_s$ measurement with these electrodes has not been well characterized.

The pKa' and the solubility coefficient, α, are both based on direct measurements in normal serum at a temperature of 37°C. Alterations in ionic strength and composition, temperature, and pH can change these constants. Hyperthermia decreases the solubility of CO_2 (α) and increases the pKa' of the HCO_3^-/Pco_2 buffer system, whereas hypothermia has opposite effects. If the specimen is brought to 37°C, $[HCO_3^-]_s$ calculated from the Pco_2 and pH should match the $[HCO_3^-]_s$ directly measured at 37°C. However, these measurements will be quite different from the *in vivo* parameters which exist at a higher or lower temperature.

When the directly measured $[HCO_3^-]_s$ does not agree with the $[HCO_3^-]_s$ calculated with the Henderson-Hasselbalch equation, an error in one of three measurements is most likely. If such errors are eliminated, unusual conditions, such as those described, may account for the difference.

The individual normal ranges for pH, Pco_2, and HCO_3^- have been noted previously. However, it is important to recognize that in a single specimen, the variance is much narrower because of the interrelationship among these three parameters. For example, if the Pco_2 is at the lower end of its normal range, the simultaneous $[HCO_3^-]_s$ cannot be in the high normal range because this would produce alkalemia. Madias et al. defined the 90% confidence range for simultaneous Pco_2 and $[HCO_3^-]_s$ measurements (Fig. 5). Normal subjects whose CO_2 tensions are relatively low have $[HCO_3^-]_s$ that also are relatively low. Normal subjects with relatively high CO_2 tensions maintain a relatively high $[HCO_3^-]_s$. Madias et al. have shown that the Pco_2 normally determines

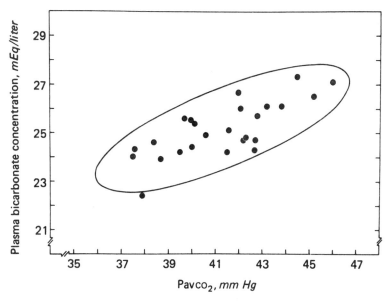

FIG. 5. The ellipse encloses the 90% confidence region in normal subjects for simultaneous plasma bicarbonate concentration and Pavco₂ (arterialized venous blood). A single set of acid-base data should fall within this ellipse with a probability of 90%. (From ref. 31.)

the $[HCO_3^-]_s$. Patients with relatively low PCO_2 levels tend to have a relatively higher pH, whereas those with CO_2 tensions in the high normal range tend to have a pH in the low normal range (Fig. 5). A patient whose PCO_2 is 45 mm Hg and whose $[HCO_3^-]_s$ is 23 mEq/liter has an acid-base disturbance despite the fact that the PCO_2 and $[HCO_3^-]_s$ each fall within their normal range. This patient has acidosis, either respiratory or metabolic or both.

PRIMARY ACID-BASE DERANGEMENTS

Definitions

A primary acid-base disorder is characterized by an abnormality in either the $[HCO_3^-]_s$ or the PCO_2 accompanied by a secondary change in the other member of the HCO_3^-/CO_2 pair. The secondary change represents compensation and acts to minimize the pH alteration produced by the primary disorder. The intensity of the secondary change is related to the severity of the primary disorder and falls into specifiable and predictable limits.

Mixed acid-base disorders represent at least two independent derangements of the $[HCO_3^-]_s$ or primary abnormalities in both the $[HCO_3^-]_s$ and PCO_2. When mixed metabolic and respiratory disturbances occur, they are identified by finding that the $[HCO_3^-]_s$ or PCO_2 falls outside the defined range of predicted compensation for a pure primary disturbance. The diagnosis of mixed metabolic disturbances requires careful analysis of the $[HCO_3^-]_s$, anion gap, and $[Cl^-]_s$ relative to $[NA^+]_s$. These concepts are discussed later in this chapter.

Metabolic acidosis is defined as a primary reduction in the $[HCO_3^-]_s$ accompanied by a fall in pH. It may be caused by accelerated HCO_3^- losses into the urine or stool. The HCO_3^- may be lost as such or indirectly in the form of decomposed bicarbonate. Metabolic acidosis also may result from acid accumulation from exogenous loads, accelerated production decreased excretion (via the kidney), or some combination of these mechanisms. The accumulating acid decomposes HCO_3^-, reducing its concentration and decreasing the pH.

Metabolic alkalosis is defined as a primary increase in the $[HCO_3^-]_s$ accompanied by a rise in pH. It may be due to exogenous alkali loads or accelerated acid excretion by the kidney, or other organs (usually the stomach).

Respiratory acidosis is defined as a primary increase in CO_2 tension accompanied by a reduction in pH. It is caused by alveolar underventilation for any given metabolic CO_2 production rate. Depression of the respiratory center, airway obstruction, and ineffective respiration each lead to respiratory acidosis. Rarely, the increase in CO_2 tension is principally the result of accelerated CO_2 production in a setting of relatively fixed ventilation (i.e., large loads of intravenous carbohydrate in critically ill patients).

Respiratory alkalosis is defined as a primary fall in CO_2 tension and increased pH. It is caused by overventilation at any given rate of CO_2 production rate. The stimulus to overventilation may be central (e.g., anxiety, trauma), peripheral (stiff lungs, hypoxia), or chemical (salicylism, increased NH_4^+ levels).

Compensation for Primary Acid–Base Disturbances (3–5,8,12–14,16, 18,22–24,27,28,34,37,40–42,44,45,48,50,51,58)

Metabolic Acidosis

Metabolic acidosis is compensated by hyperventilation, which reduces the CO_2 tension and thereby blunts the reduction in pH. The hyperventilatory response to metabolic acidosis is in part due to direct stimulation of the medullary respiratory center by the acidemia. The fall in $[HCO_3^-]_s$ acidifies brain interstitial fluid and stimulates the respiratory center in the medulla oblongata. Acidemia also is a stimulus to peripheral chemoreceptors in the carotid bodies. The relative importance of the peripheral and central chemoreceptors in the respiratory response to metabolic acidosis (and alkalosis) is still controversial.

The ventilatory response to metabolic acidosis is carefully regulated. The

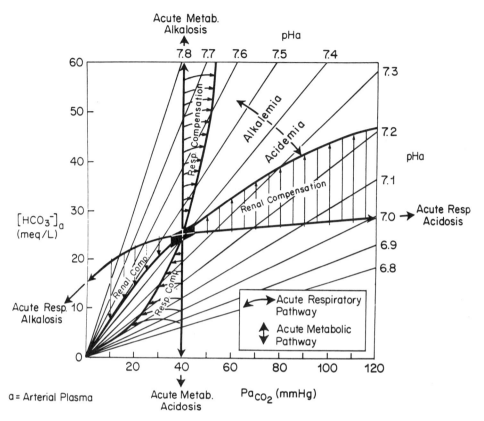

FIG. 6. Acid-base nomogram depicting the four primary acid-base disturbances (metabolic acidosis and alkalosis, respiratory acidosis and alkalosis) and expected levels of compensation. The use of the nomogram is described in the text.

CO_2 tension that develops for any given primary reduction in $[HCO_3^-]_s$ is quite predictable. Acid–base nomograms portray predictable CO_2 tensions for various degrees of metabolic acidosis (Fig. 6). The predicted P_{CO_2} may be plotted as a 95% confidence band. These data are derived from studies of large numbers of patients with primary acid-base disorders. Compensation confidence bands are then drawn to include 95% of patients with a primary acid-base disorder of given severity. The nomogram (Fig. 6) also depicts the steeper pH decline resulting if metabolic acidosis does not elicit an appropriate decrease in CO_2 tension (uncompensated metabolic acidosis). Maximal respiratory compensation for severe metabolic acidosis will reduce the P_{CO_2} to a minimal level of 12 to 15 mm Hg.

Respiratory compensation for metabolic acidosis also may be predicted by various regression equations and with several empiric rules. The respiratory response to metabolic acidosis is predicted by the following equations:

$$\text{Expected } P_{CO_2} = 1.5\,[HCO_3^-]_s + 8 \pm 2 \qquad [11]$$

$$\text{Expected } P_{CO_2} = [HCO_3^-]_s + 15 \qquad [12]$$

$$\text{Expected } P_{CO_2} = \text{last 2 digits of pH} \times 100 \qquad [13]$$

For example, if a patient develops metabolic acidosis and the $[HCO_3^-]_s$ falls to 7 mEq/liter and the pH to 7.20, the P_{CO_2} predicted by the acid-base nomogram (Fig. 6) is 20 mm Hg. Equation 11 predicts the P_{CO_2} to be 18 ± 4 mm Hg. Equation 12 predicts a $P_{CO_2} = 22$ mm Hg. Equation 13 predicts a $P_{CO_2} = 20$ mm Hg.

If metabolic acidosis does not elicit appropriate respiratory compensation (as defined by these confidence limits), a mixed acid-base disturbance exists. A P_{CO_2} that is higher than predicted indicates inadequate respiratory compensation. Under such conditions, mixed metabolic acidosis and respiratory acidosis exist and the pH falls sharply. Alternatively, if a patient with metabolic acidosis has a P_{CO_2} that is lower than predicted, mixed metabolic acidosis and respiratory alkalosis is diagnosed. The pH increases toward normal or even may become alkaline.

Since respiratory compensation for primary metabolic acidosis usually occurs within hours, the P_{CO_2} should be appropriately reduced by the time most patients with metabolic acidosis undergo evaluation.

Metabolic Alkalosis

Metabolic alkalosis is heralded by a primary increase in $[HCO_3^-]_s$ and an elevated arterial pH. Respiratory compensation is characterized by hypoventilation, increasing the CO_2 and blunting the increase in pH. The acid-base nomogram (Fig. 6) illustrates the expected respiratory response to metabolic alkalosis. The nomogram also shows the more severe alkalemia that results in the absence of appropriate respiratory compensation.

Respiratory compensation for metabolic alkalosis is less accurately predicted than compensation for metabolic acidosis. The large P_{CO_2} variation in metabolic alkalosis has several possible explanations. First, different patients with the same elevation in $[HCO_3^-]_s$ may have marked differences in intracellular pH. These differences may reflect variations in potassium balance. Potassium depletion shifts K^+ out of cells and H^+ into cells. This acidifies the cytoplasm and alkalinizes the ECF. In consequence, K^+-depleted patients with metabolic alkalosis may have a lower intracellular pH than those who are not K^+ depleted. Such variations in intracellular pH, especially in the brain, may affect the respiratory response. Second, hypoxia may accompany hypoventilation, and its development directly stimulates respiration. This can partially offset the inhibitory effect of alkalosis on respiration. Regardless of the explanation, the variable P_{CO_2} response makes prediction of compensation for metabolic alkalosis inaccurate. However, the P_{CO_2} should certainly be increased above the normal range in these patients. If the P_{CO_2} is equal to or less than 40 mm Hg in a patient with metabolic alkalosis, respiratory alkalosis also is present. At the other extreme, it is unlikely that respiratory compensation for metabolic alkalosis will increase the CO_2 tension above 55 mm Hg even when metabolic alkalosis is severe. If the P_{CO_2} is greater than 55 mm Hg, and certainly if it is greater than 60 mm Hg, respiratory acidosis exists together with metabolic alkalosis.

Metabolic Compensation for Acute Primary Respiratory Acidosis and Alkalosis

An acute alteration in CO_2 tension produces an immediate small parallel change in the $[HCO_3^-]_s$. This is partly due to the following chemical reaction.

$$CO_2 + H_2O \rightleftarrows H_2CO_3 \rightleftarrows H^+ + HCO_3^- \qquad [14]$$

When the CO_2 tension increases, the reaction is driven toward the right, increasing the $[HCO_3^-]_s$ and $[H^+]_s$. Conversely, a reduction in CO_2 tension decreases the $[HCO_3^-]_s$ and $[H^+]_s$. These small $[HCO_3^-]_s$ changes do not have any buffering effect by themselves because both HCO_3^- and H^+ are either generated or consumed in identical amounts. However, if the H^+ generated by hypercarbia is consumed by other buffers, the increase in $[HCO_3^-]_s$ will be greatly magnified and will constitute a buffering effect. Similarly, if the H^+ consumed by hypocarbia is replaced by H^+ released from other buffers, the reduction in $[HCO_3^-]_s$ will be magnified and will act to buffer the increase in pH produced by hypocarbia. Several buffer sources are used to acutely provide or remove H^+ in response to primary respiratory disorders: (1) ECF non-HCO_3^- buffers, such as albumin. (2) H^+ may be transported into or out of parenchymal cells. (3) H^+ (or HCO_3^-) may be transported into or out of red cells. (4) Organic acid concentrations may be modulated up or down in response to respiratory alkalosis or acidosis.

Acute respiratory acidosis increases the blood P_{CO_2} and $[H_2CO_3]$. The reduced pH increases H^+ binding to albumin. To the extent that this occurs, the anion gap falls slightly and the $[HCO_3^-]_s$ increases. A small amount of H^+ enters parenchymal cells in exchange for Na^+ or K^+ and thereby generates HCO_3^- in the ECF. Most importantly, the high CO_2 tension is immediately transmitted into the red cells. Here, the presence of carbonic anhydrase accelerates Eq. 14 and generates H_2CO_3. This acid dissociates, and the H^+ is partially bound by hemoglobin, leaving HCO_3^- in the cytoplasm of the red cell. As discussed previously, hemoglobin (Hb) can bind relatively large amounts of H^+ because of its rich histidine content. The following reaction occurs in the red cell.

$$H_2CO_3 \rightarrow H^+ + HCO_3^-$$
$$Hb + H^+ \rightarrow HHb^+$$

$$H_2CO_3 + Hb \rightarrow HCO_3^- + HHb^+$$

As red cell $[HCO_3^-]$ increases, it exits from the cell, exchanging for plasma Cl^-, which enters the RBC. (RBC membranes are relatively impermeable to cations.) This increases the $[HCO_3^-]_s$ and decreases $[Cl^-]_s$ and is termed the "red cell HCO_3^--Cl^- shift."

An acute Pco_2 reduction has the opposite effects. The plasma and RBC CO_2 tensions fall. Albumin and other non HCO_3^- ECF buffers release H^+ to decrease the $[HCO_3^-]_s$. H^+ exiting from parenchymal cells has the same effect. Within red cells, the fall in Pco_2 causes hemoglobin to release H^+ and decrease the $[HCO_3^-]$. HCO_3^- enters the red cell from plasma, whereas red cell Cl^- enters the plasma. The $[HCO_3^-]_s$ falls and $[Cl^-]_s$ increases.

The red cell HCO_3^--Cl^- shift is quantitatively the most important modulator of $[HCO_3^-]_s$ in acute respiratory acidosis and alkalosis.

The compensated $[HCO_3^-]_s$ expected with acute primary respiratory acidosis or alkalosis is depicted in the acid-base nomogram (Fig. 6). The curved horizontal lines define the range of acute metabolic compensation for these respiratory disturbances.

Respiratory alkalosis decreases the renal HCO_3^- reabsorptive capacity, and a transient HCO_3^- diuresis ensues; net acid excretion also decreases. These alterations each depress the $[HCO_3^-]_s$. Respiratory acidosis increases net acid excretion, principally in the form of NH_4Cl, so that $[HCO_3^-]_s$ rises; simultaneously, renal HCO_3^- reabsorption capacity increases. These renal effects begin soon after the respiratory disturbance occurs but will take days to develop fully (2–3 days for respiratory acidosis and 3–4 days for respiratory alkalosis). Compensation for chronic respiratory disturbances is discussed in the next section.

Acute metabolic compensation for respiratory acidosis increases the $[HCO_3^-]_s$ by about 1 mEq/liter for each 10 mm Hg increase in Pco_2. Therefore, if the Pco_2 increases acutely from 40 to 60 mm Hg, the $[HCO_3^-]_s$ should increase by about 2 mEq/liter. Acute respiratory alkalosis should reduce the $[HCO_3^-]_s$ by about 2 mEq/liter for each 10 mm Hg fall in Pco_2. If the Pco_2 is acutely reduced from 40 to 20 mm Hg, the $[HCO_3^-]_s$ should fall about 4 mEq/liter.

Metabolic (Renal) Compensation for Chronic
Primary Respiratory Acidosis and Alkalosis

When primary respiratory acidosis persists for several days, the kidney generates additional HCO_3^-. This is accomplished by an increase in net acid excretion, primarily in the form of NH_4Cl. In consequence, as $[HCO_3^-]_s$ rises, the $[Cl^-]_s$ falls. The established $[HCO_3^-]_s$ is dependent on the steady state CO_2 tension. Maintenance of the elevated $[HCO_3^-]_s$ is mediated principally by increased proximal H^+ secretion, resulting in accelerated HCO_3^- reabsorption. Intracellular acidosis, produced by the elevated Pco_2, appears to be the main factor responsible for enhanced HCO_3^- reabsorptive capacity. In addition, subtle ECF volume contraction may contribute.

Metabolic compensation for chronic respiratory acidosis is depicted in the nomogram (Fig. 6). For each 10 mm Hg increment in Pco_2, the $[HCO_3^-]_s$ increases by about 3.5 to 4.0 mEq/liter. For example, when the Pco_2 is elevated to 60 mm Hg for several days or more, the $[HCO_3^-]_s$ increases about 8 mEq/liter, to a level of about 32 mEq/liter.

The arterial pH of patients with chronic respiratory acidosis should remain mildly acid. Metabolic compensation for respiratory acidosis does not normalize the pH. Therefore, patients with chronic respiratory acidosis whose pH is normal must have a $[HCO_3^-]_s$ that exceeds the predicted level. Such patients probably have mixed metabolic alkalosis and chronic respiratory acidosis. Another possible explanation for such parameters is acute hyperventilation superimposed on chronic respiratory acidosis. (Arterial blood collection may generate pain and anxiety, with consequent transient hyperventilation.)

Alternatively, if the $[HCO_3^-]_s$ is lower than predicted, metabolic acidosis probably complicates the chronic respiratory acidosis.

If chronic respiratory acidosis is reversed and the Pco_2 falls into the normal range, the kidneys must excrete HCO_3^- to normalize the acid-base status. This does not occur if effective blood volume is reduced, either because of salt depletion owing to restricted intake or diuretics or a salt-retention state, such as heart failure or cirrhosis. Under such consequences, an increased renal HCO_3^- reabsorptive capacity prevents renal HCO_3^- clearance despite the fall in Pco_2. Chronic respiratory acidosis is thus converted to metabolic alkalosis. This development is called posthypercapnic metabolic alkalosis.

Metabolic compensation for chronic respiratory alkalosis decreases the $[HCO_3^-]_s$. The kidneys respond to chronic hypocarbia by excreting HCO_3^- and decreasing renal NH_4^+ and titratable acid excretion. The HCO_3^- excretion and acid retention, owing to reduced net acid excretion, combine to decrease the $[HCO_3^-]_s$. Alkalemia accelerates organic acid production and increases the concentration of lactate in blood (*see* Metabolic Regulation of Buffers). H^+ is also released from proteins. These buffer mechanisms increase the anion gap slightly (lactate and increased albumin anionic charge). However, the decrease in $[HCO_3^-]_s$ is primarily offset by a proportionate $[Cl^-]_s$ increase.

The expected $[HCO_3^-]_s$ in chronic respiratory alkalosis is illustrated in the acid-base nomogram (Fig. 6). Chronic respiratory alkalosis decreases the $[HCO_3^-]_s$ concentration approximately 5 mEq/liter for each 10 mm Hg reduction in CO_2 tension. Compensation for chronic respiratory alkalosis can reduce the $[HCO_3^-]_s$ sufficiently to normalize the pH. Therefore, chronic respiratory alkalosis is the only primary acid-base disorder that may be associated with a normal pH. Patients with chronic respiratory alkalosis, whose pH is alkaline, have a $[HCO_3^-]_s$ higher than predicted for compensation. Such patients may have mixed metabolic alkalosis and respiratory alkalosis. Conversely, patients with chronic respiratory alkalosis, whose pH is acid, have a $[HCO_3^-]_s$ that is lower than predicted. They probably have metabolic acidosis combined with chronic respiratory alkalosis.

CLINICAL EVALUATION OF ACID-BASE DISORDERS (56,57,59,62)

Acid-Base Nomogram and Predicted Compensation

Primary acid-base derangements generate compensatory responses that may be predicted with a high degree of accuracy. Acid-base nomograms, such as the one shown in Fig. 6, depict expected compensation for primary acid-base disturbances. Acid-base data plotted on this nomogram generate a point. If the point falls near a line describing a compensated disturbance, the data are consistent with a primary, compensated acid-base disorder. However, other explanations for such data are also possible. Mixed acid-base disorders can generate similar parameters. Consider a patient whose pH = 7.30, Pco_2 = 78 mm Hg, and $HCO_3^- = 40$ mEq/liter. These results are consistent with primary chronic respiratory acidosis. However, identical data may result if metabolic alkalosis is superimposed on acute respiratory acidosis. Therefore, acute mixed disturbances of this type may simulate a primary chronic disturbance.

The relationships described by acid-base nomograms define compensatory changes in CO_2 tension and $[HCO_3^-]_s$ in primary acid-base disturbances. Predicted compensatory Pco_2 tensions or $[HCO_3^-]_s$ can also be calculated with various formulae or $\Delta Pco_2/\Delta[HCO_3^-]_s$ ratios, as discussed previously. Table 1 summarizes several useful relationships that predict compensation for simple acid-base disturbances. Acid-base nomograms and these formulae and ratios will identify mixed respiratory and metabolic disorders in the steady state. The change in Pco_2 may be appropriate or inappropriate for the change in $[HCO_3^-]_s$, or vice versa. However, these relationships may become misleading when several acute disorders combine to simulate a mixed disorder. Extremely rapid alterations in Pco_2 or $[HCO_3^-]_s$ may not allow time for the compensatory reaction to occur. In consequence, a mixed disorder may be diagnosed inappropriately.

Mixed disorders that combine metabolic acidosis and metabolic alkalosis cannot be diagnosed on the basis of these nomograms or formulae. Such mixed disorders require critical analysis of the anion gap, the Δanion gap/$\Delta[HCO_3^-]_s$, $[Cl^-]_s$ relative to $[Na^+]_s$, the history, and the physical examination. These concepts are discussed in subsequent sections.

TABLE 1. *Simple and mixed acid-base disorders:*
Summary of expected compensation for simple acid-base disorders

Primary disorder	Initial chemical change	Compensatory response	Expected range of compensation
Metabolic acidosis	HCO_3^- decrease	P_{CO_2} decrease	$P_{CO_2} = 1.5\,[HCO_3^-] + 8 \pm 2$ $P_{CO_2} = $ last 2 digits of pH $\times$ 100 $\Delta P_{CO_2} = 1\text{–}1.3\,(\Delta[HCO_3^-])$ $P_{CO_2} = [HCO_3^-] + 15$
Metabolic alkalosis	HCO_3^- increase	P_{CO_2} increase	P_{CO_2}: Variable increase $P_{CO_2} = 0.9\,[HCO_3^-] + 9$ $P_{CO_2} = $ Increases 0.6 mm Hg for each mEq/liter increase in $[HCO_3^-]$
Respiratory acidosis	P_{CO_2} increase	HCO_3^- increase	Acute $\quad[HCO_3^-]$ increases 1 mEq/liter for every 10 mm Hg increase in P_{CO_2} Chronic $\quad[HCO_3^-]$ increases 3.5 mEq/liter for every 10 mm Hg increase in P_{CO_2}
Respiratory alkalosis	P_{CO_2} decrease	HCO_3^- decrease	Acute $\quad[HCO_3^-]$ falls 2 mEq/liter for each 10 mm Hg fall in P_{CO_2} Chronic $\quad[HCO_3^-]$ falls 5 mEq/liter for each 10 mm Hg fall in P_{CO_2}

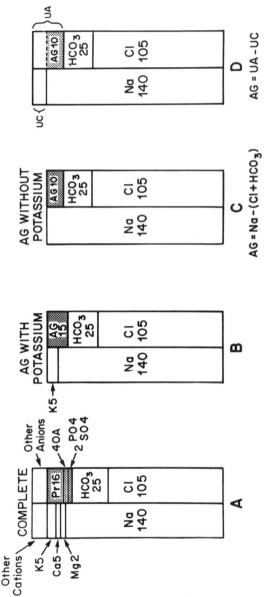

FIG. 7. The ionic anatomy of serum is depicted. **A:** The entire cation and anion composition is displayed. The total anion concentration must equal the total cation concentration. **B:** Measurement of the four major electrolytes—K^+, Na^+, Cl^-, and HCO_3^-. Under normal conditions, the concentration of the sum of $(Na^+ + K^+)$ exceeds the sum of $(Cl^- + HCO_3^-)$. This results in an anion gap, seen in **B** to be 15 mEq/liter. **C:** The anion gap calculation disregarding the $[K^+]$. The potential variation of K^+ is small compared with the other three variables, and it may, therefore, be disregarded for purposes of this calculation. As shown in the example in **C,** the anion gap, calculated as $Na^+ - (Cl^- + HCO_3^-)$, is 10 mEq/liter. **D:** The anion gap may be calculated as the difference between total unmeasured anions (UA) and unmeasured cations (UC). It can be seen that in addition to alterations of acid–base status, which may affect the anion gap as described in the text, the abnormal accumulation of unmeasured cations or depletion of unmeasured anions will depress the anion gap.

Anion Gap (19,20,56,59)

The ionic profile of normal serum is depicted in Fig. 7. The law of electro-neutrality states that the number of positive charges in any solution must equal the number of negative charges. If every ion present in serum were measured, the concentration of positive charges, or cations, would equal the concentration of negative charges, or anions. (These concentrations must be expressed in a charge unit, such as mEq/liter.) If the quantitatively most important electrolytes, Na^+, Cl^-, and HCO_3^-, are considered alone, the $[Na^+]_s$ normally exceeds the sum of $[Cl^-]_s$ and $[HCO_3^-]_s$. The difference, $[Na^+] - ([Cl^-] + [HCO_3^-])$ is the anion gap. The normal anion gap calculated in this manner is 12 ± 4 mEq/liter (± 2 SD). The $[K^+]_s$ has been excluded because of its relatively minor quantitative contribution. The anion gap is a virtual measurement; it does not represent any specific ionic constituent. It includes the net negative protein charges (primarily albumin), inorganic phosphate, sulfate, and other constituents that make a minor contribution to the anionic profile. The anion gap is a useful tool for classifying the metabolic acidosis and aids in the diagnosis and elucidation of various mixed acid-base disorders. These concepts are reviewed in the following sections.

Occasionally, the anion gap is abnormally small or even develops a negative value. This may be due to a sporadic error in the measurement of one of the electrolytes, and each measurement should be confirmed. Systematic errors that depress the $[Na^+]_s$ (pseudohyponatremia due to hyperlipidemia or hyperproteinemia) or increase the $[Cl^-]_s$ (pseudohyperchloremia due to bromism) also will reduce the anion gap. An abnormally large concentration of cations other than Na^+ (e.g., abnormal cationic myeloma proteins, extreme hypermagnesemia, lithium poisoning) can depress the anion gap, since $[Cl^-]_s$ increases without a proportionate change in $[Na^+]_s$. Table 2 lists the causes of a reduced or negative anion gap.

TABLE 2. *Causes of a low anion gap*

Reduced concentration of unmeasured anions
   Dilution
   Hypoalbuminemia
   Hyperchloremic metabolic acidosis
Systematic underestimate of $[Na^+]_s$
   Extreme hypernatremia
   Hyperviscosity
   Displacement of water by hyperlipidemia or hyperproteinemia
Systematic overestimate of $[Cl^-]_s$
   Other halides — bromide, iodide
Increased concentration of nonsodium cations
   Multiple myeloma, paraproteinemias
   Extreme hypercalcemia, hypermagnesemia, lithium
     intoxication

Hyperchloremic and Anion Gap Metabolic Acidoses (53)

When H^+ accumulates in the ECF, it is primarily buffered by the following reaction.

$$H^+ + HCO_3^- \rightarrow H_2CO_3 \rightarrow CO_2 + H_2O$$

To the extent that H^+ accumulates, a nearly equimolar decrease in $[HCO_3^-]_s$ occurs. If HA, a strong acid, accumulates in the ECF, the reduction in $[HCO_3^-]_s$ is accompanied by a similar increase in $[A^-]_s$. The net effect of HA addition is, therefore, the replacement of HCO_3^- by A^-. If HA represents HCl, the decrease in $[HCO_3^-]_s$ is counterbalanced by a similar increase in $[Cl^-]_s$, whereas the anion gap remains relatively stable.[4] Alternatively, if HA is any non-HCl acid (i.e., lactic, acetoacetic, phosphoric, sulfuric), HA accumulation in the ECF decreases the $[HCO_3^-]_s$ and reciprocally increases the anion gap.

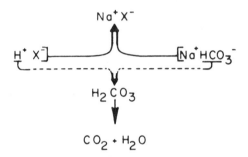

$$AG = Na^+ - (Cl^- + HCO3^-)$$

Normal Anion Gap Acidosis	High Anion Gap Acidosis
MEq/L	

	Normal Anion Gap Acidosis	High Anion Gap Acidosis
Na	140	140
Cl	115	105
HCO$_3$	15	15
AG	10	20

FIG. 8. Metabolic acidosis and the anion gap. The addition of a relatively strong acid–HX–to the ECF alters the electrolyte profile as shown. If the acid is HCl, the reduction in $[HCO_3^-]_s$ is matched by a reciprocal increase in $[Cl^-]_s$. If any non-HCl acid is added to the ECF, the reduction in $[HCO_3^-]_s$ is matched by a reciprocal increase in the anion gap, whereas the $[Cl^-]_s$ remains relatively stable.

---

[4]The anion gap actually decreases slightly because the decrease in pH increases H^+ binding by proteins. This reduces the net negative charge on proteins, principally albumin.

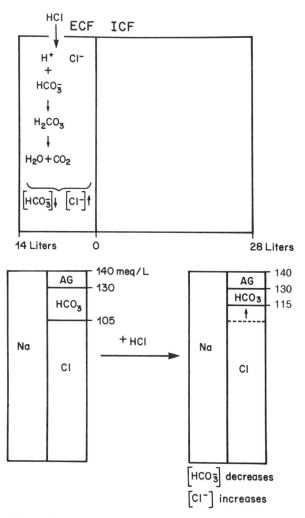

FIG. 9. The addition of 10 mmol/L of HCl to ECF results in a proportionate reduction in $[HCO_3]_s$ and increase in $[Cl^-]_s$. Hyperchloremic acidosis results. The anion gap remains stable.

Figures 8, 9, and 10 illustrate the development of hyperchloremic and anion gap metabolic acidosis.

The causes of hyperchloremic and anion gap metabolic acidosis are listed in Table 3. Recognition that a metabolic acidosis falls into one of these two groups immediately restricts the diagnostic possibilities. The specific diagnosis may then be suggested by the history, physical examination, and other readily available laboratory results.

Occasionally, patients have mixed anion gap and hyperchloremic acidosis. Such a hybrid metabolic acidosis may develop when renal failure progresses

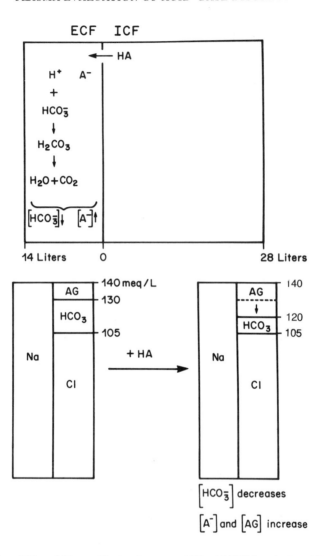

FIG. 10. The addition of 10 mmol/L of a strong non-HCl acid (HA) (i.e., lactic acid, ketoacids) reduces the $[HCO_3^-]_s$ and proportionately increases the $[A^-]$, which also increases the anion gap. The $[Cl^-]_s$ concentration remains relatively stable.

from milder to more severe stages. Hyperchloremic metabolic acidosis is common in early renal disease as a result of inadequate ammonia synthesis and excretion. The GFR is still high enough to excrete the exogenous and endogenous anion load (e.g., phosphate, sulfate). Hyperchloremic acidosis develops (type IV renal tubular acidosis). Later, when renal function deteriorates, anion retention ensues, and typical uremic-anion gap acidosis evolves. In the intervening period mixed hyperchloremic-anion gap acidosis may develop (Fig. 11).

TABLE 3. *Causes of hyperchloremic and anion gap metabolic acidoses*

Elevated anion gap acidoses
  Ketoacidosis
  Uremia
  Lactate
  Salicylate poisoning
  Ethylene glycol poisoning
  Methanol poisoning
  Paraldehyde poisoning
  D-Lactic acidosis
  Congenital organic acidoses
  Rapid hemodialysis with Na
    acetate
Hyperchloremic (normal gap) acidoses
  Renal
    Hypokalemic
      Proximal renal tubular acidosis
      Distal renal tubular acidosis
    Hyperkalemic
      Mineralocorticoid deficiency
      Mineralocorticoid resistance
      Tubular voltage defects
    Renal potential HCO_3^- losses
  Gastrointestinal
    Diarrhea
    External pancreatic fistulae
    Ingestion of resins or salts that bind HCO_3^-
      ($CaCl_2$ or cholestyramine)
  Mixed gastrointestinal–renal
    Ureterosigmoidostomy
    Rectal bladder
    Ileal loop bladder
    Ureterointestinal segments
  Other
    Posthypocapnia
    HCl or HCl precursor infusion or ingestion
    Dilution

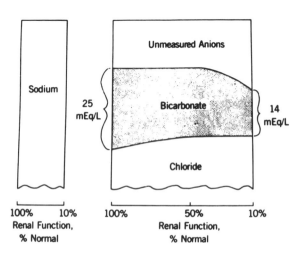

FIG. 11. Early renal failure impairs NH_4^+ excretion before anion retention develops. This results in hyperchloremic metabolic acidosis. As renal failure progresses, the GFR falls, and anion retention eventuates. Uremic-anion gap metabolic acidosis will develop. Between these extremes, combined hyperchloremic and anion gap metabolic acidosis is a common finding. (From ref. 53.)

The Effect of Multiple Acid-Base Buffering Compartments:
An Integrated Analysis (35,36,43)

The preceding discussion of alterations in anion gap and $[Cl^-]_s$ in various forms of metabolic acidosis has focused on the ECF, with little consideration of other buffering compartments. In reality, multiple compartments interact to influence the pH, electrolyte composition, and osmolality of the ECF. The impact of acid-base perturbations on the electrolyte profile may be importantly affected by these fluid and ion exchanges.

Hyperchloremic Acidosis Resulting from NaHCO₃ Losses

The loss of $NaHCO_3$ from the ECF does not occur in pure form. It is always associated with loss of other electrolytes, solutes, and water. Several examples of $NaHCO_3$ loss are analyzed to elucidate their effect on the ECF electrolyte pattern. $NaHCO_3$ might be lost as isotonic $NaHCO_3$, as an isotonic mixture of $NaHCO_3$ and NaCl, as $NaHCO_3$ without water (i.e., $NaHCO_3$ solution is lost and an equal volume of water is replaced), or as HCO_3^- loss with Cl^- replacement (i.e., $NaHCO_3$ is lost and an equal quantity of NaCl and water is replaced). Water also may be retained in excess of osmotic requirements and produce hyponatremia because volume depletion results in nonosmotic stimulation of ADH release.

If $NaHCO_3$ is lost as a pure isotonic solution, without electrolyte or water replacement, the $[Na^+]_s$ will not change. The $[Na^+]$ of the fluid that is removed is equal to the ECF $[Na^+]$. However, the $[HCO_3^-]$ of the lost fluid exceeds the ECF $[HCO_3^-]_s$ (140 mEq/liter versus 24 mEq/liter). As a consequence, the $[HCO_3^-]_s$ falls. Simultaneously, ECF volume shrinks and $[Cl^-]_s$ increases as a result of ECF contraction about a fixed quantity of Cl^-. This sequence is depicted in Fig. 12. The result is a hyperchloremic metabolic acidosis and a normal anion gap.[5]

Isotonic $NaHCO_3$ losses, which are replaced by an equal volume of free water, produce hyponatremia. Net solute loss occurs without net water loss. The administered water is distributed in total body water, whereas the $NaHCO_3$ fluid losses come primarily from the ECF. Therefore, ECF volume shrinks despite water replacement (Fig. 13). Note that mild hyponatremia coexists with mild hyperchloremia (because of contraction of the ECF). The mild hyperchloremia becomes a more significant indicator of hyperchloremic

---

[5]The anion gap may increase slightly due to ECF contraction, which concentrates proteins, phosphate, and so on. This increase is small. A 10% loss of ECF volume, as isotonic $NaHCO_3$, increases by itself $[Cl^-]_s$ from 100 mEq/liter to 110 mEq/liter while the anion gap increases from 10 mEq/liter to 11 mEq/liter. This slight increase in anion gap is partially offset because of increased H^+ binding by protein, resulting from the acidemia. This decreases the negative charge contribution of proteins to the anion gap.

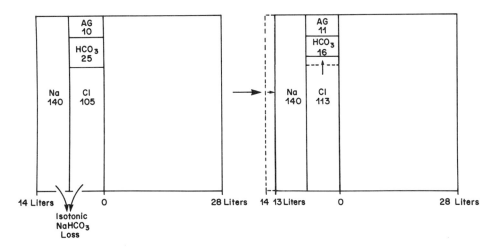

FIG. 12. The loss of isotonic $NaHCO_3$ from ECF produces hyperchloremic acidosis. The $[Na^+]_s$ remains stable, whereas the $[HCO_3^-]_s$ decreases. The $[Cl^-]_s$ increases as a result of the reduction in ECF volume. In the example, 1 liter of isotonic $NaHCO_3$ loss reduces the ECF by 1 liter, and the $[Cl^-]_s$ increases to 113 mEq/liter. The solid lines indicate the final volume after fluid shifts.

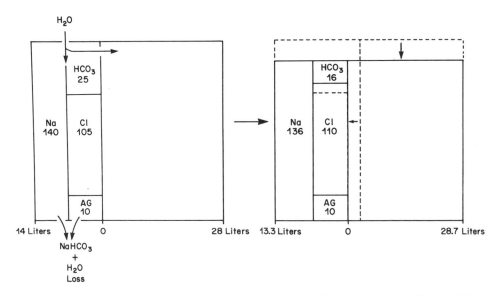

FIG. 13. Isotonic $NaHCO_3$ is lost, and an equal volume of water is replaced. To maintain osmotic equilibrium, the water distributes in total body fluid. Therefore, despite isovolemic fluid replacement, the ECF shrinks because of water entering cells. The dilution of body solutes decreases the osmolality and $[Na^+]_s$. Simultaneously, $[Cl^-]_s$ increases due to the reduction in ECF volume. The result is hyperchloremic metabolic acidosis. The anion gap changes minimally. In the example, 1 liter of $NaHCO_3$ is lost and 1 liter of H_2O is replaced. The ECF shrinks from 14 to 13.3 liters; $[Cl^-]_s$ increases to 110 mEq/liter, and $[Na^+]_s$ falls to 136 mEq/liter. The solid lines indicate the final volume after fluid shifts.

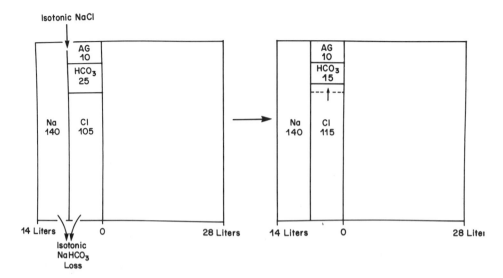

FIG. 14. The loss of isotonic $NaHCO_3$ from ECF is replaced with an equal volume of isotonic NaCl. The ECF volume is stable. The $[HCO_3^-]_s$ falls while the $[Cl^-]_s$ increases reciprocally. The net effect of this process is the replacement of HCO_3^- by Cl^-. In the example, 1 liter of $NaHCO_3$ is lost and replaced by 1 liter of NaCl. The $[Cl^-]_s$ increases to 115 mEq/liter.

acidosis when considered in relationship to the hyponatremia. The $[HCO_3^-]_s$ is reduced, and the anion gap is only minimally changed.

Figure 14 illustrates the effect of $NaHCO_3$ losses followed by replacement with water and an equivalent quantity of NaCl. The $[Na^+]_s$ and the ECF volume each remain stable. The $[HCO_3^-]_s$ falls and the $[Cl^-]_s$ increases reciprocally. The anion gap is almost unchanged.

The loss of $NaHCO_3$ in each of these situations produces hyperchloremic metabolic acidosis. The hyperchloremia is a consequence of one of the following mechanisms: (1) ECF contraction resulting from exogenous $NaHCO_3$ and fluid losses, (2) ECF contraction due to a shift of water from the ECF into cells, and (3) retention of exogenously administered NaCl. Of these potential mechanisms, the replacement of $NaHCO_3$ by exogenous NaCl is quantitatively the most common and important mechanism responsible for development of hyperchloremic acidosis after $NaHCO_3$ loss.

Hyperchloremic Acidosis Resulting from HCl Addition

Hyperchloremic metabolic acidosis also may be caused by the infusion or ingestion of HCl or an HCl precursor. HCl precursors, including NH_4Cl and various organic chloride salts, may be infused or ingested. When these salts are metabolized, they release HCl. HCl occasionally is infused into patients with profound metabolic alkalosis refractory to conservative therapy. Figure 9 represents HCl addition and the effect on the electrolyte profile. The $[Na^+]_s$ and ECF volume are unchanged by the accumulation of HCl itself. The accumulating H^+ titrates $[HCO_3^-]_s$, and the decrement is offset by an approximately equivalent increase in $[Cl^-]_s$. If the water in which the HCl or its precursor is infused is retained, $[Na^+]_s$ falls.

Anion Gap Acidosis from Organic Acid Addition

Relatively strong organic acids, such as lactic acid, ketoacids, oxalic acid, and formic acid, accumulate in the ECF in various pathologic conditions. These acids may be removed from the ECF by metabolic conversion to neutral products or to CO_2 and H_2O. They can be removed by the kidney, or they may move into another body compartment.

The exit of H^+ from the ECF may or may not be accompanied by the exit of the organic anion that originated with the acid (i.e., in the case of lactic acidosis, the H^+ may exit the ECF with or without lactate⁻). When H^+ exits from the ECF without its original anion, it must leave with some other anion, such as Cl^-, or exchange with a cation, such as Na^+ or K^+, from another compartment. Conversely, the organic acid anion may exit from the ECF without the H^+. In this case, it must exit with Na^+ or K^+ or exchange with Cl^- or another anion.

The alteration in plasma electrolyte composition produced by these various ionic movements and exchanges is best illustrated with a concrete clinical example. The evolution, stabilization, and reversal of ketoacidosis is reviewed. This disorder is a prototypical anion gap metabolic acidosis resulting from organic acid accumulation. The conceptual framework developed may then be applied to other forms of metabolic acidosis.

Ketoacidosis results when the rate of hepatic ketoacid generation exceeds peripheral utilization (primarily by muscle and brain) and the blood ketoacid concentration increases. The higher filtered load of ketoacid anions produces increasing urinary ketoacid anion losses. As the disorder progresses, blood ketone levels rise more rapidly. The pathophysiology responsible for ketoacidosis is more fully discussed in Chapter 14.

Figure 10 is representative of the initial phase of ketoacidosis. Ketoacids, symbolized by HA, move from hepatocytes into the ECF. The H^+ accumulating in the ECF decomposes $[HCO_3^-]_s$ while the $[A^-]_s$ (ketoacid anion concentration) increases. To the extent that HA enters and accumulates in the ECF, an equimolar reduction in $[HCO_3^-]_s$ and increase in anion gap supervene.

If HA exits from the ECF, the severity of the acidosis is mitigated (Fig. 15). When the acidosis improves in this fashion, the Δanion gap/ΔHCO_3^- stoichiometric relationship remains intact (i.e., the decrease in $[HCO_3^-]_s$ continues to match the increase in anion gap). HA may be removed by metabolic conver-

HA ENTERS ECF
AND HA EXITS ECF

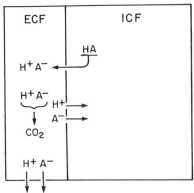

HA, NH$_4$A or Other Titratable Acid with A$^-$ } Urine

$+HA \xrightarrow[-A^-]{-H^+}$ No net effect on acid base status

HA enters the ECF and then HA exits via

1. Metabolism to neutral products or to CO$_2$

2. HA enters cells or skeleton

3. HA enters the urine as HA, as titratable acid plus A$^-$, or as NH$_4$A

FIG. 15. The entry of a relatively strong acid HA into the ECF followed by the removal of HA has no net acid-base effect. The HA may be removed by metabolism to neutral products or to CO$_2$, by HA entry into the intracellular fluids or the skeleton, or by excretion into the urine as HA or an equivalent form of HA, such as NH$_4$A or other titratable acids plus A$^-$.

sion to neutral products or CO$_2$, by movement of both H$^+$ and A$^-$ into cells,[6] or by the renal excretion of HA or an HA equivalent.

If the urine pH is 5, only 20% of the βOH-butyrate and 4% of acetoacetate present in urine are in the form of undissociated HA. The remainder of the ketoacid anions in the urine are excreted in salt forms. If these are Na$^+$ or K$^+$ salts, they represent lost potential HCO$_3^-$. If they are excreted as NH$_4^+$ salts or together with other titratable acids, they are equivalent, from an acid-base perspective, to the renal excretion of undissociated ketoacids. (βOH-butyric acid and acetoacetic acid in urine are measured with titratable acids. The excretion of other titratable acids, together with Na$_4^+$ or K$^+$ βOH-butyrate or acetoacetate is equivalent to excretion of the undissociated ketoacids. (For example, NaH$_2$PO$_4$ + NaβOH-butyrate in urine is equivalent to Na$_2$HPO$_4$ + βOH-butyric acid.) Regardless of the specific form excreted, re-

---

[6]The entry of H$^+$ into cells is equivalent to the movement of HCO$_3^-$ out of cells. Regardless of which mechanism occurs, the effect on ECF and intracellular acid-base status and electrolyte profiles is identical.

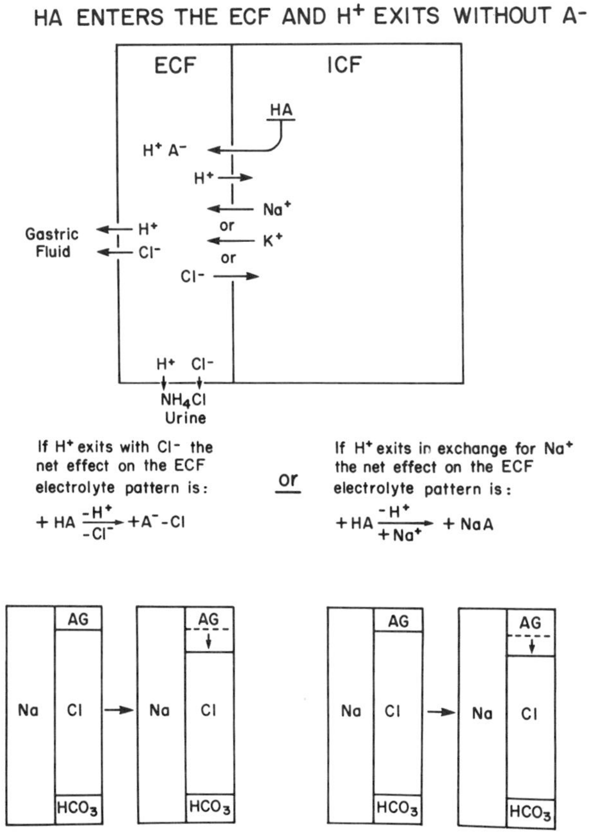

HA ENTERS THE ECF AND H$^+$ EXITS WITHOUT A$^-$

If H$^+$ exits with Cl$^-$ the net effect on the ECF electrolyte pattern is:

$$+ HA \xrightarrow[-Cl^-]{-H^+} + A^- - Cl$$

or

If H$^+$ exits in exchange for Na$^+$ the net effect on the ECF electrolyte pattern is:

$$+ HA \xrightarrow[+Na^+]{-H^+} + NaA$$

FIG. 16. Ketoacids represented by HA enter the ECF followed by H$^+$ leaving the ECF without A$^-$. The H$^+$ may exit as HCl (in gastrointestinal secretions) or as NH$_4$Cl in the urine. Alternatively, H$^+$ may exchange with Na$^+$, K$^+$, or some other cation and enter an intracellular compartment or the urine. If HCl is lost, the [HCO$_3^-$]$_s$ returns to normal while [Cl$^-$]$_s$ decreases and the anion gap remains large. If H$^+$ exchanges for Na$^+$, the net effect is similar to the addition of NaA to the ECF rather than HA. The [HCO$_3^-$]$_s$ returns to normal. [Cl$^-$]$_s$ falls as a result of ECF expansion. The net effect of such H$^+$ secretion or exchange is an amelioration of the metabolic acidosis but persistence of the large anion gap and development of relative hypochloremia.

moval of HA or its equivalent reverses the acidosis and corrects the electrolyte abnormalities.

Figure 16 illustrates the effect of H$^+$ exiting from the ECF without the organic anion A$^-$ (acetoacetate or βOH-butyrate). The H$^+$ may enter parenchymal cells, be excreted in the urine, be lost in gastric fluids (vomiting or gastric suction), or enter the skeleton. When H$^+$ exits without A$^-$, it must either be accompanied by another anion, such as Cl$^-$, or exchange for a cation, such as Na$^+$ or K$^+$. The H$^+$ excreted into the urine as NH$_4^+$ or titratable acidity is generally associated with the return of Na$^+$ to the blood. When H$^+$ enters cells without A$^-$, it may enter together with Cl$^-$ or exchange with intracellular Na^+ or K^+. The H^+ secreted by the stomach is associated with Cl^-.

The effect on the ECF electrolyte profile of H^+ exiting from the ECF without A^- may be expressed as follows.

1. If HA enters the ECF and the H^+ exits with Cl^-,

$$HA \xrightarrow{-HCl} +A^- - Cl^-$$

$[Cl^-]_s$ decreases and is reciprocally replaced by A^-. The $[Na^+]_s$ and $[HCO_3^-]_s$ are not altered. Therefore, the anion gap increases because $[Cl^-]_s$ is replaced by $[A^-]_s$.

2. If HA enters the ECF and H^+ enters cells in exchange for intracellular Na^+ (or K^+),

$$HA \xrightarrow[+ Na^+]{- H^+} + NaA$$

The result is equivalent to the addition of NaA to the ECF. The NaA will shift water into the ECF to maintain osmotic equilibrium. The ECF expands, and this decreases the $[Cl^-]_s$. The net result is a fall in $[Cl^-]_s$, and an increased anion gap.[7] Therefore, the movement of H^+ out of the ECF without the organic anion mitigates the fall in $[HCO_3^-]_s$; however, the anion gap remains large.

During the various phases of ketoacidosis, each of these H^+ exit mechanisms is used to varying degrees. H^+ has a greater volume of distribution than either acetoacetate or βOH-butyrate. Thus H^+ exits from the ECF in part by entering cells without acetoacetate or βOH-butyrate. The increase in anion gap will then exceed the reduction in $[HCO_3^-]_s$. Relative hypochloremia will develop as a result of these water and ion shifts (Fig. 16). Although this electrolyte profile occasionally occurs in patients with ketoacidosis, especially those with very poor renal function, it is an unusual finding. Other H^+ and ketoacid anion exit mechanisms that have offsetting effects which reverse this pattern.

Figure 17 illustrates the effect of the A^- exiting from the ECF without H^+. To the extent this occurs, H^+ accumulates in the ECF to a greater degree than the A^-. The decrease in the $[HCO_3^-]_s$ will then exceed the increase in $[A^-]_s$ and the increase in anion gap. Ketoacid anions enter cells to a lesser degree than does H^+; however, during the first 2 to 3 days of ketoacidosis, ketoacid anions exit from the ECF via the urine in the form of Na^+ or K^+ salts. During this time, the excretion rate of these salts exceeds the renal H^+

---

[7] If H^+ exchanges with intracellular K^+, the effect is ECF KA addition. With normal kidney function this K^+ will be largely excreted by exchanging in the distal tubule with filtered Na^+ The final result is addition of NaA to the ECF similar to that shown in Fig. 16.

HA ENTERS THE ECF AND A- EXITS WITHOUT H+

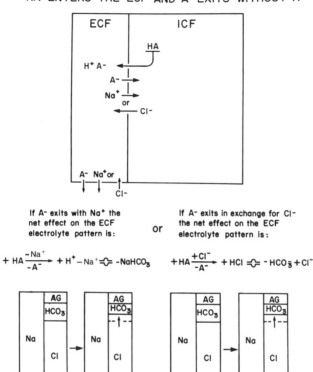

FIG. 17. Ketoacids, represented by HA, enter the ECF followed by exit of the anion (A⁻) without H⁺. The A⁻ may exit as a Na⁺ or K⁺ salt, exchange with Cl⁻ or some other anion from another compartment. The loss of NaA converts an anion gap acidosis into a hyperchloremic acidosis. The anion gap shrinks as A⁻ leaves the ECF, whereas the $[Cl^-]_s$ increases because of reduced ECF volume. To the extent A⁻ exchanges with Cl⁻ from another compartment, the anion gap will decrease while $[Cl^-]_s$ increases. In either case, the anion gap acidosis is converted to a hyperchloremic acidosis.

excretion rate (as NH_4^+ and titratable acid). To the extent that Na ketoacid salts are excreted, the following alteration in ECF electrolyte pattern occurs.

$$HA \xrightarrow{-NaA} + H^+ - Na^+ \rightarrow - NaHCO_3$$

Therefore, if ketoacids enter the ECF and then Na ketoacid salts are excreted, this is equivalent to the loss of $NaHCO_3$ from the ECF. This results in hyperchloremic acidosis. To the extent this sequence occurs, the anion gap acidosis is converted to a hyperchloremic metabolic acidosis.

In the initial stages of ketoacidosis, as ketoacids accumulate in the ECF, the reduction in $[HCO_3^-]_s$ may be approximately matched by a reciprocal increase in the anion gap. To the extent that ketoacids (both the H^+ and the ketoacid anion) are removed by metabolism or renal excretion, the anion gap acidosis is mitigated. To the extent that H^+ exits from the ECF with Cl^- or in exchange for Na^+ or K^+ while the A^- remains in the ECF, the $[HCO_3^-]_s$ increases, but the anion gap remains large and hypochloremia develops. To the extent that A^- exits from the ECF with Na^+ while H^+ remains in the ECF (i.e., renal Na ketoacid anion salt excretion), the anion gap acidosis is converted to a hyperchloremic acidosis.

Each of these processes occurs to a variable extent in patients with ketoacidosis. In many patients, these mechanisms have offsetting effects so that a reciprocal relationship between the increase in anion gap and decrease in $[HCO_3^-]_s$ is maintained (i.e., $\Delta AG = \Delta HCO_3^-$). However, it is important to recognize that this finding is usually the fortuitous result of several offsetting processes.

Correction of Hyperchloremic Acidosis and Anion Gap Acidosis

The reversal of a hyperchloremic metabolic acidosis requires a fall in $[Cl^-]_s$ and a commensurate rise in $[HCO_3^-]_s$. This correction is usually accomplished by the kidney, which excretes the equivalent of HCl in the form of NH_4Cl or titratable acid plus Cl^-. ($NaH_2PO_4 + NaCl$ in the urine is equivalent to $Na_2HPO_4 + HCl$). If exogenous NaCl is provided, the kidney can excrete the Cl^- together with H^+ and retain Na^+ and HCO_3^-. The retained $NaHCO_3$ expands the ECF and decreases the $[Cl^-]_s$. However, if the ECF is contracted, avid renal NaCl retention prevents correction of the acidosis until sufficient exogenous NaCl is provided.

Correction of an anion gap metabolic acidosis requires elimination of both accumulated anion and H^+. This can be accomplished by renal excretion of H^+ and A^-. They may be excreted in the form of NH_4A or titratable acid plus A^-. The $[HCO_3^-]_s$ increases while the anion gap falls reciprocally. If the accumulating anion is organic and can be metabolized to a neutral product or to CO_2 and H_2O, H^+ and A^- also can be removed by metabolic processes.

Correction of ketoacidosis can serve as a prototypical example of the correction of an organic anion gap metabolic acidosis. If the ketoacids entering the ECF were entirely retained in the body, the electrolyte pattern would display an increase in anion gap that exceeds the decrease in $[HCO_3^-]_s$ (Δanion gap$>\Delta[HCO_3^-]_s$). The reason for this discrepancy is the greater entry of H^+ into cells than ketoacid anions; the latter are largely restricted to the ECF. Note that $[Cl^-]_s$ is reduced due to ECF expansion as Na^+ enters the ECF from cells and Cl^- may also leave the ECF to a small extent with H^+. If the accelerated ketoacid generation is reversed and the retained ketoacids are metabolized, normal electrolyte concentrations and acid-base parameters are reestablished. This sequence might occur if ketoacidosis developed in an anephric patient in whom exogenous losses are precluded.

The presence of functioning kidneys adds a level of complexity. The renal excretion of ketoacid anions together with H^+, in the form of NH_4A or titratable acid plus A^-, reestablishes normal electrolytes and acid-base status. However, if the kidney excretes Na^+ or K^+ salts of ketoacids, the electrolyte pattern depicted in Fig. 16 is converted to the pattern shown in Fig. 17. The anion gap falls, the $[HCO_3^-]_s$ remains low, and $[Cl^-]_s$ increases. The lost Na^+ or K^+ salts of ketoacids represent lost potential HCO_3^-. The reversal of ketoacidosis following such losses leaves a residual hyperchloremic acidosis. The severity of the hyperchloremic acidosis reflects the degree of antecedent ketoacid salt losses. Reversal of this hyperchloremic metabolic acidosis requires renal HCO_3^- regeneration.

The magnitude of Na^+ and K^+ ketoacid salt loss is a function of the rapidity, severity, and duration of the ketoacidosis, the level of renal function, and the ECF volume status. Patients who are able to continue eating and drinking despite the development of ketoacidosis and thereby maintain relative euvolemia maintain reasonable renal function. These patients may excrete large quantities of Na^+ and K^+ salts of ketoacid anions. They thereby forestall the development of an anion gap acidosis and instead develop a hyperchloremic acidosis.

At the other extreme are the ketoacidotic patients with poor renal function secondary to volume depletion, intrinsic renal disease, or both. These patients retain a larger proportion of the generated ketoacid anions. The large anion gap may exceed the $[HCO_3^-]_s$ reduction (Fig. 16). Reversal of the anion gap metabolic acidosis can occur more rapidly after control of ketoacid generation because the retained ketoacid anions can be rapidly metabolized or excreted as NH_4 salts or together with titratable acid.

The treatment of ketoacidosis usually requires the infusion of large quantities of fluid containing NaCl and KCl. Some of the infused Na^+ and K^+ enters cells in exchange for H^+, which enters the ECF. The net effect of such exchange is an ECF infusion of HCl. This generates hyperchloremic acidosis. Furthermore, since the $Na^+:Cl^-$ ratio of normal saline is 1:1, whereas in the ECF it is normally 1.4:1, the $[Cl^-]$ of 154 mEq/liter in isotonic saline also can contribute to the development of hyperchloremia when large volumes are infused. Distal renal tubular acidosis has been identified occasionally during the recovery phase of ketoacidosis. Each of these factors can contribute to the development of hyperchloremic metabolic acidosis during recovery from ketoacidosis. However, the major factor responsible for this development is the loss of ketoacid salts into the urine and their replacement with administered NaCl as the ECF is reexpanded and renal function improves. Table 4 lists the potential causes of hyperchloremic acidosis developing during the reparative phase of ketoacidosis.

Increased Anion Gap Without a Proportionate
Reduction in $[HCO_3^-]_s$ (1,32,52,56,59)

Anion gap metabolic acidoses typically depress the $[HCO_3^-]_s$ and increase the anion gap in reciprocal fashion ($\Delta[\text{anion gap}] = \Delta[HCO_3^-]_s$). However,

TABLE 4. *Pathogenesis of hyperchloremic acidosis during reparative phase of ketoacidosis*

Na^+ and K^+ salts of ketoacid anions are lost into the urine.
  Losses reflect the volume status, level of renal function, and rapidity of development of ketoacidosis.
  Losses are accelerated by volume expansion during the reparative phase.
NaCl and KCl replacement produces movement of Na^+ and K^+ into cells exchanging for H^+ movement into ECF. This is equivalent to HCl infusion into ECF.
Expansion with normal saline ($Na^+:Cl^-$ = 1:1) rather than the physiologic $Na^+:Cl^-$ ratio of 1.4:1.
Development of distal renal tubular acidosis (rare).

the multiple buffering compartments into which the H^+ and anion may penetrate to variable degrees and the variable renal excretion of H^+ and the anions may disrupt this relationship. When the anion gap is increased but not accompanied by a proportionately decreased $[HCO_3^-]_s$, several possible explanations must be considered:

1. An anion gap acidosis exists, and the volume of distribution of the anion is smaller than the volume of distribution of H^+. Therefore, the anion gap increases to a greater degree than $[HCO_3^-]_s$ falls. This concept was discussed previously in relationship to ketoacidosis (see Fig. 16).

2. Metabolic alkalosis coexists with the anion gap metabolic acidosis.

3. Chronic Respiratory acidosis and anion gap metabolic acidosis coexist.

4. Metabolic alkalosis alone may be present if the $[HCO_3^-]_s$ is markedly elevated.

If metabolic alkalosis due to vomiting is superimposed on an anion gap metabolic acidosis, the $[HCO_3^-]_s$ increases, the $[Cl^-]_s$ decreases, while the anion gap remains large. This sequence is depicted in Fig. 18. If the metabolic alkalosis superimposed on the anion gap acidosis is the result of exogenous $NaHCO_3$, the sequence depicted in Fig. 19 occurs. In each case, the large anion gap remains as a telltale residue of the metabolic acidosis despite the relatively normal $[HCO_3^-]_s$. The anion gap then becomes a critically important clue to this mixed disorder in which the pH, Pco_2, and $[HCO_3^-]_s$ may all be normalized.

Compensation for chronic respiratory acidosis increases the $[HCO_3^-]_s$ and proportionately reduces the $[Cl^-]_s$. If a patient with compensated chronic respiratory acidosis then develops an anion gap metabolic acidosis, the $[HCO_3^-]_s$ falls from an elevated level toward normal, and the anion gap increases. Therefore, a large anion gap may coexist with a normal $[HCO_3^-]_s$. Even if the $[HCO_3^-]_s$ is reduced below normal, the anion gap will still be disproportion-

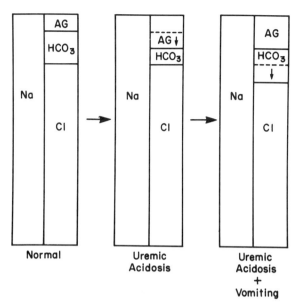

FIG. 18. A patient develops uremic anion gap metabolic acidosis. The $[HCO_3^-]_s$ falls, and the anion gap increases reciprocally. If this patient then begins to vomit, the $[HCO_3^-]_s$ increases while the $[Cl^-]_s$ falls. In the example, the $[HCO_3^-]_s$ has returned to normal (third panel). Mixed metabolic acidosis and metabolic alkalosis is now present. The correct diagnosis is suggested by the large anion gap coexisting with a normal $[HCO_3^-]_s$. From another perspective, the $[Cl^-]_s$ is reduced relative to $[Na^+]_s$. This must indicate metabolic alkalosis or compensated chronic respiratory acidosis. However, the $[HCO_3^-]_s$, which should be elevated in either case, is not elevated. This suggests that metabolic acidosis is also present (see text for details).

ately large compared with the magnitude of the reduction of $[HCO_3^-]_s$. Such patients manifest extreme acidemia because of combined metabolic acidosis and respiratory acidosis. The very low pH will distinguish such patients from those with mixed anion gap metabolic acidosis and metabolic alkalosis who have a similar electrolyte pattern but a relatively normal pH.

Severe metabolic alkalosis alone also can increase the anion gap. The expanded anion gap in these individuals has several components. First, alkalinization of cells stimulates glycolysis, increasing the cellular and blood concentrations of lactic, citric, and other organic acids. To the extent that these acids accumulate in plasma, the $[HCO_3^-]_s$ falls, and anion gap increases. Second, the contribution of plasma proteins, especially albumin, to the anion gap increases because the proteins release H^+ and thereby become more negatively charged. Third, these patients are often volume depleted. This increases the plasma protein concentration, increasing its contribution to the anion gap. Therefore, a moderately elevated anion gap in the presence of a markedly elevated $[HCO_3^-]_s$ and an alkaline pH may be due to the metabolic alkalosis alone and does not necessarily herald a mixed disturbance.

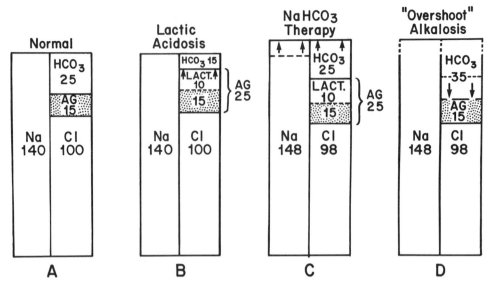

FIG. 19. Consequences of bicarbonate therapy of high AG acidosis. A patient with a normal electrolyte pattern (**A**) develops lactic acidosis (**B**). The $[HCO_3^-]_s$ reduction is matched by a proportionate increase in [lactate⁻] and the [anion gap]. (**C**): The effect of hypertonic $NaHCO_3$ infusion, which in this case has normalized the $[HCO_3^-]_s$. This infusion represents iatrogenic metabolic alkalosis superimposed on the preexistent anion gap metabolic acidosis. The anion gap remains enlarged, representing the elevated lactate concentration. It is elevated due to the increased $[Na^+]_s$ and decreased $[Cl^-]_s$ produced by the hypertonic $NaHCO_3$ infusion. The coexistent large anion gap and normal $[HCO_3^-]_s$ are characteristic of a mixed anion gap acidosis and metabolic alkalosis. Relative hypochloremia and a normal $[HCO_3^-]_s$ also suggest this mixed disorder. (A similar electrolyte pattern could be caused by metabolic acidosis superimposed on chronic respiratory alkalosis). (**D**): The reversal of the metabolic acidosis. When the lactic acidosis reverses, the 10 mEq/liter of accumulated lactate is converted to 10 mEq/liter of HCO_3^-. The anion gap shrinks as the $[HCO_3^-]_s$ increases. A residual overshoot metabolic alkalosis reflects the previous exogenous $NaHCO_3$ therapy.

Increased $[HCO_3^-]_s$ and Decreased $[Cl^-]_s$

This electrolyte pattern is produced by metabolic alkalosis and by respiratory acidosis. Aside from hypokalemia, which is much more common with metabolic alkalosis, there is nothing else in this pattern that permits differentiation of these two disorders. The history and physical examination will be helpful. Blood gas analysis will permit definitive differentiation.

Proportionate and Disproportionate Changes of $[Cl^-]_s$ Relative to $[Na^+]_s$

The normal $[Na^+]_s$ is 140 mEq/liter, and $[Cl^-]_s$ is 100 mEq/liter, establishing a ratio of 1.4:1. This normal ratio may be altered by artifacts in the measurement of $[Na^+]_s$, $[Cl^-]_s$, or both. When electrolytes are measured by any technique that requires quantitative sampling of serum or plasma, displacement errors can occur. For example, measurement of $[Na^+]_s$ by flame photometry and $[Cl^-]_s$ by colorimetric methods requires quantitative aspiration and dilution. In the presence of excess solids, due to hyperlipidemia or hyperproteinemia, water is displaced. Therefore, less than the expected volume of serum or plasma water is diluted for analysis, and this produces pseudohyponatremia or pseudohypochloremia. Such displacement artifacts do not occur if direct ion specific electrodes (ISE) are used for the measurements. These electrodes measure the ion activity in serum or plasma water directly. Fat and proteins have minimal effect on these electrodes. Many clinical laboratories are converting to ISE methodology.

Pseudohyperchloremia can result when excess nonchloride halides, such as bromide or iodide, accumulate in blood. Many $[Cl^-]_s$ measurement techniques, including ISE, are sensitive to nonchloride halides, and these interactions produce pseudohyperchloremia.

If the $[Na^+]_s$ or $[Cl^-]_s$ is abnormal and if their ratio is not 1.4:1, measurement artifacts must be excluded. In the rest of this section, we assume that such artifacts have been excluded.

Hypernatremia always represents dehydration because cells are hypertonic and shrunken. The free water deficit concentrates the blood solutes, increasing the $[Na^+]_s$ and $[Cl^-]_s$ proportionately in a 1.4:1 ratio. For example, when the $[Na^+]_s$ increases by 10% from 140 to 154 mEq/liter, the $[Cl^-]_s$ increases from 100 to 110 mEq/liter. The absolute $[HCO_3^-]_s$ increase is much less for two reasons: (1) the percentage increase translates to a smaller change (i.e., 10% concentration increases the $[HCO_3^-]_s$ from 24 mEq/liter to 26 mEq/liter), and (2) the increase in $[HCO_3^-]_s$ is mitigated by the interaction of other buffers that release H^+ and stabilize the $[HCO_3^-]_s$ and the pH.

Hyponatremia results from two general causes. (1) Hyponatremia may result from a high concentration of osmotically active substances (other than Na^+) in the ECF that are excluded from the intracellular space. They shift water from the intracellular space to the ECF. The ECF expands and dilutes the $[Na^+]_s$. In these patients, the ECF osmolality is elevated despite the presence of hyponatremia. Hyperglycemia or high mannitol levels due to exogenous infusions generate this form of hyponatremia. (2) Far more commonly, hyponatremia is due to overhydration, or water excess, relative to the content of osmotically active substances in the body.

Hyponatremia, due either to osmotic (e.g., glucose, mannitol) ECF expansion or to overhydration, is associated with a proportionate reduction in $[Cl^-]_s$. For example, a 10% decrease in $[Na^+]_s$ from 140 to 126 mEq/liter is associated with a 10% $[Cl^-]_s$ reduction from 100 to 90 mEq/liter.

If artifacts and osmotic ECF expansion have been excluded, alterations in $[Na^+]_s$ always reflect hydration disturbances. Hypernatremia reflects dehydration, and hyponatremia reflects overhydration. Under such circumstances, the $[Cl^-]_s$ should change proportionately (in a 1.4:1 ratio). On the other hand, disproportionate changes in $[Cl^-]_s$ relative to $[Na^+]_s$ always represent acid-base disorders. Increased $[Cl^-]_s$ relative to $[Na^+]_s$ indicates either hyperchloremic metabolic acidosis or chronic respiratory alkalosis. Each of these disorders decreases the $[HCO_3^-]_s$ and increases the $[Cl^-]_s$ in a near reciprocal fashion. The anion gap changes very little.[8]

Relative hypochloremia (decreased $[Cl^-]_s$ relative to the $[Na^+]_s$) is diagnostic of metabolic alkalosis or chronic respiratory acidosis. Both conditions elevate the $[HCO_3^-]_s$ and proportionately reduce the $[Cl^-]_s$.

Therefore, if artifacts and osmotic fluid shifts are excluded, alterations of $[Na^+]_s$ always reflect hydration disorders. However, $[Cl^-]$ may be altered for two reasons: (1) hydration disorders, where the $[Cl^-]_s$ remains proportionate to $[Na^+]_s$, and (2) acid-base disorders, where the $[Cl^-]_s$ changes disproportionately to $[Na^+]_s$.

If relative hypochloremia is not associated with a proportionate increase in $[HCO_3^-]_s$, a mixed disorder exists. This electrolyte profile indicates that anion gap metabolic acidosis (relative hypochloremia without an elevated $[HCO_3^-]_s$ mandates an anion gap increase) coexists with either metabolic alkalosis or chronic respiratory acidosis.

It is apparent that the concept of $[Cl^-]_s$ relative to $[Na^+]_s$, the anion gap, and the expected $[HCO_3^-]_s$ are closely interrelated. Mixed acid-base disorders can be diagnosed using either approach. If $[Cl^-]_s$ is found to be decreased relative to $[Na^+]_s$, then a diagnosis of either metabolic alkalosis or chronic respiratory acidosis is suggested. The $[HCO_3^-]_s$ should be increased in either condition. If the $[HCO_3^-]_s$ is not appropriately increased, or is reduced, then metabolic acidosis must coexist with the metabolic alkalosis or chronic respiratory acidosis. Blood gas analysis permits a more definitive diagnosis. Alternatively, the same conclusions can be reached by finding that the anion gap is increased but the $[HCO_3^-]_s$ is not appropriately reduced. The large anion gap indicates a diagnosis of metabolic acidosis, while the simultaneous relatively high $[HCO_3^-]_s$ indicates that either metabolic alkalosis or chronic respiratory acidosis must also be present. These mixed combined disturbances may develop simultaneously or sequentially. Analysis of the blood electrolytes does not define the temporal sequence. Table 5 shows examples of proportionate and disproportionate $[Cl^-]_s$ alterations with and without appropriate changes in $[HCO_3^-]_s$.

Hyperchloremia, relative to $[Na^+]_s$, whether due to hyperchloremic metabolic acidosis or chronic respiratory alkalosis, should reduce the $[HCO_3^-]_s$ proportionately. If relative hyperchloremia is not associated with a low $[HCO_3^-]_s$, the anion gap must be very small or even negative. The causes of a low or negative anion gap are outlined in Table 2.

---

[8]Actually, in hyperchloremic metabolic acidosis, the anion gap decreases slightly. This occurs because albumin buffers the acidosis by accepting H^+. This reduces the net negative charge on albumin and, hence, reduces its contribution to the anion gap. On the other hand, chronic respiratory alkalosis increases the anion gap slightly because the release of H^+ from proteins increases their net negative charge. Respiratory alkalosis also slightly increases the serum lactate level.

TABLE 5. *Relative changes in [Na]$_s$ and [Cl]$_s$ as an index of disorders in hydration or acid–base balance or both*

Proportionate changes in [Na]$_s$ and [Cl]$_s$ are always due to the disturbances of hydration alone.
  [Na]$_s$: 140→154 mEq/liter = +14 mEq/liter = 10% rise
  [Cl]$_s$: 100→110 mEq/liter = +10 mEq/liter = 10% rise
  —Dehydration
  [Na]$_s$: 140→126 mEq/liter = −14 mEq/liter = 10% fall
  [Cl]$_s$: 100→ 90 mEq/liter = −10 mEq/liter = 10% fall
  —Overhydration
Changes in [Cl]$_s$ without any change in [Na]$_s$ is always due to disturbances of acid–base alone.
  [Na]$_s$: 140→140 mEq/liter = 0 change
  [Cl]$_s$: 100→ 90 mEq/liter = −10 mEq/liter = 10% fall
  —Respiratory acidosis or metabolic alkalosis
  [Na]$_s$: 140→140 mEq/liter = 0 change
  [Cl]$_s$: 100→110 mEq/liter = +10 mEq/liter = 10% rise
  —Respiratory alkalosis or hypercholemic acidosis
Disproportionate changes in [Na]$_s$ and [Cl]$_s$ are due to disturbances in both hydration and acid–base balance.
  [Na]$_s$: 140→154 mEq/liter = +14 mEq/liter = 10% rise
  [Cl]$_s$: 100→100 mEq/liter = 0 change
  — ↑ [Na]$_s$ and normal [Cl]$_s$ → Dehydration plus respiratory acidosis or metabolic alkalosis
  [Na]$_s$: 140→126 mEq/liter = −14 mEq/liter = 10% fall
  [Cl]$_s$: 100→100 mEq/liter = 0 change
  — ↑ [Na]$_s$ and normal [Cl]$_s$ → Overhydration plus respiratory alkalosis or hypercholemic acidosis
  [Na]$_s$: 140→154 = +14 mEq/liter = 10% rise
  [Cl]$_s$: 100→ 90 = −10 mEq/liter = 25% fall
  —Dehydration plus respiratory acidosis or metabolic alkalosis
  [Na]$_s$: 140→126 = −14 mEq/liter = 10% fall
  [Cl]$_s$: 100→ 75 = −25 mEq/liter = 25% fall
  —Overhydration plus respiratory acidosis or metabolic alkalosis
  [Na]$_s$: 140→168 = +28 mEq/liter = 20% rise
  [Cl]$_s$: 100→110 = +10 mEq/liter = 10% rise
  —Overhydration plus respiratory acidosis or metabolic alkalosis

---

Potassium Concentration in Acid-Base Disorders (2,7,10,17,33,38)

The serum [K$^+$]$_s$ is only occasionally helpful in the elucidation of acid-base disorders. Alkalosis *per se* tends to shift K$^+$ into cells and decrease the [K$^+$]$_s$. In addition, metabolic alkalosis is almost always associated with K$^+$ depletion, which contributes to the low [K$^+$]$_s$. On the other hand, acute respiratory acidosis increases [K$^+$]$_s$ slightly as it exits from cells, and chronic respiratory acidosis has little effect on the [K$^+$]$_s$. Therefore, an elevated [HCO$_3^-$]$_s$ associated with a low [K$^+$]$_s$ is more likely to represent metabolic alkalosis than respiratory acidosis. A normal, or elevated, $[K^+]_s$ together with an elevated $[HCO_3^-]_s$ suggests respiratory acidosis.

The metabolic acidoses have variable effects on the $[K^+]_s$. In general, the reduction in $[HCO_3^-]_s$ and low pH produces a movement of H^+ into and K^+ out of cells. However, the magnitude of this exchange varies with different forms of metabolic acidosis. Hyperchloremic acidosis due to HCl or NH_4Cl infusion can produce significant hyperkalemia as a result of H^+-K^+ exchange across cell membranes. However, when hyperchloremic acidosis is encountered clinically it is more often associated with other confounding factors that independently affect $[K^+]_s$. For example, if hyperchloremic acidosis is due to diarrhea, stool K^+ losses are large and hypokalemia is common. Proximal and distal renal tubular acidoses generate hyperchloremic acidosis and also accelerate renal K^+ losses. Type IV renal tubular acidosis is a hyperkalemic disorder in which renal K^+ excretion is depressed because of aldosterone deficiency or renal resistance to its effect. These independent effects on K^+ balance are usually more important than any transcellular shift effects.

The organic acidoses, such as lactic acidosis and ketoacidosis, do not directly shift K^+ from cells to a significant extent. When $[K^+]_s$ does increase, this is usually the result of tissue catabolism, rhabdomyolysis, and/or decreased renal function. If fluid shifts from cells into the ECF as a result of hypernatremia or hyperglycemia, hyperkalemia may occur because this also shifts K^+ from cells into the ECF. Glycosuria and ketoacid salt losses that occur in diabetic ketoacidosis also produce renal K^+ losses. These various effects may be offsetting or additive.

Therefore the $[K^+]_s$ in patients with metabolic acidosis may be low, normal, or high and does not have much diagnostic utility. The $[K^+]_s$ most likely reflects multiple factors other than acid-base status itself.

Acute respiratory alkalosis will transiently depress the $[K^+]_s$ because of cellular K^+ entry. However, the $[K^+]_s$ returns to normal during chronic respiratory alkalosis. A low $[HCO_3^-]_s$ may be caused by metabolic acidosis or respiratory alkalosis, and the $[K^+]_s$ is not generally helpful in their differentiation.

ACKNOWLEDGMENT

The secretarial support rendered by Ann Drew is very gratefully acknowledged.

REFERENCES

1. Adrogue, H. J., Brensilver, J., and Madias, N. E. (1978): Changes in plasma anion gap during chronic metabolic acid base disturbances. *Am. J. Physiol.*, 235:F291–F297.
2. Adrogue, H. J., and Nicolaos, E. M. (1987): Changes in plasma potassium concentration during acute acid-base disturbances. *Am. J. Med.*, 71:456–467.

3. Aquino, H. C., and Luke, R. G. (1973): Respiratory compensation to potassium depletion and chloride depletion alkalosis. *Am. J. Physiol.*, 225:1444–1448.
4. Arbus, G. S., Herbert, L. A., Levesque, P. R., Etsten, B. E., and Schwartz, W. B. (1969): Characterization and clinical significance of the "significance band" for acute respiratory alkalosis. *N. Engl. J. Med.*, 280:117–121.
5. Asch, M. J., Dell, R. B., Williams, G. S., Cohen, M., and Winters, R. W. (1969): Time course for development of respiratory compensation in metabolic acidosis. *J. Lab. Clin. Med.*, 73:610–615.
6. Beattice, J. A., and Gamble, J. L. Jr. (1975): Skeletal buffering of acute metabolic acidosis. *Am. J. Physiol.*, 229:1618–1624.
7. Bia, M. J., and DeFronzo, R. A. (1981): Extrarenal potassium homeostasis. *Am. J. Physiol.*, 240:F257–F268.
8. Brackett, N. C. Jr., Cohen, J. J., and Schwartz, W. B. (1965): Carbon dioxide titration curve of normal man. Effect of increasing degrees of acute hypercapnia in an acid-base equilibrium. *N. Engl. J. Med.*, 272:6–10.
9. Burnell, J. M. (1971): Changes in bone sodium and carbonate in metabolic acidosis and alkalosis in the dog. *J. Clin. Invest.*, 50:327–331.
10. Burnell, J. M., Villamil, M. F., Uyeno, B. T., and Schribner, B. H. (1956): The effect in humans of extracellular pH change on the relationship between serum potassium concentration and intracellular potassium. *J. Clin. Invest.*, 35:935–939.
11. Burton, R. F. (1987): On calculating concentrations of "HCO_3" from pH and P_{CO_2}. *Eur. Comparative Biochem. Physiol.*, 87A:417–422.
12. Ehlers, S. M., Petzel, R. A., and Brown, D. C. (1980): Ventilatory response in lactic acidosis and diabetic ketoacidosis. Effect of coexistent shock, respiratory disease and severe acidosis. *Miner. Electrolyte Metab.*, 3:200–206.
13. Fencl, V., and Gabel, R. A. (1980): Respiratory adaptations in acid-base disturbances: Role of cerebral fluids. *Contrib. Nephrol.*, 21:145–149.
14. Fencl, V., Miller, T. B., and Pappenheimer, J. R. (1966): Studies on the respiratory response to disturbances of acid-base balance, with deductions concerning the ionic composition of cerebral interstitial fluid. *Am. J. Physiol.*, 210:459–572.
15. Fraley, D. S., and Ader, S. (1979): An extrarenal role for parathyroid hormone in the disposal of acute acid loads in rats and dogs. *J. Clin. Invest.*, 63:985–987.
16. Fulop, M. (1976): The ventilatory response in severe metabolic acidosis. *Clin. Sci. Mol. Med.*, 50:367–373.
17. Fulop, M. (1979): Serum potassium in lactic acidosis and ketoacidosis. *N. Engl. J. Med.*, 300:1087–1089.
18. Fulop, M., Dreyer, N., and Tannenbaum, H. (1974): The ventilatory response in diabetic ketoacidosis. *Clin. Sci. Mol. Med.*, 45:539–549.
19. Gabow, P. A. (1985): Disorders associated with an altered anion gap. *Kidney Int.*, 27:472.
20. Gabow, P. A., Kaehny, W. D., Fennessey, D. V., Goodman, S. I., Gross, P. A., and Schrier, R. W. (1980): Diagnostic importance of an increased serum anion gap. *N. Engl. J. Med.*, 303:854–858.
21. Garella, S., Chang, B. S., and Kahn, S. I. (1975): Dilution acidosis and contraction alkalosis: review of a concept. *Kidney Int.*, 8:279–283.
22. Gennari, F. J., Goldstein, M. D., and Schwartz, W. B. (1972): The nature of the renal adaptation to chronic hypocapnia. *J. Clin. Invest.*, 51:1722–1730.
23. Goldring, R. M., Cannon, P. J., Heinemann, H. O., and Fishman, A. P. (1968): Respiratory adjustment to chronic metabolic alkalosis in man. *J. Clin. Invest.*, 47:188–202.
24. Gougoux, A., Kaehny, W. D., and Cohen, J. J. (1975): Renal adaptation to chronic hypocapnia: Dietary constraints in achieving H^+ retention. *Am. J. Physiol.*, 229:1330–1337.
25. Hastings, A. B., Sendroy, J. Jr., and Van Slyke, D. D. (1928): Studies of gas and electrolyte equilibria in blood. XII. The value of pK in the Henderson-Hasselbalch equation for blood serum. *J. Biol. Chem.*, 79:183–192.
26. Hood, I., and Campbell, E. J. M. (1982): Is pK ok? *N. Engl. J. Med.*, 306:864–866.
27. Irsigler, G. B., Stafford, M. J., and Severinghaus, J. W. (1980): Relationship of CSF, pH, O_2, and CO_2 responses in metabolic acidosis and alkalosis in humans. *J. Appl. Physiol.*, 48:355–361.

28. Javahert, S., Clendining, A., Papadakis, N., and Brody, J. S. (1981). Changes in brain surface pH during acute isocapnic metabolic acidosis and alkalosis. *J. Appl. Physiol.*, 51:276–281.
29. Lemann, J. Jr., Litzow, J. R., and Lennon, E. J. (1966): The effects of chronic acid loads in normal man: Further evidence for the participation of bone mineral in the defense against chronic metabolic acidosis. *J. Clin. Invest.*, 45:1608–1614.
30. Maas, A. H., Rispens, P., Siggaard-Anderson, O., and Zijlsatra, W. G. (1984): On the reliability of the Henderson-Hasselbalch equation in routine clinical acid-base chemistry. *Ann. Clin. Biochem.*, 21:26–39.
31. Madias, N. E., Adrogue, H. J., Horowitz, G. L., Cohen, J. J., and Schwartz, W. B. (1979): A redefinition of normal acid-base equilibrium in man: Carbon dioxide tension as a key determinant of normal plasma bicarbonate concentration. *Kidney Int.*, 16:612–618.
32. Madias, N. E., Ayus, J. C., and Adrogue, H. J. (1979): Increased anion gap with metabolic alkalosis. The role of plasma-protein equivalency. *N. Engl. J. Med.*, 300:1421–1423.
33. Magner, P. O., Robinson, L., Halperin, R. M., Zettle, R., and Halperin, M. L. (1988): The plasma potassium concentration in metabolic acidosis: A re-evaluation. *Am. J. Kidney Dis.*, 11:220–224.
34. Monti, M., and Rooth, G. (1970): Respiratory compensation to metabolic acid-base disturbances. *Scand. J. Clin. Lab. Invest.*, 26:381–383.
35. Oh, M. S., Banerji, M. S., and Carroll, H. J. (1981): The mechanism of hyperchloremic acidosis during the recovery phase of diabetic ketoacidosis. *Diabetes*, 30:310–313.
36. Oh, M. S., Carroll, H., Goldstein, M. D., and Fein, I. A. (1978): Hyperchloremic acidosis during the recovery phase of diabetic ketosis. *Ann. Intern. Med.*, 89:925–927.
37. Oliva, P. (1972): Severe alveolar hypoventilation in a patient with metabolic alkalosis. *Am. J. Med.*, 52:817–821.
38. Perez, G. O., Oster, J. R., and Vaamonde, C. A. (1981): Serum potassium concentration in acidemic states. *Nephron*, 27:233–243.
39. Pichette, C., Chen, C-B, Goldstein, M., Steinbaugh, B., and Halperin, M. (1983): Influence of solutes in plasma on the the total CO_2 content determination: Implications for clinical disorders. *Clin. Biochem.*, 16:91–93.
40. Pierce, N. F., Fedson, D. S., Brigham, R. L., Mitra, R. C., Sack, R. B., and Mondal, A. (1970): The ventilatory response to acute base deficit in humans. Time course during development and correction of metabolic acidosis. *Ann. Intern. Med.*, 72:633–640.
41. Poppell, J. W., Vanamee, P., Roberts, K. E., and Randall, H. T. (1956): The effect of ventilatory insufficiency on respiratory compensations in metabolic acidosis and alkalosis. *J. Lab. Clin. Med.*, 47:885–890.
42. Roberts, K. E., Poppell, J. W., Vanamee, P., Beals, R., and Randall, H. T. (1956): Evaluation of respiratory compensation in metabolic alkalosis. *J. Clin. Invest.*, 35:261–266.
43. Robin, E. D. (1972): Dynamic aspects of metabolic acid-base disturbances: Phenformin lactic acidosis with alkaline overshoot. *Trans. Assoc. Am. Physicians*, 85:317–324.
44. Schwartz, W. R., Brackett, N. C. Jr., and Cohen J. J. (1965): The response of extracellular hydrogen ion concentration to gradual degrees of chronic hypercapnea: The physiologic limits of the defense of pH. *J. Clin. Invest.*, 44:291–295.
45. Stone, D. J. (1962): Respiration in man during metabolic alkalosis. *J. Appl. Physiol.*, 17:33.
46. Swan, R. C., Axelrod, D. R., Seip, M., and Pitts, R. F. (1955): Distribution of sodium bicarbonate infused into nephrectomized dogs. *J. Clin. Invest.*, 34:1795–1801.
47. Swan, R. C., and Pitts, R. F. (1955): Neutralization of infused acid by nephrectomized dogs. *J. Clin. Invest.*, 34:205–212.
48. Turino, G. M., Goldring, R. M., and Heinemann, H. O. (1974): Renal response to mechanical ventilation in patients with chronic hypercapnia. *Am. J. Med.*, 56:151–161.
49. Van Slyde, D. D., Sendroy, J. Jr., Hastings, A. B., and Neill, J. M. (1928): Studies of gas and electrolyte equilibria in blood. X. The solubility of carbon dioxide at 38° in water, salt solution, serum, and blood cells. *J. Biol. Chem.*, 78:765–799.
50. van Ypersele de Strihou, C., and Frans, A. (1970): The pattern of respiratory compensation in chronic uraemic acidosis. The influence of dialysis. *Nephron*, 7:37–50.
51. van Ypersele de Strihou, C., and Frans, A. (1973): The respiratory response to chronic metabolic alkalosis and acidosis in disease. *Clin. Sci. Mol. Med.*, 45:439–448.
52. Whang, R. (1975): Bicarbonate overshoot: An indication for acetazolamide therapy. *South. Med. J.*, 68:733–734.

53. Widmer, B., Gerhardt, R. E., Harrington, J. T., and Cohen J. J. (1979): Serum electrolyte and acid-base composition. The influence of graded degree of chronic renal failure. *Arch. Intern. Med.*, 139:1099–1102.

Review Articles

54. Boron, W. F. (1985): Control of intracellular pH. In: *The Kidney: Physiology and Pathophysiology*, edited by D. W. Seldin and G. Giebisch, pp. 1417–1440. Raven Press, New York.
55. Davenport, H. W. (1974): *The ABC of Acid-Base Chemistry*, 6th ed. University of Chicago Press, Chicago.
56. Emmett, M., and Narins, R. G. (1977): Clinical use of the anion gap. *Medicine*, 56: 38–54.
57. Emmett, M., and Seldin, D. W. (1985): Clinical syndromes of metabolic acidosis and alkalosis. In: *The Kidney: Physiology and Pathophysiology*, edited by D. W. Seldin and G. Giebisch, pp. 1567–1639. Raven Press, New York.
58. Irsigler, G. B., and Severinghouse, J. W. (1985): Respiratory regulation of cerebrospinal fluid and peripheral acid base balance. In: *The Kidney: Physiology and Pathophysiology*, edited by D. W. Seldin and G. Giebisch, pp. 1459–1470. Raven Press, New York.
59. Narins, R. G., and Emmett, M. (1980): Simple and mixed acid-base disorders: A practical approach. *Medicine*, 59:161–187.
60. Pitts, R. F. (1974): *Physiology of the Kidney and Body Fluids*, 3rd ed. Year Book, Chicago.
61. Relman, A. (1972): Metabolic consequences of acid-base disorders. *Kidney Int.*, 1: 347–359.
62. Saxton, C. R., and Seldin, D. W. Clinical interpretation of laboratory values. In: *Fluids and Electrolytes*, edited by J. P. Kokko, and R. L. Tannen, pp. 3–62, W. B. Saunders, Philadelphia.

The Regulation of Acid–Base Balance, edited
by Donald W. Seldin and Gerhard Giebisch,
Raven Press, Ltd., New York © 1989.

12

Evaluation of Acid-Base Disorders from the Urine

Melvin E. Laski and Neil A. Kurtzman

Departments of Internal Medicine and Physiology, Texas Tech University Health Sciences Center, Lubbock, Texas 79430

Urine Chemistry
Urine pH • Urine Bicarbonate • Urine P_{CO_2} • Urinary Abnormalities in Specific Forms of Acidosis
Evaluation of Urinary Acidification Defects
Relevant Physiology of Renal Tubular Acidosis • Detection of Renal Tubular Acidosis • Subclinical Disease • Specific Tests of Renal Acidifying Capacity
References

The regulation and maintenance of acid-base balance depends on the function of the kidney and the respiratory system working in concert. One may diagnose acid-base disorders and assess the response of the body to these abnormalities by the interpretation of appropriate clinical tests performed on blood and urine samples. Both primary respiratory acid-base disorders and the adaptive responses of the respiratory system to stress may be defined adequately by the analysis of arterial blood gases. On the other hand, the assessment of metabolic acidosis and alkalosis and renal response to alkalosis and acidosis requires that both blood and urine data be obtained.

The purpose of this chapter is to review the use of urine data in the evaluation of acid-base disorders. Both routine and specialized tests are discussed, and the basic physiology underlying the performance of the procedures and the interpretation of the results is considered. We first discuss the measurement and interpretation of urine chemistry in acidosis and alkalosis and then review the use of urine data and specialized tests of acidification in the diagnosis of renal tubular acidosis.

URINE CHEMISTRY

Urine pH

Methods of Determination

The first issue to be considered when approaching the assessment of urine acidification is the manner in which the urine pH is to be measured. There are only two techniques currently employed: (1) test tapes and (2) pH meter. The pH-sensitive dyes used in dipstick tapes change color in response to the pH of the fluid in which they are immersed. The results obtained are at best a gross estimate of true pH, and this technique is severely limited at the end of the spectrum most useful in diagnosis of renal acidification defects. The most common dividing line used to determine the presence of adequate acidifying capacity in the presence of acidemia is the ability to lower urine pH to less than 5.5. Test strips, which can only show that pH is somewhere between 6.0 and 5.0, are of little use in this regard. The only purposes to be served by this method are the serendipitous detection of grossly anomalous pH (7.0 or greater) in a patient with acidosis or the discovery of markedly elevated urine pH (greater than 8.0), which suggests the presence of a urinary tract infection with a urea-splitting organism. Confirmation of the presence of inappropriate urine pH in acidosis, however, rests with meter measurement of pH.

Specific measurement of fluid pH is universally accomplished by use of pH-sensitive glass electrodes. Such electrodes may stand alone or may be contained within a blood gas analyzer. The basic principle involved is that the glass at the electrode tip is far more permeable to protons than to other electrical species. Diffusion of protons across the membrane results in the creation of an electrical potential that is measured via a Wheatstone bridge. A tenfold concentration gradient for protons across the membrane produces a 60 mV potential difference. Unique forms of glass often are used in manufacture of the electrodes, but it should be noted that even standard Coke bottles have been used as electrodes. Meters in clinical usage are generally accurate to two decimal places and remain accurate in ranges well beyond those needed for clinical measurement.

Because urine pH depends on the poise of the bicarbonate–carbonic acid–carbon dioxide buffer system, accurate measurement of pH requires that the concentration or partial pressure of these substances does not change between acquisition of the sample and measurement. For this reason, either urine samples should be collected into cups containing a small amount of oil that prevents evaporation and limits the escape of carbon dioxide, or the sample may be collected into a standard container and then be aspirated immediately into a closed syringe, which is quickly capped and placed in ice. For ease of sample handling, we prefer the second method. Such collection methods are necessary for accurate measurement of urine pH, P_{CO_2}, and bicarbonate.

Urine pH in Acidosis

The pH of the urine in acidemia and acidosis, whether of metabolic or res-piratory origin, is determined by the urine buffer content, the proton mo-tive force of the distal nephron, and the ability of the distal urinary epithe-lium to resist acid backleak. Normal proton motive force (the strength of the hydrogen pump) is in excess of 180 mV, three pH units, or, in terms of proton concentration, a 1,000:1 proton concentration gradient between blood and urine. The actual proton gradient that may be achieved is limited primarily by the occurrence of significant backleak of protons at urine pH less than 4.5. Proton motive force and resistance to proton backleak, given normal renal function, are more or less invariant. The factor most important in modulation of the pH of the urine, as well as the factor that determines the total amount of acid excreted in the urine, is thus the buffer content. The greater the buffer content, the greater the total load of protons disposable before the limit gradient is achieved. In general, one expects the urine pH of an acidemic in-dividual to be between 4.5 and 5.5, but pH will vary within this range de-pending on the amount of adaptable buffer (e.g., ammonia) present in the urine. One always assumes when discussing these urinary parameters that some level of steady state has been achieved; a patient whose blood pH status has changed precipitously may have a bladder full of alkaline urine that has not yet equilibrated with newly produced urine. The full response to acidosis is not immediate; maximal response may take 2 to 3 days to be apparent. If buffer is present in quantity, pH will not reach minimal levels until a signifi-cant degree of adaptation of tubule cell membranes can occur.

Urine pH in Alkalosis

Although urine pH in acidosis is a function of the ability of the distal neph-ron to excrete acid against an electrochemical gradient, the limits and mecha-nisms of which may be extrapolated from a variety of experimental models, the pH of final urine in alkalosis is the product of delivery of bicarbonate escaping the proximal tubule, urine concentration, distal nephron acidifi-cation, and, most likely, distal bicarbonate secretion. The actual pH of the fi-nal urine may be either alkaline or acid, depending on whether the alkalotic state is being generated or maintained and also on the cause of the alkalosis. If alkalosis is the result of the administration of exogenous alkali or hyperventi-lation, for example, delivery of bicarbonate from the proximal tubule will be high, distal acidification will be suppressed, and the urine will be alkaline. The final urine bicarbonate will depend on the degree of concentration of the urine. If alkalosis is being generated and maintained by vomiting and volume depletion, respectively, the results may be quite different. The alkalosis of vomiting or nasogastric suction is generated by gastric acid loss and urinary

acid secretion driven by the secondary hyperaldosteronism of volume depletion. The urine pH during volume depletion with elevated aldosterone levels
is low because volume depletion lowers glomerular filtration rate (GFR) and
increases proximal bicarbonate reabsorption, limiting delivery of bicarbonate
out of the proximal tubule, and also because the elevated aldosterone level induces increased distal acid secretion. When volume is restored by increased
intake or saline infusion, the result is increased delivery of bicarbonate out of
the proximal tubule and high urine pH. Thus, as stated earlier, any urine pH
level may be seen. Finally, if the alkalosis is of respiratory origin, current data
suggest that both proximal and distal proton secretion will be depressed. Increased bicarbonate delivery out of the proximal tubule again occurs, and alkaline urine pH should routinely result.

Urine Bicarbonate (3,4)

Methods of Determination

Urine anion gap

Although urine bicarbonate may be measured directly, such measurement
rarely is performed in clinical practice. In contrast, urine electrolytes (Na, K,
Cl) are measured frequently. It is not generally appreciated, but these values
allow for a simple estimate of urine bicarbonate. If one subtracts urine chloride concentration from urine sodium plus potassium, the difference, in alkaline urine, reflects the urine bicarbonate concentration. This method contains
several errors. Urine ammonium is an unmeasured cation, whereas urine
phosphate, sulfate, and creatinine are unmeasured anions. The unmeasured
anions, however, are relatively constant in their production and excretion
(one must recall that penicillins and some other drugs are urine cations), and
ammonia production is suppressed in alkalosis. For clinical purposes at least,
the urine anion gap as just described gives a qualitative measure of urine bicarbonate. The use of such calculation is shown by the presence of high urinary sodium excretion but absent urine chloride in patients who are volume
depleted and alkalotic. The missing anion is bicarbonate; sodium and potassium losses during bicarbonate diuresis are obligated by the requirement for
electrical neutrality.

If the urine pH is acidic, consideration of the urine anion gap may again
reveal significant information. A patient with acidemia, a urine pH of 5.0, and
a large urine anion gap obviously is spilling large amounts of unmeasured acid
anions into the urine. If the anion happens to be acetoacetic acid, the laboratory dipstick will reveal a positive test for reducing substances, or ketones. If,
alternatively, the patient is not manufacturing acetoacetate but is making
β-hydroxybutyrate instead, the ketone dipstick will be negative, but the anion

gap still will be present in the urine, alerting the physician to the presence of unmeasured anion. The other metabolic anions (lactate, oxalate, formate) will give similar results.

In addition to the situations described, perusal of urine electrolyte composition may yield useful information if the calculated anion gap is negative. In a well-described case, a patient with hyperchloremic acidosis and urine pH greater than 5.5 was shown to have intact acidification mechanisms but relatively high urine pH because of the presence of high levels of urine ammonia; the patient was extremely volume depleted. The urine electrolyte composition revealed the presence of chloride in considerable concentration but almost no sodium or potassium. Thus, a large negative anion gap was present. Since the patient was not receiving penicillin or any other cationic drug, the obligate cation was ammonia, which served to buffer the urine pH. The solution to the case proved to be that the patient had been severely abusing cathartics and was remarkably volume depleted. Almost no sodium was delivered to the distal nephron, and that which reached the collecting tubule was rapidly reabsorbed in exchange for protons in the form of ammonium. Similar urine findings may be seen in many patients with such severe volume depletion, and the absence of urine sodium in an acidemic patient with other signs of volume loss should make one consider the possibility that urine acidification is less than optimal only because there is little or no sodium being delivered to the site of voltage-dependent acidification.

Direct determination of urine bicarbonate

The most common method of direct measurement of urine bicarbonate is, in fact, indirect. When urine is examined with a blood gas analyzer, two of the three variables in the Henderson-Hasselbalch[1] equation are measured. These devices measure pH and the partial pressure of carbon dioxide by electrode. From these two data points the bicarbonate of the solution is calculated, although this allows only relative accuracy for bicarbonate concentration. The calculation of bicarbonate depends on the use of the proper value for pK_a of the buffer pair. Unfortunately, the pK_a of carbonic acid in urine is not a constant. There is a significant change in the value of pK_a as the ionic strength of the urine is varied. This variation is not accounted for in hard-wired blood gas analyzer programs, which use values for pK_a dependent on the presence of the ionic strength of normal plasma. To calculate bicarbonate concentration in urine with ionic strength other than this specific value, one must use the formula

$$pK = 6.33 - 0.5 \sqrt{Na + K} \quad \text{(expressed as equivalents)}$$

---

[1]$pH = pK_a + \log \dfrac{[HCO_3^-]}{(0.03 \times P_{CO_2})}$

With this calculation, accuracy acceptable in research studies can be achieved.

The second method of measurement of urine bicarbonate is that of Van Slyke. A measured amount of urine is injected into a container of strong acid, the bicarbonate contained is released as carbon dioxide, and the volume of the gas released is measured. The total carbon dioxide content (carbon dioxide, bicarbonate, and carbonate) of the sample is thus measured. Given that carbonate is present in vanishingly small amounts and that carbon dioxide can account at most for but 3 to 4 mmoles/liter of total carbon dioxide (a P_{CO_2} of 100 mm Hg is equivalent to roughly 3.0 mM total CO_2), this method provides a close estimate of urine bicarbonate.

Urine Bicarbonate in Alkalosis

The presence and concentration of bicarbonate in the urine is determined by the amount of bicarbonate that escapes reabsorption by the proximal tubule and the rate of proton secretion in the distal tubule. The mass of proximal tubules is capable of reabsorption of vast but finite quantities of bicarbonate. However, under conditions of bicarbonate infusion, bicarbonate will begin to appear in the urine in quantity before the serum bicarbonate concentration reaches as high as 30, whereas patients with severe metabolic alkalosis might attain far higher levels with less bicarbonaturia. The reason for the discrepancy is that the critical quantity for the proximal tubule is not the serum bicarbonate concentration alone but rather the filtered load of bicarbonate, which is the product of serum bicarbonate concentration and the GFR. The term "filtered load" defines the amount of bicarbonate presented to the tubule, and the difference between this quantity and the maximal rate of tubular reabsorption controls the amount that escapes the proximal tubule. Considerable tubule-to-tubule variation exists with regard to the absolute maximal load that may be handled and with regard to single nephron GFR. This factor gives rise to the well-described splay of the curve for bicarbonate tubular maximum (Tm). The result of the combination of these forces is that urine bicarbonate concentration in alkalosis will vary widely depending primarily on the volume status and GFR of the individual patient. If serum bicarbonate is elevated but volume is greatly contracted and filtration is limited, little bicarbonate may escape to the urine. If, on the other hand, one administers saline to the same individual to restore volume and filtration, massive bicarbonaturia will result.

Urine Bicarbonate in Acidosis

In contrast to the variety of results observed in states of alkalosis, urine bicarbonate in conditions of acidosis is almost uniformly minimal or absent if renal function is normal. (The findings in cases of renal tubular acidosis are discussed later.) Metabolic acid consumes circulating bicarbonate, and, in addition, acidosis stimulates proximal bicarbonate reabsorption. This results in minimal delivery of bicarbonate from the proximal tubule. Since acidosis also stimulates distal acidification, any bicarbonate reaching the distal nephron will be reabsorbed. In respiratory acidosis, the situation with regard to serum levels is reversed, and bicarbonate rises through buffering and renal compensatory mechanisms. However, distal acidification is stimulated, and urine bicarbonate may remain low as a result. If respiratory acidosis is corrected partially in an abrupt manner, bicarbonaturia may occur, even if some degree of acidosis remains.

Urine P_{CO_2} (5)

Methods of Determination

There is only one method to determine the P_{CO_2} of the urine: by use of the CO_2 electrode of a blood gas analyzer. As mentioned previously, this measurement is made on freshly collected specimens that are kept under oil or in closed, gas-free syringes.

Significance of Urine P_{CO_2}

The P_{CO_2} in the urine is determined by several factors. First, since carbon dioxide partitions relatively equally in aqueous and lipid phases, no absolute permeability barrier exists to its movement between tubules and blood, and some amount of urine carbon dioxide may arise from diffusion from renal vessels. When considering this effect, one must also realize that the P_{CO_2} of renal tissue and vasculature differs from that of the body as a whole. Measurements of intrarenal P_{CO_2} in several laboratories show it to be somewhere between 50 and 65 mm Hg in the rat. There have been no direct measurements of intrarenal P_{CO_2} in the human, and thus the degree to which urine P_{CO_2} actually exceeds ambient blood P_{CO_2} in clinical situations remains a matter of speculation.

The second major determinant of P_{CO_2} in alkaline urine is the rate of acidification in the collecting tubules. This effect has been recognized and used since the days of Pitts et al. If bicarbonate is delivered in appreciable quantity to the distal acidification sites while acidification is occurring, the P_{CO_2} of the urine will reflect acidification because the addition of acid to the bicarbonate solution ultimately results in the production of carbon dioxide (Fig. 1). Since the distal renal epithelium does not contain luminal carbonic anhydrase, the intratubular result of acidification is the formation of carbonic acid, with dehydration to carbon dioxide occurring only later in the collecting system or bladder. Because of the large volume of these structures, diffusion of carbon

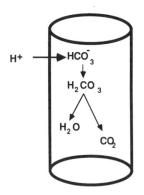

FIG. 1. The diagram indicates the basic mechanism by which distal acidification raises urine Pco_2. If bicarbonate is present in the urine and a proton is secreted, the hydrogen ion will combine with bicarbonate to form carbonic acid, which dissociates to form water and carbon dioxide. The absence of carbonic anhydrase in the lumen of the distal tubule and other effects keep the carbon dioxide from escaping back to the blood.

dioxide from urine to blood may be prevented by unstirred layer barrier effects. Although not strictly quantitative, the urine Pco_2 thus provides some measure of distal acidification under these conditions. Two methods of estimation of the relative contributions of blood to urine diffusion and urine generation are available. In older literature, the arterial blood Pco_2 is subtracted from the urine Pco_2 to arrive at a urine minus blood $(U-B)$ Pco_2. More recently, authors have measured the urine Pco_2 before and after the administration of bicarbonate loads to determine the degree of rise occurring when excess bicarbonate is present in the urine, this amount arising presumably from distal acidification. Both methods have been used in clinical studies.

A third cause of elevation of urine Pco_2 has been postulated. If bicarbonate is added to a concentrated bicarbonate solution at alkaline pH, a reaction between bicarbonate and bicarbonate to form carbonate and carbon dioxide will occur, elevating carbon dioxide tension. This process, the ampholyte effect, can be demonstrated *in vitro*. If it occurs *in vivo*, it may be a source of elevation of urine Pco_2 not dependent on distal acidification.

Urine Pco_2 in Acidosis

The degree to which urine Pco_2 is elevated in the presence of systemic acidosis and normal renal function depends on delivery of bicarbonate to the distal nephron. For this reason, spontaneous occurrence of high urine Pco_2 in patients with metabolic acidosis is unlikely. If, however, bicarbonate is infused in amounts resulting in significant bicarbonaturia, elevation of urine Pco_2 will be seen. Patients with respiratory acidosis and high bicarbonate levels may show increased Pco_2 if they are bicarbonaturic.

Respiratory Influences on Urine Pco_2

As reviewed previously, the Pco_2 of the renal vasculature contributes to the urine Pco_2. However, the exact blood Pco_2 of human renal vasculature and the effects of respiratory variation on this level are unknown. Urine P_{CO_2} rises in the presence of respiratory acidosis, but studies of the effects of respiratory acidosis and alkalosis on the difference between blood and urine P_{CO_2} have not yielded easily interpretable data.

Urinary Abnormalities in Specific Forms of Acidosis

In addition to the bicarbonate–carbon dioxide buffer set, there are at least two other specific anions of acids that may be measured in the clinical setting to aid in diagnosis and management of clinical acid-base disorders. First, in the case of ketoacidosis, one may measure both acetone (acetoacetate) and, with greater effort, β-hydroxybutyrate in the urine. These substances are cleared by the kidney and are more easily detectable in the urine than in the plasma. Acetone, which is a reducing substance, is detected by the common Acetest tablet or tape. More specific and less available methods must be used to test for β-hydroxybutyrate, which is in the reduced state.

The second specific anion of acidosis detectable by simple clinical testing is found in cases of ethylene glycol intoxication. Ethylene glycol, or antifreeze, is an infrequent cause of metabolic acidosis, but it is particularly important to diagnose this condition accurately because such intoxication may lead to acute renal failure. If diagnosis is made rapidly, renal failure may be averted through removal of the toxin via dialysis. Ethylene glycol itself does not cause toxicity or acidosis, but it is metabolized to oxalic acid, which is a cause of both. Fortunately, oxalate is easily detected by urinalysis. Oxalate precipitates in the urine, forming characteristic envelope-shaped crystals. The discovery of such crystals on urinalysis of any patient with unexplained metabolic acidosis and central nervous system depression mandates the institution of emergent dialysis if other elements of the history suggest intoxication. The possibility of discovery of oxalate crystals is an important reason for the physician to perform a personal microscopic examination of the urine. Inexperienced laboratory personnel have been known to mistake oxalate for urate, which may have tragic consequences.

EVALUATION OF URINARY ACIDIFICATION DEFECTS

Relevant Physiology of Renal Tubular Acidosis (2,6,7)

Proximal Renal Tubular Acidosis

Acidification of the urine occurs at two major sites along the nephron, the proximal tubule and the collecting duct system, although recent evidence indicates that some bicarbonate transport may take place in the ascending limb of the loop of Henle. Ninety percent of filtered bicarbonate is reabsorbed along the length of the proximal tubule (some 4,000 mEq or more per day); thus severe defects in proximal bicarbonate reabsorption result in major depression of serum bicarbonate levels. If serum bicarbonate is restored to normal levels in the face of such a defect, marked bicarbonaturia occurs that is characteristic of proximal renal tubular acidosis. To be more specific, proximal renal tubular acidosis is marked by serum bicarbonate usually around 15 mEq/liter, but if bicarbonate is given to correct this, the fractional excretion of bicarbonate

$$ FE_{HCO_3}\% = \frac{U_{HCO_3}}{P_{HCO_3}} \times \frac{P_{Cr}}{U_{Cr}} \times 100 $$

will be in the range of 15%. Hyperchloremic metabolic acidosis with low serum bicarbonate, associated with low urine pH and severe bicarbonate wastage on correction of serum levels of bicarbonate, more or less defines proximal renal tubular acidosis.

In the proximal tubule, bicarbonate is reabsorbed when protons are secreted via a sodium-proton exchanger. Carbonic anhydrase either supplies protons to the exchanger or helps dispose of base generated by acid production. Three major mechanisms for failure of bicarbonate reabsorption can thus be postulated. First, a major defect in the regulation of cell sodium may be present, as in the case of a partial absence of Na,K-ATPase activity. This would result in a decrease in the activity of all sodium-linked transport mechanisms, which include amino acid, glucose, phosphate, and organic acid transport. This postulation describes the defects seen in patients with the Fanconi syndrome. A second possibility is a defect of the sodium/proton antiporter, and a third is a defect in the generation of acid in the cell or basolateral disposal of base from the cell. The third situation occurs in congenital deficiencies of carbonic anhydrase and in patients who take a drug that inactivates the enzyme. Any of these possibilities would result in specific loss of bicarbonate reabsorption as appears in those patients with pure proximal bicarbonate wastage.

Whichever is the mechanism responsible for proximal bicarbonate wastage, a secondary result is potassium loss and hypokalemia. Diminished proximal volume absorption decreases potassium recovery at this site. In addition, patients with proximal renal tubular acidosis are volume contracted and, therefore, develop secondary elevation of aldosterone. This rise is beneficial because it tends to correct volume, but aldosterone also increases distal potassium secretion. Potassium loss is accentuated by the increased distal delivery of bicarbonate, which is a relatively nonreabsorbable anion that increases the negative potential resulting from sodium reabsorption and, thus, further aggravates the tendency to lose potassium. As might be expected from this scenario, potassium loss in this disorder is always severe.

Distal Renal Tubular Acidosis

In contrast to the proximal tubule, where electroneutral sodium-proton exchange drives proton secretion, the mechanism responsible for acidification in the distal nephron is an active, electrogenic proton pump. This process can lower urine pH at least three units below that of blood, which is equivalent to 180 mV or more of potential difference, a value identical to that seen in studies of acidification in the turtle bladder. Recent studies are consistent with the theory that this pump is a proton ATPase. As in the proximal tubule, carbonic anhydrase appears to be necessary for acid generation or cellular base disposal.

Additional characteristics are deducible from studies in turtle bladders and isolated collecting tubules. The first of these is that the limiting factor on the acid gradient achieved is backleak of acid through the mucosa. Studies with amphotericin in turtle bladders show that this agent does not alter the power or velocity of the proton pump, but it does increase backleak so that equilibrium between pump and backleak occurs at a higher pH. The second major characteristic is the relationship between acidification and the transepithelial potential difference. In the turtle bladder, this has been examined by elegant studies using a voltage clamp device that sets transepithelial potential at any desired level after sodium transport is inhibited. Such experiments show that acidification may be increased or decreased by alteration of the voltage gradient against which the pump must work. They also show that the effects of sodium transport inhibitors on acidification are caused by changing voltage and not by direct effects or sodium dependence of acidification. In the mammalian kidney, studies in isolated cortical collecting tubules reveal that sodium transport inhibitors decrease acidification in this segment by a similar mechanism, whereas in the medullary collecting tubule, where sodium transport does not occur, such drugs do not inhibit acidification. Thus, voltage-dependent, or short circuit, renal tubular acidosis is a cortical collecting tubule phenomenon.

Data from studies in isolated renal tubules have led to further understanding of the pathophysiology of distal renal tubular acidosis. Potassium excretion occurs in the cortical collecting tubule as a passive response to transepithelial potential, although net potassium transport does not normally take place in the medullary segment. Acidification defects that are associated with hyperkalemia and the inability to excrete potassium, therefore, represent disease that involves the cortical collecting tubule. It is known that aldosterone alters bicarbonate transport in the cortical collecting tubule and that it induces increased sodium transport and transepithelial potential, which secondarily increases potassium and proton transport. In the medullary collecting tubule, acidification is stimulated by mineralocorticoid in a direct manner. Aldosterone deficiency thus has effects in both segments of the collecting tubule. The exact characteristics of the medullary effect are best shown in the turtle bladder, where it has been demonstrated that the force of the pump remains intact, but the pump rate declines in the absence of aldosterone. Thus, aldosterone deficiency does not alter the minimal pH achieved but does result in decreased ability to excrete acid because of diminished rate of secretion.

Although aldosterone is a major modulator of sodium reabsorption and transepithelial potential in this segment, some sodium reabsorption occurs even in the absence of the hormone. This remaining sodium reabsorption can be maximized by increasing distal sodium delivery via salt loading, and the potential generated by this sodium reabsorption can be increased by providing a nonreabsorbable anion with sodium. Mineralocorticoid-deficient patients thus may increase acid excretion after an increase in salt intake and also respond to sodium sulfate loads by lowering urine pH.

Detection of Renal Tubular Acidosis

Overt Disease

Proximal renal tubular acidosis, when fully expressed, occurs with extreme depression of serum bicarbonate, hypokalemia, and acidemia. It usually is associated with low serum uric acid, low phosphate levels and glycosuria, aminoaciduria, phosphaturia and uricosuria, although on rare occasions, bicarbonate wastage occurs without urinary spillage of other substances. The urine always contains significant amounts of bicarbonate during bicarbonate replacement (loading), but in the absence of bicarbonate loading, the urine pH will eventually be lowered to normal levels for acidosis. When present in a child, there is attendant growth retardation, and renal ricketts occur if phosphate losses are significant.

Classic distal renal tubular acidosis (Type I) occurs as hyperchloremic metabolic acidosis with an abnormally high urine pH. If these two features are present, no further testing is needed to establish the presence of distal renal tubular acidosis. The level generally used to define normal urine pH in the face of systemic acidemia is below 5.5, but more stringent rules may be applied. Either hyperkalemia or hypokalemia may be present. Other clinical features include nephrocalcinosis and metabolic bone disease.

Latent Disease

Whereas proximal renal tubular acidosis is almost always fully expressed and clinically overt, distal forms of renal tubular acidosis often appear more subtly. There are two major ways this may happen. First, if the physiology of the disorder is that the proton pump has normal electromotive force but is deficient in overall rate, the urine pH may be be lowered normally (pH below 5.5), but overall renal acidification may not be sufficient to prevent systemic acidosis from occurring. Thus, a patient may have hyperchloremic acidosis with low urine pH. The extent of this disorder may become apparent only when external loads are applied. The second manner in which latent distal renal tubular acidosis may be discovered is by the presence of unexplained hyperkalemia. Defects in the cortical collecting tubule may affect both acidification and potassium secretion. One such lesion has been described as "short circuit" renal tubular acidosis and is postulated to be due to loss of the normal, sodium reabsorption-driven, lumen-negative transepithelial potential that drives potassium secretion and facilitates acidification. Because acidification may be normal in other, nonsodium-transporting portions of the collecting duct system, the potassium defect may be more apparent than the loss of acidification. Such patients may be able to lower pH and may even maintain normal balance if not stressed. These patients may be shown to be unable to acidify normally by specific tests of acidification.

Subclinical Disease

The final group of patients who need evaluation of acidification are those who, although showing no clinical signs or symptoms of an acidification disorder, are known to have a disease process associated with a high frequency of renal tubular acidosis. As shown in Table 1, this list is quite extensive, and it includes several conditions that are a part of every physician's practice.

The most common disease with a significant incidence of distal renal tubular acidosis due to secondary failure of aldosterone secretion is diabetes mellitus. The usual clinical picture in which the acidification disorder is discovered is the patient in whom the physician notes a tendency to hyperkalemia at a time when renal insufficiency is not of sufficient severity to explain this abnormality. Screening of patients with significant degrees of partial urinary tract obstruction will reveal a fair percentage of individuals who show subnormal capacity to excrete acid and lower urine pH when they receive acid loads in the course of clinical testing. Another set of patients who may reveal abnormalities of acidification on testing are those with inborn errors of hemoglobin synthesis. The presence of hemoglobin S, whether in the homozygous or hemizygous state, eventually leads to distal renal tubular acidification defects, which are detectable by specific testing before the occurrence of clinical disease. Of the other general categories shown in Table 1, forms of interstitial kidney injury, amyloidosis, and connective tissue disorders are most likely to be found in the average clinical practice. Unless severe acidosis of nonrenal cause occurs and brings the defects to light, they may remain unnoticed in the absence of testing.

TABLE 1. *Conditions associated with the presence of distal renal tubular acidosis*

Genetic and metabolic disorders
  Sickle cell disease
  Wilson's disease
  Hereditary fructose intolerance
  Fabry's disease
  Carbonic anhydrase deficiency
Tubulointerstitial nephritides
  Analgesia abuse
  Systemic lupus erythematosus
  Chronic pyelonephritis
  Urinary tract obstruction
  Chronic transplant rejection
  Medullary cystic disease
  Medullary sponge kidney
Drugs and Toxins
  Toluene
  Amphotericin
  Lithium
  ?Amiloride
Autoimmune disorders (?tubulointerstitial diseases)
  Sjögren's syndrome
  Cryoglobulinemia
  Thyroiditis
Hyporeninemic hypoaldosteronism
  Diabetes mellitus
  Interstitial nephritis
Mineralocorticoid deficiency
  Congenital enzyme defects
  Addison's disease
  Idiopathic hypoaldosteronism
  Chronic heparin therapy
  Mineralocorticoid resistance

Specific Tests of Renal Acidifying Capacity (1,8–11)

Summaries of specific tests are given in Tables 2 and 3.

Ammonium Chloride Loading

In those patients who have a defect in acidification but are in acid-base balance, evidence of a distal defect can be found by the ammonium chloride loading test. The effect of administering ammonium chloride is equivalent to giving the patient ammonia (which is metabolized to urea) plus hydrochloric acid and allows far more milliequivalents of effective acid to be given than would be possible if the acid itself were given. The physiology of this procedure is that the imposition of the stress of the acid load allows identification of

TABLE 2. *Characteristics of defects in renal acidification*

Defect	Fractional excretion of bicarbonate	Urine pH in acidosis	Test	
			Sodium sulfate load or furosemide test	Urine P_{CO_2} − blood P_{CO_2}
Proximal RTA[a]	> 15%	< 5.5	pH < 5.5 $U_K V$ increases	25 Urine P_{CO_2} increases after bicarbonate load
Distal RTA				
Pump failure	Normal	> 5.5	pH > 5.5 $U_K V$ increases	< 10 Urine P_{CO_2} unchanged after bicarbonate load
Aldosterone deficiency	Normal	< 5.5	pH < 5.5 $U_K V$ increases	< 10 Urine P_{CO_2} increases after bicarbonate load
Voltage-dependent defect	Normal	> 5.5	pH > 5.5 $U_K V$ unchanged	< 10 Urine P_{CO_2} unchanged after bicarbonate load
Backleak	Normal	> 5.5 (predicted)	pH > 5.5 $U_K V$ increases (predicted)	> 25 Urine P_{CO_2} increases after bicarbonate load
Rate-dependent defect	Normal	< 5.5	pH < 5.5 $U_K V$ increases	> 25 Urine P_{CO_2} increases after bicarbonate load

[a]RTA, renal tubular acidosis.

TABLE 3. *Tests of renal acidifying capacity*

Test	Normal	Abnormal	Diagnostic for
Urine pH	< 5.5 in presence of acidosis	> 5.5 in face of acidosis	Distal acidification defect
NH$_4$Cl load	Induces urine pH < 5.5; increases ammonia excretion	Urine pH remains above 5.5; ammonia excretion unchanged	Distal acidification defect; uncovers latent disease
Urine bicarbonate (FE$_{bicarb}$%)[a]	Usually < 5%	> 15% definite; 5–15% suggestive	Proximal RTA[b] (if more than 15%)
Urine P$_{CO_2}$	Urine P$_{CO_2}$ usually mm Hg greater than blood (UpH 7.8, U$_{bicarb}$ 100/dl)[c]	UP$_{CO_2}$ not 25 blood failure to rise after bicarbonate infusion	Distal acidification defects
Sulfate load	Urine pH drops to < 5.5, urine K increases	Urine pH stays over 5.5; urine K may be increased or unchanged	Distal defect, may distinguish cortical from medullary defect
Phosphate load	Increases urine P$_{CO_2}$ if given during bicarbonate load	Failure to induce rise UP$_{CO_2}$	Distal acidification defects
Furosemide	UpH drops to < 5.5 3 hrs after dose; U$_K$ increases	pH fails to drop; U$_K$ may or may not increase	Distal defect, may distinguish cortical from medullary defect

[a]FE, fractional excretion.
[b]RTA, renal tubular acidosis.
[c]U, urine.

those unable to respond. The test is appropriate for those patients suspected of having a distal acidification defect, such as patients with hyperkalemia or a condition predisposing to renal tubular acidosis, who do not have evidence of systemic acidosis.

Two basic forms of ammonium chloride loading are currently in use, a long and a short method. The long procedure is to feed the patient a dose of ammonium chloride of 0.1 g/kg daily for 3 to 5 days. The short form consists of a 1-day feeding of the same daily dose. Although it is easier to perform, the short procedure may be less reliable. Normal response is lowering of urine pH to 5.5 or less, usually under 5.0. In addition, ammonium excretion should at least triple after a 3-day load. A failure to lower urine pH in this manner is indicative of a distal acidification defect.

There are, as might be expected, difficulties with this test. Some patients are unable to ingest ammonium chloride without experiencing nausea and vomiting. In addition, ammonium chloride loading is contraindicated in patients with liver disease. In these patients, one may acid load by giving calcium chloride (2 mEq/kg body weight) in a single dose and measure the response of urine pH. Failure to lower urine pH indicates that an acidification defect is present.

Sodium Sulfate Loading

The administration of sodium sulfate loads accomplishes two ends. It lowers blood pH slightly, and sodium sulfate is presented to the distal tubule as sodium plus a nonreabsorbable anion. If the collecting tubule is capable of sodium reabsorption, the effect of infusing nonreabsorbable anion will be to increase the lumen-negative electrical potential in this segment. The conductance of sulfate is less than that of chloride, and, therefore, the potential created by sodium reabsorption will be shunted by anion movement to a lesser degree than if chloride were present. The effects of increased lumen-negative electrical potential are twofold. Potassium secretion in the collecting tubule is a passive event, driven by the lumen-negative potential. As sodium sulfate reaches a collecting tubule capable of sodium reabsorption, increased potassium secretion results. A similar, but not identical, event occurs with regard to acidification. Proton secretion in the cortical collecting tubule occurs by primary active transport and does not absolutely require the presence of sodium or favorable potential. Nevertheless, this transport, which creates a lumen-positive electrical potential, exists in the same electrical circuit as the sodium reabsorption mechanism. The effect of increasing the electrical consequences of sodium transport in this segment are to reduce the work required to transport protons into the urine and possibly to increase the rate at which such transport occurs. Thus, sodium sulfate infusion will increase potassium secretion and acidification in the collecting tubule.

This test is performed as follows. To induce a state of increased distal sodium avidity, patients should prepare for the infusion by reducing sodium intake to 20 mEq/day for 3 days before the test. One milligram of 9-fluorohydrocortisone may be given 12 hr before sulfate loading. After a control urine collection is obtained, 500 ml of 4% sodium sulfate solution is given intravenously. The effects of the infusion on urine flow, urine pH, and urine potassium concentration are recorded. In normal individuals, urine pH decreases, generally to less than 5.5, and urine potassium rises. In patients with defects of the proton pump *per se*, the pH is unchanged, but urine potassium increases. In patients with acidification defects secondary to impaired sodium reabsorption (urinary tract obstruction, hemoglobin S), acidification and potassium excretion will be impaired.

Furosemide Test

Because of the difficulty inherent in infusion tests, such as the sulfate and phosphate procedures previously described, significant interest has arisen in a simple evaluative test involving only the administration of a single dose of furosemide and two or three urine collections. The precise physiologic basis for the success of this test is unclear. Some propose that furosemide renders the collecting tubule impermeable to chloride and thus increases the lumen-negative potential, but evidence for such effect on transepithelial potential in this segment *in vitro* is lacking. Differences between rabbit and human physiology in this segment exist, however, and this explanation is at least functional at present. The furosemide test is roughly equivalent to sulfate or phosphate loading procedures.

The furosemide test is performed as follows. After a control urine collection, 40 or 80 mg of furosemide is given orally, and urine samples are collected at 1, 2, and 3 hr after the dose. Normal individuals and those with aldosterone deficiency lower urine pH to less than 5.5. Those individuals with proton pump defects or voltage-dependent defects do not respond normally to furosemide. The test is interpreted in the same manner as the sulfate loading test.

Urine P_{CO_2} Tests

The physiology of the urine P_{CO_2} response has been discussed in an earlier section. The key to test performance is the administration of adequate bicarbonate to induce bicarbonaturia and an alkaline urine. The usual manner is to give sodium bicarbonate (0.9 M) intravenously until urine bicarbonate exceeds 80 mEq/liter. Urine is collected under oil or in sealed syringes for determination of pH, bicarbonate, and P_{CO_2} before the bicarbonate infusion and after the infusion is given and urinary bicarbonate has risen. If distal urinary acidification is normal, the urine P_{CO_2} will rise after the onset of bicarbonaturia. Urine P_{CO_2} is normally greater than 70 mm Hg if urine bicarbonate is greater than 80 mEq/liter. Absence of the normal rise indicates an acidification defect in the distal tubule. This test may be performed if blood pH is normal or acidemic.

There are two modified versions of the urine P_{CO_2} test. If acidosis is not present in the patient, acidification can be stimulated by phosphate loading if urine pH is kept near phosphate pK (6.8). Such loads increase urine P_{CO_2} because phosphate may be titrated from the -2 form to the -1 form by distal acid excretion. The acid phosphate thus created may then release protons still more distally in the terminal collecting duct or ureter, and these protons can react with bicarbonate to produce carbon dioxide and water, raising urine P_{CO_2} (Fig. 2). This effect will occur only if distal acidification is present. A rise in urine P_{CO_2} will thus occur in individuals with normal distal acidification after infusion of neutral sodium phosphate (1 mmole/liter total body water in 180 ml normal saline given over 3 hr). A second version involving oral administration of phosphate (18 mg phosphorus/kg body weight as phosphate (Sandoz) [each tablet contains 1,518 mg ammonium acid phosphate, 650 mg potassium acid phosphate, and 1,540 mg, magnesium glycerol phosphate yielding 750 mg elemental phosphate]) also has been described. The general interpretation of urinary results is similar to that given to sodium sulfate load-

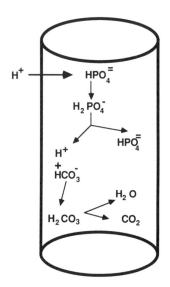

FIG. 2. Increasing the delivery of phosphate to the acidifying sites in the distal tubule results in the following sequence of events. Secreted protons titrate phosphate from the neutral (-2) to the acidic (-1) form. Acid phosphate later dissociates to release a proton, which may combine with bicarbonate to form carbonic acid, which will dissociate to carbon dioxide and water.

ing tests. If sodium phosphate loading fails to raise urine P_{CO_2}, a distal acidification defect is likely.

REFERENCES

1. Batlle, D. C. (1986): Segmental characterization of defects in collecting tubule acidification. *Kidney Int*, 30:546–554.
2. Batlle, D. C, Sehy, J. T., Roseman, M. K., Arruda, J. A. L., and Kurtzman, N. A. (1981); Clinical and pathosphysiologic spectrum of acquired distal renal acidosis. *Kidney Int.*, 20: 389–396.
3. Batlle, D. C., Von Riotte, A., and Schleuter, W. (1987): Urinary sodium in the evaluation of hyperchloremic metabolic acidosis. *N. Engl. J. Med.*, 316:140–144.
4. Goldstein, M. B., Bear, R., Richardson, R. M. A., Marsden, P. A., and Halperin, M. L. (1986): The urine anion gap: A clinically useful index of ammonia excretion. *Am. J. Med. Sci.*, 292:198–202.
5. Halperin, M. L., Goldstein, M. B., Haig, A., Johnson, M. D., and Stinebaugh, B. J. (1974): Studies on the pathogenesis of type 1 (distal) renal tubular acidosis as revealed by the urinary P_{CO_2} tensions. *J. Clin. Invest.*, 53:669–677.
6. Kurtzman, N. A. (1983): Acquired distal renal tubular acidosis. *Kidney Int.*, 24:807–819.
7. Morris, R. C. Jr. (1981): Renal tubular acidosis. *N. Engl. J. Med.*, 304:418–420.
8. Oster, J. R., Hotchkiss, J. L., Carbon, M., Farmer, M., and Vaamonde, C. (1975): A short duration renal $CaCl_2$ acidification test using calcium chloride. *Nephron*, 14:281–292.
9. Schwartz, W. B., Jenson, R. L., and Relman, A. S. (1955): Acidification of the urine and increased ammonia excretion without change in acid-base equilibrium: Sodium reabsorption as a stimulus to the acidifying process. *J. Clin. Invest.*, 34:673–680.
10. Stinebaugh, B. J., Schloeder, F. X., Gharafry, E., Suki, W. N., Goldstein, M. B., and Halperin, M. L. (1977): Mechanism by which neutral phosphate infusion elevates urine P_{CO_2}. *J. Lab. Clin. Med.*, 89:946–958.
11. Vallo, A., and Rodriguez-Soreano, J. (1984): Oral phosphate-loading test for the assessment of distal urinary acidification in children. *Miner. Electrolyte Metab.*, 10:387–390.

The Regulation of Acid-Base Balance, edited
by Donald W. Seldin and Gerhard Giebisch,
Raven Press, Ltd., New York,© 1989.

13

Uremic Acidosis

Nicolaos E. Madias and *Jeffrey A. Kraut

*Tufts University School of Medicine, and Division of Nephrology, New England
Medical Center, Boston, Massachusetts 02111; and *Division of Nephrology,
Wadsworth Veterans Administration Medical Center, West Los Angeles,
Los Angeles, California 90073*

As discussed in Chapter 10, the kidney plays a critical role in the regulation
of acid-base balance. It reabsorbs the large quantities of bicarbonate filtered
by the glomerulus and excretes sufficient quantities of net acid to match the
acid generated by cellular metabolism. Tubular secretion of hydrogen ions is
responsible for accomplishing both these tasks. Under normal conditions,
approximately 85 to 90% of the filtered bicarbonate load is reabsorbed in the
proximal tubule; the remaining 10 to 15% is delivered to the distal tubule and
the collecting duct. Hydrogen ion secretion in the distal nephron effects the
reabsorption of the remaining bicarbonate load, acidifies the urine, titrates
the urinary buffers (ammonia and phosphate), and, thus, results in the excretion of the acid burden derived from cellular metabolism. Over 98% of the
hydrogen ions secreted by the renal tubules are directed toward conservation
of the filtered bicarbonate load (approximately 4,500 mEq/day). The

remaining small percentage of hydrogen ion secretion is expended in the excretion of net acid required to balance the endogenous acid load (approximately 1 mEq/kg body weight per day). By properly completing both these tasks, the kidney enables the organism to strike external hydrogen ion balance and, thus, to maintain a stable plasma bicarbonate concentration of approximately 25 mEq/liter.

Alterations in renal function may profoundly affect the ability of the organism to maintain acid-base homeostasis. Defects in either of the processes of acidification, if uncompensated, will lead to the development of metabolic acidosis. It is apparent that even small reductions in the rate of bicarbonate reabsorption will produce substantial losses of filtered bicarbonate into the urine, thus diminishing systemic bicarbonate stores and leading to metabolic acidosis. Similarly, any reduction in net acid excretion will result in the accumulation of endogenous acids, depletion of bicarbonate stores and generation of metabolic acidosis.

With destruction of the kidney parenchyma by disease and progressive loss of nephrons, disturbances in renal acidification occur, eventually leading to the development of metabolic acidosis. It has been customary to use the term "uremic acidosis" to signify the metabolic acidosis that develops during the course of progressive renal failure. The attendant hypobicarbonatemia usually is associated with a substantial fall in glomerular filtration rate (GFR) and, therefore, a rise in the concentration of blood urea nitrogen (BUN) and creatinine—hence, the epithet "uremic" to describe this type of metabolic acidosis. Moreover, as a consequence of the reduced GFR, retention of phosphate, sulfate, and various organic anions occurs, producing a rise in the concentration of unmeasured anions (increased anion gap). The fall in plasma bicarbonate concentration is matched by an equivalent increment in the unmeasured anion concentration, producing a high anion gap (normochloremic) form of metabolic acidosis. Potassium retention and hyperkalemia are common, particularly during the late stages of uremia.

By contrast, the term "renal tubular acidosis" has been used to describe the form of metabolic acidosis developing because of impaired renal acidification in the presence of well-preserved or only minimally reduced renal function. In this form of metabolic acidosis, the attendant hypobicarbonatemia usually occurs in the company of normal or only mild rises in BUN or creatinine concentration. In addition, the reduction in plasma bicarbonate concentration is matched by an equivalent rise in plasma chloride concentration, producing a hyperchloremic (normal anion gap) form of metabolic acidosis. Both proximal renal tubular acidosis and the classic form of distal tubular acidosis are characterized by potassium wasting and hypokalemia.

The distinction between these two forms of renal acidosis, one arising as a consequence of generalized parenchymal disease and another reflecting selective defects in hydrogen ion transport, is generally warranted because of major differences in the clinical features, prognosis, and requirements for therapy in the two disorders. Several overlapping features exist, however, and, in some cases, distinguishing between the two entities may be difficult. For example, patients with certain varieties of hyperkalemic distal renal tubular acidosis (so-called Type IV renal tubular acidosis) often have diffuse parenchymal renal disease and substantial impairment in GFR. Similarly, a component of hyperchloremic metabolic acidosis has been recognized in a certain number of patients with chronic renal failure, leading to further blurring of the distinction between the two clinical syndromes. It should be emphasized, however, that in both types of metabolic acidosis, the essential underlying abnormality is an impairment in renal tubular function, producing defective hydrogen ion secretion and, thus, a reduction in net acid excretion and renal bicarbonate reabsorption. Consequently, all forms of renal acidosis are, in fact, tubular in origin.

In the discussion that follows, we focus primarily on the various aspects of uremic acidosis and consider the entity of renal tubular acidosis only as it relates to the pathogenesis and clinical features of uremic acidosis. A detailed discussion of renal tubular acidosis is given in Chapter 12. Table 1 (*see page 288*) summarizes the major contrasting features of the two syndromes.

CLINICAL AND LABORATORY FEATURES OF UREMIC ACIDOSIS

Prevalence, Onset, and Magnitude (6,9,14,17,18,24–26)

Metabolic acidosis is a common feature of chronic renal failure. Yet a reduction in plasma bicarbonate concentration is not inevitable during the course of chronic, progressive renal failure, even when the GFR is severely reduced. In this regard, Wallia, et al. examined acid-base parameters and serum electrolytes in 70 consecutive patients with severe renal failure requiring the initiation of maintenance dialysis. The renal diseases present in these patients included chronic glomerulonephritis, diabetic nephrosclerosis, and interstitial renal disease. The average serum creatinine concentration was 11 mg/dl (range, 6–19 mg/dl). Thirteen of these patients (19%) had normal plasma bicarbonate concentrations (25 ± 3 mEq/liter, mean ± SD). There was no history of vomiting, nor were any of these subjects receiving diuretics, alkali, or steroids. Although the patients with normal plasma bicarbonate concentrations had slightly lower levels of serum creatinine than those with hypobicarbonatemia (9.0 ± 2.3 mg/dl versus 13.2 ± 3.7 mg/dl), the level of serum creatinine was well within the range at which metabolic acidosis has generally been found in patients with chronic renal failure. Similarly, Oster et al. and Wrong and Davies identified a few patients with GFRs below 20 ml/min who had normal plasma bicarbonate concentrations. In other studies examining the relationship between renal function and the appearance of metabolic

TABLE 1. *Contrasting features of uremic acidosis and renal tubular acidosis*[a]

	Uremic acidosis	RTA[b] with Hypokalemia		DRTA[c] with hyperkalemia
		Proximal	Distal	
GFR[d]	Reduced	Normal or minimally reduced	Normal or minimally reduced	Reduced
Electrolyte pattern	Normochloremic and/or hyperchloremic	Hyperchloremic	Hyperchloremic	Hyperchloremic
Serum potassium	Increased	Decreased	Decreased	Increased
Urine pH	< 5.5	< 5.5	> 5.5	< or > 5.5

[a]Features refer to the condition of no alkali supplementation.
[b]RTA, renal tubular acidosis.
[c]DRTA, distal renal tubular acidosis.
[d]GFR, glomerular filtration rate.

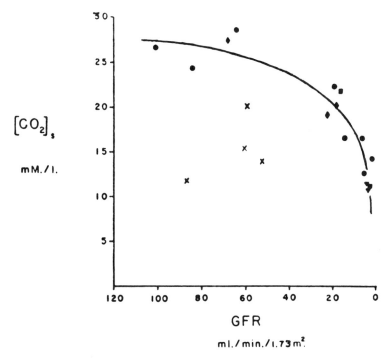

FIG. 1. Relationship between the level of serum total CO_2 concentration and glomerular filtration rate (GFR) in patients with chronic renal disease of various causes, including chronic glomerulonephritis (●), chronic pyelonephritis (■), nephrosclerosis (♦), and polycystic kidney disease (▼). Data from four patients with renal tubular acidosis also are depicted (X). (From ref. 6.)

acidosis, more than 90% of patients had some degree of hypobicarbonatemia once the GFR had fallen below 20 ml/min. Thus, as depicted in Fig. 1, although metabolic acidosis may not be present in all patients with advanced renal failure, it appears that the vast majority will have a reduction in plasma bicarbonate concentration once the GFR falls below 20 ml/min. The explanation for the normal acid-base status seen in a few patients with severe renal failure, therefore, remains unexplained but could be the consequence of better preservation of renal tubular function and increased participation of extrarenal buffers in these patients.

It has been widely held that the acidosis of chronic renal failure is a feature of advanced renal dysfunction, generally appearing when the GFR has fallen below 25% of normal and the serum creatinine concentration has exceeded 4 mg/dl. A retrospective study by Widmer et al., demonstrated, however, that metabolic acidosis may accompany even modest degrees of chronic renal insufficiency. These workers examined serum electrolyte data from 41 ambulatory patients with graded degrees of uncomplicated, stable renal failure due to diverse causes. None of these patients had other disorders or were taking medications known to influence acid-base equilibrium. Patients with serum creatinine levels of 2 to 4 mg/dl (corresponding to GFRs ranging from roughly 50% to 25% of normal) had a substantial decrease in serum total CO_2 content (average value of 22 mEq/liter compared to 28 mEq/liter for normal subjects). Moreover, as anticipated, more advanced degrees of chronic renal failure were associated with metabolic acidosis of greater severity. Thus, as shown in Fig. 2, the reduction in the level of serum total CO_2 content was correlated with the degree of renal failure as measured by the serum creatinine concentration.

In general, the more severe degrees of hypobicarbonatemia were seen at the lowest levels of GFR. An analogous relationship between the levels of measured GFR and the plasma bicarbonate concentration was reported previously and is shown in Fig. 1. The 95% confidence levels for serum total CO_2 to be expected in patients with uncomplicated chronic renal failure with various degrees of renal insufficiency are shown in Table 2. The broadness of the confidence limits at each level of renal dysfunction is substantial, presumably reflecting, at least in part, variable preservation of renal tubular function. Indeed, as can be seen in Table 2, even patients with severe degrees of renal failure may have values for serum total CO_2 content falling within the lower limits of the normal range. It is possible that prospective studies using arterial blood samples and more accurate estimates of GFR may arrive at a different relationship as well as narrower limits of plasma bicarbonate concentration during graded chronic renal failure.

It is notable that even patients with far advanced renal failure, when stable

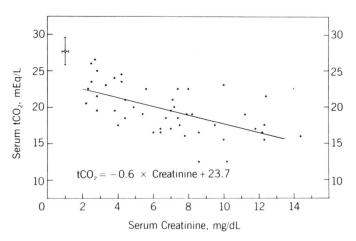

FIG. 2. Relationship between serum total CO_2 concentration and serum creatinine in patients with graded degrees of chronic renal failure. Note that a reduction in total CO_2 concentration was observed with even modest increments in serum creatinine concentration. (From ref. 25.)

TABLE 2. *Ninety-five percent significance intervals for serum total CO_2 and serum unmeasured anion concentration during chronic renal failure in humans*

Serum creatinine (mg/dl)	Serum total CO_2 (mEq/liter)	Serum unmeasured anions (mEq/liter)
2.0	16.9–28.1	7.3–17.2
4.0	15.7–26.8	8.4–18.2
6.0	14.6–25.5	9.6–19.3
8.0	13.4–24.3	10.7–20.3
10.0	12.1–23.2	11.7–21.5
12.0	10.8–22.1	12.6–22.6

From ref. 25.

and uncomplicated, are usually characterized by only mild to moderate degrees of metabolic acidosis. Plasma bicarbonate concentration usually ranges from 12 to 18 mEq/liter, and blood pH is usually 7.30 or greater. Moreover, once plasma bicarbonate is reduced, it remains stable unless a further decline in renal function occurs or an increased acid load is superimposed. The mechanisms postulated to explain the relative stability of the metabolic acidosis are considered in the section on Pathophysiology of Uremic Acidosis. Certainly, more severe degrees of metabolic acidosis may occur in patients with chronic renal failure. These occurrences, however, usually reflect a defective response to an augmented acid load (commonly the result of certain catabolic stresses, such as sepsis or the postoperative state, or the result of a substantial change in dietary intake) or superimposition of an independent acidifying process, such as diarrhea or lactic acidosis.

Earlier studies had suggested that the nature of the underlying renal disease is an important determinant of the severity of the metabolic acidosis. It was believed that patients with tubulointerstitial diseases, such as chronic pyelonephritis, urinary tract obstruction, and polycystic kidney disease, tend to develop more severe metabolic acidosis and at an earlier stage of renal insufficiency than patients with glomerular diseases. However, this view remains mostly a clinical impression and has not been subjected to rigorous investigation. Several recent retrospective studies have not comfirmed the earlier observations. In general, the degree of hypobicarbonatemia found in patients with tubulointerstitial diseases was not different from that prevailing in patients with glomerular diseases irrespective of the level of severity of the renal failure. It is worth noting, however, that some patients with tubulointerstitial diseases, particularly those with urinary tract obstruction and chronic pyelonephritis, have hyperkalemic distal renal tubular acidosis (Type IV) due to hypoaldosteronism or tubular unresponsiveness to aldosterone (aldosterone resistance). These patients will, therefore, be expected to manifest a degree of metabolic acidosis greater than anticipated on the basis of their GFR.

Signs and Symptoms

The clinical signs and symptoms related to acidosis are usually subtle in patients with uremic acidosis, reflecting the relative mildness and slowly progressive nature of the metabolic disturbance. Some degree of hypernea may be found at rest, indicative of the ventilatory response to metabolic acidosis. If bone disease is present, bone pain may be a prominent feature. Acidosis may contribute to the lethargy and mental confusion often experienced by patients with advanced renal failure. However, the dramatic clinical features of acute forms of severe metabolic acidosis, such as ketoacidosis or lactic acidosis, generally are not seen.

Anionic Patterns in Uremic Acidosis (7,14,24,25)

Until recently, it had been thought that the metabolic acidosis developing in the course of chronic progressive renal failure is predominantly of the high anion gap (normochloremic) variety, the fall in plasma bicarbonate concentration being matched by an equivalent rise in the concentration of unmeasured anions, mostly sulfate, phosphate, and various organic-acid anions. However, studies of Widmer et al. suggested, in fact, that the precise electrolyte pattern observed may depend on the stage of renal failure (Fig. 3). Thus, early in the course of chronic renal failure (serum creatinine concentrations of 2–4 mg/dl), the dominant electrolyte pattern observed was a normal anion gap or hyperchloremic metabolic acidosis in which the prevailing mild hypobicarbonatemia was entirely offset by an increase in plasma chloride concentration. At more advanced degrees of renal failure (i.e., serum creatinine concentration greater than 4 mg/dl corresponding to a GFR less than 25% of normal), the metabolic acidosis reflected a mixed normal anion gap and high anion gap pattern. Thus, the graded decrements in plasma bicarbonate were associated with equivalent increments in plasma unmeasured anions, plasma chloride concentration remaining at the elevated level presumably attained during the earlier stages of renal insufficiency.

During end-stage renal failure (GFR less than 10% of normal), a high anion gap metabolic acidosis was present predominantly, but an element of hyperchloremia persisted. Figure 4 depicts the correlation between serum unmeasured anions and the level of serum creatinine concentration, and Table 2 lists the 95% confidence intervals for unmeasured anion concentration in patients with uncomplicated renal failure. More recent studies by Wallia et al. not only confirmed the high prevalence of hyperchloremic acidosis in patients with renal failure, but also showed that this electrolyte pattern was observed by itself (i.e., in the absence of a coexisting element of high anion gap acidosis), even with severe reductions of renal function. Thus, among the subjects with severe renal failure requiring the initiation of maintenance dialysis de-

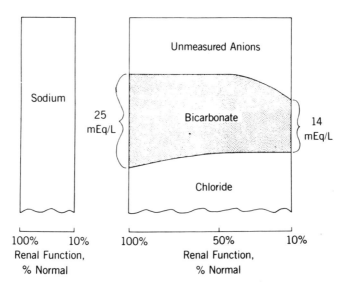

FIG. 3. Evolution of the electrolyte pattern of metabolic acidosis in patients with chronic renal failure. Vertical axis reflects serum concentration in mEq/liter. Although the serum concentration of sodium does not change appreciably in the course of progressive renal failure, considerable changes in the serum anion composition occur. During early renal dysfunction, the prevailing mild hypobicarbonatemia is entirely offset by an increase in serum chloride concentration, unmeasured anion concentration remaining normal. At more advanced degrees of renal failure (glomerular filtration rate less than 25% of normal), the graded decrements in bicarbonate concentration are associated with equivalent increments in unmeasured anion concentration, but the element of hyperchloremia established earlier persists. (From ref. 25.)

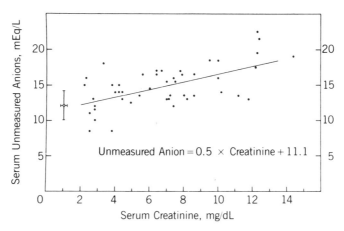

FIG. 4. Relationship between serum unmeasured anion concentration and serum creatinine in patients with graded degrees of chronic renal failure. (From ref. 25.)

scribed by these authors, 11 patients had a mixed high and normal anion gap metabolic acidosis, 21 patients had a pure normal anion gap (hyperchloremic) metabolic acidosis, and only 14 patients had a pure high anion gap metabolic acidosis. Enia et al. found some component of hyperchloremic acidosis in 30% of patients with chronic renal failure, even at GFRs below 10 ml/min.

In order to appreciate the possible reasons for the variable electrolyte pattern of metabolic acidosis in patients with chronic renal failure, it is necessary to understand how a high or normal anion gap metabolic acidosis might be generated during the course of renal failure. The pathogenesis of these two different electrolyte patterns is schematically depicted in Fig. 5. Figure 5A represents the situation prevailing in subjects with normal renal function who are in normal acid-base balance. Under usual circumstances, approximately 1

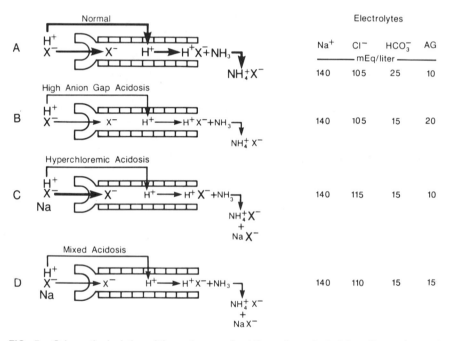

FIG. 5. Schematic depiction of the pathogenesis of the various electrolyte patterns observed in chronic renal failure. In all panels, acid anions (X^-) are shown to be excreted by glomerular filtration, whereas hydrogen ions (H^+) are secreted by the tubular epithelium and excreted in the urine combined with buffer, primarily NH_3. **A:** State of normalcy. The excretion of protons and anions ensures acid-base and electrolyte balance. **B:** Situation arising during generalized renal failure in the presence of a proportionate reduction in glomerular and tubular function. The equivalent retention of protons and anions results in a high anion gap acidosis. **C:** Situation in which tubular function is markedly disturbed, but little change has occurred in glomerular function (such as in renal tubular acidosis). Here, the retained protons are matched by an equivalent quantity of chloride, thereby producing a hyperchloremic acidosis. **D:** Situation in which both glomerular and tubular functions are disturbed but to a disproportionate degree. Retention of anions, protons, and chloride occurs, thus leading to a mixed high anion gap and normal anion gap metabolic acidosis. (Adapted from ref. 14.)

mEq/kg body weight of strong acid (designated as HX) is produced daily by cellular metabolism. The influx of this acid into the body fluids is followed by its virtually complete dissociation, resulting in a fall in plasma bicarbonate as it is titrated by the relinquished protons, and an equivalent rise in the concentration of the acid anion X^-. In essence, throughout this process, $NaHCO_3$ is being replaced by NaX. Sodium and the accompanying acid anion X^- is then filtered by the glomerulus. Replenishment of the depleted bicarbonate stores is accomplished via tubular secretion of an equivalent number of protons, which eventually are excreted in the urine bound to a urinary buffer, primarily ammonia. The ammonium thus formed is excreted with the acid anion so that electroneutrality of the urinary fluid and, in addition, acid-base and electrolyte balance are maintained. In this formulation, the excretion of the acid anion reflects primarily a glomerular function, whereas the excretion of acid is accomplished via a tubular function. Thus, retention of acid anions results when glomerular filtration is reduced, and decreased net acid excretion is a consequence of tubular dysfunction.

Figure 5B depicts the electrolyte pattern emerging during generalized renal failure in the presence of a proportionate decrease in glomerular and tubular function. Under such circumstances, there will be an equivalent reduction in acid anion excretion and net acid excretion. As a consequence, the retention of acid anions and the reduction in plasma bicarbonate concentration will be equivalent, giving rise to a pure high anion gap (normochloremic) metabolic acidosis. By contrast (Fig. 5C), if damage is primarily tubular (as occurs with renal tubular acidosis), the metabolic acid anions will continue to be filtered and excreted, whereas net acid excretion by the kidney will be compromised. Electroneutrality will be maintained by diverting some filtered sodium into the urine to accompany part of the excreted acid anions and by retaining some dietary chloride to replace the depleted plasma bicarbonate stores. As a consequence, a pattern of pure normal anion gap (hyperchloremic) metabolic acidosis will emerge. One can appreciate that when glomerular and tubular functions are decreased disproportionately (Fig. 5D), a mixed high and normal anion gap metabolic acidosis will develop, and the dominant electrolyte pattern will be determined by the locus of the greater damage. In view of this formulation emphasizing the disparate roles of glomerular and tubular function in determining the electrolyte pattern and given the heterogeneity of renal damage in parenchymal renal disease, it would in fact have been surprising if these two portions of the nephron were damaged proportionately, resulting in the consistent generation of a pure high anion gap metabolic acidosis during the course of chronic renal failure. The available evidence suggests rather that, early in the course of most renal diseases, a disproportionate reduction in tubular function must be present, accounting for the development of hyperchloremic acidosis. As renal failure progresses, glomerular function must fall sufficiently to result in a rise in unmeasured anion concentration and thereby produce a mixed hyperchloremic and high anion gap metabolic acidosis. With end-stage renal disease, in some patients, the reduction in glomerular and tubular function must be proportionate to produce a pure high anion gap metabolic acidosis. In others, a disparity between tubular and glomerular function persists, leading to a mixed type of acidosis. Recent observations suggesting that a sizable fraction of patients with severe renal failure apparently have a pure hyperchloremic acidosis without a detectable rise in the anion gap are puzzling. It is recognized, of course, that the range of the normal anion gap is wide (8–18 mEq/liter in various studies) and that the level of plasma albumin concentration (the main determinant of the plasma unmeasured anion concentration) has not been reported in the various studies of the electrolyte pattern of uremic acidosis. Nonetheless, careful examination of the available evidence supports the intriguing conclusion that a substantial portion of patients with end-stage renal failure do indeed have a pure hyperchloremic acidosis.

Although some earlier studies had suggested that, in comparison to patients with glomerular diseases, the metabolic acidosis in patients with tubulointerstitial diseases tends to appear earlier, is more severe at the same level of glomerular filtration, and is more likely to be hyperchloremic, this impression has not been borne out by more recent studies. They have indicated that the hyperchloremic form of metabolic acidosis was just as likely to be observed in patients with glomerular diseases as in those with tubulointerstitial diseases. Furthermore, as noted earlier, the severity of the acidosis was no different between subjects with the two different types of diseases.

It should be recognized, however, that a critical deficiency in all the reported studies is that the diagnosis of the type of renal disease was often made on the basis of the clinical findings rather than by renal biopsy. In fact, even when renal biopsy was available, no comments on the extent of coexisting glomerular and tubulointerstitial disease were made. The coexistence of a substantial component of tubulointerstitial disease might account, at least in part, for the development of a pattern of hyperchloremic acidosis in some patients with presumed pure glomerular disease.

It is unknown to what extent the various studies on uremic acidosis have been complicated by the inclusion of patients with the syndrome of hyperkalemic distal renal tubular acidosis. In this syndrome, commonly observed in patients with such diverse disorders as obstructive uropathy, sickle cell disease, systemic lupus erythematosus, and diabetes mellitus, tubular function is impaired out of proportion to the reduction in GFR, resulting in substantial hyperchloremic metabolic acidosis in association with hyperkalemia. Although GFR often is only moderately reduced, this syndrome even has been described in patients with GFRs as low as 20 ml/min.

High anion gap acidosis, hyperchloremic (normal anion gap) acidosis, and mixed types of metabolic acidosis may be observed in patients with chronic renal failure. The electrolyte pattern observed does not appear to be a clue to the type of underlying renal disease. Moreover, recent studies suggest that, in contrast to previous beliefs, the hyperchloremic form of metabolic acidosis may be seen by itself in a substantial portion of patients with end-stage renal failure.

Ventilatory Response in Uremic Acidosis (27)

Careful observations have documented that the ventilatory response to the metabolic acidosis of chronic renal failure is virtually indistinguishable from that noted in other types of metabolic acidosis. Thus, on average, $PaCO_2$ falls by 1.0 to 1.3 mm Hg for each mEq/liter fall in plasma bicarbonate concentration, and the slope of the relationship between $PaCO_2$ and plasma bicarbonate is not altered when the patient is maintained on chronic hemodialysis.

Effect of Uremic Acidosis on Serum Electrolytes (2,5)

The impact of the acidemia of uremic acidosis on the compartmental distribution of body potassium and, therefore, the level of serum potassium is difficult to discern, since impaired renal function decreases potassium excretion. As noted previously, uremic acidosis of the high anion gap variety is associated with retention of phosphate, sulfate, and various organic acid anions. Evidence suggests that in various high anion gap organic acidoses (e.g., ketoacidosis, lactic acidosis), the increment in serum potassium is less for the same degree of acidemia than with mineral acid acidoses, presumably because the high intracellular penetrance of the corresponding organic anions does not obligate translocation of cellular potassium to the extracellular fluid in the process of buffering of protons. Since chronic renal failure primarily is associated with an increment of inorganic anions, such as phosphate and sulfate, rather than organic acid anions, it has been postulated that the attendant acidemia would have essentially the same effect as administration of hydrochloric acid in favoring potassium egress from the cell. Although this thesis remains to be tested, it seems reasonable to suggest that the acidemia of chronic renal failure tends to elevate the serum potassium concentration by affecting its cellular distribution.

Hyperphosphatemia is an inevitable consequence of chronic renal failure and is primarily due to reduced excretion of phosphate as a consequence of a decreased GFR. However, studies in humans and experimental animals suggest that the metabolic acidosis of uremia may contribute to the rise in serum phosphorus. Thus, serum phosphorus was higher in uremic acidotic rats than in nonacidotic controls, and Barsotti et al. and Cochrane and Wilkinson showed that, in patients with chronic renal failure maintained on chronic dialysis or treated with conservative therapy, a significant fall in serum phosphorus was noted when metabolic acidosis was corrected by bicarbonate therapy. The reduction in serum phosphorus was not a result of increased excretion of phosphorus, since urinary phosphorus excretion was in fact reduced by alkali therapy. The reduction in serum phosphorus could result from incorporation of phosphorus into bone as bone is healing during treatment with alkali. This situation is analogous to the hungry bone syndrome observed after parathyroidectomy in patients with secondary hyperparathyroidism. It is worth emphasizing, however, that the increment in serum phosphorus with acidosis makes only a minor contribution to the rise noted with chronic renal failure.

Hypocalcemia is a common finding in chronic renal failure. The depression in serum calcium is accounted for largely by the combination of reduced intestinal calcium absorption and the increased level of serum phosphorus, both characteristic features of uremia. Metabolic acidosis may contribute to the prevailing hypocalcemia, however, by promoting urinary calcium excretion and thereby contributing to negative calcium balance. On the other hand, metabolic acidosis actually may contribute to a rise in the level of ionized calcium. Such increment in ionized calcium may be due both to a pH-related reduction in binding of calcium to protein and to increased release of calcium from bone into the extracellular fluid in the process of extrarenal buffering.

PATHOGENESIS OF UREMIC ACIDOSIS (14,17,21)

The basic defect responsible for the metabolic acidosis of chronic renal failure is tubular dysfunction leading to reduction in net acid excretion to levels below that of endogenous acid production. Although under certain circumstances, alterations in all three components of net acid excretion (i.e., ammonium plus titratable acid minus bicarbonate) may contribute to the fall in urinary acid output, the predominant culprit is a decrease in ammonium excretion. In this section, we first discuss the mechanisms underlying the stability of the metabolic acidosis of uremia and then proceed with an analysis of the precise alterations that lead to a fall in net acid excretion.

Stability of Uremic Acidosis (9,11,15)

Careful balance studies performed in patients with stable chronic renal failure (GFRs between 12 and 40 ml/min) established that the daily production of endogenous acid is not different from that of subjects with normal renal function. In both cases, endogenous acid production is approximately 1.0 mEq/kg body weight per day.[1] Furthermore, the same studies established

---

[1] In some patients with chronic renal failure, a decrease in appetite or therapeutic intervention may lead to ingestion of lower quantities of protein. In view of the direct correlation between protein intake and acid production, endogenous acid production may actually be less than that observed in subjects with normal renal function.

that net acid excretion in patients with chronic renal failure falls short of endogenous acid production, daily hydrogen ion balance being on the average 10 to 20 mEq positive. Strikingly, despite this continual acid retention, plasma bicarbonate concentration and the degree of metabolic acidosis remain stable as long as renal function is also stable. Some extrarenal mechanism must, therefore, serve as a repository for retained hydrogen ions, thereby sparing the circulating bicarbonate stores.

The nature of this extrarenal buffering mechanism has not been established with certainty. Nonetheless, several lines of indirect evidence suggest strongly that the stability of the uremic acidosis is made possible through buffering of the retained hydrogen ions by bone carbonate and phosphate, but at the expense of progressive bone mineral dissolution. First, studies in normal humans have demonstrated that the progressive hydrogen ion retention characteristic of stable ammonium chloride-induced metabolic acidosis occurs in association with marked hypercalciuria and negative calcium balance. Second, the positive hydrogen ion balance characteristic of patients with chronic stable uremic acidosis is accompanied by negative calcium balance. Administration of bicarbonate led to neutral acid balance and a significant reduction in urinary calcium losses, presumably because the need for buffering of hydrogen at the expense of bone mineral dissolution was obviated. Third, loss of bone mineral is a common feature of chronic renal failure. Indeed, analysis of bone biopsies from dialysis patients or bone specimens obtained at autopsy of uremic patients has revealed reduced concentrations of calcium carbonate, a potential source of base. Fourth, chronic administration of mineral acid to dogs or rats causes bone decalcification and reductions in bone carbonate. Furthermore, prevention of bone-buffer mobilization by administration of diphosphonates or colchicine to animals with experimental acute renal failure produced by ureteral ligation leads to greater hypobicarbonatemia when compared to animals receiving vehicle alone.

Although the evidence implicating the skeleton as the site of buffering of protons retained during the course of chronic renal failure is strong, the factors that govern the recruitment of bone buffers remain to be delineated. Some studies have suggested that buffering of protons occurs as a result of physicochemical dissolution of labile bone mineral, primarily calcium carbonate, by the reduced pH. Under certain experimental conditions, this process appears to be triggered by only minor reductions in pH that are well within the range of those observed in uremic acidosis. On the other hand, it also has been suggested that metabolic acidosis is associated with stimulation of cell-mediated bone resorption, with resultant release of bone buffers. Animals with acute renal failure have an impaired capacity to buffer the endogenous acid load when cell-mediated bone resorption is blocked by pretreatment with colchicine. Most of the available evidence suggests that both of these mechanisms of release of bone buffers function independently of parathyroid hormone. On the other hand, parathyroid hormone might play a modulating role in the release of bone buffers. Chronic renal failure is associated with secondary hyperparathyroidism, and in some studies, chronic metabolic acidosis induced by the administration of mineral acid has led to a rise in parathyroid hormone levels. Animals with chronic renal failure were shown in one study to have reduced buffering capacity for an acute acid load after their parathyroid glands had been removed. However, no long-term observations are available, and further work is needed to clarify the role of parathyroid hormone in the buffering process during chronic renal failure.

Urine pH (21,26)

Early studies by Palmer and Henderson indicated that the ability to acidify the urine is reasonably well preserved in patients with chronic renal failure. Thus, during spontaneous hypobicarbonatemia and in the absence of alkali therapy, the urine contains no appreciable quantities of bicarbonate, urine pH being consistently less than 6.0 and usually close to 5.0. The preservation of distal hydrogen ion secretory capacity is further attested to by the increase in titratable acid excretion observed when a phosphate load is administered. In contrast to distal renal tubular acidosis, the urine − blood P_{CO_2} gradient is found to be in the normal range in chronic renal failure when correction is applied for the attendant concentrating defect. On the other hand, when plasma bicarbonate is normalized by alkali administration, urine pH is usually greater than 6.0 and substantial bicarbonaturia commonly occurs. The relatively high urine pH observed under these circumstances has been attributed to increased delivery of bicarbonate to the distal nephron and, therefore, exhaustion of the limited distal nephron secretory capacity.

By contrast, when spontaneous hypobicarbonatemia prevails, the modest distal bicarbonate delivery allows expression of the preserved distal acidification capacity and, thus, generation of a low urine pH. This formulation is supported by the observations of Seldin et al., who examined the ability of patients with chronic renal failure (average GFR of 15 ml/min) to acidify their urine in response to an infusion of hypertonic sodium sulfate. Administration of this nonreabsorbable anion to normal subjects induces consistently intense urine acidification. Just as in normals, sodium sulfate infusion in patients with chronic renal failure and intrinsic hypobicarbonatemia led to a lowering of urine pH. On the other hand, urine pH actually rose in response to this infusion in uremic patients whose plasma bicarbonate had been normalized previously by alkali administration, presumably because sodium sulfate augmented the already heightened distal bicarbonate delivery.

Notwithstanding the spontaneous attainment of a urine pH that is usually near 5.0 by the large majority of patients with chronic renal failure, the fact remains that this level of acidification falls short (by at least 0.5 pH units) of that achieved by normal subjects after experimentally induced acidemia. This difference in urine pH remains when normal subjects and patients with chronic renal failure are exposed to the same high phosphate and hydrogen load. On the basis of this and additional evidence, it has been suggested that a certain defect in collecting tubule acidification occurs in chronic renal failure. The consequence of such a defect is imposition of a limitation on the titration of urinary buffers and, therefore, the excretion of titratable acidity. In a relatively small, but currently undefined, fraction of patients with chronic renal failure, substantial bicarbonaturia is manifest at subnormal plasma bicarbonate concentration, and urine pH remains greater than 5.5 despite moderately severe hypobicarbonatemia. In these patients, an even greater limitation on the titration of urinary buffers is, therefore, imposed.

Ammonium Excretion (3,18,21,23)

As noted in Chapter 9, ammonia is the most important urinary buffer for the excretion of acid. Ammonium excretion is increased markedly in response to an acid load, rising as much as tenfold in such disorders as severe diabetic ketoacidosis (Table 3). Ammonium excretion is strikingly reduced in chronic renal failure to levels less than 50% of normal (Table 3) and constitutes the principal abnormality leading to the fall in net acid excretion characteristic of uremia. This reduction in ammonium excretion is considerably greater than the fall in titratable acid excretion, leading to a reversal of the normal urinary ammonium/titratable acid ratio from a value greater than 1.0 in individuals with normal renal function to less than 1.0 in those with chronic renal failure (Table 3).

The decrease in ammonium excretion characteristic of chronic renal failure appears largely to be a result of a reduction in ammonia production because of reduced renal mass rather than impaired ammonia synthetic capacity. In studies of unilateral renal disease in humans and animals, although ammonium excretion by the involved kidney was less than by the normal kidney, the excretion of ammonium expressed per milliliter of GFR was similar in both kidneys. This finding indicates that the ammonia synthetic capacity of

TABLE 3. *Urinary excretion rates of ammonium and titratable acidity during health, diabetic ketoacidosis, and advanced chronic renal failure*

Condition	$U_{NH_4}V$ (mEq/day)	$U_{TA}V$ (mEq/day)
Health	30–50	10–30
Diabetic ketoacidosis	300–500	70–150
Chronic renal failure (advanced)	0.5–15	2–20

Adapted from ref. 16.

UREMIC ACIDOSIS

the residual nephrons of the involved kidney is normal. Moreover, although ammonium excretion is reduced in patients with bilateral renal disease, the level of ammonium excretion actually is extremely high when factored for the fall in GFR. As shown in Table 4 and Fig. 6, the excretion of ammonium expressed per milliliter of glomerular filtrate may be fourfold greater in patients with chronic renal failure and metabolic acidosis than in normal subjects in the absence of acidosis. However, as shown in Table 4, it is still substantially less than that observed in normal subjects with ammonium chloride-induced metabolic acidosis.

The adaptive rise in ammonia production by residual nephrons reflects largely adaptive changes in the proximal nephron, the principal site for renal ammonia synthesis. Evidence in support of both a rise in cellular ammonia synthetic capacity and an increase in the population of ammonia producing cells per nephron has been obtained. Thus, studies in rats with chronic renal failure induced by subtotal nephrectomy have detected an increase in cellular ammonia synthetic capacity in association with a rise in the activity of phosphate-dependent glutaminase and glutamate dehydrogenase, enzymes involved in the metabolic pathway for ammonia synthesis. Work in the same experimental model by other investigators, however, has failed to detect such a rise in cellular ammonia synthetic capacity but found instead an increase in the rate of ammonia production per milligram of DNA. This finding implicates formation of additional ammonia-producing cells to account for the adaptive increase in ammonia production by residual nephrons. It is conceivable that both mechanisms proposed might contribute to this adaptation, in view of the fact that, depending on the experimental conditions, the compensatory process in the proximal tubule of remnant nephrons comprises variable elements of cellular hypertrophy and hyperplasia.

Micropuncture studies by Buerkert et al. have suggested an additional mechanism whereby urinary ammonium excretion might be decreased in chronic renal failure, even in the absence of an absolute decrease in renal ammonia production. Under normal conditions, countercurrent exchange

TABLE 4. *Urinary excretion rates of ammonium and titratable acidity during health, NH_4Cl acidosis, and uremic acidosis expressed per unit of glomerular filtration rate*

Condition	$U_{NH_4^+}$ V/GFR[a] (μEq/ml)	U_{TA} V/GFR (μEq/ml)
Normal subjects	0.21 ± 0.06[b]	0.13 ± 0.06
Normal subjects with NH_4Cl acidosis	1.52	0.30
Uremic acidosis	0.81 ± 0.23	1.07 ± 0.69

[a]GFR, glomerular filtration rate.
[b]Values are mean $\pm$ SD.
Adapted from ref. 21.

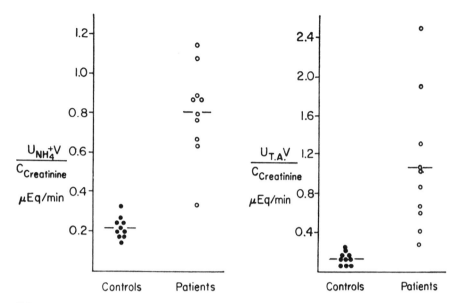

FIG. 6. Urinary excretion of ammonium and titratable acid expressed per milliliter of glomerular filtrate in normal subjects and patients with uremic acidosis. (From ref. 21.)

mechanisms favor the generation of high medullary ammonia concentration and, therefore, the trapping of ammonia by the acidified luminal fluid of the collecting duct. When the number of nephrons was decreased by subtotal nephrectomy, the countercurrent exchange mechanisms in the remnant kidney apparently were disturbed, leading to impaired reentrapment of ammonia along the collecting duct. As a result, even though in these studies ammonia addition to the luminal fluid by the proximal tubule was actually increased compared to animals with intact renal function, urinary ammonium excretion was depressed substantially. Furthermore, ammonium excretion is strikingly reduced in animals with renal failure induced by papillectomy, supporting the critical role of ammonia recycling in the excretion of ammonium. These data may provide a partial explanation for the development of metabolic acidosis early in the course of some renal diseases that primarily affect the renal medulla.

Additional abnormalities in ammonia metabolism have been reported in chronic renal failure. Thus, in contrast to the situation in normal subjects in whom extracted glutamine largely accounts for ammonia production, in chronic renal failure no more than 35% of renal ammonia production can be attributed to the renal uptake of glutamine. These studies have suggested rather that ammonia production in chronic renal failure relies heavily on the intrarenal generation of glutamine via breakdown of various proteins and peptides.

Recent studies in subjects with chronic renal insufficiency and metabolic acidosis have shown that reduction of plasma potassium concentration may lead to increased ammonium excretion and amelioration of the prevailing hypobicarbonatemia. Although most of the reported patients had hyporeninemic hypoaldosteronism, an occasional subject featured normal levels of plasma aldosterone. Since it is well known that hyperkalemia exerts a suppressive influence on ammonia production, it is possible that hyperkalemia may contribute to reduced ammonium excretion in some patients with chronic renal failure.

Decreased ammonium excretion in renal failure is primarily due to decreased ammonia synthesis as a consequence of reduced renal mass. However, impaired reentrapment of ammonia in the luminal fluid of the collecting duct and suppression of ammonia synthesis by hyperkalemia also may contribute.

Titratable Acid Excretion

As renal ammonium excretion decreases, the kidney becomes increasingly dependent on urinary excretion of titratable acids (largely phosphate) to excrete the endogenous acid load. Several studies have indicated that titratable acid excretion is normal or only mildly decreased until the late stages of chronic renal failure. The maintenance of titratable acid excretion reflects the reasonably good preservation of the ability to acidify the urine as well as the excretion of normal quantities of phosphate, assuming an unrestricted protein intake. Maintenance of normal urinary phosphate excretion despite a reduced filtered load is assured by suppressed fractional reabsorption largely mediated by secondary hyperparathyroidism. Given the near normalcy of the absolute level of titratable acid excretion in chronic renal failure, titratable acidity is, in fact, increased by severalfold over that in normals when expressed per milliliter of GFR (Table 4, Fig. 6). In addition, the diseased kidney responds to increased phosphate intake by increasing titratable acid excretion very much similar to the response of the normal kidney. Normalization of plasma bicarbonate concentration by alkali administration results in a relatively alkaline urine and reduction in titratable acid excretion. Similarly, limitation of urinary phosphate will impair titratable acid excretion. Such a limitation may result from a reduction in dietary protein intake (whether due to a decrease in appetite from uremia or to imposed protein restriction) or reduced gastrointestinal absorption of phosphate by administered phosphate binders. It should be noted, however, that the potential adverse effect of dietary protein restriction on the regulation of acid-base balance is ameliorated by the consequent reduction in endogenous acid load. Once GFR falls below 10 to 15 ml/min, urinary phosphate excretion is markedly reduced and, therefore, titratable acid excretion also will be greatly diminished (Table 3).

Reduced Bicarbonate Reabsorption (1,8,12,13,19,20,22)

The contribution of reduced renal bicarbonate reabsorption to the metabolic acidosis of chronic renal failure remains unclear. Early bicarbonate titration studies (using hypertonic solutions to limit volume expansion) in uremic humans or animals had concluded that absolute bicarbonate reabsorptive capacity was either unchanged or decreased. In subsequent studies, however, that used similar infusion protocols but factored bicarbonate reabsorption by chloride reabsorption to reflect the degree of volume expansion produced, an increment in absolute bicarbonate reabsorptive capacity was detected. Moreover, in these studies, the ratio of bicarbonate reabsorption to chloride reabsorption was inversely proportional to the prevailing GFR, suggesting that as GFR falls, sodium bicarbonate is preferentially absorbed over sodium chloride. Most, but not all, micropuncture observations in dogs and rats with remnant kidneys have revealed an increase in absolute bicarbonate reabsorption in the proximal tubule, whereas, fractional proximal bicarbonate reabsorption has variably ranged from slightly decreased to slightly increased. Several mechanisms have been proposed to account for the enhanced absolute proximal bicarbonate reabsorption in the remnant kidney, including the attendant hyperfiltration (resulting in increased luminal flow) and proximal tubule hypertrophy and hyperplasia (leading to increased membrane surface area). In addition, increased Na^+-H^+ antiporter activity, reflecting an increased V_{max} of the antiporter, has been demonstrated in proximal tubule brush border microvesicles from dogs and rats subject to partial ablation of renal mass.

On the other hand, despite experimental evidence for increased bicarbonate reabsorption, it is clear from clinical studies that some patients with chronic renal failure exhibit bicarbonaturia, which may manifest itself even at subnormal plasma bicarbonate concentrations (on the order of 15–20 mEq/liter), indicating the presence of a defect in bicarbonate reabsorption. In this regard, as noted earlier, most azotemic patients with established metabolic acidosis usually excrete an acid urine devoid of appreciable quantities of alkali. Schwartz et al. attempted to expose an underlying defect in bicarbonate reabsorption by transiently restoring plasma bicarbonate to normal with exogenous alkali and observing urinary bicarbonate excretion during the reemergence of metabolic acidosis after discontinuation of the alkali. By using this protocol, these investigators hoped to circumvent the potential limitation of bicarbonate titration studies in detecting small reductions in bicarbonate reabsorptive capacity.

Complete metabolic balance studies were performed in four patients with chronic glomerulonephritis and mild to moderate metabolic acidosis. Serum creatinine concentrations ranged from 8 to 13 mg/dl. The diet was supplemented with sodium bicarbonate to raise plasma bicarbonate concentration to about 25 mEq/liter. After the bicarbonate supplement was discontinued,

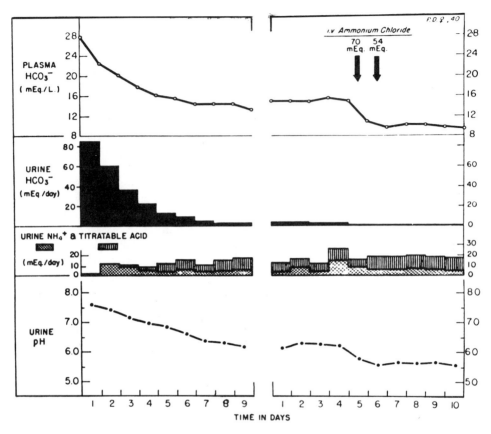

FIG. 7. Changes in plasma bicarbonate concentration, urine pH, and daily urinary excretion of bicarbonate, ammonium, and titratable acid in a patient with chronic renal failure and bicarbonate wasting. Observations were begun the day after the metabolic acidosis had been corrected by administration of bicarbonate and supplements had been discontinued. The break in the middle of the observations represents an interval of 7 days during which bicarbonate supplements were held. (From ref. 20.)

plasma bicarbonate fell to baseline levels (12–15 mEq/liter) over 5 to 8 days in three of the four patients in association with a relatively alkaline urine pH and substantial bicarbonaturia (Fig. 7). Urine bicarbonate excretion was as high as 40 to 60 mEq/day even though plasma bicarbonate concentration was subnormal. Once plasma bicarbonate had fallen to the baseline level of 12 to 15 mEq/liter, bicarbonaturia ceased and an acidic urine was again present. The very fact that a decrement in plasma bicarbonate of 10 to 13 mEq/liter developed over the course of several days attests to the presence of a bicarbonate wasting defect. A much longer period of time would have been required for such a decline in plasma bicarbonate to occur if it were merely due to partial retention of the endogenous acid load. Bicarbonate wasting, how-

ever, was not observed in the fourth patient whose urine was acidic and virtually free of bicarbonate by day 2 after discontinuation of alkali. Almost 2
weeks were required for plasma bicarbonate to stabilize at its baseline value
of approximately 14.5 mEq/liter (Fig. 8). Similarly, among eight additional
patients with chronic renal failure who were studied by the same investigators
without performing complete metabolic balances, only two excreted substantial quantities of bicarbonate at plasma bicarbonate levels below 24 mEq/liter.
The factors contributing to the presence of bicarbonate wasting in some but
not in other patients were not apparent from this study.

Additional studies have provided evidence for a bicarbonate wasting defect
in some patients with uremia. Thus, Lamiere et al. observed that after discontinuation of bicarbonate supplements, some patients with chronic renal failure
continued to excrete large amounts of bicarbonate at plasma bicarbonate
concentrations ranging from 17 to 23 mEq/liter (fractional bicarbonate excretion as high as 17%. When plasma bicarbonate was reduced to 13 mEq/liter

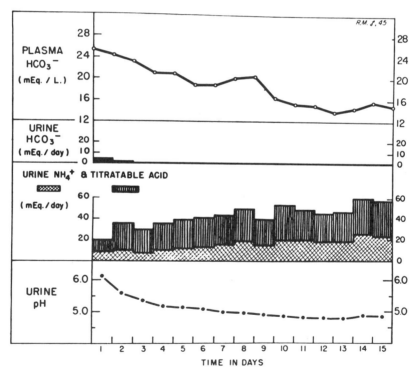

FIG. 8. Changes in plasma bicarbonate concentration, urine pH, and daily urinary excretion
of bicarbonate, ammonium, and titratable acid in a patient with chronic renal failure but no
bicarbonate wasting. Observations were begun the day after the metabolic acidosis had been
corrected by administration of bicarbonate and supplements had been discontinued. (From ref.
20.)

by administration of ammonium chloride, bicarbonaturia disappeared in more than half of the patients. Yet a slight degree of bicarbonaturia persisted, and urine pH was greater than 6.0 in some subjects even at this low level of plasma bicarbonate. In addition, Muldowney et al. have documented bicarbonate wastage in two patients with polycystic kidney disease and severe renal failure.

Various mechanisms have been proposed to account for the impaired bicarbonate reabsorption encountered in some patients with chronic renal failure. Although structural damage of remaining nephrons might well play a role, it is notable that bicarbonate wastage has been observed in patients with either glomerular or tubulointerstitial renal disease. Secondary hyperparathyroidism, a common occurrence in chronic renal failure, also has been implicated. It has been shown that acute administration of parathyroid hormone augments urinary bicarbonate excretion in both animals and humans with normal renal function, and some patients with primary hyperparathyroidism manifest bicarbonate wastage. Studies in isolated perfused proximal tubules have shown inhibition of bicarbonate reabsorption by parathyroid hormone. Moreover, parathyroid hormone has been demonstrated to decrease Na^+-H^+ antiporter activity in a cell line resembling proximal tubule epithelium, and parathyroidectomy increased Na^+-H^+ antiporter activity in proximal tubule brush border microvesicles from dogs subject to partial renal ablation. It is reasonable, therefore, to implicate an excess of parathyroid hormone in the bicarbonate wastage of chronic renal failure. Muldowney et al. carried out studies in two patients with advanced polycystic kidney disease (GFRs of 6 and 15 ml/min), impaired bicarbonate reabsorption, and elevated levels of parathyroid hormone. Bicarbonate reabsorption was normalized after reduction of parathyroid hormone concentration by rising serum calcium concentration via either intravenous administration of calcium or oral administration of vitamin D. Lamiere et al. observed that parathyroid hormone levels were higher in those uremic patients who manifested persistent bicarbonaturia despite marked metabolic acidosis compared to those without bicarbonaturia. In general, parathyroid hormone levels are higher with advancing degrees of chronic renal failure. It is plausible, therefore, that the role of excessive parathyroid hormone levels in contributing to the bicarbonate wasting of uremia may be more important in severe chronic renal failure.

A degree of chronic extracellular volume expansion developing in the course of chronic renal failure also may contribute to impaired proximal bicarbonate reabsorption and, thus, to bicarbonate wastage. In this regard, Espinel examined plasma and urinary acid-base parameters in rats with graded degrees of chronic renal failure induced by sequential partial renal ablation. The control group received a constant dietary intake of sodium chloride during the course of progressive chronic renal failure; the experimental group was given a proportionally reduced sodium chloride intake at each fall in GFR. In the rats given a constant dietary intake of salt, plasma bicarbonate concentration and bicarbonate reabsorptive capacity were both reduced. Reduction of salt intake in the experimental group substantially ameliorated the decrease in both plasma bicarbonate concentration and in the bicarbonate reabsorptive capacity. In accord with these observations, recent studies in uremic humans by Lamiere et al. demonstrated amelioration of impaired bicarbonate reabsorption by reduction of dietary sodium chloride intake in four patients. With the loss of renal function, residual nephrons are exposed to an increased solute load similar to that seen in individuals with normal renal function receiving mannitol or urea infusions. The resultant solute diuresis impairs the reabsorption of sodium and its attendant anions and could, therefore, contribute to decreased bicarbonate reabsorption in chronic renal failure. The exact role of a solute diuresis is somewhat unclear, since in studies of unilateral renal disease, removal of the normal kidney failed to produce bicarbonaturia despite exposing the remaining diseased kidney to an increased solute load.

The bulk of the available experimental studies and some clinical observations suggest that there is augmentation of absolute bicarbonate reabsorptive capacity in chronic renal failure. There is also undisputed evidence that some, but certainly not all, uremic patients feature a depressed threshold for bicarbonate excretion and, therefore, exhibit bicarbonate wastage. In these patients, reduced bicarbonate reabsorption plays a contributory role in the pathogenesis of uremic acidosis. The reasons that bicarbonate wastage is seen in only some patients remain unclear but in all likelihood reflect, at least in part, differential activation of the several factors that alter bicarbonate reabsorption.

It would appear that two distinct patterns of disturbed acidification may be observed in chronic renal failure depending on whether or not an element of bicarbonate wastage is present. During spontaneous steady state metabolic acidosis, patients of either pattern generally are characterized by urine pH below 5.5, although some patients with underlying bicarbonate wastage tend to have a higher urine pH and low-grade bicarbonaturia despite substantial hypobicarbonatemia. In both patterns, net acid excretion in the steady state lags behind endogenous acid production largely because of decreased ammonium excretion. One would envision, however, a difference between the two patterns of disturbed acidification during the generation of metabolic acidosis. Only patients with bicarbonate wastage would manifest substantial bicarbonaturia until plasma bicarbonate had fallen below the reabsorptive threshold. With both patterns, the level of plasma bicarbonate eventually reached (barring further changes in renal function and assuming a stable endogenous acid load) is a function of the extent of the reduction in net acid excretion and the contribution of extrarenal buffering. The latter process succeeds in maintaining the stability of plasma bicarbonate concentration despite the fact that net acid excretion falls short of endogenous acid production (Fig. 9).

The underlying difference in the pathogenesis of metabolic acidosis in these two patterns is exposed during treatment with alkali. Substantially larger

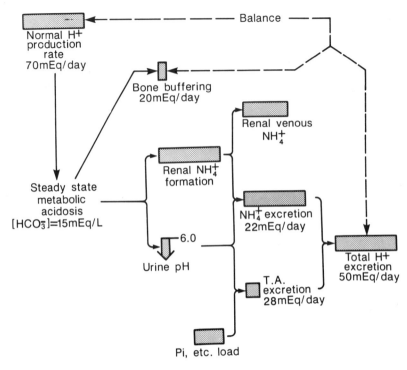

FIG. 9. Hydrogen ion balance in uremic acidosis. Endogenous acid production is normal, but net acid excretion lags behind largely due to a decrease in ammonium excretion. Retained protons are disposed of by an extrarenal mechanism, most likely bone buffering, and stability of the plasma bicarbonate concentration and the degree of metabolic acidosis are maintained as long as renal function remains stable. (Adapted from ref. 21.)

amounts of alkali are required to achieve a certain level of plasma bicarbonate concentration in patients with bicarbonate wastage as long as that level exceeds the reabsorptive threshold for bicarbonate. Under such circumstances, frank bicarbonaturia occurs, urine pH is high, and urinary titratable acidity and ammonium excretion are reduced. Patients without bicarbonate wastage, however, will continue to excrete urine characterized by a low pH, reduced ammonium content, and slightly reduced titratable acidity as long as plasma bicarbonate concentration remains subnormal.

ADVERSE EFFECTS OF METABOLIC ACIDOSIS

The adverse effects of uremic acidosis generally are similar to those produced by other causes of metabolic acidosis. Although uremic acidosis is usually mild to moderate in severity, some of the resultant morbidity may be more consequential and profound than in other types of metabolic acidosis be-

TABLE 5. *Adverse effects of uremic acidosis*

Effects on intermediary metabolism
   Protein wasting
   Altered triglyceride metabolism

Effects on hormonal secretion
   Increased catecholamines
   Increased aldosterone
   Increased corticosteroids

Hemodynamic effects
   Impaired cardiac contractility
   Arteriolar dilatation
   Peripheral venoconstriction
   Increased pulmonary vascular resistance
   Sensitization to ventricular arrhythmias

Effects on the gastrointestinal system
   Nausea
   Vomiting
   Gastric atony

Effects on the skeletal system
   Increased bone resorption
   Decreased bone formation
   Enhancement of parathyroid hormone action

---

cause of its sustained nature which often spans many years. On the other hand, because of the moderateness and relatively slow development of the acidosis, adverse effects typical of acute severe metabolic acidosis—especially those affecting the cardiovascular system—are only rarely seen in patients with chronic renal failure. When they do occur, it is usually in association with a rapid, further reduction in renal function or during the superimposition of an independent acidifying process.

The most important adverse effects of uremic acidosis are listed in Table 5.

Effects on Intermediary Metabolism

Protein wasting regularly attends the course of chronic renal failure and has been attributed to both reduced dietary intake and the uremic state. A substantial body of evidence indicates that metabolic acidosis stimulates the breakdown of endogenous tissue proteins. In accord with these observations, recent studies in both humans and experimental animals suggest the metabolic acidosis may contribute to the impaired protein metabolism characteristic of chronic renal failure. Using metabolic balance techniques, nitrogen balance was studied in six chronic renal failure patients (average GFR of 10 ml/min) and moderate metabolic acidosis (average plasma bicarbonate concentration of 16 mEq/liter) both before and after correction of metabolic acidosis with sodium bicarbonate. The subjects received equivalent quantities of sodium as the chloride salt during the control phase. Despite comparable protein intake, averaging 47 g/day during both periods of the study, BUN decreased and nitrogen balance was significantly more positive after administration of sodium bicarbonate. If correction of metabolic acidosis improved protein metabolism by increasing protein synthesis or reducing protein degradation could not be determined using the metabolic balance techniques. Observations in experimental animals, however, have served to define the mechanism of this effect. Perfused hindquarters of rats with chronic renal failure induced by subtotal nephrectomy were used to estimate protein synthesis and degradation. The animals were studied both before and after correction of metabolic acidosis with sodium bicarbonate. Mild metabolic acidosis (average plasma bicarbonate concentration of 18 mEq/liter) was associated with a 90% increase in protein degradation compared to sham-operated controls with normal renal function. Protein degradation was normalized after correction of metabolic acidosis with alkali. Protein synthesis was reduced with renal failure, but this inhibition of protein synthesis was not altered by alkali therapy. These data indicate that metabolic acidosis, even when mild in severity, plays an important role in the abnormalities of protein metabolism occurring during chronic renal failure.

Abnormalities in lipid metabolism often are prominent in chronic renal failure, including elevated triglyceride levels, increased very low density lipoproteins, and decreased high density lipoprotein cholesterol. Recent studies have suggested a possible role of metabolic acidosis in the hypertriglyceridemia of uremia. Thus, triglyceride removal from blood was reduced during the development of uremic acidosis in rats and was improved when the acidosis was corrected by bicarbonate administration. These studies have not yet been extended to cholesterol metabolism. Similarly, corresponding observations have not been carried out in humans.

Effects on Hormonal Secretion

Metabolic acidosis is associated with stimulation of secretion of a host of hormones, including catecholamines, aldosterone, and cortisol. Importantly, as arterial pH values decrease below 7.20, there is a progressive attenuation of myocardial responsiveness to catecholamines, and, therefore, the direct negative inotropic effect of acidemia on the myocardium becomes dominant. Augmented aldosterone secretion represents an important adaptive mechanism in the defense against hyperkalemia via increased renal and colonic secretion of potassium and possibly through enhanced cellular uptake of potassium. The rise in cortisol levels may contribute to the muscle wasting of uremia, since recent studies have shown that the protein catabolism associated with metabolic acidosis could be attenuated by adrenalectomy.

Hemodynamic Effects

Metabolic acidosis exerts an array of adverse hemodynamic effects, including impairment of cardiac contractility, arteriolar dilatation, peripheral venoconstriction (leading to central redistribution of blood volume, thereby augmenting the workload of a depressed myocardium), increase in pulmonary vascular resistance, and sensitization to various malignant ventricular arrhythmias. These effects are most prominent at an arterial pH below 7.20 and may culminate in the development of severe hypotension and congestive heart failure.

Effects on the Gastrointestinal System

Metabolic acidosis commonly is accompanied by nausea, vomiting, and gastric atony and may contribute to the gastrointestinal abnormalities of uremia.

Effects on the Skeletal System (4,5)

In view of the sustained nature of uremic acidosis, its most important and prevalent effects in chronic renal failure probably are exerted on mineral metabolism and the skeletal system. Studies in normal humans and experimental animals have revealed that metabolic acidosis is associated with marked calciuria. Because in the majority of reported studies gastrointestinal calcium absorption is either reduced or unaltered, negative calcium balance ensues. As a consequence, metabolic acidosis leads to dissolution of bone mineral. Recent studies using double tetracycline labeling of bone have shown that chronic metabolic acidosis induced in animals with normal renal function is associated with increased bone resorption and marked reduction in bone formation. These pathologic disturbances may lead to the development of osteoporosis in experimental animals and osteomalacia in man. Marked stunting of growth may occur in children with renal tubular acidosis, which is reversed merely by correction of the metabolic acidosis.

Abnormalities in vitamin D metabolism have been reported with metabolic acidosis in nonuremic animals. It appears that basal levels in both experimental animals and humans are not substantially altered by metabolic acidosis. In contrast, the stimulation of vitamin D synthesis by various factors appears to be strikingly blunted by metabolic acidosis.

Much less is known about the effects of uremic acidosis on mineral metabolism and the skeletal system. Recent data in rats have shown that correction of uremic acidosis decreases the fractional excretion of calcium by approximately 60%, although correction of uremic acidosis in humans did not alter urinary calcium excretion significantly. Moreover, histomorphometric studies performed in rats with chronic renal failure showed greater loss of trabecular bone and increased bone resorption in rats in whom metabolic acidosis was superimposed by administration of mineral acid than in nonacidotic uremic controls. Of note, uremia was associated with the expected decrease in vitamin D level, but superimposition of acidosis did not produce any further alterations in vitamin D metabolism.

It is uncertain if spontaneous metabolic acidosis occurring in the course of chronic renal failure would have effects on bone similar to those produced by exogenous provision of mineral acid. Nonetheless, autopsy studies of patients with severe chronic renal failure have demonstrated marked decreases in bone calcium carbonate content consistent with loss of this mineral in the buffering process. In addition, bone mineralization was studied in five patients with severe renal failure (GFRs of 6–13 ml/min) and renal osteodystrophy both before and after correction of metabolic acidosis. Correction of metabolic acidosis was associated with a significant rise in skeletal mineralization, suggesting that metabolic acidosis may be playing a role in the pathogenesis of renal osteodystrophy. In this regard, Burnell et al. documented that progression of renal osteodystrophy in humans from an early phase to osteofibrosis was associated with a decline in bone carbonate, yet the degree of bone carbonate loss was not related to the severity of the acidemia.

There are several possible mechanisms whereby uremic acidosis could contribute potentially to uremic osteodystrophy. There are data to suggest that acidemia causes dissolution of bone mineral, stimulates cell-mediated bone resorption, augments the secretion of parathyroid hormone, and enhances the biologic actions of parathyroid hormone on bone. If metabolic acidosis is an important contributory factor to the pathogenesis of renal osteodystrophy, correction of metabolic acidosis early in the course of renal failure should lessen the severity of bone disease observed in these patients. Heretofore, rigorous studies examining the possible beneficial effects of such therapeutic strategy have not been performed.

TREATMENT OF UREMIC ACIDOSIS (10)

The value of treating the metabolic acidosis of chronic renal failure in the adult patient remains conjectural. One might argue against treatment, since uremic acidosis usually is mild to moderate in degree and most life-threatening complications of acidemia occur when plasma bicarbonate is below 10 to 12 mEq/liter and arterial pH is below 7.20. On the other hand, treatment can be supported on the grounds that it will neutralize the acid retained during the course of chronic renal failure and thereby prevent the potential adverse effects on bone. Although there is no firm evidence to indicate that treatment of uremic acidosis attenuates or prevents the development of bone disease, available evidence incriminates the sustained acidosis as a contributory factor in the pathogenesis of uremic osteodystrophy. As noted previously, metabolic acidosis may play a role in the development of various metabolic abnormalities in uremia, including protein wasting. Treatment of the metabolic acidosis provides a margin of protection against the superimposition of independent acidifying processes. We consider it advisable, therefore, to maintain the plasma bicarbonate concentration at the near normal levels of 20 to 23 mEq/liter. We recognize, however, that this goal of treatment is arbitrary.

Unless substantial bicarbonate wasting exists, this therapeutic goal usually can be accomplished by the daily provision of 0.5 to 2.0 mEq/kg body weight of alkali in the form of sodium bicarbonate, calcium carbonate, or alkali precursors, such as sodium citrate. Administration of sodium bicarbonate or calcium carbonate may induce abdominal bloating and discomfort due to generation of carbon dioxide in the stomach as the ingested base reacts with the protons of the gastric fluid. These untoward effects can be avoided by administering the bicarbonate precursor, sodium citrate, while attaining the same alkalinizing effect. The citrate ion is metabolized readily by the liver to generate equivalent quantities of bicarbonate. The usual formulation of sodium citrate, Shohl's solution, contains 1 mEq of citrate/ml of solution. Once end-stage renal failure has been reached, provision of base is generally accomplished via the dialysis procedure. In patients in whom normalization of plasma bicarbonate concentration is not achieved with dialysis alone, however, administration of alkali may be warranted.

The most common complication of treatment of uremic patients with alkali is volume overload and exacerbation of hypertension as a result of retention of the accompanying sodium ion. This complication can be largely avoided by careful monitoring of the patient for evidence of clinical signs of sodium retention, including rapid weight gain. Any sodium retention produced by administration of sodium bicarbonate or its precursors can be countered by the judicious administration of diuretics. It is notable that in chronic renal failure, the retention of sodium, when administered as the bicarbonate salt, is significantly less than when given as sodium chloride. Studies in patients with chronic renal failure (creatinine clearance ranging from 3.0 to 17.0 ml/min) showed that excretion of sodium was much higher when 200 mmoles of sodium bicarbonate was administered than when 200 mmoles of sodium chloride was given, consistent with the previous clinical impressions that alkali therapy does not usually aggravate edematous states. When a mixture of 100 mmoles of sodium bicarbonate and 100 mmoles of sodium chloride was given in these studies, the quantity of sodium retained was similar to that noted in patients receiving 200 mmoles of sodium chloride. Therefore, an important requirement to minimize sodium retention in patients with chronic renal failure during treatment with sodium bicarbonate is to curtail markedly the ingestion of sodium as the chloride salt.

Obviously, given the limitation on the quantity of bicarbonate that can be

excreted in the urine by the diseased kidney, one should always be vigilant of
the potential for generating metabolic alkalosis secondary to retention of
ingested alkali. Protein restriction (and thus a decrease in the endogenous
acid load) and volume depletion are factors that tend to promote generation of
such hyperbicarbonatemia.

In contrast to the situation in the adult, administration of bicarbonate to
children with chronic renal failure is widely accepted therapy. Persistent
metabolic acidosis may strikingly impair growth, and in children with renal
tubular acidosis, stunting of growth is reversed by treatment of metabolic acidosis with bicarbonate. Thus, although the precise contribution of metabolic acidosis to the growth retardation seen in children with chronic renal
failure is not clear, it seems prudent to maintain the plasma bicarbonate at
near normal levels in these patients.

REFERENCES

1. Arruda, J. A. L., Carrasquillo, T., Cubria, A., Rademacher, D. R., and Kurtzman, N. A. (1976): Bicarbonate reabsorption in chronic renal failure. *Kidney Int.*, 9:481–488.
2. Barsotti, G., Lazzerri, M., Cristofano, C., Cerri, M., Lupetti, S., and Giovannetti, S. (1986): The role of metabolic acidosis in causing uremic hyperphosphatemia. *Miner. Electrolyte Metab.*, 12:103–106.
3. Buerkert, J., Martin, D., Trigg, D., and Simon, E. (1983): Effect of reduced renal mass on ammonium handling and net acid formation by the superficial and juxtamedullary nephron of the rat. Evidence for impaired reentrapment rather than decreased production of ammo- nium in the acidosis of uremia. *J. Clin. Invest.*, 71:1661–1675.
4. Burnell, J. M., Teubner, E., Wergedal, J. E., and Sherrard, D. J. (1974): Bone crystal matu- ration in renal osteodystrophy in humans. *J. Clin. Invest.*, 53:52–58.
5. Cochrane, M., and Wilkinson, R. (1975): Effect of correction of metabolic acidosis on bone mineralization rates in patients with renal osteomalacia. *Nephron*, 15:98–110.
6. Elkinton, J. R. (1962): Hydrogen ion turnover in health and in renal disease. *Ann. Intern. Med.*, 57:660–684.
7. Enia, G., Catalano, C., Zoccali, C., et al. (1985): Hyperchloraemia: A non-specific finding in chronic renal failure. *Nephron*, 41:189–192.
8. Espinel, C. H. (1975): The influence of salt intake on the metabolic acidosis of chronic renal failure. *J. Clin. Invest.*, 56:286–291.
9. Goodman, A. D., Lemann, J., Jr., Lennon, E. J., and Relman, A. S. (1965): Production, ex- cretion and net balance of fixed acid in patients with chronic renal acidosis. *J. Clin. Invest.*, 44:495–506.
10. Husted, F. C., Nolph, K. D., and Maher, J. F. (1975): NaHCO₃ and NaCl tolerance in chronic renal failure. *J. Clin. Invest.*, 56:414–419.
11. Litzow, J. R., Lemann, J., Jr., and Lennon, E. J. (1967): The effect of treatment of acidosis on calcium balance in patients with chronic azotemic renal disease. *J. Clin. Invest.*, 46:280– 286.
12. Lubowitz, H., Purkerson, M. L., Rolf, D. B., Weisser, F., and Bricker, N. S. (1971): Effect of nephron loss on proximal tubular bicarbonate reabsorption in the rat. *Am. J. Physiol.*, 220:457–461.
13. Muldowney, F. P., Donohue, J. F., Carroll, D. V., Powell, D., and Freaney, R. (1972): Para- thyroid acidosis in uremia. *Q. J. Med.*, 41:321–342.
14. Narins, R. G. (1978): The renal acidoses. In: *Acid-Base and Potassium Homeostasis*, edited by B. M. Brenner, and J. H. Stein, pp. 30–64. Churchill Livingstone, New York.

15. Pellegrino, E. D., and Biltz, R. M. (1965): The composition of human bone in uremia. Observations on the reservoir functions of bone and demonstration of a labile fraction of bone carbonate. *Medicine*, 44:397–418.
16. Pitts, R. F. (1945): The renal regulation of acid–base balance with special reference to the mechanism for acidifying the urine. *Science*, 102:49–54, 81–85.
17. Relman, A. S. (1964): Renal acidosis and renal excretion of acid in health and disease. *Adv. Intern. Med.*, 12:295–347.
18. Sabatini, S. (1983): The acidosis of chronic renal failure. *Med. Clin. North Am.*, 67:845–858.
19. Schmidt, R. W., and Gavellas, G. (1977): Bicarbonate reabsorption in experimental renal disease: Effects of proportional reduction of sodium and phosphate intake. *Kidney Int.*, 12:393–402.
20. Schwartz, W. B., Hall, P. W. III, Hays, R. M., and Relman, A. S. (1959): On the mechanism of acidosis in chronic renal disease. *J. Clin. Invest.*, 38:39–52.
21. Simpson, D. P. (1971): Control of hydrogen ion homeostasis and renal acidosis. *Medicine*, 50:503–541.
22. Slatopolsky, E., Hoffsten, P., Purkerson, M., and Bricker, N. S. (1970): On the influence of extracellular fluid volume expansion and of uremia on bicarbonate reabsorption in man. *J. Clin. Invest.*, 49:988–998.
23. Tizianello, A., De Ferrari, G., Garibotto, G., Gurreri, G., and Robaudo, C. (1980): Renal metabolism of amino acids and ammonia in subjects with normal renal function and in patients with chronic renal insufficiency. *J. Clin. Invest.*, 65:1162–1173.
24. Wallia, R., Greenberg, A., Piraino, B., Mitro, R., Puschett, J. B. (1986): Serum electrolyte patterns in end-stage renal disease. *Am. J. Kidney Dis.*, 8:98–104.
25. Widmer, B., Gerhardt, R. E., Harrington, J. T., and Cohen, J. J. (1979): Serum electrolyte and acid-base composition: The influence of graded degrees of chronic renal failure. *Arch. Intern. Med.*, 139:1099–1102.
26. Wrong, O., and Davies, H. E. F. (1959): The excretion of acid in renal disease. *Q. J. Med.*, 28:259–313.
27. Ypersele de Strihou, C. V., and Frans, A. (1970): The pattern of respiratory compensation in chronic uremic acidosis. *Nephron*, 7:37–50.

The Regulation of Acid–Base Balance, edited
by Donald W. Seldin and Gerhard Giebisch,
Raven Press, Ltd., New York © 1989.

14

Hyperchloremic Metabolic Acidosis

Daniel C. Batlle

*Department of Medicine, Northwestern University Medical School and Lakeside
Veterans Administration Medical Center, Chicago, Illinois 60611*

In this type of metabolic acidosis, in its pure form, there is an increase in the plasma chloride equivalent to the fall in the plasma bicarbonate, so that the sum of the concentrations of these two anions remains unchanged. The plasma anion gap in pure hyperchloremic acidosis is not increased and, in fact, may be somewhat reduced owing to buffering of protons by proteins. As blood pH falls, protons are taken up by proteins, thereby reducing their anionic charge. This process spares bicarbonate titration and thereby mini-mizes the fall in plasma bicarbonate while lowering the plasma anion gap. Conversely, protons are released from proteins when the blood pH increases. Thus, independent of the type of acid-base disturbance, pH-dependent changes in the anionic charge of protein influence the plasma anion gap. The change in the anion gap attributable to changes in blood pH *per se*, however, is modest and does not alter the plasma anion gap greatly.

A basic alteration underlying the generation of hyperchloremic metabolic acidosis is the loss of bicarbonate, usually in the urine or in the stools. In this setting, the extracellular fluid is rendered hyperchloremic owing to enhanced renal sodium chloride retention caused by the attendant volume contraction. As acidosis develops, retention of chloride by the kidney is facilitated also by the fall in tubular bicarbonate concentration resulting from the decrease in filtered bicarbonate load. Under these circumstances, luminal chloride reabsorption is enhanced because no other reabsorbable anions are available in the tubular lumen.

With the administration of HCl or HCl-generating compounds, the generation of hyperchloremic metabolic acidosis is simply the result of titration of extracellular bicarbonate, which is replaced by exogenous chloride. The source of the rise in extracellular fluid chloride can be partly exogenous, as seen, for instance, during the treatment of diabetic ketoacidosis. In this setting, hyperchloremic acidosis can develop while the ketoanions are rapidly eliminated by the kidney and sodium chloride is administered.

MIXED HYPERCHLOREMIC AND HIGH
ANION GAP METABOLIC ACIDOSIS (23)

When the decrement in plasma bicarbonate (Δ HCO_3) is not matched by either an equivalent increment in plasma chloride or in the plasma anion gap (Δ AG), a mixed hyperchloremic and high anion gap metabolic acidosis is present (Table 1). The relative contribution of each type of acidosis can be estimated from the Δ AG/Δ HCO_3 ratio. This ratio is near unity (or 100%) in a pure high anion gap acidosis and near 0 (or 0%) in a pure hyperchloremic metabolic acidosis. For instance, in normal subjects in whom serum lactate levels are transiently increased to about 15 mEq/liter by maximal exercise, there is a corresponding fall in plasma bicarbonate so that the ratio would be near unity. Conversely, in a normal individual afflicted with diarrhea causing a similar fall in plasma bicarbonate, there may be an equivalent increase in plasma chloride and no change in the anion gap. In this setting, the Δ AG/Δ HCO_3 ratio would be 0 (or 0%),denoting the presence of a pure hyperchloremic metabolic acidosis (Table 1).

TABLE 1. *Patterns of metabolic acidosis*

Types	Na	K	Cl	HCO_3	AG^a	ΔAG	ΔHCO_3	$\Delta AG/\Delta HCO_3$ ratio
			mEq/liter					%
Normal	138	4.0	102	24	16	0	0	—
Pure high anion gap	138	4.0	102	14	26	10	10	100
Pure hyperchloremic	138	4.0	112	14	16	0	10	0
Mixed	138	4.0	106	14	22	6	10	60

[a]AG, anion gap; ΔAG, plasma anion gap.

Several factors can modify the Δ AG/Δ HCO$_3$ ratio during metabolic acidosis and thereby result in a mixed type of metabolic acidosis. This may occur in situations where the initial acid-base disorder is a pure high anion gap metabolic acidosis and in situations where the initial problem is a pure hyperchloremic metabolic acidosis. A good example of the latter situation is the metabolic acidosis that occurs during the diarrhea of cholera. Losses of bicarbonate in the stool should lead to a pure nonanion gap, hyperchloremic metabolic acidosis. When formally studied, however, the anion gap has been found to be elevated in most patients with cholera who had severe dehydration (Table 2). When the acidosis is partially corrected, the anion gap diminishes. During convalescence, the mean serum bicarbonate concentration and mean anion gap are further corrected into the normal ranges.

The increased anion gap, which resolves promptly after rehydration, can be attributed to a number of processes coexisting with gastrointestinal bicarbonate losses. First, there may be substantial chloride losses in the watery stools of patients with cholera. Second, in this type of diarrhea, there is rapid and profound dehydration, which results in hyperproteinemia and, thus, a rise in the anion gap as a result of an increment in the concentration of anionic serum protein. In the study summarized in Table 2, the contribution of serum anionic protein to the anion gap was estimated at 5.5 mEq/liter, or about half the total increase in the anion gap. Third, lactic acidemia generated as a consequence of hypovolemic shock resulting from severe fluid depletion may contribute to the observed increase in the anion gap. Another factor contributing to the increase in the plasma anion gap in patients with diarrhea due to cholera is the rise in plasma phosphate that results from the combination of renal failure and severe acidosis (Table 2).

These observations underscore that a mixed hyperchloremic and high anion gap metabolic acidosis can develop in a setting where the metabolic acidosis originates from loss of bicarbonate in the stool, an alteration which in and of itself should cause a pure hyperchloremic metabolic acidosis. The transition towards the mixed type should alert the physician to the existence of other coexisting factors, such as severe volume contraction, hypovolemic shock, and renal impairment, that render the acidosis more severe than it would be solely on the basis of loss of bicarbonate in the stool.

A mixed metabolic acidosis, sometimes a pure hyperchloremic acidosis, can be seen in conditions traditionally said to result in a pure high anion gap acidosis. Such is the case, for instance, in patients with diabetic ketoacidosis and in patients with renal failure treated by chronic hemodialysis. The Δ AG/Δ HCO$_3$ ratio also is altered in the presence of chronic respiratory alkalosis. For instance, when a patient with preexisting respiratory alkalosis develops a high anion gap metabolic acidosis (e.g., lactic acidosis), the ratio will not be 100% because of preexisting hyperchloremia associated with the underlying respiratory alkalosis.

TABLE 2. *Serum electrolyte levels and anion gap, anionic serum protein, lactate, in patients with*

	Sodium (mEq/liter)	Potassium (mEq/liter)	Chloride (mEq/liter)
Before rehydration (n = 21)	134.8 ± 3.5	4.6 ± 0.6	103.2 ± 4.4
After rehydration (n = 11) +	139.5 ± 1.2	4.7 ± 1.2	107.1 ± 1.9
During convalescence (n = 16)	138.6 ± 2.6	4.0 ± 0.6	104.6 ± 3.1
p value	< 0.001	< 0.01	NS[a]

Adapted from ref. 22.
[a]NS, not significant.

CAUSES OF HYPERCHLOREMIA (9,11)

The causes of hyperchloremia other than those associated with hyperchloremic metabolic acidosis are few (Table 3). The plasma chloride concentration changes in response to changes in hydration and changes in acid-base balance. In the absence of metabolic acidosis, two conditions can account for hyperchloremia: hemoconcentration during severe dehydration and chronic respiratory alkalosis. The former can be recognized easily because it is usually accompanied by hypernatremia. If serum sodium is not elevated, dehydration is not a likely cause of hyperchloremia. The plasma sodium concentration increases only as a result of water loss. If a rise in plasma chloride is not matched by a proportionate increase in plasma sodium, the presence of an acid-base disorder should be suspected. To determine whether hyperchloremia is a result of metabolic acidosis or respiratory alkalosis, one must measure blood pH, blood P_{CO_2}, and plasma bicarbonate.

In patients with multiple myeloma, serum electrolytes often reveal increased chloride but normal sodium and bicarbonate concentrations, so that the plasma anion gap is reduced. This occurs with IgG myeloma because the cationic nature of the paraprotein obligates a rise in chloride anions to neu-

TABLE 3. *Causes of hyperchloremia*

Hyperchloremic metabolic acidosis
Chronic respiratory alkalosis
Dehydration
Multiple myeloma
Spurious hyperchloremia
  Hyperlipidemia
  Bromide intoxication
  Iodide exposure

and phosphate, before rehydration, after rehydration, and during convalescence severe cholera

Bicarbonate (mEq/liter)	Anion Gap (mEq/liter)	Protein (mEq/liter)	Lactate (mEq/liter)	Phosphate (mEq/liter)	Creatinine (mg/dl)
11.4 ± 4.0	20.2 ± 4.8	17.1 ± 2.2	4.05 ± 1.96	4.4 ± 1.3	2.48 ± 1.01
17.8 ± 2.8#	14.6 ± 2.8	11.8 ± 1.4	—	2.0 ± 0.8	1.70 ± 0.81
22.6 ± 4.0#	11.4 ± 3.0	11.6 ± 1.1	1.61 ± 0.90	1.9 ± 0.5	1.02 ± 0.92
< 0.001	< 0.001	< 0.001	< 0.001	< 0.001	< 0.001

tralize the protein's cationic charge. In this situation, metabolic acidosis is not present unless there is an associated renal acidification defect. Although the anion gap may be low in patients with IgG myeloma, it is normal in other types of multiple myeloma (Fig. 1). This difference in the anion gap pattern has been well documented to be accounted for by differences in the isoelectric points of IgA and IgG paraproteins. IgG paraproteins have isoelectric points higher than physiologic pH and are positively charged in serum. To maintain electrical neutrality in serum, this large accumulation of positive

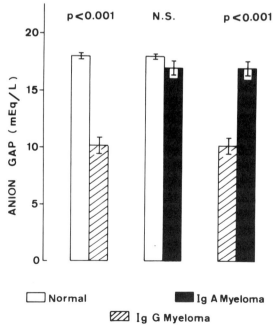

FIG. 1. Mean values for plasma anion gap in 29 patients with IgG myeloma, 18 with IgA Myeloma, and 150 normal control subjects (From ref. 9.)

charges has to be counterbalanced by an increase in anions, resulting in lowering of the anion gap. Inversely, IgA paraproteins have isoelectric points slightly below physiologic pH. Therefore, they behave like anions in normal serum, so that if they are present in large circulating concentrations, the anion gap should increase. The fact that in IgA myeloma the anion gap is normal instead of being elevated, may be due, at least in part, to concomitant hypoalbuminemia. Hypoalbuminemia, a frequent complication of myeloma, could indeed reduce to normal an otherwise elevated anion gap.

Hyperlipidemia is an often unrecognized cause of spurious hyperchloremia. Hyperlipidemia can lead to overestimation of plasma chloride levels as a result of a technique-dependent error of measurement due to a light-scattering effect. Overestimation of chloride levels, as found using colorimetric procedures, does not occur if a titrimetric or potentiometric technique is used. Still, such spurious hyperchloremia is seen only when triglyceride levels are markedly increased, usually over 1,000 mg/dl. In this setting, the light-scattering effect produces errors of a large magnitude, sometimes 50 mEq/liter above the true plasma chloride concentration, which should prompt suspicion of laboratory error. The lipid space-occupying effect usually also causes spurious hyponatremia. Thus, the findings of hyponatremia, hyperchloremia, and a low anion gap, sometimes a negative anion gap, should alert the clinician to look for hyperlipidemia as a cause of spurious hyperchloremia. Ultracentrifugation of serum to remove lipid excess allows for a correct measurement of chloride levels.

Other causes of spurious hyperchloremia include iodide overexposure and bromide intoxication. Hyperchloremia has been described in patients topically treated with povidone-iodine (Betadine) for surgical wounds and decubitus ulcers. Transcutaneous absorption of iodine may occur in burn patients and neonates treated topically with povidone-iodine. Accumulation of iodide is more likely in the presence of renal impairment because the kidney is the major route for its excretion. Hence, in patients with renal insufficiency, iodine intoxication may occur as hyperchloremic metabolic acidosis of unknown etiology. Spurious elevations of serum chloride by iodide intoxication have been noted using autoanalyzer methods that rely on the displacement of thiocyanate (SCN^-) from the $Hg(SCN)_2$ molecule by anions, such as iodide, bromide, or chloride. Since iodide and bromide have a greater affinity for Hg than does chloride, spurious hyperchloremia occurs with either form of intoxication.

EXTRARENAL CAUSES OF HYPERCHLOREMIC METABOLIC ACIDOSIS

Hyperchloremic metabolic acidosis can develop under a variety of settings. For convenience, the causes of hyperchloremic metabolic acidosis can be clas-

TABLE 4. *Causes of hyperchloremic metabolic acidosis*

Extrarenal	Renal

HCl-generating compounds
  NH$_4$Cl administration
  HCl administration
  L-Arginine, L-Lysine administration
  Chlorine gas inhalation
  Hyperalimentation
Gastrointestinal HCO$_3$ losses
  Diarrheal states
  Ileus
  Pancreatic and biliary fistulas
  Drug-induced (laxatives, CaCl$_2$,
    cholestyramine)
	Renal HCO$_3$ losses
	  Proximal renal tubular acidosis (RTA)
	Reduced renal acid excretion
	  Distal RTA syndromes
	  Defects in ammoniagenesis
	  Hyperkalemia
	  Aldosterone deficiency
	  Renal insufficiency[a]

Gastrointestinal–ureteral connections Dilutional acidosis Posthypocapnic acidemia KCl administration Potassium depletion Diabetic ketoacidosis[a]	

[a]Denotes that these conditions are often classified as high-anion gap acidosis.

sified into those of primarily renal origin and those of primarily extrarenal origin (Table 4). The renal tubular acidosis (RTA) syndromes that account for many of the causes of metabolic acidosis of primary renal origin are discussed in Chapter 15. Uremic acidosis is discussed in detail in Chapter 13.

Hydrochloric Acid-Generating Substances (2,6,8,12,14,17,20)

The administration of hydrochloric acid or compounds that generate it after metabolism results in hyperchloremic metabolic acidosis (Table 4). Ammonium chloride, widely used as a test of urinary acidifying capability, is metabolized by the liver to urea and hydrochloric acid. Cationic amino acids, such as arginine, lysine, histidine, and hydroxylysine, usually are prepared as HCl salts. The administration of these compounds results in the release of HCl after liver metabolism into neutral compounds. In addition to the generation of hyperchloremic metabolic acidosis from the acid load, basic amino acids, such as L-arginine and L-lysine, exert an inhibitory effect on proximal tubule bicarbonate reabsorption, which is concentration-dependent. This effect is stereospecific for the L form of dibasic amino acids, and it is not seen after the administration of neutral and acidic amino acids. The extent of the contribution of decreased proximal tubule bicarbonate reabsorption to the development of metabolic acidosis after L-arginine administration, however, is

probably very modest. Although L-arginine infusions produce massive bicarbonaturia in the dog, they do not substantially increase bicarbonate excretion
in humans. In fact, in humans, L-arginine infusion is sometimes used as an
acid-loading test because of its ability to cause a fall in urine pH (to less than
5.5) in normal people. It is likely that in the face of depressed proximal tubule
bicarbonate reabsorption, distal bicarbonate reabsorption is capable of reclaiming the fraction rejected in the proximal tubule, thereby preventing bicarbonaturia from occurring.

Hyperchloremic metabolic acidosis has been reported after accidental inhalation of chlorine gas. Chlorine combines with tissue water according to the
reaction

$$2 \, Cl_2 \, + \, 2 \, H_2O \rightarrow 4 \, HCl \, + \, O_2$$

The generation of sufficient HCl to cause significant metabolic acidosis by
this mechanism, however, would in theory require the absorption of large
concentrations of Cl_2 gas, which could be fatal. Hyperchloremic metabolic
acidosis of transient duration (1 day) has been documented in a patient who
survived after inhalation of Cl_2 gas released from the accidental mixture of
chloride bleach and phosphoric acid.

Hyperchloremic metabolic acidosis ensues after the administration of sulfuric and nitric acid. A high anion gap is not seen because the anions of these
acids are excreted readily by the kidneys. For instance, elemental sulfur ingestion results in formation of sulfuric acid after metabolism by gut bacteria.
Accumulation of sulfuric acid would result in a high anion gap metabolic acidosis if it were not for the rapid renal excretion of sulfate, which exceeds the
rate of acid excretion. As long as the renal excretion of acid cannot keep up
with the more rapid excretion of the anion, a hyperchloremic metabolic acidosis ensues. Plasma chloride increases because sodium chloride retention by
the kidney is enhanced owing to volume contraction caused by losses of sodium as sodium sulfate. Metabolic acidosis from the ingestion of mineral acids
rarely is encountered in the clinical setting. This type of acidosis has been
widely studied experimentally as a model of hyperchloremic metabolic acidosis and is discussed in some detail in the following sections.

Renal Adaptation to Mineral Acid Loading

Much of our knowledge about renal adaptation to hyperchloremic metabolic acidosis has been derived from studies involving the administration of
mineral acids to humans and to experimental animals. The renal regulation of
plasma bicarbonate concentration during prolonged mineral acid loading depends largely on the interplay of various factors that affect distal urinary acidification. The proximal tubule, however, has a major role in the initial renal
adaptation to an acid load by increasing ammonia production and by reclaim-

ing most of the filtered bicarbonate load. Shortly after metabolic acidosis is induced, urinary bicarbonate excretion falls to barely detectable amounts. The
fall in plasma bicarbonate is accompanied by enhanced proximal tubule reabsorption of bicarbonate so that its delivery beyond this nephron segment
markedly diminishes. This process not only ensures maximal bicarbonate reclamation within the proximal nephron but, in addition, permits proton secretion in the distal nephron to be used for the formation of ammonium and
titratable acidity rather than for the reclamation of bicarbonate escaping from
proximal reabsorption. Consequently, the excretion of ammonium and titratable acidity in the urine increases. The increase in acid excretion continues
progressively over several days of acid loading but not to the level of acid input, and positive acid balance ensues.

Regulation of distal acidification during prolonged acid feeding is influenced
by the rate of distal sodium delivery, the avidity of the distal nephron for sodium reabsorption, and the characteristics of the administered acid anion. Sodium avidity refers to a state of enhanced capacity for sodium reabsorption
within the distal nephron that may accelerate sodium-dependent distal acidification. Sodium-dependent acidification within the distal nephron takes place
mainly in the cortical collecting tubule and is under the control of aldosterone. This hormone has been assumed to be the major mediator of distal
sodium avidity. Sodium excretion, however, can be reduced substantially
despite the total absence of aldosterone (i.e., in adrenalectomized animals).
Thus, factors in addition to aldosterone—possibly an intrinsic tubular adaptation or some other hormonal influences, such as hypersecretion of vasopressin
in response to volume depletion—may contribute to sodium avidity. No matter how generated, sodium avidity will favor the achievement of transtubular
voltage (lumen-negative), which will then favor H^+ ion secretion and thereby
help mitigate the severity of the acidosis caused by the ingested mineral acid.
Adequate distal sodium delivery, however, must be present for distal sodium
avidity to play a significant role in the regulation of sodium-dependent distal
urinary acidification.

An important role for sodium delivery in distal urinary acidification can be
inferred from the finding that the administration of acid with anions with
different degrees of reabsorbability (chloride, sulfate, or nitrate) produces
a different degree of metabolic acidosis. For instance, after 2 to 3 weeks of
acid administration, the steady state value of plasma bicarbonate is about 9
mEq/liter below control in dogs given HCl but only about 4 mEq/liter below
control in those given H_2SO_4 (Fig. 2). If the anion is easily reabsorbable, as it
is in the case of the chloride anion in hydrochloric acid, chloride retention in
the proximal tubule as sodium chloride will limit distal sodium delivery. The
finding that maneuvers that inhibit proximal chloride reabsorption and, therefore, enhance sodium chloride distal delivery attenuate the severity of hydrochloric acid-induced acidosis supports this concept. If the anion is poorly
reabsorbable, as in the case of sulfuric and nitric acids, there is no constraint

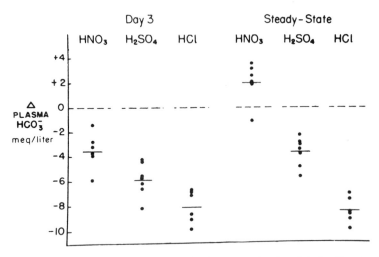

FIG. 2. Effect of acid loading on Δ plasma bicarbonate at day 3 and during the steady state in animals receiving HNO_3, H_2SO_4, or HCl while on a low NaCl diet. (From ref. 8.)

on distal sodium delivery. Thus, the mechanism whereby distal acid excretion increases to a greater extent after H_2SO_4 than after HCl has been ascribed to differences in distal sodium delivery. The anions of the acids produced by the metabolism of dietary protein are largely those that are poorly reabsorbable, such as sulfate or nitrate, which may enhance urinary acidification. The administration of HCl in itself does not affect the excretion of sulfate, but it does increase the excretion of phosphate, with an attendant increase in titratable acid excretion.

Influence of Sodium Depletion on Renal Adaptation to Metabolic Acidosis

Although the properties of the administered mineral acid anion are important in regulating distal urinary acidification, at least in sodium depletion, it is perhaps more clinically relevant to examine the role of sodium depletion *per se* on the renal adaptation to hyperchloremic metabolic acidosis. The role of preexisting sodium depletion on the renal acidification response to acid loading in humans has been studied using brief periods of ammonium chloride loading. In two studies, plasma bicarbonate fell to a comparable level in the presence and in the absence of sodium depletion. In both studies, a highly acidic urine (pH less than 5.3) was obtained despite preexisting sodium depletion. One study, however, disclosed a subtle but significant difference in the minimal urine pH observed after ammonium chloride loading before and after sodium depletion (4.65 ± 0.04 and 5.07 ± 0.06, respectively). In the aggregate, the available information suggests that despite preexisting sodium depletion, plasma bicarbonate concentration during acid loading can be maintained at a level equal or only slightly lower than that seen while on a normal dietary salt intake. The data also indicate that the rate of acid excretion by the kidneys increases substantially despite sodium depletion. In fact, the rate of ammonium excretion after acid loading has not yet been found to be significantly different between sodium-depleted and sodium-repleted animals. Before considering the mechanism(s) that permit a near normal renal acidification response to acid loading despite reduced sodium intake, one must stress that some patients may be in a state of volume depletion for periods longer than those used in the experimental settings described previously. Under these circumstances, maintenance of an optimal urinary acidification response to acidosis is no longer possible (*see sections* Diarrheal States and Laxative Abuse).

The increase in urinary acidification in response to acid loading that takes place despite sodium depletion is made possible, at least in part, by an increase in aldosterone release triggered by volume contraction. In addition, metabolic acidosis in and of itself stimulates aldosterone release. A rise in plasma potassium, as may be seen in early states of hyperchloremic acidosis caused by mineral acid administration, also can contribute to hyperaldosteronism. There are several mechanisms whereby aldosterone stimulates renal acidification. Aldosterone promotes enhanced ammonium excretion both by a direct effect on ammoniagenesis and indirectly by causing hypokalemia. Aldosterone also stimulates cortical, medullary, and papillary collecting tubule hydrogen ion secretion. Of note, the stimulator effect of aldosterone on hydrogen ion secretion is sodium-dependent in the cortical but not in the medullary portion of the collecting tubule.

Mineralocorticoid administration has been shown to augment renal acidification in animals subjected to chronic HCl feeding and correct the metabolic acidosis caused by the continued ingestion of the acid load (Fig. 3). In contrast, it had no effect on renal acid excretion or plasma bicarbonate when it was given to sodium-restricted dogs fed HCl. Before desoxycorticosterone acetate administration, both groups of animals had comparable levels of plasma bicarbonate, plasma potassium, and similar rates of acid excretion. Aldosterone levels were not reported but presumably were higher in sodium-depleted than in sodium-repleted animals. It is entirely possible that in the sodium-depleted group, plasma bicarbonate was not depressed below the level of sodium-repleted animals owing to preexisting hyperaldosteronism, which, thus, completely compensated for the limitation on renal acidification imposed by sodium depletion.

That exogenous administration of mineralocorticoid failed to improve the acidosis of sodium-depleted animals is not surprising if one postulates that a maximal level of mineralocorticoid activity (owing to volume contraction) had already been achieved. In contrast, sodium-repleted animals with normal or only slightly elevated levels of aldosterone may have benefited from the added effect of exogenous mineralocorticoid, causing an increase in both

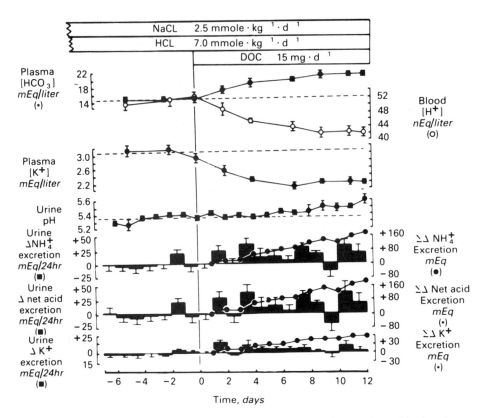

FIG. 3. Effect of desoxycorticosterone acetate (DOC) administration on plasma bicarbonate, hydrogen ion, and potassium concentrations, urine pH, and changes in urine ammonium, net acid, and potassium excretion in acidotic animals receiving a normal sodium intake. Cumulative changes ($\varepsilon\Delta$) in urine acid and potassium excretion also are depicted. (From ref. 12.)

sodium-independent acidification in the collecting tubule. Owing to unrestricted distal sodium delivery these animals excreted more potassium and developed profound hypokalemia, which, in turn, could have increased ammonia production greatly and thereby account for the observed increase in the rate of ammonium excretion and correction of acidosis. The importance of stimulation of sodium-independent acidification by aldosterone is apparent from more recent studies in adrenalectomized rats. In this rat model, plasma aldosterone could be controlled at the desired level by the administration of the hormone by implantation of osmotic minipumps. Under conditions of blockade of sodium-dependent distal acidification by amiloride and low sodium diet, net acid excretion was higher in rats that had high levels of plasma aldosterone than in those that had normal levels of this hormone. Although sodium-dependent distal acidification is important in the adaptive renal response to acidemia, there is also an important contribution of stimulation of sodium-independent acidification by aldosterone.

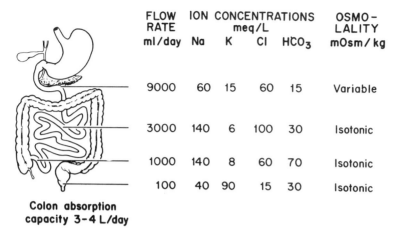

	FLOW RATE ml/day	ION CONCENTRATIONS meq/L				OSMO-LALITY mOsm/kg
		Na	K	Cl	HCO₃	
	9000	60	15	60	15	Variable
	3000	140	6	100	30	Isotonic
	1000	140	8	60	70	Isotonic
	100	40	90	15	30	Isotonic

Colon absorption capacity 3–4 L/day

FIG. 4. Estimates of electrolyte composition at the end of various gastrointestinal tract segments. (From ref. 21.)

Gastrointestinal Bicarbonate Losses (3,5,21,23,24)

Overview of Intestinal Electrolyte Transport

The hyperchloremic metabolic acidosis and electrolyte disturbances occurring in diarrheal states and gastrointestinal–ureteral connections can be understood best on the basis of the transport characteristics of the different bowel segments. The normal composition and flow rate of the intestinal fluids as they course through the small and large bowels are summarized in Fig. 4. About 9 liters of fluid enter the jejunum daily. Most of this volume consists of saliva, gastric, pancreatic, bile, and duodenal secretions. A smaller portion (1.5–2 liters) is derived from liquid intake and food contents. HCl secreted by the stomach is neutralized, in part, by bicarbonate-rich pancreatic and biliary fluids. The large volume of fluid entering the jejunum is reduced to about 3 liters at the end of the jejunum and to about 1 liter of fluid at the end of the ileum (Fig. 4). Normally, the total daily fecal output is only 100 ml because of water reabsorption in the colon. The fluid reaching the terminal portion of the ileum is rich in Na, Cl, and HCO₃ are all reduced as compared to fluid entering the colon (Fig. 4).

Like the renal proximal tubule, the luminal membrane of the jejunum contains a Na⁺-H⁺ exchanger. The sodium entering the cell in exchange for H⁺ is extruded at the basolateral membrane of a Na,K-ATPase. The Na⁺-H⁺ exchanger allows for net reabsorption of sodium bicarbonate. The high paracellular permeability of the jejunum, however, allows for much of the Na reabsorbed to move back into the intestinal lumen, driven by the electrical potential (lumen-negative) prevailing in this bowel segment. As in the renal proximal tubule, the luminal membrane of the jejunum transports hexose sugars and amino acids in a Na^+-dependent fashion. The osmotic gradient produced by sugar and amino acid reabsorption favors the movement of large quantities of water and solutes through paracellular channels. Consequently, the flow rate is reduced markedly when the intestinal contents reach the end of the jejunum (Fig. 4).

Unlike the jejunum, the ileum and the colon display active electroneutral sodium chloride reabsorption against electrochemical gradients and do not require Na^+/sugar and Na^+/amino acid cotransport for osmotically mediated fluid and solute reabsorption. In the ileum, there is a marked decrease in Cl concentration while HCO_3 increases (Fig. 4). This change in ionic composition is a result of the ability of this bowel segment to actively secrete HCO_3 and to absorb Na^+ and Cl^- against a large electrochemical gradient. A luminal membrane Cl^-/HCO_3 exchanger normally operates in the direction of HCO_3 secretion and Cl absorption and seems to account for the low Cl concentration to above 60 mM reverses net Cl movement from absorption to secretion. Conversely, increased amounts of chloride in the lumen facilitate HCO_3 secretion. This explains the HCO_3 wasting that occurs when chloride-rich urine is diverted into the ileum or other bowel segments possessing a Cl^-/HCO_3 exchanger.

The net amount of HCO_3 normally lost in the stool is small. The concentration of HCO_3 in the colon is reduced by its reaction with organic acids, such as acetic, propionic, butyric, and lactic acid, that are produced by bacteria. This reaction produces organic anions (e.g., acetate) and carbonic acid, which dehydrates to H_2O and CO_2. The stool anion gap $[(Na + K) - (Cl^- + HCO_3)]$ is an approximation of unmeasured anion (organic anions) representing decomposed HCO_3. The measured HCO_3 concentration plus decomposed HCO_3 represent the net stool alkali. Decomposed HCO_3 usually exceeds intact HCO_3 and accounts for much of net alkali loss leading to acidosis in diarrheal states. Thus, an increase in the stool anion gap is a better marker of the rate of net alkali loss (i.e., net acid retention) than the HCO_3 concentration in the stool. The normal stool anion gap is around 85 mEq/liter (Fig. 4).

The colon has the ability to secrete K, thereby regulating the excretion of this cation in the final stool water. Colonic potassium secretion is driven by the large electrical potential (lumen-negative) prevailing in this bowel segment. The electrical potential in this segment increases (i.e., becomes more lumen-negative) under conditions of mineralocorticoid excess and decreases in states of mineralocorticoid deficiency. Aldosterone influences the electrical potential and, thus, the rate of K secretion by enhancing Na absorption via sodium channels in the apical membrane. Colonic K secretion also is stimulated in hyperkalemic states and in renal insufficiency and is reduced in hypokalemic states not associated with mineralocorticoid excess. The colonic adaptation to states characterized by potassium excess or deficiency, in general, parallels the renal adaptation that takes place in the renal cortical collecting tubule.

Diarrheal States

Except for patients who surreptitiously abuse laxatives, the cause of diarrhea usually is apparent from the patient's history. The stool osmolar gap is useful in the distinction between osmotic and secretory diarrheas. In osmotic diarrheas, the measured total stool osmolarity exceeds the calculated osmolality $[(Na^+ + K+) \times 2]$, whereas in secretory diarrheas, there is no osmolar gap. The osmolar gap in osmotic diarrheas is approximately equivalent to the concentration of the unreabsorbable solute (e.g., Mg, SO_4) causing diarrhea. An osmolar gap is considered significant if greater than 50 mOsm/kg H_2O. Further information is obtained from the stool pH, which is normal (around 7.0) in osmotic diarrheas caused by poorly reabsorbable mineral salts and high in diarrheas induced by $Mg(OH)_2$-containing preparations. For example, milk of magnesia causes an osmotic diarrhea with a high stool pH (7.5–8.). In contrast, stool pH is low (5–6 pH units) in osmotic diarrheas associated with carbohydrate malabsorption because of the production of organic acids from bacterial carbohydrate metabolism.

A basic mechanism underlying the pathogenesis of many diarrheal states is a change in the pattern of intestinal electrolyte transport from net sodium chloride absorption to net sodium chloride secretion. This basic alteration is best exemplified by the action of *Vibrio cholerae* toxin on intestinal electrolyte transport. Exposure of the intestinal wall to the cholera toxin results in an increase in intracellular cyclic adenosine monophosphate (cAMP) levels. This, in turn, increases luminal membrane Cl^- conductivity in crypt cells, thereby favoring Cl^- secretion from cell to lumen (i.e., a process opposite to that operating under normal conditions). In addition, a rise in intracellular cAMP in villous cells inhibits sodium chloride reabsorption, resulting in massive sodium chloride and H_2O loss. Bicarbonate loss has been ascribed to the action of the cholera toxin in promoting secretion of bicarbonate-rich fluid by small intestinal mucosal cells. A rise in intracellular cAMP is well known to promote bicarbonate secretion in the turtle bladder and in cortical collecting tubules studied *in vitro*. A similar but seemingly more dramatic effect is operative in intestinal cells exposed to the cholera toxin. Importantly, agents that inhibit cAMP, such as chlorpromazine and nicotinic acid, attenuate the hyperchloremic acidosis caused by cholera toxin and that following urinary tract diversion through intestinal segments. This further suggests that intestinal bicarbonate secretion is mediated, at least in part, by cAMP.

The diarrhea characteristic of pancreatic cholera is caused by hypersecretion of vasoactive intestinal polypeptide by the tumor. Experimentally, infusion of the polypeptide at a dose sufficient to mimic the plasma concentration prevailing in patients with the pancreatic cholera syndrome results in profuse watery diarrhea and hyperchloremic metabolic acidosis. Results in stool analysis reveal significant increases in fecal sodium and bicarbonate concentrations as well as a rise in pH. It seems likely that other causes of secretory diarrhea result in hyperchloremic metabolic acidosis by causing large fecal bicarbonate loss. It should be emphasized that no alteration in HCO_3 transport *per se* is required to result in substantial HCO_3 wastage. Frank hyperchloremic metabolic acidosis can originate as a result of activation of the normal mechanisms that produce low chloride and high HCO_3 levels within intestinal fluid.

In many patients with diarrhea, the acidosis is more severe than that accounted for by loss of bicarbonate in the stool. For instance, in a typical patient with severe cholera, the acidosis usually is out of proportion to that anticipated from an average loss of bicarbonate of 200 mEq/liter calculated based on a stool bicarbonate concentration of 50 mEq/liter and a fecal output of 4 liters. The actual HCO_3 concentration of the stools, however, underestimates HCO_3 loss because of the presence in the intestine of organic acids formed from bacterial products. Titration of intestinal HCO_3 by these organic acids lowers its final concentration in the stool so that the net alkali loss is underestimated. Even if this is taken into account, however, the difference between the expected plasma bicarbonate value and the observed value may be substantial in many cases. The measured plasma bicarbonate is often lower than expected from HCO_3 losses because of coexisting lactic acidemia or renal failure, common complications of severe cholera.

Aside from these complications, volume contraction from diarrhea may be sufficiently severe to constrain maximal renal tubular acidification. Euvolemic individuals faced with a chronic acid challenge can increase acid excretion to as much as 200 mEq/day while experiencing only a modest fall in plasma bicarbonate. The acidosis seen in patients with cholera, and probably other types of diarrhea, would not be severe if the expected adaptive renal acidification response was not jeopardized by coexisting sodium depletion. Although data on renal acid excretion from cholera patients are not available, it seems reasonable to speculate that it may not increase maximally, owing to a limitation in distal acidification imposed by impaired distal sodium delivery. This can be inferred from studies in individuals with metabolic acidosis associated with protracted laxative abuse.

Laxative Abuse

The virtual absence of urine sodium in some of these patients (sodium excretion may be less than 1 mEq/24 hr) may impede a maximal distal acidification response to the prevailing acidemia. When sodium excretion is increased to normal by salt replacement, there is a maximal fall in urine pH, an

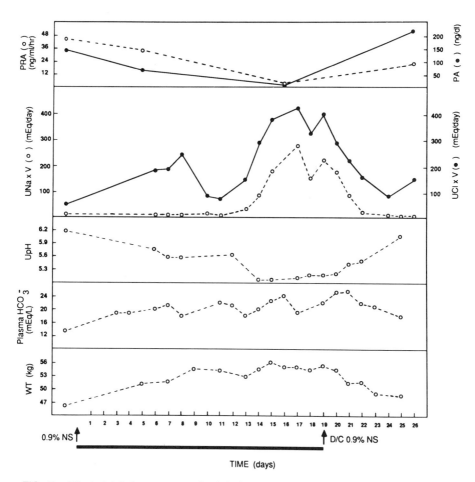

FIG. 5. Effect of daily intravenous saline infusion (0.9% NaCl) on plasma renin activity (PRA), sodium and chloride excretion, urine pH, plasma bicarbonate, and total body weight in a patient who continued to abuse laxatives throughout the observation period. Note the reversible improvement in plasma bicarbonate and the fall in urine pH that occurred during saline administration. (From ref. 5.)

increase in acid excretion, and amelioration of the metabolic acidosis (Fig. 5). Correction of plasma bicarbonate may require the administration of sodium chloride for several days because the volume deficit in people with protracted diarrhea may be severe.

Volume depletion in laxative abusers, however, may go unrecognized clinically because such patients often are asymptomatic. They seem to tolerate, for instance, low blood pressures (systolic 80–100 mm Hg) without displaying postural symptoms. Blood pressure is in the normal range in other patients. These patients are often difficult to recognize, since they learn to stop taking the laxative before clinical evaluation. Unlike other types of secretory diarrhea, laxative-induced secretory diarrhea may stop after fasting. Verification of laxative abuse sometimes can be accomplished by the finding of a high fecal fluid Mg^{2+} (i.e., more than 12 mM) or by the use of screening tests for phenolphthalein-containing laxatives. A clue to the diagnosis is the virtual absence of sodium in the urine.

These individuals often come to medical attention for evaluation of hypokalemia of unknown etiology. Indeed, in diarrheal states caused by laxative abuse, hypokalemia is seen more commonly than hyperchloremic metabolic acidosis. In laxative overusers, hypokalemia is often severe because of coexisting diuretic abuse and self-induced vomiting, common practices among these individuals. Many of such patients have a picture of hypokalemic metabolic alkalosis rather than hyperchloremic metabolic acidosis. Aside from diuretic abuse or vomiting, several factors determine the predominance of hypokalemia in laxative abusers. The relatively high potassium content of the normal stool, if associated with large fecal output, will produce significant potassium wastage. It should be noted, however, that fecal potassium losses, unlike renal potassium excretion, do not increase linearly as a function of fecal output. The contribution of colonic potassium secretion to fecal losses of this cation in diarrheal states has not been defined. It may be substantial because of increased colonic potassium secretion driven by hyperaldosteronism secondary to volume contraction. Aldosterone enhances colonic potassium secretion by increasing lumen-negative electrical potential generated by sodium absorption.

Renal potassium losses, likewise, could be incurred as a result of the stimulatory action of the hormone on cortical collecting tubule potassium secretion. This effect, however, may not occur despite hyperaldosteronism if distal sodium delivery is severely impaired by coexisting sodium depletion. In this setting, urinary potassium is very low as long as urinary sodium is low. In summary, renal potassium losses are not important for the generation of hypokalemia of diarrheal states if sodium depletion is severe. If sodium delivery is adequate, renal potassium losses are substantial because of hyperaldosteronism. Hyperchloremic metabolic acidosis, if present, also impairs maximal renal conservation of potassium.

Drug-induced Bicarbonate Wastage

Various substances result in hyperchloremic metabolic acidosis by causing gastrointestinal HCO_3 wastage. $CaCl_2$ when ingested orally reacts with secreted HCO_3 in the intestinal lumen as follows

$$CaCl_2 + 2\ NaHCO_3 \rightarrow CaCO_3 + 2\ NaCl + H_2O + CO_2$$

$CaCO_2$ is lost in the stool, whereas NaCl is absorbed, and the net effect is loss of HCO_3 and Cl gain, thereby resulting in hyperchloremic metabolic acidosis. Oral $CaCl_2$ administration occasionally is used as a test of urinary acidification in individuals with liver disease in whom NH_4Cl administration is contraindicated.

Cholestyramine is an anionic resin that is given as a chloride salt. In the intestine, chloride is absorbed by the Cl^-/HCO_3 exchanger, and the secreted HCO_3 is bound to the resin, thereby resulting in HCO_3 wastage. Cholestyramine has been documented to cause hyperchloremic metabolic acidosis when given to some patients with biliary cholestasis or renal insufficiency.

Ileus, Fistulas, and Gastroenterostomies

Large bicarbonate losses can be incurred by sequestration of secreted HCO_3 in the intestine of patients with ileus. Thus, although rarely recognized, hyperchloremic metabolic acidosis is a predictable complication of intestinal obstruction.

The pancreas and the biliary tract produce bicarbonate-rich secretions. Consequently, high-output fistulas may cause substantial bicarbonate losses, leading to hyperchloremic metabolic acidosis usually accompanied by severe volume depletion. Metabolic acidosis can be particularly severe when a fistula develops between the biliary tree and the colon. In this setting the direct delivery of large amounts of bile acids to the colon can promote massive secretory diarrhea. Hyperchloremic metabolic acidosis usually does not occur in patients with conventional ileostomies. There are, however, excessive losses of sodium chloride (the average sodium concentration is 120 mEq/liter as opposed to a normal stool sodium of 40 mEq/liter) that may cause subclinical volume depletion. Severe hyperchloremic metabolic acidosis also has been reported after jejunoileal bypass for morbid obesity.

Gastrointestinal–Ureteral Connections (19)

Diversion of urine through intestinal segments can result in hyperchloremic metabolic acidosis, hypokalemia, and other electrolyte abnormalities, i.e., hypomagnesemia and hypocalcemia. Various intestinal segments have been used as conduits to receive urine when the urinary bladder has been removed or is nonfunctioning (Table 5). The anastomosis of one or both ureters into the sigmoid colon (ureterosigmoidostomy) almost always results in hyperchloremic metabolic acidosis. This diversion technique is now employed rarely because of the high rate of metabolic complications associated with its use. Isolated loops of ileum or jejunum are employed instead as urine conduits. The incidence of electrolyte abnormalities, e.g., hyperchloremic hypokalemic metabolic acidosis, has declined since the introduction of the ileal conduit method. Hyperchloremic metabolic acidosis is still a problem in about 10% of

TABLE 5. *Gastrointestinal–ureteral connections that may cause metabolic acidosis*

Ureterosigmoidostomy
Ureterojejunostomy
Ileal conduit (obstructed)
Colon conduit
Ileal ureter
Enterourinary fistula
Rectosigmoid bladder

patients with an ileal conduit. In these cases, however, the ileal conduit usually is obstructed.

The length of time that the urine–feces mixture is in contact with the intestinal mucosa is a main determinant of the severity of the acidosis. This is suggested by the clinical observation that in patients with ureterosigmoid anastomosis, the acidosis is made worse by constipation and ameliorated in the face of fecal incontinence. Another determinant of the severity of acidosis is related to the surface of intestine exposed to urine. The incidence and severity of acidosis in patients with an ileal conduit, a colon conduit, or a rectosigmoid bladder are much less than in those with ureterosigmoid anastomosis.

Several mechanisms have been proposed to account for the development of hyperchloremic metabolic acidosis after ureterosigmoidostomy. Those include (1) selective chloride absorption by the intestinal mucosa (2) reabsorption of chloride with ammonium present in the urine plus additional ammonium generated from the metabolism of urea to ammonia by urease-producing bacteria within the intestinal segment, and (3) bicarbonate secretion owing to activation of the Cl^--HCO_3 exchanger. In addition, the presence of a renal acidifying defect attributable to renal tubular damage from pyelonephritis or high colonic pressures may contribute to the generation of metabolic acidosis. If renal acidification is abnormal often remains unknown owing to the difficulties of studying urinary acidification from the urine–feces mixture that results when urine is diverted into the gastrointestinal tract. In any event, if plasma creatinine is elevated or there is radiologic evidence of urinary obstruction, it is the prevalent idea to consider that a distal acidification defect may be contributing to the hyperchloremic metabolic acidosis. Hyperchloremic metabolic acidosis, however, does occur after urinary tract diversion in patients with normal renal function as judged by a normal plasma creatinine. Plasma blood urea nitrogen (BUN) levels may be misleading, since absorption of urea can lead to elevations of the BUN, even when kidney function is normal.

The pathogenesis of hyperchloremic metabolic acidosis associated with urinary tract diversion has been studied in detail in patients with ureterosigmoid anastomosis. To obtain a urine–feces mixture free of bacterial contamination, a dialysis technique *in vivo* using cellulose bags was used. Patients with ureterosigmoid anastomosis pass a highly alkaline urine–feces mixture with a concentration of both bicarbonate and total ammonia higher than the fecal dialysate from normal subjects. Interestingly, the concentrations of bicarbonate and total ammonia are higher in specimens from acidotic patients than in those from patients receiving bicarbonate to correct the acidosis. A significant negative correlation was found between urine–feces bicarbonate and plasma bicarbonate levels (Fig. 6). Thus, it appears that there is a paradoxical increase in bicarbonate excretion with worsening acidemia.

Because the kidney excretes more acid as plasma bicarbonate falls, it has been postulated that it is the acidity of the urine entering the colon that provides the primary stimulus to colonic bicarbonate secretion. It may very well be that bicarbonate secretion increases because of enhanced chloride-bicarbonate exchange driven by increasing concentrations of chloride in the acid urine delivered to the colon. This comment is based on the known inhibitory effect of acidemia on renal tubular chloride reabsorption. The colon, like the ileum, has a Cl^--HCO_3 exchanger that is activated by the presence of chloride in its lumen. The role of urinary chloride also can be inferred from the observation that when isotonic saline is instilled into the colon of normal individuals, the chloride concentration falls while the bicarbonate concentration increases.

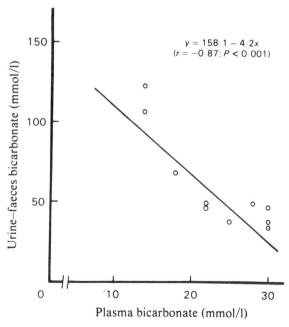

FIG. 6. Correlation of urine–feces bicarbonate with plasma bicarbonate concentration in six patients with a ureterosigmoid anastomosis. (From ref. 19.)

In keeping with this notion, chloride concentration decreases concomitant with the increase in bicarbonate concentration in the urine–feces mixture obtained from patients with a uterosigmoidostomy. The finding of relatively low bicarbonate and ammonia concentrations in nonacidotic patients with ureterosigmoid anastomosis suggests that the delivery of neutral or only slightly acidic urine, not so rich in chloride, results in less bicarbonate secretion than when the delivered urine is acid. Thus, the acidity of urine excreted by the kidney may determine the amount of urinary chloride draining into the colon and the extent of bicarbonate secretion. Administration of sodium bicarbonate in such persons serves a double purpose; it corrects the acidosis and it reduces bicarbonate wastage.

Of note is the high concentration of ammonium in the urine–feces mixture of untreated (acidotic) patients with a ureterosigmoidostomy. This suggests that the source of ammonium is the kidney, which increases its excretion owing to systemic acidemia. The content of ammonium and bicarbonate in urine–feces specimens from patients with ureterosigmoidostomy obtained by catheter immediately after a bowel movement is higher than that when the mixture is obtained after permanence in the intestine. This suggests that NH_4^+ and HCO_3^- are absorbed. Absorption of NH_4^+ could worsen the acidosis, since it reduces the net amount of acid excreted by the kidneys. Ammonium can be reabsorbed as its conjugate free base, ammonia, whereas the liberated hydrogen ion is either excreted as titratable acid or reabsorbed with chloride. In this regard, it is worth mentioning that ammoniagenic coma after urinary diversion has been described in the presence of underlying liver disease.

Dilutional Acidosis (10)

The concept of dilutional acidosis has been validated experimentally. The fall in plasma bicarbonate that may be anticipated from an increase in extracellular volume, however, is of little clinical relevance. The magnitude of the depression in plasma bicarbonate is small (2–3 mEq/liter) despite acute infusions of isotonic saline graded to produce a large (24–34%) increase in extracellular fluid. A fall in bicarbonate caused by dilution could cause a fall in pH only if PCO_2 were not to fall proportionally. This condition can be met after rapid volume expansion because PCO_2 falls only transiently owing to ongoing cellular metabolism and respiratory control. Even when blood PCO_2 is kept constant at 40 mm Hg, however, the degree of depression of plasma bicarbonate is much less pronounced than would have been predicted purely on the basis of volume expansion. This indicates that new extracellular bicarbonate is generated presumably from the interaction of the bicarbonate and carbonic acid buffer pair with nonbicarbonate buffers.

That nonbicarbonate buffers participate in the titration of hydrogen ions during volume expansion has been demonstrated in *in vitro* and *in vivo* ex-

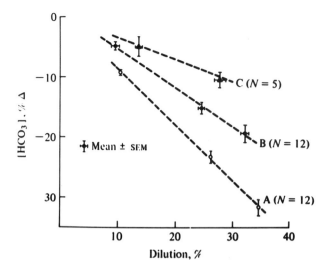

FIG. 7. Percent decrease in bicarbonate concentration as a function of progressive dilution of plasma (line A), whole blood (line B), or whole body (line C). Linear regressions calculated for individual points are as follows: y = 0.91 × − 0.44 for plasma, y = 0.63 × − 1.05 for whole blood, and y = 0.35 × − 0.15 for whole body. Correlation coefficients are 0.98, 0.96, and 0.66, respectively. (From ref. 10.)

periments (Fig. 7). *In vitro* after dilution of plasma with normal saline, while Pco_2 was kept constant at 40 mm Hg, bicarbonate concentration decreased approximately in a 1:1 proportion with the degree of dilution. This reflects the lack of any significant amounts of nonbicarbonate buffer in plasma. The fall in bicarbonate was greatly attenuated when whole blood was studied *in vitro*. An even greater protection was found when isotonic expansion was produced by infusing isotonic saline to intact animals (Fig. 7). Generation of bicarbonate was ascribed to participation of nonbicarbonate buffers, such as hemoglobin (in the case of the whole blood experiments) and to the additional participation of nonbicarbonate buffers from bone and other intracellular sources (in the *in vivo* experiments). If these studies are extrapolated to humans, one can calculate that extracellular fluid volume would have to be expanded by an estimated 38% to produce only a minor fall in plasma bicarbonate (about 2 mEq/liter). It should be further emphasized that, even though plasma bicarbonate may fall by the dilution effect, the total amount of bicarbonate in extracellular fluid does not fall. In fact, it increases by the generation of new bicarbonate from intracellular nonbicarbonate buffers. Accordingly, correction of the acidosis simply requires renal excretion of the fluid excess. Administration of bicarbonate is, therefore, not necessary.

Well-documented cases of patients with dilutional acidosis are difficult to find despite earlier studies portraying a fall in plasma bicarbonate after rapid infusions of isotonic saline, hypertonic saline, mannitol, or glucose. There is some experimental evidence suggesting that when the extracellular fluid is expanded with hypotonic solutions, plasma bicarbonate falls much less than when expansion is produced by hypertonic solutions. In this regard, it is important to recognize that metabolic acidosis does not occur in patients with the syndrome of inappropriate antidiuretic hormone secretion, a prototypic state of hypotonic volume expansion. Such patients could be protected against dilutional metabolic acidosis owing to a stimulatory effect of antidiuretic hormone (ADH) on distal acidification, an action for which there is some preliminary experimental evidence. Alternatively, hypotonic volume expansion may be associated with enhanced extrarenal bicarbonate generation. Although aldosterone secretion has been shown experimentally to increase with severe hyponatremia, there is no documentation that the levels of the hormone are elevated in patients with the syndrome of inappropriate ADH secretion. In any event, the lack of acidosis in patients with the syndrome of inappropriate ADH secretion clearly illustrates that dilution of the extracellular fluid compartment has very little impact on acid-base balance.

Potassium Excess (16)

Hyperkalemia often is associated with metabolic acidosis, and treatment of hyperkalemia usually is accompanied by amelioration of the associated metabolic acidosis. The association between hyperkalemia and metabolic acidosis usually occurs in the setting of advanced renal insufficiency causing both potassium and acid retention or as a consequence of more specific alterations in distal tubular function associated or not with mineralocorticoid deficiency (see Chapter 15).

The relationship of hyperkalemia to the generation of metabolic acidosis independently of renal disease and mineralocorticoid deficiency probably is due to impaired renal ammoniagenesis. Hyperkalemia decreases renal ammonia production, which, in turn, may predispose to metabolic acidosis by diminishing net acid excretion. In addition, hyperkalemia seems to inhibit proximal tubule bicarbonate reabsorption presumably by increasing renal tubule cell pH, thereby limiting the availability of protons for secretion. The effect of hyperkalemia on distal nephron acidification has not been well defined. Under euvolemic, but not during volume expanded conditions, dogs infused with potassium bicarbonate cannot generate a large urinary P_{CO_2}, a finding that suggests impaired collecting tubule hydrogen ion secretion.

In adrenalectomized dogs subjected to chronic potassium loading and maintained on a fixed steroid replacement, hyperchloremic metabolic acidosis develops in association with a decrease in net acid excretion. In this model of chronic stable hyperkalemia (potassium 6.7 ± 0.3 mEq/liter), the decrease in acid output can be largely accounted for by a decrease in ammonium excretion (Fig. 8, bottom panel). In addition, an inverse relationship between the

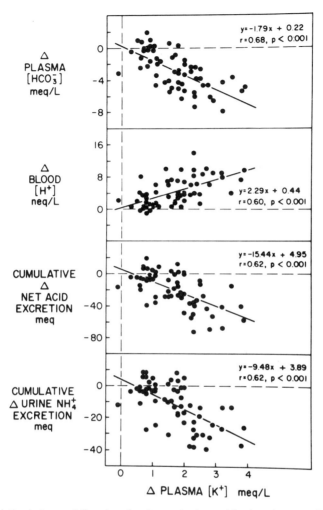

FIG. 8. Relation between daily values for change in plasma bicarbonate concentration, blood hydrogen ion concentration cumulative change (Δ) in net acid excretion, cumulative Δ ammonium excretion, and Δ plasma potassium concentration, from control to period of oral KCl loading in fixed steroid-replaced ADX dogs. (From ref. 16.)

fall in plasma bicarbonate and the rise in plasma potassium was found (Fig. 8, top panel). The latter finding is consistent with an acidosis-producing effect of hyperkalemia due to extrarenal shifts of hydrogen ions from cells to the extracellular fluid compartment. The quantitative contribution of renal versus extrarenal components to the observed changes in plasma bicarbonate induced by potassium loading has not been determined. It should be emphasized that hyperkalemia stimulates aldosterone release, an effect that would clearly attenuate the acidosis-producing effect of potassium excess. In the study just described, plasma aldosterone levels were kept constant thereby precluding extrapolation to hyperkalemia individuals with adequate aldosterone reserve.

Potassium Deficiency (13,15,18,22)

Potassium deficiency may alter acid-base status by virtue of several mechanisms that potentially have opposite effects on the regulation of plasma bicarbonate (Table 6). Potassium deficiency, if associated with mineralocorticoid excess, clearly results in profound metabolic alkalosis. The use of diuretics and syndromes of primary mineralocorticoid excess are prime examples of hyperkalemic metabolic alkalosis developing under these circumstances.

If potassium deficiency in itself can cause sustained metabolic alkalosis, in the absence of other alkalosis-producing alterations that are usually associated with the clinical syndromes of potassium deficiency, has been the subject of some debate. In rats with potassium depletion induced by a diet low in potassium but normal in chloride, metabolic alkalosis develops in association with a decrease in muscle cell pH. The fall in cell pH has been ascribed to entry of protons to replace intracellular losses of potassium. In addition to the extrarenal alkalosis-generating effect, potassium depletion, perhaps by causing intracellular acidosis in renal cells, is apt to enhance proton secretion in both the proximal and the distal nephron. It is well known that in experimental potassium depletion, the rate of bicarbonate reabsorption in the proximal and in the distal nephron is enhanced. The aggregate of these effects taken together with the known stimulatory effect of potassium depletion on ammonia production should lead to the development of metabolic alkalosis. In normal volunteers subjected to potassium deprivation of 15 days duration, a small but significant increase in plasma bicarbonate concentration (1.8 ± 0.3 mEq/liter) has been observed. Renal net acid excretion decreased and remained slightly

TABLE 6. *Effects of potassium deficiency on acid-base balance*

Alkalosis-generating effects	Acidosis-generating effects
Translocation of H^+ into cells	Impairment of maximal lowering of urine pH
Enhancement of ammonia production	
Enhancement of proximal HCO_3 transport	Decreased titratable acid excretion
Enhancement of collecting tubule H^+ secretion	
Potentiation of mineralocorticoid action on collecting tubule H^+ secretion	Hypoaldosteronism
Impairment of chloride reabsorption in the cortical collecting tubule	

but significantly below control. As anticipated, plasma aldosterone concentration decreased significantly when plasma potassium fell. Hence, potassium depletion of moderate severity (plasma potassium 3.0 ± 0.1 mEq/liter) caused and maintained a small but significant increase in plasma bicarbonate concentration. Importantly, this was observed in the absence of confounding variables, such as hyperaldosteronism and chloride depletion. A more pronounced metabolic alkalosis develops if a dietary sodium chloride intake is markedly reduced while potassium intake is restricted. Under these conditions, net acid excretion increases, indicating that a renal mechanism contributes to the generation and maintenance of the alkalosis.

Both renal and extrarenal effects of potassium depletion are involved in the pathogenesis of this form of metabolic alkalosis. In the initial phase of potassium depletion, an extrarenal mechanism may be operative by causing translocation of hydrogen ions into cells as a consequence of the efflux of potassium that occurs when the deficit of body potassium is developing. The role of the kidney in the development of metabolic alkalosis, however, is less clear. Net acid excretion in potassium-deprived people on a normal salt intake is decreased below control levels, whereas it is increased when salt intake is restricted. In the latter setting, renal mechanisms contribute to the development of metabolic alkalosis. Preexisting NaCl deficiency may potentiate the alkalosis-generating effect of potassium deprivation by several mechanisms: (1) direct stimulation of sodium-independent distal H^+ secretion by K depletion, (2) amplification of this effect by a level of plasma aldosterone higher than that prevailing when NaCl intake is not restricted, and (3) decreased availability of the readily reabsorbable Cl^- anion, which, in the face of increased avidity for Na^+ reabsorption, could stimulate voltage-dependent H^+ secretion in the cortical collecting tubule.

It is noteworthy that, in contrast to these findings in humans, potassium deprivation has not yet been shown to produce a clear-cut increase in net acid excretion in experimental animals. In fact, in dogs with severe potassium deficiency, renal net acid excretion is markedly decreased, and a hyperchloremic metabolic acidosis rather than alkalosis develops. This decrease in net acid excretion appears to be the consequence of a rise in urine pH and a fall in titratable acid excretion. Ammonium excretion may be normal, increased, or decreased. The administration of KCl to correct hypokalemia results in a prompt rise in plasma bicarbonate that is associated with a fall in urine pH and an increase in acid excretion (Fig. 9). In humans and dogs subjected to potassium deprivation, the ability to lower urinary pH normally in response to an acid load is impaired. This has led to the suggestion that potassium deprivation produces a defect in collecting tubule proton secretion akin to that seen in patients with distal renal tubular acidosis. Although experimental potassium depletion has been shown to produce hyperchloremic metabolic acidosis in dogs, clinical examples of this type of acidosis have not been described. The hypokalemia seen in patients with classic renal tubular acidosis,

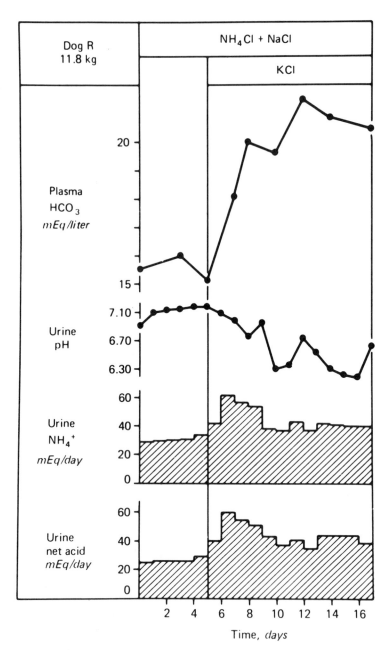

FIG. 9. Effect of correction of Kayexalate-induced potassium deficit on acid-base equilibrium in a representative dog ingesting 1.7 mmoles of ammonium chloride per kg of body weight. Provision of potassium chloride resulted in a rapid plasma bicarbonate rise and a fall in urine pH associated with an increase in ammonia excretion. (From ref. 22)

for instance, is thought to be an associated feature rather than a cause of acidosis. In these patients, plasma aldosterone levels usually are elevated. In contrast, the decrease in net acid excretion observed during experimental severe potassium depletion is largely accounted by inhibition of aldosterone secretion.

Posthypocapnic Hyperchloremic Metabolic Acidosis (4)

This acid-base disorder usually is transient and self-limited and occurs in individuals with chronic respiratory alkalosis with normal renal compensation when the underlying cause leading to hyperventilation is removed. Because plasma bicarbonate falls during chronic respiratory alkalosis, the return of blood PCO_2 to normal levels will result in a fall in blood pH and thereby a picture of posthypocapnic acidemia. The fall in plasma bicarbonate that occurs during chronic sustained hypocapnia is sufficient to prevent a substantial rise in blood pH that, during the steady state of hypocapnia, stabilizes at a level only slightly higher than before hypocapnia. When blood PCO_2 returns to normal, a period of posthypocapnic acidemia ensues until augmentation of acid excretion restores plasma bicarbonate to normal levels in approximately 2 to 5 days. During the phase of sustained chronic hypocapnia, there is a reduction in the rate of bicarbonate reabsorption and a decrease in the rate of acid excretion accompanied by a loss of sodium into the urine. The loss of sodium results in volume contraction, which, in turn, enhances sodium chloride reabsorption and contributes to hyperchloremia. The increase in plasma chloride, however, may not always match the fall in plasma bicarbonate so that the acid-base picture may be one of a mixed hyperchloremic and high anion gap acidosis. This has been ascribed to accumulations of organic acid anions, namely, lactic acid, during the acute phase of hypocapnia. Elevations in plasma lactate levels, however, are not a feature of chronic hypocapnia or posthypocapnic acidemia.

The return to normal of the plasma bicarbonate may be delayed by suppression of collecting tubule hydrogen ion secretion, which remains diminished for at least several hours after recovery from chronic hypocapnia. This has been documented in rats made hypocapnic by placing them in an environmental chamber and forcing them to inhale a low O_2 mixture. Evidence for decreased collecting tubule acidification was the finding that, at a normal blood PCO_2, maximal alkalinization of the urine by bicarbonate infusion failed to result in a normal rise in urinary PCO_2. Alkalemia could not account for the subnormal urine PCO_2 of posthypocapnic rats because blood pH is reduced in posthypocapnic states, an effect that should stimulate collecting tubule acidification. Possible explanations for the finding of suppressed collecting tubule H^+ secretion include generation of non-CO_2 buffers during protracted hypocarbia leading to increased intracellular pH, reduced cell metabolism, decreased conductance for protons, and decreased distal sodium transport. Regardless of the mechanism, this effect persists for a period of time after recovery from hypocapnia (i.e., there is a memory effect that influences acidification by renal tubules).

Since respiratory alkalosis is the most frequent of all acid-base disorders among hospitalized patients, the chances of encountering posthypocapnic metabolic acidosis are likewise high. Such patients may develop posthypocapnic acidosis when the underlying disease (e.g., sepsis, pulmonary edema, hypoxia) is brought under control. Pregnant women usually have mild chronic respiratory alkalosis, which is exacerbated by acute superimposed hypocapnia during parturition. A picture of mild posthypocapnic acidosis should, therefore, be expected for several days postpartum.

Diabetic Ketoacidosis (1)

The generation of metabolic acidosis in diabetic ketoacidosis results from the titration of bicarbonate and other buffers by protons from the ketoacids. Accumulation of ketoanions leads to an increase in unmeasured anions and should result in a high anion gap type of metabolic acidosis. Patients admitted with diabetic ketoacidosis, however, have a wide spectrum of acid-base patterns, including pure hyperchloremic acidosis, pure anion gap acidosis, and a combination of both disturbances.

The relationship between the plasma anion gap and plasma bicarbonate concentration has been investigated in a large series of patients admitted with diabetic ketoacidosis. In a pure high anion gap type of acidosis, the decrement in plasma bicarbonate should have been roughly similar to the increment in the plasma anion gap. A striking finding of this study, however, was the lack of relationship between the initial level of plasma bicarbonate and the plasma anion gap. However, a highly significant correlation was present between the plasma anion gap and BUN. This correlation could not be accounted for by retention of anions (sulfate, phosphate, and creatinine) as a result of renal insufficiency because the patients with the highest BUN did not have the lowest plasma bicarbonate. The relation between the plasma anion gap and the BUN was ascribed to different degrees of retention of ketone salts depending on the degree of extracellular fluid volume depletion. In other words, an increase in BUN was used as a marker of prerenal azotemia, a reasonable assumption, since the elevated BUN levels on admission returned to normal after the administration of fluids. Accordingly, in the face of severe volume contraction, the excretion of ketoacids is retarded, thereby contributing to the development of a high anion gap metabolic acidosis.

As ketoanions are excreted by the kidneys, a hyperchloremic type of metabolic acidosis develops because of retention of chloride in excess of sodium. Sodium can be retained as chloride or as sodium bicarbonate. Since plasma bicarbonate is low, the reabsorption of filtered bicarbonate is already complete, and the only anion available to be reabsorbed with sodium is chloride. Sodium retention is minimized because of its obligatory excretion with the ketoanions.

These observations suggest that the type of metabolic acidosis on admission may determine the speed of recovery from metabolic acidosis. If volume contraction is severe, ketoacids are retained, leading to a high anion gap type of metabolic acidosis. In this type of acidosis, the retained ketoacids provide a source of potential bicarbonate. This may contribute to a faster recovery from acidosis owing to the equimolar conversion of retained ketone salts to bicarbonate. In contrast, the hyperchloremic form of metabolic acidosis is associated with delayed time in recovery. According to this notion, administration of bicarbonate seems more indicated in diabetic patients with a hyperchloremic type of acidosis than in those with a high anion gap type.

Renal Failure Treated by Hemodialysis (7)

Renal failure, both acute and chronic, is a common cause of metabolic acidosis that has been typically classified as a high anion gap type. It should be appreciated, however, that the fall in plasma HCO is largely due to an absolute decrease in ammonium excretion as a result of reduced renal mass and that a reciprocal increase in the anion gap does not need to occur. Variable degrees of anion retention (sulfate, phosphate, and organic anions) occurring as renal insufficiency progresses determine the development of a high anion gap metabolic acidosis. The predominant pattern of metabolic acidosis among patients on maintenance hemodialysis is a mixed one, that is, a combined high anion gap and hyperchloremic metabolic acidosis. Although the mixed pattern is the more dominant (46% of all observations), hyperchloremic acidosis also is frequently seen (24%) (Fig. 10A). Together, hyperchloremic and mixed acidosis have been documented in as many as 70% of predialysis observations. During dialysis the mean Δ TCO_2/Δ AG ratio falls near the range expected in patients with nonanion gap metabolic acidosis. The pattern most frequently encountered at the end of dialysis is that of hyperchloremic metabolic acidosis (48%, or double the predialysis percentage). This pattern is followed by that of mixed acidosis (33%), and the pattern seen least frequently is that of a high anion gap acidosis (19%) (Fig. 10B).

Since the plasma anion gap reflects the difference between anions and cations not routinely measured, it follows that the impact of dialysis on the type of metabolic acidosis must be the consequence of changes in unmeasured anions or unmeasured cations occurring during the procedure. A decrease in the unmeasured anions could result in a fall in the anion gap and, thus, a shift toward a nonanion gap metabolic acidosis during hemodialysis. The dialysis procedure results in the removal of anions, such as phosphate and sulfate, that

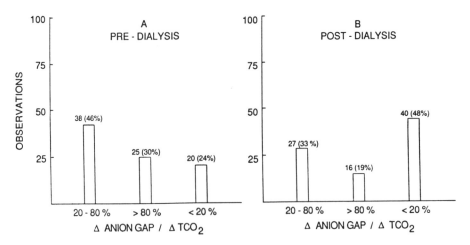

FIG. 10. The distribution of acid-base patterns on the basis of the $\Delta AG/\Delta TCO_2$ ratio before (A) and after (B) dialysis. The vertical axis shows the number of observations. (From ref. 7.)

account for the majority of unmeasured anions contributing to the increased anion gap in patients with renal failure. In essence, the swing toward a non-anion gap type of acidosis during acetate dialysis is the result of removal of anions at a rate that exceeds the correction of the plasma bicarbonate deficit. This situation is reminiscent of the development of hyperchloremic acidosis in patients with diabetic ketoacidosis, which results, at least in part, from rapid renal excretion of ketoanions in the face of avid retention by kidney of endogenous chloride and exogenous chloride administered in the form of sodium chloride as part of the therapeutic effort.

REFERENCES

1. Adrogue, H. J., Wilson, H., Boyd, A. E., Suki, W. N., and Eknoyan, G. (1982): Plasma acid-base patterns in diabetic ketoacidosis. *N. Engl. J. Med.*, 307:1603–1610.
2. Batlle, D. C., and Chan Y. L. (1988): Effect of amino acids on renal bicarbonate transport. *Membrane Biophysics III: Biological Transport*, pp. 173–183. Alan R Liss, New York.
3. Batlle, D. C., Hizon, M., Cohen, E., Gutterman, C., and Gupta, R. (1988): The use of the urinary anion gap in the diagnosis of hyperchloremic metabolic acidosis. *N. Engl. J. Med.*, 318:594–599.
4. Batlle, D. C., Itsarayoungyuen, K., Downer, M., Foley, R., Arruda, J. A. L., and Kurtzman, N. A. (1983): Suppression of distal urinary acidification after recovery from chronic hypocapnia. *Am. J. Physiol.*, 245, F433–F442.
5. Batlle, D. C., Von Riotte, A., and Schlueter,W. (1987): Urinary sodium in the evaluation of hyperchloremic metabolic acidosis. *N. Engl. J. Med.*, 316:140–144.
6. Clarke, E., Evans, B. M., Macintyre, E. I., and Milne, M. D. (1955): Acidosis in experimental electrolyte depletion. *Clin. Sci.*, 14:421–440.
7. Cohen, E., Liu, K., and Batlle, D. C. (1988): Patterns of metabolic acidosis in patients with end-stage renal disease: Impact of Hemodialysis. *Int. J. Artif. Organs* (in press).
8. De Sousa R. C., Harrington, J. T., Ricanati, E. S., Shelkrot, J. W., and Schwartz, W. B.

(1974): Renal regulation of acid-base equilibrium during chronic administration of mineral acid. *J. Clin. Invest.*, 53:465–476.

9. De Troyer, A., Stolarczyk, A., Zegers de Beyl, D., and Stryckmans, P. (1977): Value of anion-gap determination in multiple myeloma. *N. Engl. J. Med.*, 296:858–860.

10. Garella, S., Chang, B. S., and Kahn, S. I. (1975): Dilution acidosis and contraction alkalosis: Review of a concept. *Kidney Int.*, 8:279.

11. Graber, M. L., Quigg, R. J., Stempsey, W. E., and Weis, S. (1983): Spurious hyperchloremia and decreased anion gap in hyperlipidemia. *Ann. Intern. Med.*, 98:607–609.

12. Harrington, J. T., Hulter, H. N., Cohen, J. J., and Madias, N. E. (1986): Mineralocorticoid-stimulated renal acidification: The critical role of dietary sodium. *Kidney Int.*, 30:43–48.

13. Hernandez, R. E., Schambelan, M., Cogan, M. G., Colman, J., Curtis Morris, R. Jr., and Sebastian, A. (1987). *Kidney Int.*, 31:1356–1367.

14. Hizon, M., and Batlle, D. C. (1988): Role of aldosterone (A) on renal acidification during chronic acid loading: Primacy of the Na-independent effect. *Kidney Int.*, 33:401.

15. Hulter, H. N., Sebastian, A., Sigala, J. F., et al. (1980): Pathogenesis of renal hyperchloremic acidosis resulting from dietary potassium restriction in the dog: Role of aldosterone. *Am. J. Physiol.*, 238:F79–F91.

16. Hulter, H. N., Toto, R. D., Ilnicki, L. L., and Sebastian, A. (1983): Chronic hyperkalemic renal tubular acidosis induced by KCl loading. *Am. J. Physiol.*, 244:F255–F264.

17. Jacobson, H. R., and Seldin, D. W., (1983): On the generation, maintenance, and correction of metabolic alkalosis. *Am. J. Physiol.*, 245:F425–F432.

18. Jones, J. W., Sebastian, A., Hulter, H. N., Shambelan, M., Sutton, J. M., and Biglieri, E. G. (1982): Systemic and renal acid-base effects of chronic dietary potassium depletion in humans. *Kidney Int.*, 21:402–410.

19. McConnell, J. B., Murison, J., and Stewart, W. K. (1979): The role of the colon in the pathogenesis of hyperchloraemic acidosis in ureterosigmoid anastomosis. *Clin. Sci.*, 57:305–312.

20. Perez, G. O., Oster, J. R., and Vaamonde, C. A. (1977): The effect of sodium depletion on the renal response to short-duration NH_4Cl acid loading (39719). *Proc. Soc. Exp. Biol. Med.*, 154:562–567.

21. Sleisinger, M. H., and Fordtran, J. S. (eds.). *Gastrointestinal Diseases*, 3rd ed. W. B. Saunders, Philadelphia.

22. van Ypersele de Strihou, C., and Dieu, J. P. (1977): Potassium deficiency acidosis in the dog: Effect of sodium and potassium balance on renal response to a chronic acid load. *Kidney Int.*, 11:335–347.

23. Wang, F., Butler, T., Rabbani, G. H., and Jones, P. K. (1986): The acidosis of cholera. Contributions of hyperproteinemia, lactic acidemia, and hyperphophatemia. *N. Engl. J. Med.*, 315:1591–1595.

24. Weinberg, J. (1986): Fluid and electrolyte disorders and gastrointestinal diseases. In: *Fluids and Electrolytes*, edited by J. P. Kokko and R. L. Tannen, pp. 742–759. Saunders, Philadelphia.

The Regulation of Acid–Base Balance, edited
by Donald W. Seldin and Gerhard Giebisch,
Raven Press, Ltd., New York © 1989.

15

Renal Tubular Acidosis

Daniel C. Batlle

Department of Medicine, Northwestern University Medical School
and Lakeside Veterans Administration Medical Center,
Chicago, Illinois 60611

Overview of the Renal Tubular Acidosis Syndromes (1,7,21,23,26)

Metabolic acidosis is found in most patients with renal disease whose glomerular filtration rate (GFR) is markedly reduced (usually to less than 25 ml/min). A form of acidosis of renal origin distinctive from that associated with renal insufficiency was first described in children afflicted with nephrocalcinosis in the early 1930s. Unlike in patients with renal insufficiency, the urine of these patients was not as acidic as one would expect in the face of metabolic acidosis. The development of hyperchloremic acidosis was thought to result from some kind of tubular dysfunction because GFR was normal or only moderately reduced. The seminal studies of Albright et al. characterized the features of the syndrome, including the frequent occurrence of rickets, osteomalacia, and kidney calcium deposition. These authors recognized that the syndrome they were describing was entirely different from the renal tubular acidosis (RTA) that was known to occur in association with the Fanconi syndrome.

Until the late 1950s, cases of RTA were reported only sporadically and appeared to be genetically determined in some patients. Subsequently, other studies showed that the urine pH of patients afflicted with the clinical features described by Albright et al. could never be lowered below 5.5 regardless of the degree of acidemia present. Other patients, however, were found to have a distinctive pattern of urinary acidification characterized by urinary bicarbonate wasting. The latter patients were capable of lowering urine pH when plasma bicarbonate concentration was lowered to a critical level at which tubular bicarbonate reabsorption was sufficient to generate an almost bicarbonate-free urine. Because the great bulk of bicarbonate filtered is reabsorbed in the proximal nephron, the defect of patients with severe bicarbonate wastage is believed to reside in this site of the nephron. The acidosis of these patients was referred to as proximal (or type II) RTA (Table 1). The term distal, or type I, RTA was introduced to designate patients in whom urine pH was above 5.5 in the face of metabolic acidosis (i.e., the classic form of RTA described by Albright et al.). A variant of distal RTA characterized by the absence of spontaneous metabolic acidosis was described in some relatives of patients with hereditary distal RTA. This variant was designated as incomplete distal RTA to describe the fact that the disorder requires the administration of an acid load to become manifest. In patients with distal RTA, unlike in those with proximal RTA, urinary bicarbonate losses are not large (i.e., usually much less than 10% of the filtered bicarbonate is excreted in the urine at normal plasma bicarbonate concentrations). In both types, hypokalemia is frequently, but not always, seen in association with hyperchloremic metabolic acidosis.

Infants in whom bicarbonate wastage coexisted with failure to lower urine pH during severe acidemia were also described and the term type III RTA designates this pattern of renal dysfunction. These infants, however, do not

TABLE 1. *General types of acidosis of primary renal origin*

Uremic acidosis
Distal RTA[a] (classic or type I RTA)
Proximal RTA (bicarbonate wastage or type II RTA)
Distal RTA with bicarbonate wastage (type III RTA)
Hyperkalemic RTA associated with aldosterone deficiency
  (type IV RTA)
Hyperkalemic forms of distal RTA not primarily caused by
  aldosterone deficiency

---

[a]RTA, renal tubular acidosis.

have a unique type of RTA. Their bicarbonate wastage probably is the consequence of diminished proximal bicarbonate reabsorption as a result of incomplete maturation of tubular function. Increased distal bicarbonate delivery, in turn, overwhelms an already impaired distal reabsorptive apparatus. This pattern is rare and has not been delineated in the adult population. In children with this abnormality, bicarbonate wastage appears to be transient. Hence, the term type III RTA should be abandoned and the disorder should be considered a variant of distal RTA in infants (Table 1).

Hyperchloremic metabolic acidosis also occurs frequently in association with hyperkalemia and aldosterone deficiency. That the acidosis is of renal tubular origin is apparent from the finding of a decrease in ammonium excretion that is out of proportion to the degree of renal insufficiency. The disorder is due, in part, to reversible suppression of renal ammoniagenesis caused by hyperkalemia. Unlike patients with classic RTA, these patients retain the ability to lower urine pH below 5.5 during acidosis. Renal clearance of potassium is reduced greatly, and hyperkalemia ensues even though GFR is only moderately decreased. This constellation of features would be predicted to occur as a result of aldosterone deficiency. Indeed, many but not all patients with these characteristics have selective aldosterone deficiency (i.e., mineralocorticoid deficiency unassociated with glucocorticoid deficiency). The disorder usually occurs in patients with some degree of renal insufficiency as a result of underlying tubulointerstitial renal disease, many of whom have diabetes mellitus.

Because the tubular dysfunction associated with aldosterone deficiency is clearly distinguishable from that associated with proximal (type II) and distal (type I) RTA and for the sake of continuing to use a typologic classification of the RTA syndromes, the term type IV RTA was introduced by Sebastian et al. to designate patients with the characteristics just outlined (Table 1). Since the term type IV RTA was introduced, many patients with hyperkalemic hyperchloremic metabolic acidosis with apparently normal levels of plasma aldosterone, however, have been described. A distinctive pattern of urinary acidification characterized by failure to lower urine pH not only during acidemia but also after stimulation of sodium-dependent acidification by the administration of mineralocorticoid and sodium sulfate has been well delineated in some hyperkalemic patients. Thus, the renal tubular acidification defect of these patients appears to be physiologically distinct from that occurring in patients with pure selective aldosterone deficiency. The clinical presentation and the plasma electrolytes, however, are indistinguishable between the two groups of patients. In fact, both entities often coexist, and they may even evolve from one to the other. Other patients with drug-induced hyperkalemic hyperchloremic metabolic acidosis have clinical features akin to either group of patients. Rare syndromes of hyperkalemic hyperchloremic metabolic acidosis associated with or without salt wastage and aldosterone resistance (pseudohypoaldosteronism) rather than aldosterone deficiency also have been delineated.

The term type IV RTA as it is commonly used by clinicians refers to any

patient with hyperkalemic hyperchloremic metabolic acidosis not attributable
to advanced renal insufficiency. In this regard, it is a vague and undescriptive
term that may imply that the same mechanism is responsible for all cases of
hyperkalemic hyperchloremic metabolic acidosis associated with normal GFR
or only moderately reduced GFR. Because the recognition of each of the
causes of hyperkalemic RTA is feasible after a basic evaluation of urinary
acidification, it is not appropriate to place all such patients under the designa-
tion type IV RTA. The use of a typologic classification of the RTA syndromes
is problematic if one considers that different alterations in urinary acidification
possibly affecting discrete nephron segments can have the clinical features
characteristic of distal (type I) RTA. Moreover, many patients have subtle
defects in urinary acidification not manifested by hyperchloremic metabolic
acidosis. For these reasons, the identification and classification of the various types of RTA are best approached from a mechanistic point of view and
should take into consideration the site of the nephron responsible for the
defect in acidification.

PROXIMAL RENAL TUBULAR ACIDOSIS (8,18)

In normal individuals, the urine bicarbonate concentration usually is low.
In patients with proximal RTA, a large fraction of the filtered load of bicarbonate is excreted when the concentration of bicarbonate in plasma is normal. In
contrast, the urine is virtually bicarbonate-free when the concentration of
bicarbonate in plasma is below the patient's renal threshold (Fig. 1). The
renal bicarbonate threshold in patients with proximal RTA varies between 15
and 20 mEq/liter. Except for reduced renal bicarbonate threshold, the shape
of the bicarbonate reabsorption curve in patients with proximal RTA is of
normal configuration (Fig. 1). When plasma bicarbonate is below the renal
bicarbonate threshold, urine pH falls to levels comparable to those seen in
normal subjects given ammonium chloride to produce metabolic acidosis
(Table 2). The fall in urine pH also is associated with a substantial increase in
ammonium and titratable acid excretion. Ammonium excretion, however,
does not increase to the level of normal subjects challenged with an acid load.

The urinary PCO_2 in a highly alkaline urine also increases normally (i.e.,
above 70 mm Hg), suggesting that collecting tubule hydrogen ion secretion is
normal. This parameter, however, has been evaluated in only a few patients
with proximal RTA, precluding the conclusion that distal acidification is normal in all cases. The possibility remains that, at least in some patients with
proximal RTA, bicarbonate reabsorption beyond the proximal tubule may be
diminished. The capacity for bicarbonate transport of segments distal to the
proximal convoluted tubule (pars recta of the proximal tubule, the thick ascending limb of Henle, the distal tubule, and the collecting tubule) is substantial. Enhanced bicarbonate reabsorption in all or some of these nephron

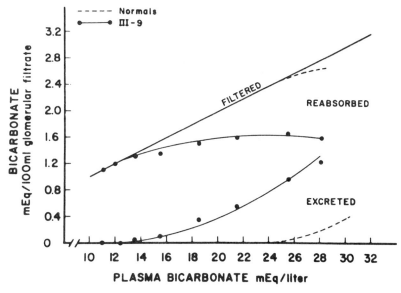

FIG. 1. Bicarbonate reabsorption and excretion plotted as a function of plasma bicarbonate concentration. In a patient with proximal RTA, bicarbonate reabsorption is incomplete, resulting in its excretion at low levels of plasma bicarbonate concentration at which normal individuals display complete reabsorption.

segments may be sufficient to reclaim much of the bicarbonate not reabsorbed in the proximal tubule and thereby prevent large bicarbonate urinary losses. Bicarbonate reabsorption in the distal tubule increases in a load-dependent manner. Thus, the finding of massive bicarbonaturia at normal plasma bicarbonate concentrations (fractional excretion greater than 15%) characteristic of patients with proximal RTA could be due, in part, to additional defects in bicarbonate reabsorption beyond the proximal convoluted tubule, the site of the nephron believed to be primarily responsible for the disorder. Immaturity of the renal tubules, as seen in infants, may contribute to the massive bicarbonaturia characteristic of proximal RTA.

The finding of only moderate bicarbonaturia at normal plasma bicarbonate

TABLE 2. *Features of urinary acidification in proximal renal tubular acidosis*

Reduced renal HCO_3 threshold (15–20 mEq/liter)
Intact ability to lower urine pH < 5.5 during acidosis
Bicarbonate wastage at normal or high plasma HCO_3
  concentrations
Normal urine Pco_2 (> 70 mm Hg) in a highly alkaline
  urine

concentration (i.e., fractional excretion between 3 and 15%) in an adult is not sufficient, in my view, to exclude the presence of a defect in proximal tubule acidification. This is suggested by the finding of only modest bicarbonaturia (fractional bicarbonate excretion less than 5%) after the administration of L-arginine, a compound that clearly inhibits bicarbonate transport in the rat proximal convoluted tubule. To detect more subtle forms of urinary bicarbonate wastage, it is preferable to perform a bicarbonate titration study and determine the renal bicarbonate threshold rather than simply measuring fractional bicarbonate excretion.

Urinary potassium wasting and hypokalemia often occur in proximal RTA. The kaliuresis of patients with proximal RTA is due to reduced sodium and bicarbonate reabsorption in the proximal nephron. This results in increased delivery of both ions to the distal nephron, thus favoring distal secretion of potassium. Sodium bicarbonate wastage leads to volume contraction, which results in secondary hyperaldosteronism, thereby increasing distal potassium secretion. It is important to realize that sodium bicarbonate administration to patients with proximal RTA, at least those with the Fanconi syndrome, aggravates the hypokalemia because of its attendant kaliuretic effect.

Pathogenesis

The nature of the defect in bicarbonate transport underlying proximal RTA is not known. Bicarbonate reabsorption in the proximal tubule is, to a large extent, mediated by Na^+-H^+ exchange. Proximal reabsorption of sodium and water, estimated from clearance techniques, is decreased in patients with proximal RTA, which would be consistent with inhibition of Na^+-H^+ exchange. A primary alteration of the Na^+-H^+ exchanger, however, has not been characterized in any experimental model of proximal RTA. In the widely studied experimental model of proximal RTA associated with Fanconi syndrome produced by the injection of maleic acid, renal cortical Na,K-ATPase activity is markedly inhibited. This effect could be secondary to inhibition of sodium transport in the proximal tubule by maleic acid. This compound also inhibits renal cortical Na,K-ATPase *in vitro* in a dose-dependent manner. This suggests that inhibition of sodium-coupled transport at the brush border of the proximal tubule may be the consequence of inhibition of Na,K-ATPase in the basolateral membrane.

Massive bicarbonaturia has been demonstrated after the infusion of 4-pentenoic acid to one renal artery. This compound, an inhibitor of fatty acid oxidation and gluconeogenesis, also causes profound natriuresis, a finding consistent with an inhibitory effect on the Na^+-H^+ exchanger or a more diffuse interference with energy production for active transport. Alteration(s) in energy-supplying reactions could interfere with functioning of the proton-translocating ATPase in the luminal membrane. The precise contribution of this pump to H^+ secretion by the proximal tubule, however, remains to be elucidated.

Another possibility is that a deficiency in carbonic anhydrase activity might cause the syndrome of isolated proximal RTA. Patients with isolated proximal RTA display many of the features seen in individuals given carbonic anhydrase inhibitors, such as acetazolamide. A patient with proximal RTA was described in whom the administration of a large dose of acetazolamide did not result in significant bicarbonaturia, strongly suggesting the absence of functional carbonic anhydrase activity in the proximal tubule. In other patients with isolated proximal RTA, however, the rate of bicarbonate excretion increased markedly when acetazolamide was infused. Hence, although renal carbonic anhydrase deficiency may play a role in some patients, one cannot conclude that this alteration underlies the pathogenesis of isolated proximal RTA in all cases. In families with an enzymatically inactive red cell carbonic anhydrase B, an RTA picture has been described. A deficiency in cytosolic carbonic anhydrase in renal cells should be manifested by a reduction in both proximal and distal acidification. Indeed, the defect in urinary acidification found in members of families in whom red cell carbonic anhydrase is inactive, although not fully studied, has features consistent with both distal and proximal RTA.

PATHOGENESIS OF DISTAL RENAL TUBULAR ACIDOSIS
(2,3,7,9,10,13,14,16,20,24,25)

Until the late 1970s, all cases of distal RTA were considered to result from a similar mechanism. The prevailing view was that the mechanism responsible for distal RTA was an inability to either generate or maintain a steep hydrogen ion concentration gradient across the distal nephron. A steep hydrogen ion gradient could not be maintained if backleak of normally secreted H^+ (or carbonic acid) was increased as a result of altered distal nephron permeability. The finding in the late 1960s that amphotericin B, a drug that clearly alters membrane permeability *in vitro*, caused distal RTA made this hypothesis very attractive. Hence, for a while, distal RTA was often referred to as "gradient" RTA.

In 1974, Halperin et al. proposed a different mechanism based on the observation that urinary PCO_2 after alkalinization of the urine (an index of collecting tubule H^+ secretion) was low in patients with distal RTA. These authors elegantly argued that this finding was incompatible with a gradient mechanism because, during alkalinization of the urine, the tubular pH is raised to a value higher than peritubular blood so that the chemical gradient is favorable for H^+ secretion but unfavorable for H^+ backleak. Accordingly, they proposed that the low urinary PCO_2 of patients with distal RTA indicated the existence of a secretory rather than a backleak defect as the mechanisn underlying the basic tubular abnormality causing distal RTA.

This postulation was soon challenged on the basis of theoretical and technical considerations. Some authors argued that a gradient type of defect resulting from an acid backleak could also be associated with a low urine Pco_2 during sodium bicarbonate loading. The rise in urinary Pco_2 is dependent on the presence of carbonic acid in the collecting duct. The delayed dehydration of carbonic acid (due to the absence of carbonic anhydrase activity in the distal lumen of the nephron) permits the generation of Pco_2 in the terminal nephron. Thus, if carbonic acid were to backdiffuse when the urine is alkaline, urine Pco_2 would not rise normally despite normal distal H^+ ion secretion. This theoretical criticism, however, is no longer tenable because experimentally induced H^+ backleak distal RTA is associated with a normal rise in urinary Pco_2.

The validity of the use of the urine Pco_2 as an index of distal H^+ secretion was seriously questioned because the concentrations of bicarbonate in the urine were not taken into account in the original study of Halperin et al. Arruda et al. showed that the relationship between urine Pco_2 and urine bicarbonate concentration is linear. Hence, subjects in whom sufficiently high urine bicarbonate concentrations cannot be achieved may have a low urine Pco_2 as a result of failure to concentrate the urine rather than to acidify it. This is the case, for example, in patients with advanced renal insufficiency in whom fractional water excretion is augmented, and maximal urine bicarbonate concentrations are difficult to achieve. Subsequent human studies, however, showed that even when urinary bicarbonate concentration is increased to the level of normal subjects, urine Pco_2 in patients with distal RTA is reduced, reflecting that collecting tubule H^+ secretion is decreased.

The view of a single mechanism underlying all cases of distal RTA was challenged by the work of Steinmetz and of Arruda and Kurtzman, which suggested that various derangements in the process of distal acidification could lead to distal RTA. Mechanistic classifications of distal RTA based on data from experimentally induced defects in distal acidification and from studies in humans with different causes of acquired distal RTA were proposed. In particular, the existence of a proton secretory type and a voltage-dependent type of distal RTA was reasonably well characterized. These studies, however, did not focus on the precise site in the distal nephron involved in the pathogenesis of the syndrome. Much of the knowledge applied to the characterization and classification of experimental and clinical defects in distal H^+ secretion originated from studies in the urinary turtle bladder. This membrane has transport characteristics that in the mammalian collecting tubule appear to be well demarcated to the cortical and medullary segments. Accordingly, extrapolation of data from turtle bladder studies to the whole animal setting does not permit the localization of a defect in acidification to the cortical or medullary portions of the collecting tubule. A basic understanding of the normal characteristics of urinary acidification in the various segments of the distal nephron is, therefore, required to approach the nephron site and mechanism of the possible defects causing distal RTA.

OVERVIEW OF COLLECTING TUBULE ACIDIFICATION AND ITS CLINICAL ASSESSMENT (4,7,14,16)

The collecting tubule is now recognized as a major site of urinary acidification within the distal nephron. This nephron site displays axial heterogeneity both anatomically and functionally. Studies of acidification of luminal fluid by rabbit cortical collecting tubules perfused *in vitro* indicate that H^+ secretion is individually coupled to sodium transport. Active sodium reabsorption generates an electrical potential (lumen-negative) that favors the secretion of H^+ and potassium. In contrast, in outer medullary collecting tubules, H^+ secretion does not appear to be under the influence of sodium transport and is accompanied by chloride secretion. In this segment, the potential difference is oriented lumen-positive presumably as a result of electrogenic H^+ secretion. This is in contrast with the lumen-negative electrical potential usually prevailing in the cortical segment that is thought to be generated by active sodium reabsorption (Fig. 2).

Both nephron segments are sensitive to mineralocorticoid stimulation. In the outer medullary portion, mineralocorticoid stimulates H^+ secretion, and adrenalectomy reduces it. The stimulatory effect of mineralocorticoid on H^+ secretion in this nephron segment is sodium-independent. In the cortical collecting tubule, mineralocorticoid also stimulates H^+ secretion, in part, by enhancement of active sodium reabsorption. In addition, mineralocorticoid exerts a direct effect on active H^+ secretion as deduced from an increase in lumen-positive electrical potential when the hormone is applied in the absence of luminal sodium. Although the relative contribution of each of these two nephron segments to net acidification *in vivo* has not been delineated, there is remarkable agreement from studies using rabbit isolated tubules perfused *in vitro* showing that the rate of acidification is considerably greater in the medullary than in the cortical segment of the collecting tubule. The cortical portion is distinctive in that it is capable of bicarbonate secretion or bicarbonate reabsorption depending on dietary, acid-base, and hormonal influences.

The clinical evaluation of the function of the collecting tubule is, to some extent, possible using maneuvers that either stimulate or inhibit proton secretion in this nephron site. A segmental approach would require a maneuver that acts selectively in each portion of the collecting tubule. The acidemic stimulus, usually provided by the administration of ammonium chloride, is not selective because acidemia enhances acidification throughout the entire distal nephron. Because H^+ secretion in the medullary collecting tubule is

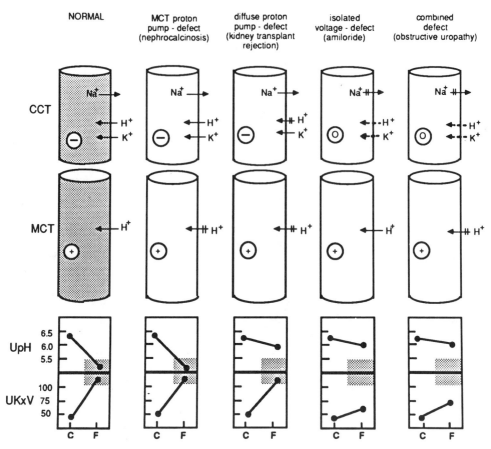

FIG. 2. Possible sites of segmental tubular dysfunction within the collecting tubule as judged by the urine pH and kaliuretic response to furosemide (F). (CCT) cortical collecting tubule; (MCT) medullary collecting tubule. (From ref. 4.)

sodium-independent, one can assume that maneuvers that produce a sodium-dependent increase or decrease in H^+ secretion do not have an impact on this nephron segment. Amiloride, at low doses that inhibit apical sodium conductance but not Na^+-H^+ exchange, inhibits sodium-dependent acidification and potassium secretion in the cortical collecting tubule. Loop diuretics, by blocking NaCl reabsorption in the thick ascending loop of Henle, increase Na delivery to the collecting tubule. Part of the sodium delivered to the cortical collecting tubule is reabsorbed, whereas chloride is not, resulting in the creation of a favorable transtubular voltage (lumen-negative) for H^+ and K^+ secretion. That the increase in distal Na reabsorption secondary to furosemide administration results in enhancement of voltage-dependent acidification in the cortical collecting tubule can be inferred from the finding that

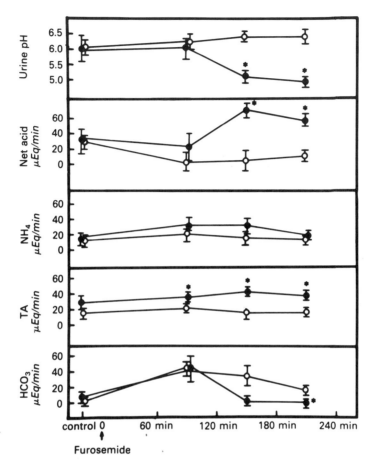

FIG. 3. The stimulating effect of furosemide (closed circles) on urinary acidification in normal subjects is obliterated by amiloride (open circles). Asterisk denotes a significant difference between the two experimental conditions. (From ref. 4.)

the fall in urine pH and the increase in net acid excretion elicited by furosemide are obliterated by amiloride (Fig. 3). Amiloride also lessens the kaliuretic effect of furosemide, indicating that the increase in K^+ secretion observed when furosemide is given alone is due, in part, to an increase in transepithelial voltage. An additional effect of furosemide on renal K^+ excretion independent of its indirect effect on transephithelial voltage is apparent from the finding that K^+ excretion increases linearly as a function of urine flow (Fig. 4). The difference in K^+ excretion observed at comparable urine flow rates when furosemide is given alone and when it is given with amiloride portrays to a large extent the contribution of the amiloride-sensitive (that is, sodium-dependent) component of distal nephron H+ secretion (Fig. 4).

Sodium-dependent acidification also can be stimulated by the infusion of

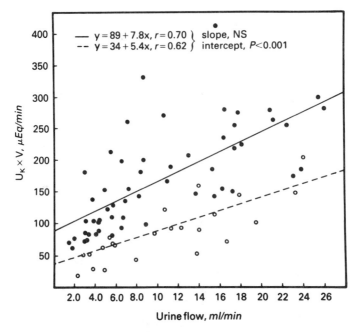

FIG. 4. The relationship between potassium excretion ($U_K \times V$) and urine flow in normal subjects given a single oral dose of furosemide (closed circles) or given furosemide and amiloride together (open circles). (From ref. 4).

sodium sulfate. The infusion of sodium sulfate provides a poorly reabsorbable anion as well as Na load that, when reabsorbed by the cortical collecting tubule, results in an increase in transepithelial voltage. An increase in the cortical collecting tubule transepithelial voltage in response to furosemide would occur only if Na were to be reabsorbed well in excess of Cl. Both furosemide and sodium sulfate administration result in enhanced tubular reabsorption of Na but differ in that Cl reabsorption relative to Na is depressed after furosemide administration because in this circumstance Cl behaves as a poorly reabsorbable anion.

CLASSIFICATION AND CHARACTERIZATION OF THE DISTAL RENAL TUBULAR ACIDOSIS SUBTYPES

A classification of distal RTA based on the deranged cellular mechanism of urinary acidification is presented in Table 3. Some of the proposed mechanisms are represented by relatively well defined clinical entities, whereas others are theoretical.

Permeability Defects (2,15,16,19,25)

A remarkable property of the collecting tubule is that H^+ secretion can occur against a transepithelial H^+ gradient until the H^+ concentration in the mucosal fluid is approximately 1,000 times greater than in the serosal fluid. When this large H^+ gradient is attained, H^+ secretion ceases but backleak of H^+ from mucosal fluid into the serosal site is virtually negligible. The existence of a defect in membrane permeability, however, could facilitate H^+ backleak. A permeability defect also could impair net acidification by causing an increased influx of HCO_3 into the lumen. Studies in the urinary turtle bladder and in mammalian collecting tubules have shown that amphotericin B, applied to the mucosal site, results in H^+ backdiffusion (lumen to blood). The drug also increases potassium permeability but does not affect HCO_3 permeability. On the basis of these findings, it has been inferred that H^+ backleak is the mechanism causing distal RTA in patients receiving amphotericin B.

The distinctive theoretical features of proton backleak distal RTA are summarized in Table 3. As in most types of distal RTA, urine pH in patients treated with amphotericin B is higher than 5.5 despite acidemia. The inability to lower urine pH despite unimpaired H^+ secretion is attributable to H^+ backleak, which is more evident when the tubular urine is acidic. Theoretically, it is conceivable that the creation of a large transtubular electrical gradient (lumen-negative) by the administration of sodium sulfate or furosemide could attenuate H^+ backleak and permit lowering of urine pH to normally low values. One would also anticipate that H^+ backleak should be minimized when the urine is made highly alkaline. That this is the case is suggested by the finding of a normal rise in urine P_{CO_2} when sodium bicarbonate is infused to amphotericin B-treated rats. As a point of fact, this is the only experimental model of distal RTA in which urine P_{CO_2} in a highly alkaline urine is normal (i.e., more than 70 mm Hg). Urine P_{CO_2} should rise normally after the infusion of neutral sodium phosphate, but data on this point are not available. This is the only type of experimental distal RTA in which an acid disequilibrium pH in the collecting tubule has been documented during the infusion of sodium bicarbonate. This finding strongly suggests that amphotericin B does not reduce collecting tubule H^+ secretion.

It must be emphasized that there are no patients described who displayed all of the features outlined in the amphotericin B model of experimental H^+ backleak distal RTA (Table 3). At present, it seems highly unlikely that any form of hereditary or acquired distal RTA, other than that associated with amphotericin B, is caused by a H^+ backleak mechanism. Some forms of drug-induced hypokalemic distal RTA, such as that caused by toluene sniffing, originally thought to originate from H^+ backleak do not appear to cause it. This can be inferred from the finding of failure to increase urine P_{CO_2} after bicarbonate infusions in individuals with hypokalemic distal RTA associated with toluene sniffing. In urinary turtle bladders exposed to high concentrations of toluene, the rate of H^+ secretion is reduced, but unlike in amphotericin B-treated bladders, there is no discernible H^+ backleak. The cortical collecting tubule is capable, under certain circumstances, of HCO_3 secretion. The role of HCO_3 secretion in urinary acidification, however, is not well

TABLE 3. *Mechanistic classification of distal renal tubular acidosis*

Type	Example	Urine pH		Urine P_{CO_2}		Plasma K
		Acidemia	Furosemide or Na$_2$SO$_4$	Na$_2$HCO$_3$	Phosphate	
I. Permeability defects						
A. H$^+$ backleak	Amphotericin B	>5.5	<5.3	>70	>70	Low or normal
B. HCO$_3$ secretion	Unknown	>5.5	>5.5	>70	>70	Low or normal
II. Secretory defects						
A. Diffuse collecting tubule proton pump failure	Chronic kidney transplant rejection	>5.5	>5.5	<55	<55	Normal or low
B. Medullary collecting tubule proton pump failure	Nephrocalcinosis	>5.5	<5.3	<55	>70	Normal or low
C. Diffuse proton pump failure + impaired Na transport and K secretion	Obstructive uropathy	>5.5	>5.5	<55	<55	Increased
III. Rate-dependent defects						
A. Voltage-dependent						
1. Primary impairment of Na transport	Amiloride	>5.5	>5.5	<55	<55	Increased

2. Secondary impairment of Na transport	Lithium	<5.5	<5.3	<55	>70	Normal
3. Enhanced chloride transport	"Cl shunt" or type I pseudo-hypoaldosteronism	<5.5	<5.2	?	>70	Increased
B. Aldosterone deficiency	Selective aldosterone deficiency	<5.5	<5.3	?	>70	Increased
C. Aldosterone resistance						
1. Without salt wastage	Tubular interstitial disease	<5.5	<5.3	?	>70	Increased
2. With salt wastage	Type II pseudo-hypoaldosteronism	<5.5	<5.3	?	>70	Increased
IV. Reduced concentration of urinary buffers						
A. Defective ammoniagenesis	Hyperkalemia	<5.5	<5.5	>70	>70	Increased
B. Impaired collecting tubule ammonia delivery	Unknown	<5.5	<5.5	>70	>70	Normal
C. Phosphate depletion						Normal
V. Reduced availability of cellular H$^+$						
A. Deficiency of cell carbonic anhydrase	Hereditary deficiency	>5.5	>5.5	<55	<55	Normal
B. Impaired exit of OH$^-$ or HCO$_3^-$ from the cell	Unknown					

defined. Conceivably, a defect in collecting tubule permeability causing an increase in HCO_3 secretion could result in a decrease in net collecting tubule acidification, leading to distal RTA. There is no experimental or clinical evidence, however, for such a defect. Theoretically, this defect could be distinguished from proton secretory defects by the finding of a high urine P_{CO_2} during bicarbonate loading (Table 3). The reason for this is that the addition of bicarbonate to tubular urine would markedly stimulate carbonic acid and CO_2 generation. The mechanism leading to the rise in P_{CO_2} would be identical to that observed if one adds sodium bicarbonate to a beaker of water. Failure to lower the urine pH during acidemia would simply be the result of bicarbonate wastage.

Secretory Defects (4,5,7,11,14,16)

Under this terminology are considered any alteration causing an impairment of collecting tubule acidification by primarily interfering with active H^+ secretion. The collecting tubule is believed to contain a proton pump at its luminal surface. This pump, a proton translocating ATPase, secretes H^+ in an electrogenic manner (i.e., is capable of translocating a net positive charge into the lumen) and can operate independently of sodium transport and despite an unfavorable transtubular electrical gradient. The rate of sodium transport and the electrical voltage, however, importantly influence the rate of H^+ secretion. Alterations in transepithelial voltage caused by either inhibition of sodium transport or enhancement of chloride transport can reduce the rate of H^+ secretion and thereby cause distal RTA. These alterations are considered under the heading of rate-dependent defects (Table 3). A primary H^+ secretory defect, by definition, is limited to the proton pump.

The existence of a secretory type of distal RTA has been reasonably well characterized in patients with different diseases causing acquired distal RTA. Derangements of collecting tubule function determined genetically (e.g., hereditary distal RTA), associated with structural abnormalities (e.g., medullary sponge kidney), immunologically mediated (e.g., chronic renal transplant rejection) or caused by impaired metabolic cell function could all interfere with the proton pump secretory apparatus. One can envision a spectrum of secretory defects ranging from reduction in the number of proton pumps to severe proton pump dysfunction as well as defects in the active transport pathway due to altered metabolic energy production or use. Given the variety of disease states causing distal RTA and the numerous basic mechanisms on which they could have an impact, there is no reason to believe that they all have to alter the proton secretory apparatus in the same way. There is also no *a priori* reason to believe that proton pump dysfunction has to involve the entire collecting tubule. It is conceivable that the lesion causing proton pump dysfunction may be confined to a portion of the collecting tubule. For instance, one could anticipate from the anatomic distribution of some disease states causing distal RTA that their defect in acidification would be confined to the medullary collecting tubule. Before considering the possible ways to evaluate the site of abnormal H^+ secretion within the collecting tubule, the general features characteristic of a secretory type of distal RTA are discussed (Table 3).

Plasma potassium in patients with secretory distal RTA is not increased because potassium secretion in the distal nephron is unimpaired. In fact, hypokalemia develops often as a consequence of secondary hyperaldosteronism and accelerated sodium for potassium exchange in the distal nephron. Urine pH during spontaneous acidosis or after acid loading usually cannot be lowered below 5.5, and the rate of acid excretion is decreased. Ammonium excretion is reduced, a finding that can be inferred at bedside from the finding of a positive urine anion gap. The urine Pco_2 measured after bicarbonate loading does not increase normally, reflecting that the rate of collecting tubule H^+ secretion is reduced. This feature is useful in distinguishing a secretory from a permeability defect (Table 3). It is not useful, however, in differentiating a secretory from a voltage-dependent defect, which also decreases the rate of H^+ secretion (albeit indirectly). The value of measuring urine Pco_2 in a highly alkaline urine stems from its exquisite sensitivity in portraying the rate of H^+ secretion. For instance, environmental factors that reduce collecting tubule H^+ secretion, such as an alkaline diet or exposure to hypocapnia, are associated with a subnormal rise in urine Pco_2 during bicarbonate loading. Except for permeability defects, any other perturbation leading to a decrease in the rate of collecting tubule H^+ secretion could impair the generation of a high urine Pco_2.

A distinctive feature of a secretory type of distal RTA is the inability to secrete H^+ when sodium-dependent distal acidification is stimulated and when backleak of secreted H^+ is eliminated or minimized. Such conditions are provided by the administration of sodium sulfate and neutral sodium phosphate. The infusion of sodium sulfate stimulates distal H^+ secretion by enhancing lumen electronegativity. In addition, any potential backleak of secreted H^+ should be minimized under these conditions. In patients with a secretory type of distal RTA, urinary pH cannot be lowered below 5.5 by sodium sulfate infusions (except when the defect spares the cortical portion of the collecting tubule). Administration of neutral sodium phosphate also stimulates distal H^+ secretion and should retard acid backleak. The rise in urinary Pco_2 normally seen after the administration of neutral sodium phosphate does not occur when H^+ secretion in the collecting tubule is impaired.

Segmental Localization of Defects in Collecting Tubule H^+ Secretion

Although patients with distal RTA display an abnormally high urine pH during acidemia and a low urine Pco_2 during bicarbonate loading, they may or may not respond normally to the administration of sodium sulfate or loop diuretics. The response to the latter two maneuvers has been proposed to be of use in localizing the site of the H^+ secretory defect within the collecting tubule.

A scheme for the interpretation of the distinctive responses to furosemide and sodium sulfate found in patients with distal RTA is presented in Fig. 2. This scheme assumes that with administration of these agents, tubular fluid pH falls below 5.3 at the level of the cortical collecting tubule as a consequence of enhanced Na-dependent H^+ secretion. This nephron segment could be deranged in that either the number (or function) of proton pumps is reduced or in that the ability to transport sodium and thereby generate a transepithelial voltage (lumen-negative) is impaired. The latter alteration is seen when amiloride is given to normal subjects. Under these conditions, urine pH cannot be lowered below 5.3 (Fig. 3), and the kaliuretic effect of furosemide is blunted (Fig. 4). If only the proton pump were impaired, the administration of either furosemide or sodium sulfate should increase transepithelial voltage in the cortical collecting tubule. In this situation, K^+ excretion would increase normally, but urine pH could not be lowered maximally owing to failure of the proton pump. According to this scheme, patients who exhibit a normal increase in K^+ excretion but are unable to lower urine pH below 5.3 after furosemide or sodium sulfate administration can be classified as having a proton pump defect involving the cortical collecting tubule (Fig. 2).

In some patients with distal RTA, K^+ secretion increases and urine pH falls below 5.3 after either furosemide or sodium sulfate administration. The fall in urine pH suggests that the cortical collecting tubule has sufficient intact proton pumps to secrete H^+ when a favorable transepithelial voltage is imposed by these maneuvers. By exclusion, their defect in distal acidification, uncovered by the failure to lower urine pH despite acidemia, must be located in the medullary collecting tubule and confined to this nephron segment (Fig. 5). This notion has the support of experimental work showing that acidemia causes a fall in luminal pH in the medullary collecting tubule. One could argue that normal lowering of urine pH after furosemide or sodium sulfate in some patients with distal RTA simply denotes the existence of a mild proton pump defect. Inasmuch as the response to these agents in some patients with distal RTA is similar to that observed in normal individuals, however, it seems reasonable to conclude that sodium-dependent H^+ secretion in the cortical collecting tubule of such patients is normal.

In some patients with hyperkalemic distal RTA, the response to sodium sulfate and furosemide is characterized by both inability to lower urine pH and a subnormal K excretion. In patients with hyperkalemic metabolic acidosis associated with selective aldosterone deficiency, furosemide and sodium sulfate administration result in lowering of urine pH below 5.3. The pattern found in the former patients could be explained solely on the basis of an isolated voltage-dependent defect in the cortical collecting tubule, such as is

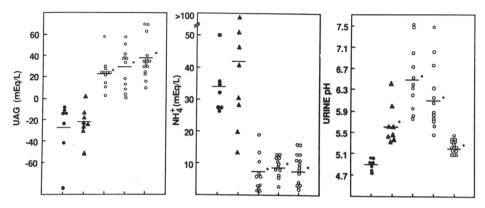

FIG. 5. Urine anion gap (UAG), ammonium (NH$_4^+$), and pH values in five groups of patients with hyperchloremic metabolic acidosis. Normal subjects treated with NH$_4$Cl (controls) are represented by solid circles, patients with diarrhea by triangles, and patients with distal renal tubular acidosis by open circles; those with classic renal tubular acidosis are to the left, those with hyperkalemic distal renal tubular acidosis are in the middle, and those with selected aldosterone deficiency are to the right. Each asterisk denotes a significant difference ($p<0.01$) between the mean value for a patient group and that for the control group. (From ref. 11.)

seen in normal subjects given amiloride (Fig. 5). In addition to a voltage-dependent defect in the cortical collecting tubule, patients with hyperkalemic distal RTA likely have a proton pump defect affecting the entire collecting tubule (Fig. 5). Thus, these patients are best classified as having a diffuse proton pump secretory defect in the collecting tubule that is associated with impaired sodium and potassium transport in the cortical collecting tubule (Table 3). This kind of structural involvement could also be anticipated from the type of renal disease (e.g., obstructive uropathy) usually associated with this form of hyperkalemic distal RTA.

Rate-dependent Defects (4,6,7,9,10,22)

One can classify under the heading of rate-dependent defects a variety of alterations that have in common that the rate of H$^+$ secretion in the collecting tubule is reduced, not because of primary proton failure but rather as a consequence of reduced availability of intracellular H$^+$, failure to sustain an adequate transtubular electrical gradient (voltage-dependent defects), aldosterone deficiency, and aldosterone resistance (Table 3).

A mechanism that could result in a decrease in the rate of collecting tubule H$^+$ secretion is reduced availability of intracellular H$^+$ (Table 3). A rise in intracellular pH could be expected, for example, in states associated with potassium depletion. Urinary pH cannot be lowered maximally under these conditions (*see* Chapter 14). Since the proton pump generates an intracellular OH$^-$ for each H$^+$ secreted into the tubular lumen, the ability to remove OH$^-$

is required for continued H^+ secretion. The removal of OH^- is facilitated by cytosolic carbonic anhydrase, an enzyme that catalyzes the reaction of OH^- with CO_2. Deficiency of cytosolic carbonic anhydrase in the renal intercalated cells of the collecting tubule (carbonic anhydrase type II) could, therefore, slow down the rate of H^+ secretion by interfering with intracellular OH^- disposal. Likewise, a defect in the exit step for HCO_3 (or OH^-) could reduce the rate of collecting tubule H^+. The features of urinary acidification in this type of defect remain to be studied. In patients with hereditary carbonic anhydrase deficiency, urine pH is higher than 5.5 during acidosis. The defect in H^+ should also impair urine P_{CO_2} formation after bicarbonate loading, but data on this parameter are not available.

In a more restricted sense, the term "rate-dependent" distal RTA was first introduced to designate patients with a pattern of urinary acidification characterized by failure to increase urine P_{CO_2} in a highly alkaline urine but otherwise intact ability to lower urine pH during ammonium chloride-induced acidosis. Many of the patients were not acidotic but had clinical evidence of tubulointerstitial renal disease, which prompted investigation of urinary acidification. In this regard, it represents a variant of incomplete distal RTA. This pattern is common among patients on well-controlled chronic lithium therapy. The concentration of lithium in the urine of these patients ranges from 10 to 40 mmoles/liter, a concentration sufficient to inhibit voltage-dependent H^+ secretion in the urinary turtle bladder and in rabbit cortical collecting tubules perfused *in vitro*. The reduced rate of collecting tubule H^+ secretion, disclosed *in vivo* by the failure to increase urine P_{CO_2} in a highly alkaline urine, has been inferred to result from failure to generate a normal transtubular voltage (lumen-negative) when lithium is present in the lumen of the cortical collecting tubule. This cation appears to compete for sodium reabsorption. The impairment in sodium reabsorption, in turn, lessens the voltage (lumen-negative) required for optimal H^+ and K^+ secretion (Table 3). Hyperkalemia, however, is not a feature of lithium-treated patients possibly because of the high urine flow (due to impaired concentrating capacity), which increases K^+ secretion.

Voltage-dependent Renal Tubular Acidosis

Examples of voltage-dependent defects in collecting tubule acidification due to an isolated impairment of sodium transport are so far confined to lithium and to drugs that primarily block apical sodium transport, such as amiloride and triamterene (Table 3). As alluded to earlier, there are patients with hyperkalemic RTA in whom furosemide or sodium sulfate administration does not result in lowering of urine pH below 5.5. The kaliuretic response to these agents also is blunted. These findings suggest that voltage-dependent (i.e., sodium-dependent) H^+ and K^+ secretion in the cortical collecting tubule is impaired. In addition to hyperkalemic hyperchloremic metabolic acidosis, one would anticipate a salt-wasting tendency reflecting impairment of sodium transport in such patients. Although systematic studies of sodium balance have not been performed, clinical observations of defective sodium conservation have been made on occasional patients. Some of them may display sodium wastage on a normal salt diet, whereas others may manifest sodium wastage only when they are salt restricted. A consequence of salt wastage is the functional deterioration of GFR, which is reversible on fluid replacement. Although inhibition of sodium transport in the cortical collecting tubule results in a decrease in the rate of H^+ secretion, this effect could be compensated by enhanced H^+ in the medullary collecting tubule, a segment with a greater capacity for urinary acidification. Unlike individuals treated with amiloride or lithium, these patients develop marked metabolic acidosis, a finding that suggests a more diffuse impairment of collecting tubule acidification. Patients with this form of hyperkalemic distal RTA probably have a proton pump secretory defect that involves the entire collecting tubule (Table 3).

Selective Aldosterone Deficiency

Hyperkalemic metabolic acidosis associated with selective aldosterone deficiency (SAD) is the most common type of RTA in adults. It also is the commonest cause of hyperkalemia among patients with mild to moderate insufficiency. Most of these patients have evidence of tubulointerstitial renal disease and reduced GFR. The rate of collecting tubule H^+ secretion is stimulated by aldosterone and reduced in its absence. The urine of these patients is acidic (pH 5.0–5.5) during mild metabolic acidosis. Relative to their reduced rate of ammonium excretion, however, urine pH is slightly higher than that of normal subjects made acidotic by ammonium chloride. This finding reflects that the rate of collecting tubule H^+ secretion is reduced. The P_{CO_2} in a highly alkaline urine should be reduced, but data from patients are not available regarding this parameter. In addition to the direct stimulatory effect of aldosterone on the rate of collecting tubule H^+ secretion and its indirect effect mediated by changes in distal sodium transport, aldosterone increases ammonia production. Aldosterone deficiency results in hyperkalemia, which inhibits ammonium excretion.

The features characteristic of SAD are summarized in Table 3. The main factor responsible for the acidosis is a decrease in ammonium excretion. In this regard, this type of RTA could be mechanistically classified under the category of reduced concentration of urinary buffers (ammonia) (Table 3). Correction of hyperkalemia, no matter how accomplished, results in amelioration of metabolic acidosis by enhancement of ammonium excretion. Some of the patients with aldosterone deficiency also display end-organ resistance to the action of the hormone, as evidenced by the persistence of hyperkalemia despite chronic administration of large amounts of mineralocorticoid. The typical patient, however, responds reasonably well to mineralocorticoid administration. It is important to recognize that some patients have a combination of both SAD and hyperkalemic distal RTA. Such patients have low ammonium excretion and low aldosterone levels and, in addition, cannot lower urinary pH below 5.5 regardless of the degree of acidosis. The clinical implication of this observation is that a patient with hyperkalemic acidosis with an inappropriately high urine pH (i.e., 5.5) has, by definition, hyperkalemic distal RTA regardless of whether plasma aldosterone is low, normal, or high. If the patient has low aldosterone and cannot lower urinary pH below 5.5 in the face of acidosis, he or she suffers from both hyperkalemic distal RTA and SAD.

Types of Renal Tubular Acidosis Associated with Aldosterone Resistance and Normal Glomerular Filtration Rate

The term "aldosterone resistance" (or pseudohypoaldosteronism) is used to designate those patients with hyperkalemic hyperchloremic metabolic acidosis in whom aldosterone deficiency clearly is not present and in whom there is no evidence of diffuse tubulointerstitial nephropathy. Two clinical pictures fit this definition: (1) the syndrome of classic pseudohypoaldosteronism of infancy characterized by salt-wastage and hypotension and (2) a rare syndrome of aldosterone-resistant acidosis and hyperkalemia usually characterized by salt retention and hypertension (chloride shunt type of disorder).

The clinical picture of classic pseudohypoaldosteronism is characterized by dehydration and hyponatremia due to renal salt wastage, hyperkalemia, and hyperchloremic metabolic acidosis. It occurs in infants as a congenital disorder. The severity of salt-wastage and potassium retention diminishes with time, but hyponatremia and hyperkalemia may recur if dietary salt is restricted. This condition appears to be a pure form of tubular aldosterone resistance not associated with discernible tubulointerstitial damage at kidney biopsy. It has been proposed that the syndrome results from a deficiency of Na^+,K^+-ATPase because absence of this enzyme from proximal and distal nephron segments was documented in kidney biopsy material obtained from one patient with classic pseudohypoaldosteronism.

As in any state of end-organ responsiveness, the circulating levels of the hormone are greatly elevated in patients with pseudohypoaldosteronism. The features characteristic of the acidification defect associated with aldosterone resistance should be identical to those seen in states of aldosterone deficiency (Table 3). Data on urinary acidification from patients with pseudohypoaldosteronism of infancy, however, are sparse. Like patients with aldosterone deficiency, those with aldosterone resistance should have a low urine pH during acidosis but reduced rates of ammonium excretion. Whether the rate of collecting tubule H^+ secretion assessed by the rise in urine PCO_2 in a highly alkaline urine is diminished or not remains to be investigated.

Another aldosterone-resistant type of disorder associated with normal GFR and hyperchloremic hyperkalemic metabolic acidosis has been characterized and is referred to as type II pseudohypoaldosteronism. This disorder corresponds to a similar clinical picture known as Gordon's syndrome. Evidence for aldosterone resistance in such patients is inferred from the persistence of hyperkalemia despite the administration of exogenous mineralocorticoid. In contrast, potassium excretion increases markedly after the administration of sodium sulfate or sodium bicarbonate. Hyperkalemia and metabolic acidosis can be corrected by restriction of dietary sodium or by the administration of thiazide diuretics. The primary abnormality is believed to be a tubular defect characterized by increased chloride reabsorption in the distal nephron. This results in increased NaCl reabsorption, thereby resulting in volume expansion and low-renin hypertension. Plasma aldosterone also may be suppressed and remains low relative to the prevailing hyperkalemia. Enhanced chloride transport limits the sodium-dependent and mineralocorticoid-dependent voltage driving force for potassium and hydrogen ion secretion. This defect can be classified as a voltage-dependent type of distal RTA due to enhanced chloride transport (Table 3). Unlike the voltage-dependent defect caused by amiloride, the one caused by a chloride shunt type of defect does not appear to interfere with lowering of urine pH during acidosis.

Reduced Availability of Urinary Buffers (25)

The rate of H^+ secretion by the collecting tubules is higher when the tubular fluid is alkaline than when it is acid. The rate of H^+ secretion may be decreased owing to a lack of buffer in the tubular fluid. In the absence of H^+ acceptors, tubular fluid is acidified rapidly, and the H^+ pump inhibits its own transport rate by the pH gradient it generates. In quantitative terms, ammonia is the most important H^+ acceptor. Disease states causing decreased ammonia production, such as advanced renal insufficiency, hyperkalemia, and aldosterone deficiency—usually acting in combination—result in impaired ammonium excretion. Delivery of ammonia to the medullary collecting tubule may be decreased and thus limit H^+ secretion. This situation occurs whenever the kidneys are underperfused. Phosphate depletion not only results in decreased titratable acidity from hypophosphaturia but also interferes with ammonium excretion.

PATHOPHYSIOLOGY

General Features of the Basic Types of Renal Tubular Acidosis

The pathophysiology of the major types of RTA is different not only with regard to the pattern of urinary acidification but also with regard to biochemical and clinical expression (Table 4). Proximal RTA as an isolated abnormality in bicarbonate transport occurs only in children with male sex predominance. In both children and adults, bicarbonate wastage usually occurs as a part of a generalized defect in proximal tubular transport that results in inhibition of reabsorption of glucose, phosphate, uric acid, and amino acids (the so-called Fanconi syndrome). In this setting, glycosuria develops at normal plasma glucose concentrations, and the excretion of uric acid, phosphate, and amino acids is increased. Therefore, reduced plasma phosphate and plasma uric acid levels may be found in patients with proximal RTA.

A common feature of children with proximal and distal RTA is failure to thrive (Table 4). Acidemia, by mechanisms not yet delineated, appears to interfere with normal growth. This is supported by the universal finding that when alkali therapy is started early in the course of the disease, growth is normalized. Failure to thrive is indeed one of the most common manifestations of RTA in children. Workup to exclude RTA usually is recommended in any child with failure to thrive.

Symptoms of hypokalemia might be a dominant feature of both proximal

TABLE 4. *General features of renal tubular acidosis*

| | | Distal renal tubular acidosis | |
| | | Hypokalemic or | |
Features	Proximal renal tubular acidosis	normokalemic	Hyperkalemic[a]
Hyperchloremic metabolic acidosis	Present	Present	Present
Serum potassium	Usually low	Low or normal	Increased
Serum phosphate, serum uric acid	Usually low	Normal	Normal
Glycosuria, amino aciduria, hyper-phosphaturia, hyperuricorsuria	Common	Absent	Absent
Fractional HCO^- excretion at normal plasma HCO^- concentrations	> 15%	< 5%	< 5%
Maximal reduction in urinary pH during acidosis	< 5.5	> 5.5[b]	> 5.5
Net acid excretion during acidosis	Low at urine pH > 6.0, normal at urine pH < 5.5	Low	Low
Urinary potassium excretion	Increased	Increased	Low
Urinary calcium excretion	Normal	Increased	Decreased
Urinary citrate excretion	Normal	Low	Unknown
Nephrocalcinosis and renal stones	Rare	Common	Rare
Bone disease	Common	Uncommon	Unknown
Growth failure	Common	Common	Uncommon

[a]Refers to the type of hyperkalemic distal RTA not attributable to selective aldosterone deficiency.

[b]Although patients with distal renal tubular acidosis typically have a urine pH above 5.5 during acidosis, some may retain the ability to lower urinary pH below 5.3 during acidosis. Others lower it after stimulation of Na-dependent H^+ secretion.

RTA and distal RTA. They usually consist of muscle weakness, paresthesias, polyuria, and thirst. At times, the diagnosis of distal RTA is suspected from the incidental finding of nephrocalcinosis on a simple x-ray study of the abdomen. Sometimes, a renal stone, usually composed of calcium phosphate, is the initial presentation of distal RTA. Severe complications of chronic acidosis, such as myocardial failure, lethargy, and coma, are rare. Buffering of acid by bone salts is enhanced markedly during chronic metabolic acidosis. Bone demineralization may result from release of calcium carbonate from bone to neutralize excess hydrogen ions. This process can lead to rickets and growth retardation in children and osteopenia and osteomalacia in adults.

The hyperkalemic types of distal RTA usually develop in patients with tubulointerstitial renal disease and reduced GFR. Patients with uncomplicated chronic renal insufficiency do not develop hyperkalemia until the GFR falls to very low levels (i.e., usually < 10 ml/min). Hence, the presence of hyperkalemia in patients with moderate renal insufficiency should prompt the search for a specific cause. The acidosis of patients with advanced chronic renal insufficiency usually, but not always, is of the high anion gap variety. The finding of high plasma chloride and potassium levels and a normal anion gap suggests the presence of selective aldosterone deficiency, hyperkalemic distal RTA, or both. The finding of hyperkalemic hyperchloremic metabolic acidosis in an individual with normal plasma creatinine should alert to the possibility of a chloride shunt type of disorder if the patient has hypertension.

Bone Disease (17)

Until recently, skeletal abnormalities were thought to be rare in patients with proximal RTA and relatively frequent in patients with distal RTA. This traditional view must be altered in view of a recent report examining the prevalence of skeletal abnormalities in 92 patients with various types of RTA as determined radiographically. In this study the prevalence of radiographically evident bone disease was extremely low in patients with distal RTA. In fact, only one patient with this type of RTA had radiographically detectable bone disease. Moreover, this patient had renal insufficiency. Thus, on the basis of this study, one could conclude that the incidence of bone disease is rare in patients with distal RTA (Table 4). Earlier studies had shown a higher incidence of bone disease in patients with RTA, although the distinction between the proximal and distal forms was not made with clarity. It is likely that the lower incidence of bone disease reported in this study reflects, at least in part, the result of aggressive alkali therapy because now patients with distal RTA are diagnosed and treated early in the course of the disease.

In contrast, radiographic evidence of skeletal abnormalities was found in 10 of 15 patients with proximal RTA. All of them had osteopenia, as evidenced by generalized bone demineralization. Eight of the ten had rickets defined radiographically as widened and irregular epiphyseal metaphyseal junctions or evidence of bone softening of the long bones. The incidence of bone disease in patients with proximal RTA may be related to hypophosphatemia and vitamin D deficiency. Amelioration of metabolic bone disease in response to vitamin D therapy has been reported in patients with Fanconi syndrome and proximal RTA. Metabolic acidosis suppresses 1α-hydroxylase in the proximal convoluted tubule by inhibiting PTH-dependent adenylate cyclase. This effect of acidosis, which has been observed in the vitamin D-deficient animal, leads to a reduction in the conversion of 25-hydroxyvitamin D_3 to 1,25-hydroxyvitamin D_3.

Induction of metabolic acidosis of several days duration, however, is without effect on the synthesis of $1,25(OH)_2D_3$ in vitamin D-repleted humans. This suggests that the vitamin D deficiency observed in patients with proximal RTA may not be related to metabolic acidosis *per se*. Rather, preexisting structural damage in the proximal tubule may interfere with the formation of $1,25(OH)_2D_3$. In the experimental model of proximal RTA induced by the administration of maleic acid, the conversion of 25-hydroxyvitamin D_3 to $1,25(OH)_2D_3$ is impaired. Hence, the available evidence suggests that the development of bone disease in patients with proximal RTA may be related to abnormalities in vitamin D synthesis rather than an effect of metabolic acidosis *per se*. Hypophosphatemia, if present, is a major factor in the development of $1,25(OH)_2D_3$ deficiency and a determinant of bone disease and growth retardation in children with proximal RTA. In patients with hyperkalemic hyperchloremic metabolic acidosis associated with selective aldosterone deficiency, skeletal abnormalities were observed frequently. All patients in this category, however, had renal insufficiency, which itself may cause bone disease.

Renal Calcium Abnormalities (12,17)

Renal stone formation and nephrocalcinosis are common in patients with classic form of distal RTA. In contrast, hypercalciuria, renal stone formation, and nephrocalcinosis are rare in patients with proximal RTA (Table 4). A recent study found nephrocalcinosis in 24 of 56 patients with distal RTA, whereas it was not observed in any of the 13 patients with proximal RTA. Proximal RTA is usually a disease of childhood and may disappear with time. The short duration of disease in patients with proximal RTA may explain the lack of nephrocalcinosis and nephrolithiasis in such patients. Aside from differences in the duration of the disease, the most likely determinant of the development of nephrocalcinosis and nephrolithiasis is the presence of hypercalciuria.

Hypercalciuria is a common finding in patients with distal RTA, whereas it is rare in patients with proximal RTA. The reason for the difference in calcium excretion is not understood completely. A major determinant of hypercalciuria in patients with distal RTA is the degree of acidemia. The lower the plasma bicarbonate, the higher is the excretion of calcium. When plasma bicarbonate concentration is higher than 21 mEq/liter, urinary calcium excretion tends to decrease to the normal range. This emphasizes the importance of bicarbonate therapy in the correction of hypercalciuria associated with distal RTA. However, if acidemia were the sole determinant of hypercalciuria, calcium excretion should also be increased in patients with proximal RTA. Calcium excretion in patients with proximal RTA may not be increased because of increased distal delivery of bicarbonate. It is well known that administration of sodium bicarbonate enhances distal calcium reabsorption. Enhancement of distal calcium reabsorption by the large amounts of bicarbonate rejected in the proximal tubule could, therefore, attenuate or prevent the calciuric effect of acidosis in patients with proximal RTA. In patients with distal RTA, the decrease in calcium reabsorption secondary to systemic acidosis would not be counterbalanced by increased distal bicarbonate delivery.

Plasma parathyroid hormone (PTH) levels have been reported to be increased in some patients with classic RTA. If the anticalciuric effect of PTH was fully operative during acidosis, hypercalciuria should be minimized in such patients. Experimental studies in the dog, however, showed that PTH does not exert its normal anticalciuric effect during chronic metabolic acidosis. This could contribute to the development of calciuria despite PTH excess in acidotic subjects. Whether the lack of anticalciuric effect of PTH during acidosis contributes significantly to calcium wastage in patients with distal RTA remains to be shown.

Another factor that may account for the differences in renal calcium excretion between patients with proximal and those with distal RTA may be related to differences in urinary citrate excretion. Whereas citrate is excreted in the urine in normal amounts in patients with proximal RTA, citrate excretion is markedly reduced in patients with classic RTA (Table 4). Citrate is an organic anion that interferes with precipitation of calcium salts in the urine by sequestering calcium as a soluble calcium–citrate complex. Hypocitraturia may be a major determinant in the development of nephrocalcinosis and nephrolithiasis seen in patients with distal RTA. Conversely, the low incidence of nephrocalcinosis observed in patients with proximal RTA can be explained, in part, by a protective effect of citrate against the precipitation of calcium salts in the urine. As in normal subjects, administration of sodium bicarbonate to patients with distal RTA increases urinary citrate excretion. This may contribute to the decrease in calcium excretion and prevention of nephrocalcinosis that occurs in such patients when chronic alkali therapy is instituted.

ETIOLOGY OF RENAL TUBULAR ACIDOSIS (5,6,14)

RTA can be primary or secondary to a wide variety of diseases. Some of the diseases that cause proximal RTA can also cause distal RTA (Table 5). The

TABLE 5. *Causes of proximal and distal renal tubular acidosis*

Distal renal tubular acidosis	Proximal renal tubular acidosis
Primary or idiopathic 　Sporadic 　Genetically transmitted (hereditary)	Primary or idiopathic 　Sporadic 　Genetically transmitted
Secondary to inherited diseases 　Osteopetrosis 　Nerve deafness 　Carbonic anhydrase B deficiency or dysfunction 　Hereditary fructose intolerance 　Ehlers-Danlos syndrome	Secondary to inherited diseases 　Cystinosis 　Thyrosinosis 　Hereditary fructose intolerance 　Lowe's syndrome 　Wilson's disease 　Carbonic anhydrase B deficiency 　Pyruvate carboxylase deficiency 　Osteopetrosis 　Metachromatic leukodystrophy 　Galactosemia
Drugs and toxic agents 　Amphotericin B 　Lithium 　Toluene 　Amiloride 　Cyclamate	Drugs and toxic agents 　Heavy metal toxicity (lead, 　　cadmium, copper and mercury, 　　uranium, cisplatin) 　Carbonic anhydrase inhibitors 　Outdated tetracyclines 　L-Arginine and L-lysine 　Streptozotocin 　G-mercaptopurine 　Toluene 　Sulfanilamide 　Valproic acid 　Gentamicin
Altered calcium metabolism causing nephro- 　calcinosis 　Nephrocalcinosis (primary) 　Idiopathic hypercalciuria 　Urolithiasis 　Hypervitaminosis D 　Hyperthyroidism 　Hyperparathyroidism 　Fabry's disease	
Autoimmune and hypergammaglobulinemic 　disorders 　Idiopathic hypergammaglobulinemias 　Multiple myeloma 　Systemic lupus erythematosus 　Sjögren's syndrome 　Thyroiditis 　Pulmonary fibrosis 　Hepatic cirrhosis 　Primary biliary cirrhosis 　Chronic active hepatitis 　Pulmonary fibrosis	Miscellaneous 　Hyperparathyroidism 　Multiple myeloma 　Sjögren's syndrome 　Amyloidosis 　Nephrotic syndrome 　Renal transplantation 　Hypervitaminosis D 　Vitamin D deficiency or resistance 　Chronic active hepatitis 　Paroxysmal nocturnal hemo- 　　globinuria 　Balkan nephropathy 　Renal vein thrombosis in newborns
Tubulointerstitial nephropathies 　Obstructive uropathy 　Rejection of renal transplant 　Sickle cell hemoglobinopathies 　Medullary sponge kidney 　Analgesic nephropathy 　Balkan nephropathy 　Leprosy 　Hyperoxaluria	

primary (or idiopathic) form of both proximal and distal RTA can occur in relatives of affected patients. Proximal RTA can be associated with inherited systemic diseases that are usually diagnosed during childhood. Of these, cystinosis is the most common. In hereditary fructose intolerance, the features of Fanconi's syndrome and bicarbonate wastage become manifest only after fructose ingestion.

Proximal RTA associated with Fanconi's syndrome has been reported occasionally in recipients of renal transplants. Deposition of heavy metals in the renal tubules also can cause proximal RTA. This is the case in inherited diseases of copper metabolism, such as Wilson's disease, or after exposure to heavy metals due to occupation or accident. The most common drug to cause isolated proximal RTA is acetazolamide, a diuretic widely used in the treatment of glaucoma. In general, the occurrence of bicarbonate wastage in the absence of glucose, phosphate, amino acid, or uric acid wasting is very rare. Most cases of proximal RTA are, therefore, associated with a combination of the features of Fanconi's syndrome. In infants, however, isolated bicarbonate wastage can occur, although it is usually a transient phenomenon.

Although the majority of cases of distal RTA are sporadic, there are several families described with two or more members afflicted with the classic form of distal RTA. Some individuals have only hypercalciuria, whereas other have the incomplete form of distal RTA. The abnormal gene appears to be inherited as an autosomal dominant trait with complete expression in affected individuals. The development of nephrocalcinosis in most patients with distal RTA is probably the result of hypercalciuria secondary to acidosis. In some patients, however, hypercalciuria or nephrocalcinosis was noted before the development of distal RTA. It was proposed that hypercalciuria, inherited in an autosomal dominant manner, was the primary genetic defect that led to the development of nephrocalcinosis and later distal RTA. Although calcium deposition in the kidney may be the cause rather than the consequence of distal RTA in some patients, distal RTA appears to be the initiating event that alters calcium metabolism in the majority of patients. Support for this view is derived from the impressive arrest of the progression of calcium deposition in the kidney after early alkali therapy and correction of acidosis in patients with distal RTA.

Reports of distal RTA associated with rare inherited disorders are appearing with increasing frequency. The clinical association of osteopetrosis (or marble bone disease) and distal RTA is believed to be inherited in an autosomal recessive manner. This form of osteopetrosis has a relatively benign course, unlike the malignant variety of osteopetrosis that also is inherited in an autosomal recessive form. It is interesting to note that some of these patients achieve maturity with spontaneous resolution of bone modeling and osteosclerosis, perhaps as a result of an inhibitory effect of acidosis on the bone hyperformation characteristic of the disease. Thus, although chronic acidosis in patients with RTA may interfere with body growth and cause bone osteopenia, acidosis may, on the other hand, exert a salutory effect in this particular type of RTA. Another interesting association is childhood deafness and distal RTA, which also appear to be inherited in an autosomal recessive fashion.

Aside from the hereditary and drug-induced forms, distal RTA has been reported to occur mainly in association with autoimmune and hypergammaglobulinemic disorders. In the autoimmune disorders, tubulointerstitial infiltration of inflammatory cells is believed to result in tubular dysfunction, causing distal RTA. Both proximal and distal RTA have been reported in recipients of kidney transplants, but the distal form is more common and can be an early and persistent sign of chronic transplant rejection. In some patients, immunofluorescence staining of renal tubules is positive, suggesting that distal RTA is the functional expression of tubulointerstitial damage caused by chronic transplant rejection.

The association between liver disease and distal RTA is interesting. Hepatic cirrhosis, chronic active hepatitis, and primary biliary cirrhosis have all been associated with distal RTA. Common to all these entities is the fact that exaggerated renal sodium reabsorption can limit the amount of sodium delivered to the distal nephron, thereby decreasing distal hydrogen ion secretion. The fact that maneuvers that enhance distal sodium delivery may improve distal acidification in some patients with cirrhosis supports this view. In patients with primary biliary cirrhosis and possibly in patients with Wilson's disease, deposition of copper in the renal tubules may underlie the defect in distal acidification. In addition, it should be noted that patients with hepatic insufficiency usually have respiratory alkalosis and acid-base disorder, which in itself decreases collecting tubule H^+ secretion.

Distal RTA often is found in association with tubulointerstitial nephropathies, such as obstructive uropathy and sickle cell disease, which cause a hyperkalemic type of distal RTA. Patients with interstitial nephritis of diverse etiology and associated hyperkalemic hyperchloremic metabolic acidosis may have hyperkalemic distal RTA as well (Table 6). This form of distal RTA probably is the result of a generalized defect in the distal nephron that interferes with sodium reabsorption, hydrogen ion secretion, and potassium secretion.

Table 7 lists the causes of aldosterone deficiency. Selective aldosterone deficiency usually is associated with renin deficiency. Less often, low aldosterone production occurs in association with normal or even high levels of plasma renin activity. This has been documented in critically ill patients. Chronic heparin therapy and converting enzyme inhibitors may cause hyperkalemic metabolic acidosis associated with normal plasma renin activity and reduced plasma aldosterone. Numerous conditions can result in combined aldosterone and glucocorticoid deficiency. The most common cause is Addison's disease in its primary or idiopathic form, which is probably an autoimmune disorder. Other classic causes of Addison's disease, such as tuberculosis

TABLE 6. *Causes of hyperkalemic hyperchloremic metabolic acidosis other than aldosterone deficiency*

Hyperkalemic distal renal tubular acidosis
   Obstructive uropathy
   Sickle cell hemoglobinopathies
   Renal amyloidosis
   Acute hypersensitivity interstitial nephritis
   Interstitial nephritis of uncertain etiology
   Amiloride administration

Aldosterone resistance
   Pseudohypoaldosteronism of infancy
   Adult aldosterone hyporesponsiveness and renal insufficiency
   Enhanced tubular chloride reabsorption ("chloride shunt")
   Spironolactone administration

and other infectious conditions, also should be considered. Rarely, adrenal insufficiency can result from congenital enzymatic defects, such as 21-hydroxylase deficiency (congenital adrenal hyperplasia). Women who underwent bilateral adrenalectomy for treatment of cancer of the breast represent another example of acquired adrenal insufficiency. Adrenal insufficiency also can result from hemorrhage into the adrenal gland in patients receiving anticoagulants.

The syndromes associated with selective aldosterone deficiency are typified by the syndrome of hyporeninemic hypoaldosteronism. Most patients are middle-aged or elderly and have cardiovascular disease. Hyperkalemia is the

TABLE 7. *Causes of aldosterone deficiency*

Aldosterone + glucocorticoid deficiency (low cortisol, high plasma renin activity)	Selective aldosterone deficiency (normal cortisol)
Addison's disease	Low renin
21-Hydroxylase deficiency	Hyporeninemic hypoaldosteronism
Bilateral adrenalectomy	Prostaglandin synthesis inhibitors
Adrenal gland hemorrhage	
	Normal or high renin
	Normoreninemic hypoaldosteronism
	Hyperreninemic hypoaldosteronism
	in critically ill patients
	Converting-enzyme inhibitors
	Corticosterone methyloxidase
	deficiency
	Heparin therapy
	Cyclosporine A (?)[a]

[a]It is uncertain if the hypoaldosteronism observed in patients treated with cyclosporine occurs despite hyperreninism.

usual manifestation of this syndrome. The development of hyperchloremic metabolic acidosis in these patients is very common (more than 75% of cases). The hyperkalemia usually is not severe (in the range of 5.5–6.5 mEq/liter) and is not associated with ECG manifestations. In some cases, hyperkalemia is only intermittent. Most patients have mild to moderate renal insufficiency (i.e., plasma creatinine level 2–5 mg/dl). The syndrome, however, can occur in patients with normal GFR.

TREATMENT (7,17)

Treatment of distal RTA consists of alkali therapy. The alkali requirements of these patients are usually small compared with those of patients with proximal RTA. A dose of 1 to 2 mEq/kg body weight of sodium bicarbonate daily is sufficient in most cases. Many patients with hereditary distal RTA have a bicarbonate wastage tendency during the first years of life that gradually abates with advancing age. Hence, the dose of alkali needed to correct the acidosis decreases beyond 6 years of age. Alkali can be provided in the form of a sodium citrate solution, which is well tolerated because it causes less abdominal distention than bicarbonate. Each milliliter of citrate solution provides 1 mEq of bicarbonate after hepatic conversion of citrate into bicarbonate. Potassium supplements are indicated in patients with hypokalemia.

The treatment of patients with proximal RTA is more difficult because much of sodium bicarbonate administered is lost in the urine as fast as it is given. Maneuvers that enhance proximal bicarbonate reabsorption, however, are effective in reducing bicarbonate wastage. Either moderate salt restriction or administration of thiazide diuretics ensures a state of mild volume contraction that enhances proximal bicarbonate reabsorption. Using these maneuvers, the dose of alkali can be reduced. The magnitude of bicarbonate wastage is the major determinant of the amount of alkali necessary to sustain the correction of acidosis. This amount might range from 3 to 8 mEq/kg body weight per day. During periods of rapid growth, children might require much larger doses of alkali, ranging from 5 to 13 mEq/kg body weight per day. Treatment of even mild acidosis should be aggressive in children. Adults with mild compensated metabolic acidosis, however, might not need treatment because the acidosis is self-limited, and its consequences not well delineated. This is the case, for instance, in patients treated with acetazolamide for glaucoma.

The most impressive result of treatment of distal RTA is the achievement of normal growth in children when therapy is started early. No prospective studies on the progression of bone disease are available in adults with distal RTA, but it is possible that alkali therapy corrects bone osteopenia. This is strongly suggested by the virtual absence of bone disease as determined radiographically among patients with distal RTA reported in a series. There is good evidence that hypercalciuria and renal stone formation are prevented by correction of the acidosis. Nephrocalcinosis usually is not reversible, but its development can be prevented if alkali therapy is started in the early stages of distal RTA. The incomplete form of distal RTA usually does not require treatment. When associated with hypercalciuria, however, it should be managed in the same manner as idiopathic hypercalciuria. The hypokalemic (classic) form of distal RTA is not associated with deterioration of renal function, as shown by preservation of normal GFR over many years of follow-up. Progressive deterioration of GFR, however, is common in patients with selective aldosterone deficiency and hyperkalemic distal RTA.

Identification of the cause of hyperkalemic distal RTA is the first priority for the management of this acid-base disorder. Rapid correction of hyperkalemia or acidosis usually is not necessary unless the patient is symptomatic. An effort to treat the underlying disease has priority. For instance, correction of urinary tract obstruction could reverse the defect for potassium and acid excretion. Studies showing a reversal of hyperkalemic distal RTA after release of urinary tract obstruction, however, are currently lacking. We have observed a few patients in whom hyperkalemic hyperchloremic metabolic acidosis persisted for several months after prostatectomy, probably because permanent distal nephron damage already had occurred. Nevertheless, prompt correction of the cause of obstructive uropathy prevents further deterioration of overall renal function. In this respect, the presence of hyperkalemic hyperchloremic metabolic acidosis may be a clue to the diagnosis of unsuspected obstructive uropathy.

Patients with hyperkalemic distal RTA should be differentiated from those with pure selected aldosterone deficiency because some of the patients with the latter condition are more likely to respond to treatment with mineralocorticoids. Tubular unresponsiveness or hyporesponsiveness to the action of exogenous mineralocorticoid, however, is common in some patients with the syndrome of selective aldosterone deficiency. The reason why some patients with pure selective aldosterone deficiency respond to physiologic replacement with mineralocorticoid whereas others do not is not readily apparent, except that clinical evidence of tubulointerstitial nephropathy is usually present in such patients. Presumably, those who do not respond to large amounts of exogenous mineralocorticoid have more extensive tubular damage, which diminishes the number or function of aldosterone receptors. The acidosis can be corrected easily with the administration of sodium bicarbonate tablets. Hyperkalemia can be treated using exchange resins, such as sodium polysterene sulfonate, which increase gastrointestinal potassium excretion. Correction of hyperkalemia has an additional salutory effect in that it improves the acidosis by increasing ammonium excretion. Loop diuretics are effective in increasing K excretion, and they also ameliorate the metabolic acidosis associated with selective aldosterone deficiency.

DIAGNOSTIC APPROACH TO HYPERCHLOREMIC
METABOLIC ACIDOSIS (9–11)

After history and physical examination, the next step in the diagnostic approach to hyperchloremic metabolic acidosis is to determine whether or not urinary acidification is normal (Table 8). This involves measurement of urine pH, titratable acidity, and ammonium excretion. An increase in urine ammonium is an important element of the renal adaptation to metabolic acidosis. This parameter, however, is not measured routinely by clinical laboratories. Whether ammonium is increased or not can be inferred at bedside by a simple calculation of the urine anion gap (Na + K − Cl). In a relatively acid urine (pH < 6.5), urine bicarbonate concentration is very low, and its contribution to the urine anion gap can be considered negligible. If the urine pH is higher than 6.5, the urine anion gap should be calculated as

$$(Na + K) - (Cl^- + HCO_3)$$

The rationale for calculating the urine anion gap is based on the principle of electroneutrality, which also underlies the use of the plasma anion gap—that is, the sum of all anions and all cations present in the urine must be equal. The anions normally present in the urine that are not routinely measured (UA) include bicarbonate, sulfate, phosphate, and organic anions, and the cations not routinely measured (UC) include ammonium, calcium, and magnesium. Since only urinary chloride, sodium, and potassium are routinely measured, it follows that

$$Cl^- + UA = Na^+ + K^+ + UC$$

or

$$UA - UC = Na^+ + K^+ - Cl^- = UAG$$

Thus, the urine anion gap (UAG), like the plasma anion gap, unravels the difference between unmeasured anions and unmeasured cations. Accordingly, the UAG will decrease whenever there is a decrease in unmeasured anion or an increase in unmeasured cation (i.e., NH_4^+). Conversely, the UAG will increase if there is an increase in unmeasured anions or if there is a decrease in unmeasured cations. The latter circumstance should obtain whenever ammonium excretion does not increase appropriately in response to endogenous or exogenous acid loads. In keeping with this notion, the UAG is positive in patients with various types of defects in urinary acidification and negative in normal subjects given an acid load (Fig. 5, left). This difference reflects to a large extent the inability of patients to excrete ammonium appropriately in the face of spontaneous acidosis (Fig 5, middle). Thus, the UAG can be used to estimate whether ammonium excretion is normal or decreased during metabolic acidosis.

The UAG is most useful in the separation of patients with reduced ammo-

TABLE 8. *Diagnostic approach to hyperchloremic metabolic acidosis*

I. Hyperchloremic acidosis with normal or low plasma potassium

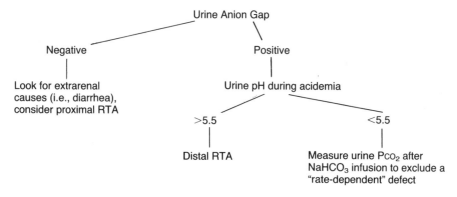

II. Hyperchloremic acidosis with hyperkalemia

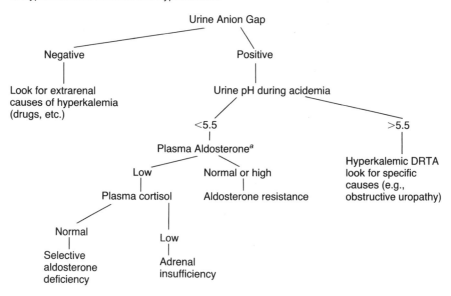

[a]Plasma renin activity should also be measured; it is usually low in patients with selective aldosterone deficiency and high in patients with adrenal insufficiency and aldosterone resistance.

nium excretion because of impaired distal acidification from those with hyper-chloremic metabolic acidosis from other causes, namely, gastrointestinal bicarbonate losses (Table 8). In the latter patients, renal acidification is greatly stimulated by acidemia, and the urine pH should be low. In some patients, however, urine pH rises because of the addition of large amounts of ammonia buffer into the collecting tubule. Many of these patients are volume depleted from protracted diarrhea, so that the delivery of sodium to the collecting tubule is impaired. In this situation, urine pH may not be lowered below 5.5 despite acidemia until distal sodium delivery is restored by the administration of salt or diuretics. In patients with spontaneous or laxative-induced diarrhea, the clinical picture may be further complicated by the presence of potassium depletion, which may interfere with the ability to lower urine pH maximally during metabolic acidosis. The findings of hypokalemia, hyperchloremic met-abolic acidosis, and a high urine pH suggest the diagnosis of distal RTA in these patients. The key differential finding is the UAG, which is positive if the patient has distal RTA but negative if the patient has hypokalemic hyper-chloremic metabolic acidosis associated with diarrhea (Table 8). Patients with proximal RTA should display a negative UAG insofar as they are capable of excreting substantial amounts of ammonium when plasma bicarbonate is reduced.

Those patients with a positive UAG should be suspected of distal RTA, which can be separated into hyperkalemic and hypokalemic (classic) distal RTA on the basis of the plasma K (Table 8). The diagnosis of distal RTA can be confirmed by the finding of a urinary pH above 5.5 in the face of spontane-ous or ammonium chloride-induced metabolic acidosis.

In general, if the patient is spontaneously acidotic (pH < 7.35), there is no need to induce severe acidosis in order to evaluate urinary acidification. If the patient is suspected of having distal RTA and acidosis is not present, am-monium chloride is given orally in a dose of 0.1 g/kg body weight daily for 3 consecutive days. Urinary pH falls below 5.5 (usually below 5.0) by the first day and remains low thereafter. This approach also allows evaluation of net acid excretion. In nonacidotic subjects, the failure to lower urinary pH in response to the administration of ammonium chloride can uncover a defect in distal acidification (i.e., incomplete distal RTA). Some individuals might have impaired distal acidification despite preserved capacity to lower urinary pH during acidosis. Patients whose urinary pH is appropriately low in response to ammonium chloride loading but whose urinary PCO_2 fails to increase normally in response to sodium bicarbonate loading also should be considered to have incomplete distal RTA. Any patient with unexplained hyperchloremic meta-bolic acidosis and a low urine pH should have urinary PCO_2 evaluated during sodium bicarbonate loading. The performance of this test, however, is not necessary in the majority of patients suspected of having distal RTA because the diagnosis usually can be made on the basis of the findings of a positive UAG and a high urine pH during acidosis. Measurement of urinary ammo-nium and titratable acidity can then be performed to confirm this diagnosis.

REFERENCES

1. Albright, F., Burnett, C. H., Parson, W., et al. (1946): Osteomalacia and late rickets. The various etiologies met in the United States with emphasis on that resulting from a specific form of renal acidosis, the therapeutic indications for each etiological subgroup, and the relationship between osteomalacia and Milkman's syndrome. *Medicine*, 25:399.
2. Arruda, J. A. L., and Kurtzman, N. A. (1980): Mechanism and classification of deranged distal urinary acidification. *Am. J. Physiol.*, 8:F515–523.
3. Arruda, J. A. L., Nascimento, L., Mehta, P. K., et al. (1977): The critical importance of urinary concentrating ability in the generation of urinary carbon dioxide tension. *J. Clin. Invest.*, 60:922–935.
4. Batlle, D. C. (1986): Segmental characterization of defects in collecting tubule acidification. *Kidney Int.*, 30:546–553.
5. Batlle, D. C. (1986): Sodium-dependent urinary acidification in patients with aldosterone deficiency and in adrenalectomized rats. *Metabolism*, 35:852–860.
6. Batlle, D. C. (1981): Hyperkalemic hyperchloremic metabolic acidosis associated with selective aldosterone deficiency and distal renal tubular acidosis. *Semin. Nephrol.*, 1:260–274.
7. Batlle, D. C., Arruda, J. A. L., and Kurtzman, N. A. (1981): Hyperkalemic distal renal tubular acidosis associated with obstructive uropathy. *N. Engl. J. Med.*, 304:373–380.
8. Batlle, D. C., and Chan, Y. L. (1988): Effect of L-arginine on renal tubular bicarbonate reabsorption by the rat kidney. *Min. Electrolyte Metab.* (in press).
9. Batlle, D. C., Gaviria, M., Grupp, M., Arruda, J. A. L., Wynn, J., and Kurtzman, N. A. (1982): Distal nephron function in patients receiving chronic lithium therapy. *Kidney Int.*, 21:477–485.
10. Batlle, D. C., Grupp, M., Gaviria, M., and Kurtzman, N. A. (1982): Distal renal tubular acidosis with intact ability to lower urine pH. *Am. J. Med.*, 72:751–758.
11. Batlle, D. C., Hizon, M., Cohen, E., Gutterman, C., and Gupta, R. (1988): The use of the urinary anion gap in the diagnosis of hyperchloremic metabolic acidosis. *N. Engl. J. Med.*, 318:594–599.
12. Batlle, D. C., Itsarayoungyuen, K., Hays, S., Arruda, J. A. L., and Kurtzman, N. A. (1982): Parathyroid hormone is not anticalciuric during chronic metabolic acidosis. *Kidney Int.*, 22:269–271.
13. Batlle, D. C., and Kurtzman, N. .A. (1982): Distal renal tubular acidosis. Pathogenesis and classification. *Am. J. Kidney, Dis.*, 1:328–344.
14. Batlle, D. C., Moses, M. F., Manaligod, J., Arruda, J. A. L., and Kurtzman, N. A. (1981): The pathogenesis of hyperchloremic metabolic acidosis associated with renal transplantation. *Am. J. Med.*, 70:786–796.
15. Batlle, D. C., Sabatini, S., and Kurtzman, N. A. (1988): On the mechanism of toluene-induced renal tubular acidosis. *Nephron* 49:210–218.
16. Batlle, D. C., Sehy, J. T., Roseman, M. K., Arruda, J. A. L., and Kurtzman, N. A. (1981): Clinical and pathophysiologic spectrum of acquired distal renal tubular acidosis. *Kidney Int.*, 20:389–396.
17. Brenner, R. J., Spring, D. B., Sebastian, A., et al. (1982): Incidence of radiographically evident bone disease, nephrocalcinosis, and nephrolithiasis in various types of renal tubular acidosis. *N. Engl. J. Med.*, 307:217–221.
18. Capasso, G., Jaeger, P., Giebisch, G., Guckian, V., and Malnic, G. (1987): Renal bicarbonate reabsorption in the rat. *J. Clin. Invest.*, 80:409–414.
19. DuBose, T. D. Jr., and Calflisch, C. R., (1985): Validation of the difference in urine and blood carbon dioxide transport during bicarbonate loading as an index of distal nephron acidification in experimental models of distal renal tubular acidosis. *J. Clin. Invest*, 75:1116–1123.
20. Halperin, M. L., Goldstein, M. B., Haig, A., et al. (1974): Studies on the pathogenesis of type 1 (distal) renal tubular acidosis as revealed by the urinary P_{CO_2} tensions. *J. Clin. Invest.*, 53:669–677.
21. Rodriguez-Soriano, J., Boichis, H., Stark, H., et al. (1967): Proximal renal tubular acidosis: A defect in bicarbonate reabsorption with normal urinary acidification. *Pediatr. Res.*, 1:81.
22. Schambelan, M., Sebastian, A., and Rector, F. C., Jr. (1981): Mineralocorticoid-resistant renal hyperkalemia without salt wasting (type II pseudohypoaldosteronism): Role of increased renal chloride reabsorption. *Kidney Int.*, 19:716.

23. Sebastian, A., Schambelan, M., Lindenfeld, S., et al. (1977): Amelioration of metabolic acidosis with fluorocortisone therapy in hyporeninemic hypoaldosteronism. *N. Engl. J. Med.*, 297:576–589.
24. Seldin, D. W., and Wilson, J. D. (1972): Renal tubular acidosis. In: *Metabolic Basis of Inherited Diseases*, 3rd ed., edited by J. B. Stanbury, J. B. Wyngarden, and D. Frederickson, pp. 1548–1566. McGraw-Hill, New York.
25. Steinmetz, P. R. (1971): Cellular mechanisms of urinary acidification and renal tubular acidosis. In: *Physiology of Membrane Disorders*, edited by T. E. Andreoli, J. Hoffman, and D. Fanestil, pp. 987–1017. Plenum Press, New York.
26. Wrong, A., and Davies, H. E. F. (1959): The excretion of acid in renal diseases. *Q. J. Med.*, 28:259–313.

The Regulation of Acid–Base Balance, edited
by Donald W. Seldin and Gerhard Giebisch,
Raven Press, Ltd., New York © 1989.

16

Overproduction Acidosis

Michael Emmett and *Donald W. Seldin

*Nephrology/Metabolism Division, Baylor University Medical Center,
Dallas, Texas 75246; and *University of Texas Southwestern Medical Center at Dallas,
Dallas. Texas 75235*

Lactic Acidosis
   Pyruvate, Lactate, and Energy Metabolism • Lactate-Pyruvate Relationship • Normal Lactic Acid Metabolism • Ischemia and Lactic Acidosis • Clinical Syndromes of Lactic Acidosis • Therapy of Lactic Acidosis
Ketoacidosis
   Fat Oxidation, Ketogenesis, and Ketone Metabolism • Diabetic Ketoacidosis • Starvation Ketosis • Alcoholic Ketoacidosis • Glucose-6-Phosphatase and Fructose-1,6-Bisphosphatase Deficiency
Poison-Associated Anion Gap Acidosis
   Osmolality and the Osmolal Gap • Methanol Poisoning • Ethylene Glycol Poisoning • Isopropyl Alcohol Poisoning • Paraldehyde Poisoning • Salicylate Poisoning
Unusual Anion Gap Metabolic Acidoses
   Congenital Organic Acidoses • D-Lactic Acidosis
References

Four distinctive pathophysiologic states will lead to the development of metabolic acidosis: (1) *acid underexcretion*, (2) *renal bicarbonate loss*, (3) *gastrointestinal bicarbonate loss*, and (4) *acid overproduction or exogenous loads exceeding excretory and metabolic capacity.*

Underexcretion metabolic acidosis usually is a result of decreased renal excretion of the normal acid load derived from the diet, metabolic organic acid production in excess of organic base production, and gastrointestinal alkali losses. Examples of underexcretion acidosis include uremic acidosis and distal renal tubular acidosis.

Renal bicarbonate loss results from the direct urinary loss of bicarbonate salts. Proximal renal tubular acidosis is characterized by renal $NaHCO_3$ and $KHCO_3$ wasting. Acetazolamide also produces direct bicarbonate losses.

Gastrointestinal bicarbonate loss usually is due to the development of diarrhea or enteric fistulae.

Overproduction or exogenous metabolic acidosis results from the generation, ingestion, or infusion of relatively strong acids at rates that exceed the renal excretory and metabolic clearance capacities. The overproduction metabolic acidoses include lactic acidosis, ketoacidosis, metabolic acidosis due to congenital enzyme defects, and several poison-associated acidoses. To the extent that salts of acid anions are lost into the urine, these disorders are converted into hybrid forms with features of both overproduction and renal loss of decomposed HCO_3^-.

LACTIC ACIDOSIS (12,98–100,102,103,105–107)

Pyruvate, Lactate, and Energy Metabolism (41,46)

The key reactions that produce pyruvic and lactic acid and the metabolic fate of these acids are depicted in Fig. 1. Pyruvate is derived primarily from glucose oxidation. The deamination of alanine also generates pyruvate. Pyruvate may enter one of four metabolic sequences.

1. It may enter mitochondria for oxidation to acetyl-CoA.

2. It may enter mitochondria for carboxylation to form oxaloacetate.

3. It may be aminated in the cytosol to yield the amino acid alanine.

4. It may be reduced in the cytosol to form lactic acid.

Mitochondrial pyruvate uptake is a major metabolic pathway, and this uptake usually increases in parallel with increased pyruvate generation to maintain normal cytosolic pyruvate concentrations. If mitochondrial uptake does not increase in response to accelerated pyruvate generation, the cytosol pyruvate concentration increases. If mitochondrial uptake should decrease at a time when generation was rapid, cytosol pyruvate levels would increase sharply.

Pyruvate that enters the mitochondria may be oxidized to acetyl-CoA via pyruvate dehydrogenase (PDH), or pyruvate may combine with CO_2 to yield oxaloacetate via pyruvate carboxylase (PC).

Acetyl-CoA derived from pyruvate can be further oxidized in the Krebs cycle, producing CO_2, H_2O, and energy. Alternatively, acetyl-CoA can be used to synthesize fatty acids, cholesterol, and steroid hormones. Fatty acid and cholesterol synthesis occur primarily in the cytosol. Therefore, acetyl-

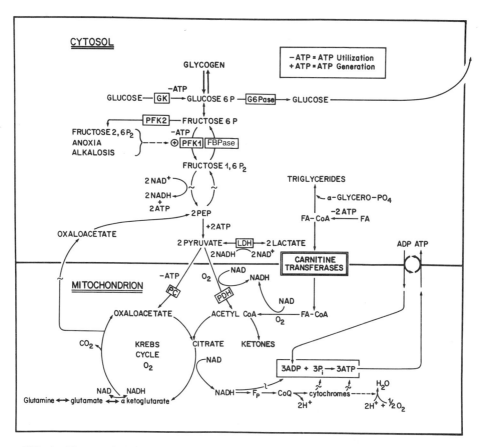

FIG. 1. The metabolic pathways that generate pyruvate and lactate and the pathways that consume pyruvate are summarized. (GK) glucokinase; (G6Pase) glucose-6-phosphatase; (PFK) phosphofructokinase; (FBPase) fructose bisphosphatase; (LDH) lactate dehydrogenase; (PC) pyruvate carboxylase; (PDH) pyruvate dehydrogenase.

CoA generated in mitochondria must first cross the mitochondrial membrane to enter the cytosol if fat is to be synthesized. However, the mitochondrial membrane is relatively impermeable to acetyl-CoA. It must, therefore, exit by an indirect mechanism (see Fig. 3B).[1]

Acetyl-CoA is formed in the mitochondria from pyruvate as described and by the β-oxidation of fatty acids. When acetyl-CoA generation is very rapid, the metabolic pathways described previously may not be adequate to prevent

---

[1]Within mitochondria, acetyl-CoA condenses with oxaloacetate to form citrate, which then crosses the mitochondrial membranes. In the cytoplasm, citrate is split back to acetyl-CoA and oxaloacetate. The acetyl-CoA can then be carboxylated, yielding malonyl-CoA, an intermediate committed to the synthesis of fatty acid.

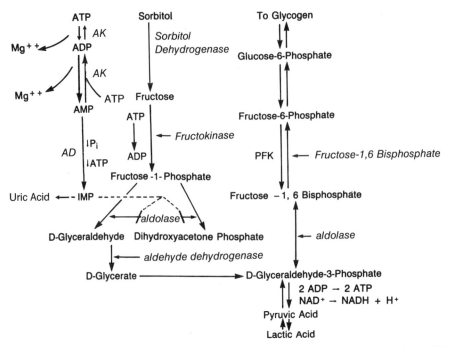

FIG. 2. The metabolism of fructose in the liver (and renal cortex). AK, adenylate kinase; AD, adenylate deaminase.

mitochondrial acetyl-CoA accumulation. Under such conditions, acetyl-CoA molecules can condense and be converted (via the β-OH β-methylglutaryl-CoA cycle) to acetoacetic acid. Ketoacidosis may result when fatty acids rapidly enter the mitochondria and are oxidized to acetyl-CoA, producing this compound at very rapid rates (*see* Ketoacidosis).

The other mitochondrial reaction for pyruvate is catalyzed by pyruvate carboxylase and generates oxaloacetate. Oxaloacetate may condense with acetyl-CoA to form citrate. In the Krebs cycle, citrate yields CO_2, H_2O, and energy as it is oxidized and ultimately converted back to oxaloacetate. Alternatively, citrate can exit from the mitochondria to be used for cytosol fat synthesis, as mentioned previously. Oxaloacetate can exit also from the mitochondria (indirectly as malate or aspartate) to be used for glucose synthesis. The cellular metabolic-hormonal set determines the predominant metabolic reaction sequences taken by pyruvate, acetyl-CoA, and oxaloacetate.

The oxidation of acetyl-CoA yields energy as electrons and protons are removed from this compound and eventually transferred to molecular O_2. NAD^+ is first reduced to $NADH + H^+$, thus transferring chemical potential energy. The energy is subsequently released in a stepwise fashion when these electrons flow down the mitochondrial respiratory (or electron transport) chain. As the catalytic components of this system are sequentially reduced by the electron pair, the released energy is transferred to adenine nucleotides. The removal of two electrons and two protons from $NADH + H^+$ regenerates NAD^+. The sequential oxidation-reduction reactions associated with the movement of these electrons down the respiratory chain generates three ATP molecules.

$$3 \text{ ADP} + 3 \text{ P}_i \rightarrow 3 \text{ ATP}$$

The final transfer of the electron/H^+ pair from cytochrome A_3 to oxygen yields H_2O.

$$1/2 \text{ O}_2 + 2 \text{ H}^+ + 2 \text{ E}^- \rightarrow H_2O$$

Lactate-Pyruvate Relationship (40,46,98,106)

The lactate dehydrogenase (LDH) enzyme system interconverts pyruvic and lactic acids. It requires as cosubstrates the NAD^+/NADH couple. The dynamic equilibrium that exists between these compounds may be expressed as follows.

$$NAD^+$$
$$\text{Lactate} \rightleftharpoons \text{LDH} \rightleftharpoons \text{Pyruvate}$$
$$NADH + H^+$$
$$10 \quad : \quad 1$$

This reaction occurs in the cell cytoplasm. It is normally poised toward the left, resulting in a lactate/pyruvate ratio of about 10:1. At equilibrium, the reactants are interrelated as follows.

$$(\text{Pyruvate})(\text{NADH})(\text{H}^+) \, \alpha \, (\text{lactate})(\text{NAD}^+)$$

$$\text{Lactate} \, \alpha \, \frac{(\text{Pyruvate})(\text{NADH})(\text{H}^+)}{(\text{NAD}^+)}$$

or

$$\text{Lactate} = K \frac{(\text{Pyruvate})(\text{NADH})(\text{H}^+)}{(\text{NAD}^+)}$$

where K is the equilibrium constant for the LDH reaction. Therefore, the cytosol lactate concentration is a function of the cytosol pyruvate concentration, the NADH/NAD^+ ratio (redox), and the pH. On the basis of this analysis, it is evident that lactate can increase for three reasons.

1. Lactate may increase solely as a consequence of an increased pyruvate concentration. Under these conditions, the lactate/pyruvate ratio remains normal at 10:1.

2. Lactate may increase due to a high $NADH/NAD^+$ ratio. This increases the lactate/pyruvate ratio, which may reach levels of 40:1 or more.

3. Lactate may increase as a result of an increased pyruvate concentration and an increased $NADH/NAD^+$ ratio. This is usually the case in patients with severe lactic acidosis.

If the pyruvate concentration doubles but the $NADH/NAD^+$ ratio remains normal, lactate also doubles. *Epinephrine infusions* may increase plasma lactate elevations to values of about 2 to 3 mEq/liter. Epinephrine accelerates glycogenolysis and glycolysis while inhibiting mitochondrial pyruvate uptake. The cytosol pyruvate and lactate concentrations rise proportionately. *Rapid intravenous glucose infusions and respiratory alkalosis* also accelerate pyruvate generation. The pyruvate and lactate levels increase, but the redox state remains normal. These conditions rarely increase lactate levels above 5 mEq/liter.

When an $NADH/NAD^+$ redox increase is associated with a simultaneous rise in pyruvate, lactate levels increase markedly. Huckabee suggested that the lactate acidoses be separated into two types on the basis of the $NADH/NAD^+$ ratio (reflected in the lactate/pyruvate ratio). He proposed the concept of "excess lactate," which represents that component of lactate elevation not directly attributable to a pyruvate increase. Excess lactate results from an $NADH/NAD^+$, or redox, shift that increases the lactate/pyruvate ratio. Clinically significant lactic acidosis does not occur in the absence of a redox shift.

Although pyruvate levels are not generally available, a redox shift (increased $NADH/NAD^+$ ratio and a lactate/pyruvate ratio greater than 10:1) may be assumed if the blood lactate concentration exceeds 5 mEq/liter.

Normal Lactic Acid Metabolism (46,98)

Normally, the rates of lactic acid generation and utilization are perfectly matched. Tissues that normally release lactic acid are the skin, brain, exercising muscle, renal medulla, intestine, and red blood cells. The liver is the major organ that takes up and metabolizes lactic acid, although the kidneys and other tissues can also use lactate. Anaerobic glycolysis in peripheral tissues generates lactic acid, which is subsequently taken up by the liver and converted back to glucose (the Cori cycle).

Normal rates of lactic acid generation and utilization are about 15 to 20 mEq/kg/day (1,000–1,400 mEq/day). These rates can increase markedly. Accelerated lactate production must be matched immediately by accelerated uptake, or the lactate concentration will increase rapidly. For example, strenuous exercise accelerates lactate production (in muscles) and simultaneously depresses hepatic perfusion and lactate uptake. Therefore, following exhaustive exercise, lactate levels may increase to about 10 to 15 mEq/liter (and reciprocally reduce the $[HCO_3^-]$).

The normal steady state serum lactate level is 1 to 2 mEq/liter.

Ischemia and Lactic Acidosis

Tissue ischemia reduces lactate use and simultaneously triggers multiple metabolic events that accelerate lactate production (Fig. 1).

A drastic fall in tissue perfusion, as occurs in shock, for example, sharply reduces the delivery of oxygen to tissues. Since oxygen is the final physiologic acceptor of protons derived from NADH, the failure of oxygen delivery results in an NADH accumulation; simultaneously NAD^+ falls, since it cannot be regenerated from NADH. In consequence, the $NADH/NAD^+$ ratio rises sharply. A second consequence of a tissue oxygen deficit is a failure of oxidative phosphorylation: The energy required to drive the reaction ADP $+ P_i \rightarrow$ ATP is derived from transfer of protons from NADH along the electron transport chain to oxygen. Since this process is blocked, the accumulation of NADH is paralleled by reduced ATP formation together with an increase in the ADP/ATP ratio.

Simultaneously with the rise in the $NADH/NAD^+$ ratio, the concentration of pyruvate in the cytoplasm increases. This increase results from diminished use and accelerated production. Mitochondrial pyruvate uptake is closely linked to oxidative metabolism. Pyruvate oxidation via pyruvate dehydrogenase requires NAD^+, whereas carboxylation via pyruvate carboxylase requires ATP. Mitochondrial hypoxia will, therefore, decrease pyruvate flux through each reaction sequence and thus decrease mitochondrial uptake. As the cell becomes energy (ATP) depleted, it compensates by accelerating anaerobic glycolysis via the Embden-Meyerhof pathway (the Pasteur effect). This reaction sequence is primarily under the control of the rate limiting enzyme phosphofructokinase (PFK-1). This allosteric enzyme is activated (deinhibited) by hypoxia and energy-depleted states. A high ADP/ATP ratio and the ATP breakdown products inorganic phosphate and AMP are potent

---

[2]Phosphofructokinase-1 irreversibly phosphorylates fructose-6-phosphate to fructose-1,6-bisphosphate. The enzyme is activated by AMP, ADP, and phosphate and inhibited by ATP. The glucose regulatory hormones, insulin and glucagon, also affect this enzyme. They act through another metabolic intermediate, fructose-2,6-bisphosphate, which is also derived from fructose-6-phosphate (F-6-P). The enzyme phosphofructokinase-2 converts F-6-P to F-2,6-bisphosphate. Fructose-2,6-bisphosphate exerts a strong positive effect on phosphofructokinase-1. Fructose-2,6-bisphosphate levels are increased by insulin, thereby stimulating glycolysis, and decreased by glucagon, inhibiting glycolysis. There is no evidence that hypoxia or ischemia directly affects the fructose-2,6-bisphosphate level.

activators of PFK-1. This enzyme also is activated by intracellular alkalosis and by the intermediate fructose-2,6-bisphosphate.[2]

Ischemic stress, therefore, simultaneously accelerates glycolysis and pyruvate generation while slowing mitochondrial pyruvate uptake and metabolism. The ischemia increases the NADH/NAD$^+$ ratio, which drives pyruvate toward lactate. Therefore, lactic acid levels increase sharply as elevated pyruvate levels combine with a high NADH/NAD$^+$ ratio.

Clinical Syndromes of Lactic Acidosis (3,7–10,16,18,21–25,33,34, 37,39,40,47,56–59,61,67,69,72,74,75,78,91,93,95)

Table 1 lists the major clinical syndromes associated with lactic acidosis. Most commonly, lactic acidosis is the result of an inadequate supply of oxygen to a large mass of tissue. *Circulatory failure* is the classic cause of lactic acidosis. The generalized underperfusion produces cellular ischemia and triggers the metabolic cascade outlined previously. In addition, circulatory failure reduces hepatic perfusion and lactate use. The blood lactate concentration, in states of circulatory collapse, reflects the severity of the process and can be used as a prognostic indicator. In early circulatory failure, lactate levels may increase while the blood pressure is still normal. At this time, the decreased cardiac output is compensated by intense peripheral vasoconstriction to maintain the blood pressure, while the lactate levels reflect the state of reduced tissue perfusion.

Severe acute arterial hypoxemia, in the absence of decreased perfusion, can result in lactic acidosis. However, severe chronic hypoxemia rarely produces lactic acidosis. Chronic hypoxemia triggers multiple compensatory mechanisms that serve to maintain tissue oxygenation. Increased cardiac output, polycythemia, and a decreased hemoglobin-oxygen affinity owing to high red cell 2,3-diphosphoglyceric acid levels improve oxygen delivery and unloading in these patients. Therefore, patients with uncomplicated chronic obstructive lung disease rarely develop lactic acidosis despite severe hypoxemia. When lactic acidosis develops in these patients, it is usually because of a superimposed process, such as hypotension, sepsis, or acute hypoxia.

Carbon monoxide poisoning frequently produces lactic acidosis. Carbon monoxide binds to hemoglobin more avidly than does oxygen. Therefore, it displaces the oxygen-carrying capacity of hemoglobin. In addition, the carbon monoxide–hemoglobin complex shifts the oxygen-hemoglobin dissociation curve of the remaining CO free hemoglobin toward the left. This increases hemoglobin-oxygen affinity and decreases oxygen release to tissues. Less oxygen is carried to tissues, and its release is simultaneously decreased.

TABLE 1. *Lactic acidosis*

Decreased ATP production
  Circulatory failure
    Volume depletion
    Severe heart failure
    Massive pulmonary emboli
    Vascular collapse
      Septic shock
      Anaphylaxis
      Vasodilators (nitroprusside)
  Severe acute tissue hypoxemia
    Acute respiratory failure
    Carbon monoxide poisoning
    Severe anemia
    Methemoglobinemia
  Defective mitochondrial oxygen use/energy production
    Electron transport defect
      Carbon monoxide
      Cyanide
      Severe iron deficiency
    Decreased oxidative phosphorylation
      Salicylate intoxication
      2,4-Dinitrophenol
    Mitochondrial enzyme defect
      Pyruvate carboxylase
      Pyruvate dehydrogenase
      Cytochrome oxidase defects
    Decreased pyruvate use
      Phenformin
      Acute beriberi
    Phosphate trapping
      Fructose
      Xylitol
      Sorbitol
      Glucose-6-phosphatase deficiency (von Gierke's
        disease)
Lactate overproduction (with relative ATP deficiency)
  Muscle hyperactivity
    Severe exertion
    Seizure
    Hypothermia—?shivering (and decreased perfusion)
    Exertional heat stroke
  Disseminated tumor, especially leukemia or lymphoma
  Tumor lysis syndrome
  Gluconeogenic enzyme defects
    Glucose-6-phosphatase defect (von Gierke's
      disease)
    Fructose-1,6-diphosphatase defect
  Catecholamine excess
  Methanol
  Ethylene glycol
Decreased lactate use
  Advanced liver disease

Furthermore, the cardiac output, which usually increases in hypoxic states, does not increase in patients with carbon monoxide poisoning. Oxygen chemoreceptors, which constitute the afferent limb of this response, respond primarily to a fall in arterial Po_2, but the Po_2 is not depressed with carbon monoxide poisoning. The displaced oxygen-carrying capacity, left shift of the oxyhemoglobin dissociation curve, and deficient cardiovascular response combine to reduce tissue oxygenation markedly. Finally, carbon monoxide binds directly to cytochrome a_3 in the electron transport chain and thereby interferes with oxidative phosphorylation and mitochondrial respiration. These toxic effects accelerate lactic acid production and produce lactic acidosis.

Severe anemia, especially iron deficiency anemia and methemoglobinemia, may lead to the development of lactic acidosis. Anemia directly reduces the oxygen-carrying capacity of blood. In addition, iron is an important constituent of several electron carriers of the respiratory chain. Severe iron deficiency may impair cytochrome function. The abnormality of mitochondrial oxidation combined with decreased oxygen delivery can produce lactic acidosis.

Certain poisons block mitochondrial oxygen use despite normal oxygen delivery. *Cyanide* combines with cytochromes a and a_3, blocking the flow of electrons to oxygen. ATP generation and the oxidation of NADH to NAD^+ are decreased. The arterial-venous O_2 gradient across vascular beds decreases as a result of depressed oxygen uptake. Cyanide poisoning may be due to attempted suicide or homicide. However, iatrogenic cyanide poisoning may occur during prolonged nitroprusside use. This vasodilator is metabolized to cyanide and then to thiocyanate. If renal and hepatic function are poor, cyanide poisoning can result.

2,4-Dinitrophenol is a classic example of another family of mitochondrial poisons. These are agents that uncouple oxidative phosphorylation. Uncouplers do not block NADH oxidation to NAD^+, and the electrons can still flow to oxygen, which is reduced to H_2O. However, the uncouplers separate these reactions from the phosphorylation of ADP to ATP. The oxidation of NADH, uncoupled from ATP generation, becomes unregulated and rapid. Chemical energy is converted to heat, and calories are burned. This is the basis for the use of such compounds to accelerate weight loss. However, these dangerous agents can produce life-threatening complications, including lactic acidosis.

Toxic concentrations of *salicylate* and *phenformin* also can act in the mitochondria to inhibit or uncouple oxidation. These effects may result in lactic acidosis. These drugs also have other effects that accelerate lactic acid production (discussed later).

Many *congenital mitochondrial enzyme defects* that affect lactate metabolism have been described. The defects may involve various components of pyruvate carboxylase, pyruvate dehydrogenase, and the cytochrome electron transport system (Fig. 1). Severe impairment of these enzyme systems is incompatible with life. However, individuals with subtle defects may survive and then develop chronic lactic acidosis. The acidosis may be exacerbated by exercise, which increases the load on these enzyme systems. These patients often also develop severe myopathies and neurologic abnormalities as a result of enzyme defects in muscle and the central nervous system (CNS).

Thiamine is a critical cofactor for several enzyme complexes, including pyruvate dehydrogenase. *Severe thiamine deficiency* impairs pyruvate dehydrogenase activity and thereby depresses mitochondrial pyruvate oxidation (Fig. 1). This defect is partially responsible for the lactic acidosis that occurs in patients with beriberi. High output heart failure, common with beriberi, also contributes to the lactic acidosis. Beriberi-associated lactic acidosis is promptly reversed by the administration of thiamine.

Acute inorganic phosphate depletion, as a result of metabolic phosphate trapping, can result in ATP depletion and lactic acidosis. If a compound (such as fructose—see below) is rapidly phosphorylated and subsequent metabolism of the phosphorylated products is relatively slow, these products accumulate in the cell. This acutely reduces the intracellular inorganic phosphate concentration. The phosphate depletion impedes ATP generation.

The metabolic effects of combining acute inorganic phosphate depletion with ATP depletion and relatively high concentrations of ADP and AMP can be seen when *fructose is rapidly infused* intravenously or when smaller fructose loads are administered to *fructose-intolerant individuals* (Fig. 2). Fructose is rapidly phosphorylated by the liver and, to a lesser extent, the kidney, to fructose-1-phosphate. This phosphorylation step is unregulated. Fructose-1-phosphate aldolase splits this to dihydroxyacetone phosphate and glyceric acid. The fructose-1-phosphate aldolase step is a relatively slow, rate-limiting reaction. The activity of this aldolase is markedly depressed in patients with *hereditary fructose intolerance*. When these patients ingest fructose, fructose-1-phosphate accumulates rapidly in the liver and renal cortex and produces a phosphate trap. Inorganic phosphate levels fall sharply in the cells of the liver and renal cortex, producing acute phosphate depletion and restricted ATP synthesis. While ATP levels fall, the ADP and AMP levels increase. The low ATP and high ADP and AMP levels accelerate anaerobic glycolysis (the Pasteur effect). Restricted oxidative phosphorylation is, therefore, coupled with accelerated glycolysis, and this combination generates lactic acidosis. Hepatic and renal cortical cell dysfunction also result from the ATP depletion. In the renal cortex, proximal tubule dysfunction produces a Fanconi syndrome. Hepatic cell necrosis increases serum transaminase levels. Although ATP and energy depletion probably is the major cause of hepatic and renal toxicity, the accumulation of fructose-1-phosphate also may produce toxicity directly.

The adenine nucleotides ATP, ADP, and AMP are in equilibrium via the reaction catalyzed by adenylate kinase (Fig. 2). When the ATP/ADP ratio falls, the enzymes that degrade the adenylate pool are activated. Inorganic phosphate depletion also activates adenylate deaminase, which catabolizes the adenine nucleotides. These catabolic reactions produce IMP, which is then converted to the end product (in humans), uric acid. Therefore, acute inorganic phosphate depletion combines with ATP depletion to accelerate markedly uric acid generation. The renal secretion of uric acid may be reduced by high lactate levels. Lactate competes with uric acid for renal tubular secretion by the organic acid pathway. The accelerated hepatic production and decreased renal secretion of uric acid increase blood uric acid levels sharply. Hyperuricemia is a characteristic feature of the metabolic phosphate trapping syndromes. Hypermagnesemia also typically occurs and probably reflects the release of magnesium from the adenine nucleotide pool, (both ATP and ADP are normally complexed with magnesium).

The biochemical derangements that develop after modest fructose loads in fructose-intolerant patients also may occur in normal individuals after *rapid intravenous fructose infusions*. This occurs because fructose-1-phosphate aldolase, even in normal individuals, is a relatively low capacity enzyme. Also, IMP accumulation reduces aldolase activity toward fructose-1-phosphate (Fig. 2). Therefore, the rapid infusion of fructose results in fructose-1-phosphate accumulation, inorganic phosphate depletion, lactic acidosis, and hyperuricemia. *Sorbitol* is rapidly converted to fructose by sorbitol dehydrogenase (Fig. 2) and can produce similar abnormalities if rapidly infused or absorbed.

Several enzyme abnormalities in the gluconeogenic pathway can produce fasting hypoglycemia, lactic acidosis, and ketoacidosis. *Glucose-6-phosphatase deficiency (von Gierke's disease)* blocks the release of glucose from glucose-6-phosphate. The gluconeogenic and glycogenolytic pathways are stimulated when these patients fast. Glucose-6-phosphate is generated but cannot be converted to glucose owing to deficient glucose-6-phosphatase activity (Fig. 1). The resultant hypoglycemia inhibits insulin and stimulates the counter-regulatory hormones glucagon, growth hormone, glucocorticoids, and catecholamines. Gluconeogenesis, glycogenolysis, lipolysis, and proteolysis are further activated by these hormonal changes. Glucose-6-phosphate, other phosphorylated intermediates of the Embden-Meyerhof pathway, and pyruvate accumulate, since metabolic precursors cannot be converted to glucose. The accumulating phosphorylated intermediates constitute a phosphate trap and deplete the cellular inorganic phosphate pool. As described previously, this reduces mitochondrial oxidative phosphorylation and blunts pyruvate uptake. The cytosol pyruvate concentration increases, and simultaneously the high $NADH/NAD^+$ ratio drives pyruvate toward lactate.

During the initial phase of fasting hypoglycemia in patients with glucose-6-phosphatase deficiency, fatty acid entry into mitochondria is relatively slow. Cytosol malonyl-CoA levels are high enough to inhibit the entry of fatty acids into mitochondria (*see* Ketoacidosis). Later, as glucagon levels increase, the malonyl-CoA levels fall, and long-chain fatty acid mitochondrial entry, oxidation, and ketogenesis accelerate. Therefore, these patients initially develop lactic acidosis and later ketoacidosis during fasting.

Fasting also increases the uric acid concentration in these patients. The biochemical mechanisms responsible for hyperuricemia are analogous to those described for hereditary fructose intolerance. The inorganic phosphate and ATP depletion trigger degradation of the adenylate pool to generate uric acid. Frequent feedings, including nocturnal enteral tube feedings, are used to prevent these metabolic derangements in patients with glucose-6-phosphatase deficiency.

Similar biochemical derangements develop in patients with *fructose-1,6-bisphosphatase deficiency*. This enzyme is not required to release glucose from glycogen but is needed to generate glucose via gluconeogenesis (Fig. 1). During a fast, these patients initially use glycogen. After glycogen depletion, additional glucose synthesis from gluconeogenic precursors is blocked. The metabolic cascade triggered by the resulting hypoglycemia is similar to that which occurs during fasting in patients with glucose-6-phosphatase deficiency.

The syndromes of lactic acidosis discussed to this point are largely the result of abnormal mitochondrial energy generation. The energy deficit may result from decreased oxygen delivery or use, congenital or acquired mitochondrial enzyme defects, or acute inorganic phosphate depletion. Other forms of lactic acidosis are due primarily to accelerated lactate production. The lactate uptake rate may be increased, normal, or decreased. Lactic acidosis that follows strenuous exercise is one example of rapid lactic acid generation that temporarily exceeds the hepatic removal rate. The source of the lactic acid is anaerobic glycolysis in muscle. During *strenuous exercise*, hepatic blood flow decreases, depressing lactate delivery and uptake. Following exhaustive exercise, lactate levels may increase to 12 mEq/liter or more. Similar mechanisms generate *postictal lactic acidosis*. Cessation of the exercise, or seizure, slows lactic acid generation, permitting the accumulated lactic acid to be metabolized rapidly. Lactate levels are normal within 1 hr.

Malignancies, especially certain leukemias, lymphomas, and oat cell lung cancer, may produce chronic lactic acidosis. These patients generally have a large tumor mass. Multiple factors may contribute to the lactic acidosis in these patients: (1) The malignant cells, present in large quantities, often have a rapid metabolic rate. (2) Rapidly growing and bulky tumors may develop hypoxic foci as they outstrip their blood supply. (3) Acquired enzymatic defects, which accelerate lactate production or decrease lactate use, have been identified in some cases. (4) Extensive metastatic liver disease may decrease hepatic lactate uptake. These patients may manifest chronic lactic acidosis that persists for weeks or months. It is refractory to treatments other than those directed at controlling the malignancy itself. Exogenous $NaHCO_3$ usually is not helpful and has been shown actually to accelerate lactic acid synthesis in some patients.

Severe hepatic disease may decrease lactate uptake and use. However, lactic acidosis is not common in patients with liver disease. If lactic acidosis develops, there is usually some other cause for accelerated lactate generation, such as hypotension or sepsis. However, some patients with chronic liver disease, severe renal failure (frequently on dialysis), and severe malnutrition may develop chronic lactic acidosis that is not due to hypotension, decreased tissue perfusion, or hypoxia. The acidosis often develops with fasting and usually is associated with hypoglycemia. These patients are glycogen depleted and, therefore, critically dependent on gluconeogenesis to maintain blood glucose levels during a fast. Low insulin levels and high counterregulatory hormones—glucagon, growth hormone, glucocorticoid and catecholamine —accelerate gluconeogenesis and also lypolysis and proteolysis. However, the hepatic uptake of glucose precursors, especially alanine, is decreased owing to poor hepatic function. In addition, malnutrition may sharply reduce alanine release from muscle. These processes blunt the gluconeogenic response and result in hypoglycemia. Simultaneously, lactic acid levels increase as decreased hepatic lactate uptake combines with accelerated peripheral generation. Lactic acidosis further depresses hepatic alanine uptake and thereby exacerbates the hypoglycemia. A vicious cycle ensues. Most of the biochemical abnormalities, including the hypoglycemia and lactic acidosis, are rapidly reversed by intravenous glucose infusions. The complex interrelationships among the liver disease, renal disease, lactic acidosis, and hypoglycemia have not been fully elucidated. However, because exogenous glucose rapidly reverses most of the metabolic abnormalities, including the lactic acidosis, hypoglycemia must play a central role.

Increased catecholamines, as a result of either endogenous secretion or exogenous infusion, increase lactic acid levels slightly. Epinephrine accelerates glycogen breakdown and glycolysis while inhibiting mitochondrial pyruvate uptake. This increases pyruvate and, in parallel, lactate levels. However, if the $NADH/NAD^+$ ratio remains normal, lactate increases are relatively small. When catecholamine levels increase markedly, tissue perfusion may be compromised owing to intense peripheral vasoconstriction and cardiac dysfunction. The $NADH/NAD^+$ ratio then increases, and clinically significant lactic acidosis can occur. Severe lactic acidosis may occur in patients with *pheochromocytomas* and when large exogenous doses of catecholamines are used.

Therapy of Lactic Acidosis (13,70,76,77,88,90)

The treatment of lactic acidosis requires that the underlying pathophysiology be addressed. When lactic acid is overproduced, the root cause of overproduction must be identified and reversed. The therapeutic approach in patients with shock, sepsis, asphyxia, and various poisonings is generally self-evident, if not always successful. Treatment directed at later steps in the metabolic cascade that eventuates in lactic acidosis generally is unsuccessful. For example, strategies designed to furnish the mitochondria with nonoxygen electron acceptors usually fail. Methylene blue, a strong oxidant that accepts electrons from NADH, oxidizing the cofactor to NAD^+, has been infused in attempts to normalize the $NADH/NAD^+$ ratio and reverse lactic acidosis. Unfortunately, any improvement that occurs is transient unless the underlying pathology is simultaneously reversed.

Recently, a novel biochemical approach has been used to treat lactic acidosis. The compound dichloroacetate stimulates pyruvate dehydrogenase and accelerates mitochondrial pyruvate oxidation (Fig. 1). Increased mitochondrial pyruvate uptake should decrease the cytosol concentrations of pyruvate and lactate. However, if effective mitochondrial oxygen delivery and use are not restored simultaneously, the beneficial effect of dichloroacetate also will be transient. Dichloroacetate has been shown to improve cardiac performance. This may result from stimulation of the pyruvate dehydrogenase complex in myocardial cells. If dichloroacetate improves the hemodynamic status, this effect may be the explanation for the clinical improvement that sometimes occurs with this drug. The potential clinical use of this drug remains uncertain. Perhaps it can be used to provide more time to reverse the underlying cause of the lactic acidosis. Dichloroacetate appears to be relatively nontoxic when used acutely but may have neurotoxic effects when used on a chronic basis.

Treatment of lactic acidosis with infusions of $NaHCO_3$ or other alkalinizing salts generally is ineffective. Even when the pH and $[HCO_3^-]_s$ can be increased, the basic abnormality responsible for the generation of lactic acidosis usually persists, and acidemia recurs. Although severe acidemia may depress cardiovascular function and blunt catecholamine responsiveness, $NaHCO_3$ therapy usually affords only minor and short-lived beneficial effects. More worrisome are experimental data showing that $NaHCO_3$ therapy may decrease survival in lactic acidosis. $NaHCO_3$ infusions acutely increase CO_2 generation and may increase the P_{CO_2}. A higher P_{CO_2} will accentuate intracellular acidosis. In addition, if large quantities of hypertonic $NaHCO_3$ are required, hypernatremia will result. When hypernatremia is forestalled by appropriate hydration, excessive volume expansion may produce pulmonary edema. Finally, if the patient survives the acidosis and large quantities of $NaHCO_3$ have been administered, rebound metabolic alkalosis develops during recovery (*see* Chapter 17). Hemodialysis or peritoneal dialysis, using $NaHCO_3$ dialysate, simultaneously infuses HCO_3^-, removes lactate, normalizes electrolytes, and stabilizes the extracellular fluid (ECF) volume. Occasional patients apparently have benefited from such therapy. However, the simultaneous correction of multiple abnormalities, especially the volume status, may be responsible for the improvement, rather than the infusion of $NaHCO_3$.

KETOACIDOSIS (52,96,97,99,103,104,107)

Ketoacidosis is the result of an accumulation of acetoacetic acid and βOH-butyric acid (acetoacetic acid is a true ketoacid; βOH-butyric acid is not). Mild ketoacidosis develops in normal individuals during prolonged starvation, whereas severe ketoacidosis occurs most commonly in patients with poorly controlled, or uncontrolled, insulin-dependent diabetes mellitus. Patients with hereditary glucose-6-phosphatase deficiency (von Gierke's disease) and fructose-1,6-bisphosphatase deficiency can develop mixed ketoacidosis and lactic acidosis during a fast (*see* Lactic Acidosis). Some chronic alcoholics develop severe ketoacidosis when they fast. Each of these clinical settings generates low insulin levels and variable elevations of glucagon, cortisol, growth hormone, catecholamines, and glucocorticoids. This hormone profile is necessary for the development of the ketoacidosis.

Fat Oxidation, Ketogenesis, and Ketone Metabolism (51,68)

The reactions responsible for fatty acid release and oxidation are shown in Figs. 3A and 3B. A hormone sensitive lipase in adipose tissues releases free fatty acids (FFA) from the triglyceride in adipose stores. The fatty acids that enter the blood are transported to the liver for further metabolism. In hepatocyte cytoplasm, fatty acids can be reesterified with glycerol to reform triglycerides or be used to synthesize phospholipids or lipoproteins. Alternatively, fatty acids can enter the mitochondria of hepatocytes to undergo β-oxidation. β-Oxidation sequentially splits two carbon fragments of acetyl-CoA from the fatty acid. The regulation of fatty acid oxidation is achieved primarily at two metabolic sites. First, the lipase that releases fatty acids from triglycerides in adipose is hormone sensitive. It is inhibited by relatively low levels of insulin and activated by catecholamines, cortisol, growth hormone, and very high glucagon levels. Accelerated FFA release is a prerequisite for the development of severe ketoacidosis. Second, the entry of long-chain fatty acids into the hepatic mitochondria for β-oxidation is tightly regulated at the inner membrane of the mitochondria (Fig. 3B).

Within hepatic cytoplasm, long-chain fatty acids are activated by enzymatic conversion to their respective acyl-CoA derivatives. If mitochondrial oxidation is to occur, the activated fatty acid is next linked to carnitine by the enzyme carnitine palmitoyl transferase I (CPT I). The acyl-carnitine complex crosses the inner mitochondrial membrane, and on its inner surface, CPT II catalyzes the reformation of fatty acyl-CoA and carnitine. The activated fatty acid is now in the mitochondrial matrix and may undergo β-oxidation; the carnitine recycles to the outer surface of the inner membrane and can be reused as a fatty acid carrier molecule. The mitochondrial fatty acid entry rate is regulated at the level of CPT I. This enzyme is competitively inhibited by the in-

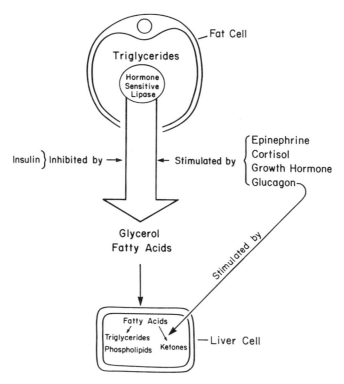

FIG. 3A. The release of fatty acids from adipose triglyceride stores under the control of hormone-sensitive lipase.

termediate malonyl-CoA. When cytosolic fatty acid generation occurs acetyl-CoA is first converted to malonyl-CoA. This intermediate is committed to the synthesis of fatty acid. In the fed state, relatively high insulin and low glucagon levels stimulate fatty acid synthesis, and the cytosolic concentration of malonyl-CoA increases. This inhibits CPT I and reduces the flow of long-chain fatty acids into mitochondria. During a fast or with uncontrolled insulin-dependent diabetes mellitus, insulin levels fall and glucagon levels are elevated. Acetyl-CoA carboxylase, the enzyme responsible for conversion of acetyl-CoA to malonyl-CoA, is now inhibited by cyclic AMP (cAMP)-mediated phosphorylation a consequence of the high gluagon/insulin ratio. The fall in cytoplasmic malonyl-CoA levels, deinhibits CPT I and accelerates the entry of long-chain fatty acids into mitochondria. Mitochondrial fatty acid β-oxidation and acetyl-CoA generation are thereby accelerated.

Acetyl-CoA generated in the mitochondria from fat oxidation (or from pyruvate via pyruvate dehydrogenase) can be further oxidized in the Krebs cycle to yield CO_2, H_2O, and energy, exit the mitochondria for fat synthesis (indirectly; *see* Footnote 1), or be converted to ketoacids. When rapid acetyl-CoA generation, due to rapid fatty acid oxidation, occurs in a setting of low in-

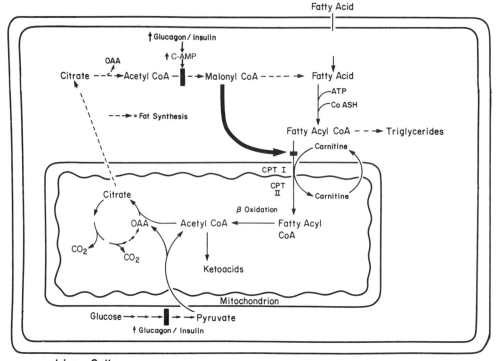

Liver Cell

FIG. 3B. Fat metabolism in hepatic parenchymal cells. The oxidation of long-chain fatty acids requires that they first be activated in cytoplasm and then transported into the mitochondria. Mitochondrial entry is controlled at the level of carnitine palmitoyl transferase I (CPT I) by malonyl CoA. Liver cells can also synthesize fatty acids from acetyl-CoA. The fat synthetic pathway is indicated by the dashed arrows. The synthetic and oxidative pathways are under the control of insulin and glucagon. OAA, oxaloacetate.

sulin and high glucagon levels, ketoacids may become the dominant metabolic products. Krebs cycle oxidation will be limited, in part because oxaloacetate, which is necessary to condense with acetyl-CoA to form citrate, is exported from the mitochondria for gluconeogenesis when insulin is low and glucagon is high. (The oxaloacetate also exits the mitochondria indirectly in the form of malate or aspartate.) This hormone profile also inhibits cytoplasmic fat synthesis from acetyl-CoA. Therefore, the rapid generation of acetyl-CoA occurs in a setting of depressed mitochondrial Krebs cycle and cytoplasmic fatty acid synthetic activity, and the acetyl-CoA is driven toward formation of ketoacids. Two acetyl-CoA molecules condense to form acetoacetyl-CoA, which is subsequently converted to acetoacetic acid (via 3-hydroxy-3-methylglutaryl- CoA).

The ketoacids produced in the liver are acetoacetic acid and βOH-butyric acid (βOH-butyric acid is not a true ketoacid). These two acids are interconverted by the βOH-butyrate dehydrogenase reaction, which requires as cosubstrates the $NAD^+/NADH$ couple (Fig. 4). At equilibrium, the βOH-butyrate/acetoacetate ratio is proportional to the mitochondrial $NADH/NAD^+$ ratio and is normally about 2:1. Both acetoacetic and βOH-butyric acid are relatively strong acids (pK 3.6 and 4.4, respectively). To the extent that they accumulate in the ECF, the $[HCO_3^-]_s$ falls and the anion gap increases. The severity of the anion gap metabolic acidosis reflects the sum of the βOH-butyric and acetoacetic acid levels. Although βOH-butyrate usually predominates (2:1), the magnitude of the acidosis is independent of the specific accumulating acid. However, the two anions have important differences with respect to diagnostic studies. Nitroprusside reagent, most often used to detect ketoacids in blood and urine, reacts with acetoacetate, which usually accounts for only about 30% of blood ketoacids, but does not react with the predominant species, βOH-butyrate. If the $NADH/NAD^+$ ratio increases, βOH-butyrate levels increase further and acetoacetate levels decrease (Fig. 4). The nitroprusside test will then become less positive, or even negative, despite significant ketoacidosis. This situation may occur when ketoacidosis and lactic acidosis coexist because lactic acidosis is usually associated with an $NADH/NAD^+$ redox shift. Patients with alcoholic ketoacidosis also typically have a high $NADH/NAD^+$ ratio, which leads to relatively weak nitroprusside tests.

Acetone is nonenzymatically derived from acetoacetic acid (Fig. 4). Acetone is not an acid; its accumulation does not reduce the $[HCO_3^-]_s$ or increase the anion gap. It is volatile and is largely excreted by the lungs. Small amounts are excreted by the kidneys and metabolized to glucose. Serum acetone levels increase markedly during prolonged, severe ketoacidosis. The elevated levels may persist for several days after ketoacidosis has resolved.

Acetone also reacts with nitroprusside, and this may introduce diagnostic errors. As ketoacidosis improves, persistent acetone levels are responsible for a positive nitroprusside test despite otherwise improved or normal acid-base parameters. A persistent osmolal gap without an anion gap suggests that the

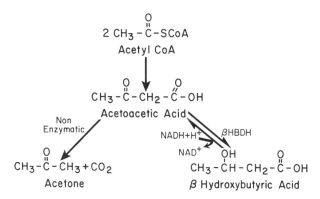

FIG. 4. Ketone body metabolism. The interrelationship between acetoacetic acid, β-hydroxybutyric acid (not a true ketoacid), and acetone is shown. The arrow from acetyl-CoA to acetoacetic acid encompasses the intermediate formation of acetoacetic-CoA and β-OH β-methylglutaryl-CoA. (βHBDH) β-hydroxybutyrate dehydrogenase.

positive nitroprusside test is attributable to acetone and not ketoacids. Indeed, if these findings occur during recovery from diabetic ketoacidosis, they indicate that ketoacid overproduction has been reversed, and insulin requirements probably have reverted to basal levels. Since acetone may accumulate in concentrations as high as 50 mm/liter and is slowly eliminated, the positive nitroprusside test may persist for days. Isopropyl alcohol poisoning also leads to acetone accumulation, with similar potential diagnostic confusion (see below).

Diabetic Ketoacidosis (1,96)

The central cause of diabetic ketoacidosis is absolute, or relative, insulin deficiency and glucagon excess. Insulin deficiency may develop in a previously undiagnosed diabetic or in a diabetic patient who discontinues insulin therapy. It also commonly occurs in a setting of increased insulin resistance resulting from infection or some other stress. The levels of glucagon and other counterregulatory hormones increase. This results in catabolism of peripheral tissues, which release substrate that the liver uses to synthesize glucose (amino acids derived from protein and glycerol from fat are used for gluconeogenesis). Glucose also is liberated from glycogen stores. Fatty acids are rapidly oxidized to ketoacids. Simultaneously, glucose and ketoacid uptake by peripheral tissues is inhibited so that blood glucose and ketoacid levels rise sharply.

Starvation Ketosis (65,66)

Starvation will generate modest ketoacidosis in normal individuals. Initially (first 10–14 hours of fast), glucose levels are maintained primarily by glycogenolysis. After several days, as glycogen stores are depleted, gluconeogenesis increases and becomes dominant. At this time, hepatic energy requirements are met largely by oxidation of fatty acids. The accelerated mobilization and mitochondrial oxidation of fatty acids generate ketosis. After 1 to 2 weeks, the blood ketoacid level reaches 5 to 6 mEq/liter. More fulminant ketoacidosis is aborted by several features unique to uncomplicated starvation. Ketosis itself directly stimulates the pancreatic islet cells to release insulin, despite continued starvation. These tonic insulin levels inhibit lipolysis. This lipolysis brake does not exist in the diabetic who develops ketoacidosis. During prolonged starvation, the elevated glucagon and catecholamine levels also return toward normal as the ketoacidosis stabilizes.

Alcoholic Ketoacidosis (15,28,42,48)

Alcoholic ketoacidosis develops in certain susceptible individuals who chronically abuse alcohol. Its development requires that an alcohol debauch be followed by a period of nausea, vomiting, and starvation (thereby depleting the liver of glycogen). Alcoholic ketoacidosis may represent an extreme form of starvation ketosis. However, in these subjects, starvation combines with alcohol withdrawal and volume depletion to elevate markedly counterregulatory hormones, especially the catecholamines. This accelerates fatty acid release from adipose stores and markedly increases blood fatty acid levels. The fatty acids are presented to the liver, which is primed for fatty acid entry into mitochondria and fat oxidation by the high glucagon/insulin ratio. This sequence culminates in ketoacidosis. A major distinction from uncomplicated starvation ketosis is the greatly accelerated release of fatty acids from adipose tissue.

As mentioned previously, the NADH/NAD ratio in alcoholic ketoacidosis is increased, which is reflected in a high βOH-butyrate/acetoacetate ratio. This may be the result of rapid NADH generation produced by alcohol oxidation and/or diminished tissue perfusion resulting from volume depletion. The nitroprusside reaction may be reduced by this redox shift despite severe ketoacidosis.

Glucose-6-Phosphatase and Fructose-1,6-Bisphosphatase Deficiency (3,34,95)

Patients who have glucose-6-phosphatase deficiency cannot liberate glucose from glucose-6-phosphate. Consequently, gluconeogenesis and glycogenolysis cannot generate glucose normally. A relatively brief fast produces hypoglycemia, reducing insulin levels, and increasing the levels of counterregulatory hormones. Exaggerated starvation ketoacidosis will develop. It is usually preceded by lactic acidosis (*see* Clinical Syndromes of Lactic Acidosis).

Patients with fructose-1,6-bisphosphatase deficiency also develop similar abnormalities during a fast. These patients can mobilize glucose from glycogen but cannot generate glucose via the gluconeogenic pathway (*see* Clinical Syndromes of Lactic Acidosis).

Many other inherited enzyme disorders produce metabolic acidosis owing to the accumulation in blood of a spectrum of unusual organic acids. Some of these acids are ketoacids, including acetoacetic acid and other longer-chain ketoacids (*see* Congenital Organic Acidosis).

POISON-ASSOCIATED ANION GAP ACIDOSIS (97,100,104)

Virtually every type of poison can produce lactic acidosis as a result of cardiovascular collapse. However several poisons can contribute to the anion gap acidosis, either by generating acid metabolites or inhibiting normal enzymatic reactions which, in turn, result in organic acid accumulation. Such poisons include methanol, ethylene glycol, paraldehyde, and salicylate.

Exposure to short-chain aliphatic alcohols and related compounds can produce many toxic manifestations. CNS sedation and depression are common direct effects of these poisons. The native compounds are oxidized to a variety of toxic products. In some cases, the metabolic products are more toxic than the parent compounds. Poisoning usually results from ingestion, but volatile compounds may be absorbed in the lungs or through the skin. This is more likely in infants and young children.

Osmolality and the Osmolal Gap (30,100)

Most toxic alcohols and glycols have a relatively low molecular weight. When they accumulate in blood, the total osmotic pressure increases.[3] Normally, the major solutes responsible for the blood osmotic pressure are sodium salts (e.g., NaCl, $NaHCO_3$). If the urea or glucose concentrations increase markedly, they also contribute significantly to the measured osmolality. Plasma osmolality can be approximated by the following equation.

$$\text{Osmolality} = 2\,[\text{Na}]_s + \frac{\text{BUN mg/100 ml}}{2.8} + \frac{\text{glucose mg/100 ml}}{18}$$

The osmolality, calculated with this equation, should agree with the measured osmolality to within 10 to 15 mOsm/liter. When the measured osmolality exceeds the calculated osmolality by greater than 15 mOsm/liter, several possible explanations must be considered. First, the calculated osmolality may be spuriously low due to artifactual depression of the $[\text{Na}^+]_s$, i.e., pseudohyponatremia. Pseudohyponatremia may result from hyperlipidemia or hyperproteinemia, displacing plasma water. This artifact of $[\text{Na}^+]_s$ measurement occurs only if the measurement technique requires a quantitative aliquot of serum or plasma, for example, flame photometry. Hyperviscosity also can spuriously reduce the $[\text{Na}^+]_s$ as measured with certain instruments. (Hyperviscosity interferes with quantitative aspiration required with some methods.) Displacement errors and hyperviscosity do not affect the osmolality measurements. Therefore, the osmolality reflects the true $[\text{Na}^+]$ in serum water, whereas the measurement of $[\text{Na}^+]_s$ may be spuriously reduced when plasma solids are markedly increased.

Another explanation for an osmolal gap (the measured osmolality exceeds the calculated value) is the presence in blood of osmotically active substances not included in the equation. For example, mannitol infusions will elevate the measured blood osmolality, but mannitol does not appear in the osmolality equation. Furthermore, mannitol is restricted to the ECF and shifts water from the intracellular space to the ECF. The ECF expansion decreases

---

[3]The osmotic effects of volatile alcohols are only apparent when measured by freezing point depression osmometry. If a vapor pressure osmometer is used, dissolved alcohols do not generate osmotic pressure because volatile substances contribute only minimally to an alteration of the measured water vapor pressure.

TABLE 2. *Compounds that can accumulate in the blood*

Substance	Molecular weight	mOSM/liter generated by a concentration of 100 mg/dl
Acetone	58	17
Ethanol	46	22
Ethyl ether	26	38
Isopropanol	60	17
Methanol	32	31
Ethylene glycol	62	16
Mannitol	182	5

$[Na^+]_s$. Therefore, the measured osmolality increases while simultaneously the calculated osmolality falls.

The presence of alcohols, glycols, and acetone in blood will also raise the measured osmolality. Unlike mannitol or glucose, these compounds readily penetrate cells. Therefore, they do not induce any fluid shifts and $[Na^+]_s$ is not directly altered. The difference between the measured and calculated osmolality (the osmolal gap) is proportional to the concentration of alcohol, glycol, or acetone in the blood. For example, the molecular weight of methanol is 32. Therefore, a methanol level of 100 mg/dl represents a methanol concentration and osmolal gap of 31 mOsm/liter. Table 2 lists the molecular weight and osmolal contributions of several compounds that potentially can accumulate in blood.

Methanol Poisoning (6,14,32,44,45,49,50,53–55,83,86,87)

Methanol, or wood alcohol, is a widely used industrial solvent, antifreeze ingredient (especially in windshield washing solutions), and canned solid fuel component. The potential lethal dose of methanol in adults is 60 to 250 ml. Methanol poisoning produces initial inebriation similar to ethanol intoxication. After a latent period of 6 to 24 hr, the patient may develop vomiting, abdominal pain, visual disturbances, confusion, and coma. During the latent period, methanol is oxidized, primarily in the liver, to formaldehyde and to formic acid (Fig. 5).

Anion gap metabolic acidosis develops frequently. It is largely the result of formic acid accumulation. Hypoxia and hypotension also occur commonly. If cardiovascular function deteriorates, lactic acidosis will ensue. Methanol and toxic metabolites also may interfere with normal mitochondrial function and thereby contribute to lactic acid accumulation.

Ocular toxicity is a frequent complication of methanol poisoning. Both formic acid and formaldehyde are toxic to retinal cells and the optic nerve. Blurred vision, optic disc swelling, papillary dilation, and blindness may oc-

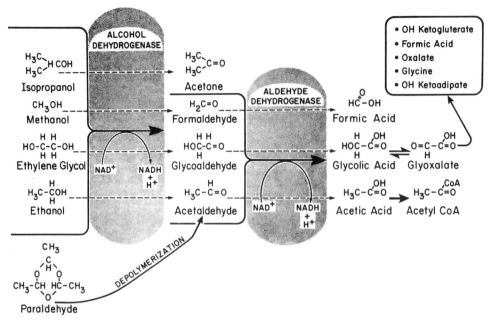

FIG. 5. The hepatic metabolism of several alcohols, ethylene glycol, and paraldehyde to their derivative compounds.

cur. Nausea, vomiting, and abdominal pain may be due to pancreatitis. CNS involvement can produce confusion, seizures, and coma.

Methanol poisoning requires aggressive therapy. First, if methanol ingestion is recent, the unabsorbed alcohol that remains in the stomach is removed by the induction of vomiting in alert patients (i.e., ipecac syrup 15–20 ml orally) or by gastric lavage when patients are less alert or unconscious. Next, an aqueous slurry of activated charcoal, 30 to 50 g, is administered by mouth or via nasogastric tube. This may be followed by a purgative, such as sorbitol (30–50 ml of 70% solution) to hasten the transit of unabsorbed alcohol and charcoal through the gastrointestinal tract.

Methanol toxicity is largely the result of its metabolic product. Therefore, the next phase of therapy is directed at inhibition of alcohol dehydrogenase, the major methanol-oxidizing enzyme. Relatively specific and potent inhibitors of alcohol dehydrogenase, such as 4-methylpyrazole, can completely block the development of anion gap metabolic acidosis and other toxic consequences of methanol poisoning. Since this compound has not yet been approved for human use, the metabolism of methanol by alcohol dehydrogenase may be competitively inhibited with ethanol. Alcohol dehydrogenase has a greater affinity for ethanol than for other alcohols, so that ethanol competitively inhibits their oxidation. A therapeutically effective blood ethanol level is 100 to 150 mg/dl. Ethanol can be administered by mouth, nasogastric tube, intravenously, or via dialysis. An initial loading dose of approximately 600 mg/kg produces the requisite level. In a 70 kg adult, this represents 42 g of ethanol. The alert patient may ingest 4 ounces of 80-proof whiskey. Alternatively 500 ml of a 10% ethanol solution may be infused intravenously. Subsequent dosing will vary depending on the rate of ethanol metabolism. Patients who chronically abuse alcohol have greater alcohol dehydrogenase activity and, consequently, more rapidly metabolize ethanol. Nonalcoholic subjects require 5 g/hr of ethanol to maintain an adequate level (about 60 ml/hr of a 10% infusion); chronic alcoholics require about 10 g/hr (120 ml/hr of a 10% infusion). If dialysis is initiated, the ethanol infusion rate must be doubled, or ethanol may be added to the dialysate at a concentration of about 100 mg/dl.

Reversal of the metabolic acidosis may decrease methanol toxicity. Therefore, aggressive alkalinization has been recommended. This may be accomplished by parenteral $NaHCO_3$ infusion. However, volume expansion and hypernatremia may complicate hypertonic $NaHCO_3$ infusions. Alkalinization is achieved more rapidly and effectively by means of hemodialysis. Hemodialysis also rapidly removes methanol and toxic metabolic products. Hemodialysis should be initiated promptly if the blood methanol level exceeds 50 mg/dl. Progressive metabolic acidosis is also an indication to initiate hemodialysis. Peritoneal dialysis is much less effective and is a poor second choice to hemodialysis when rapid methanol removal is deemed necessary. Forced diuresis is relatively ineffective because renal clearance of methanol is very low.

Ethylene Glycol Poisoning (11,27,62,63,79,82,92)

Ethylene glycol is a principal constituent of most automobile engine antifreeze preparations and is a widely used organic solvent. Although its use as a pharmaceutical solvent has largely been eliminated in the United States, some drugs obtained abroad still contain potentially toxic amounts of ethylene glycol. Ethylene glycol is still used illegally to sweeten wine.

Chronic alcoholics may knowingly ingest ethylene glycol as an inexpensive ethanol substitute. However, poisoning is more commonly accidental or suicidal. The lethal dose is about 100 ml, although occasional individuals have survived ingestion of up to 900 ml. Similar to methanol, ethylene glycol itself is not extremely toxic but is oxidized to multiple more toxic products, especially glycolates and oxalates. Several of these metabolic products are relatively strong acids. Their accumulation is largely responsible for the development of an anion gap metabolic acidosis. In addition, cardiovascular collapse is common in these patients and may precipitate lactic acidosis.

Ethylene glycol poisoning usually produces inebriation, nausea, and vomiting soon after ingestion. However, the ingestion of a large quantity may rapidly result in coma, seizures, and death. The initial symptoms persist for about 12 hr and typically are followed by a second wave of clinical and biochemical alterations. During the early latent period, toxic metabolic products accumulate and generate a progressive anion gap metabolic acidosis. A large quantity of oxalate is produced and precipitates in the lungs, heart, kidneys, and brain as calcium oxalate. Calcium precipitation and complex formation with oxalate result in reduced ionized calcium concentrations. Hypocalcemic tetany and seizures may result.

If the patient survives the initial phases of ethylene glycol poisoning, oliguric renal failure, often associated with flank pain, becomes the dominant clinical problem. This is partially the result of calcium oxalate deposition in the kidneys. Patients who are long term survivors may develop permanent neurologic deficits, perhaps also secondary to calcium oxalate deposits.

Ethylene glycol intoxication should be considered when a patient has confusion, obtundation, or coma and an unexplained metabolic acidosis. Suspicion increases if the patient has a psychiatric, suicidal, or chronic alcohol abuse history. The laboratory constellation that characterizes ethylene glycol poisoning is a large osmolal gap (that cannot be attributed to ethanol), anion gap metabolic acidosis, and calcium oxalate crystals in the urine. Identification of ethylene glycol in blood, urine, or gastric fluid establishes the definitive diagnosis.

The initial management of ethylene glycol poisoning is similar to that described for methanol poisoning. Unabsorbed poison is removed from the gastrointestinal tract by emesis or gastric lavage. A charcoal slurry is then administered to bind residual ethylene glycol. Purgatives that speed gastrointestinal transit also may be useful. Ethylene glycol is oxidized by alcohol dehydrogenase in the cytoplasm of hepatic cells. Inhibition of this enzyme markedly reduces ethylene glycol toxicity. As indicated in the discussion of methanol intoxication, the most potent inhibitor of alcohol dehydrogenase is 4-methylpyrazale, a compound that is effective orally and intravenously; unfortunately, it may not be readily available. Ethanol is, therefore, used as a competitive substrate for alcohol dehydrogenase. A blood ethanol concentration of about 100 mg/100 ml is considered optimal. The specific details of therapeutic ethanol administration have been discussed (*see* Methanol Poisoning).

Severe metabolic acidosis may be treated with parenteral $NaHCO_3$. However, large quantities of $NaHCO_3$ will produce volume expansion and may precipitate pulmonary edema. Cardiac and pulmonary toxicity resulting from calcium oxalate deposition increases the likelihood of pulmonary edema in response to a volume challenge.

Unlike methanol, the renal excretion of toxic products of ethylene glycol may be enhanced, in the presence of adequate renal function, by forced diuresis with furosemide and mannitol. Precautions must be taken to forestall sodium and other electrolyte deficits that can be induced by the diuresis. The effectiveness of diuretics in accelerating urinary losses will be greatly amplified if metabolism of ethylene glycol is reduced by inhibition of the alcohol dehydrogenase enzyme system. Hemodialysis may be used effectively to treat ethylene glycol poisoning. It removes ethylene glycol and toxic metabolic products, reverses the metabolic acidosis, corrects electrolyte abnormalities, and stabilizes volume status.

Ionized calcium levels are reduced as a result of calcium oxalate precipitates and chelates. Metabolic acidosis ameliorates the fall in ionized calcium by reducing calcium binding to proteins. Therefore, alkalinization exacerbates hypocalcemic symptomatology and may produce tetany and seizures. Dialysis simultaneously corrects the acidosis and hypocalcemia because oxalate is removed and calcium is infused simultaneously with alkalinization.

Isopropyl Alcohol Poisoning (26,43)

Isopropyl alcohol is used in rubbing compounds, as a solvent and as an antiseptic. Isopropyl alcohol poisoning may be accidental or suicidal. This alcohol is very volatile and may be absorbed across the skin or the lungs. Poisoning by absorption is most common in infants and young children. The ingestion of 200 to 250 ml of isopropyl alcohol is potentially lethal in adults.

The initial toxic effect of isopropyl alcohol is neurologic. Inebriation, confusion, coma, and respiratory failure may occur. Early gastric and hepatic toxicity also are common.

Isopropyl alcohol, like the other alcohols described, is oxidized by alcohol dehydrogenase (Fig. 5). However, unlike methanol and ethylene glycol, its metabolic products are not acids. The major metabolic product of isopropyl alcohol is acetone, which is primarily excreted by the lungs and, to a lesser extent, the kidneys. Acetone also can be metabolized to glucose.

Isopropyl alcohol poisoning generates an osmolal gap representing both the alcohol and acetone. The nitroprusside test becomes positive in blood and urine, and the breath develops a fruity smell due to the acetone. These findings suggest ketoacidosis. However, hyperglycemia and anion gap metabolic acidosis usually are absent. An osmolal gap, positive ketone tests, normal acid-base parameters, and a normal anion gap are a constellation of findings that, in the appropriate setting, strongly suggest isopropyl alcohol poisoning. If gastrointestinal bleeding, hypotension, or liver toxicity intervenes, lactic acidosis may also develop.

The treatment of isopropyl alcohol poisoning is largely supportive. As with most other ingested poisons, the unabsorbed fraction still present in the gastrointestinal tract should be removed with purgatives or lavage and adsorption to charcoal (*see* Methanol Poisoning). Careful attention to the cardiorespiratory status and fluid balance may be the only other necessary treatment. If the patient remains stable, the alcohol will be excreted and metabolized. If lactic acidosis develops, cardiovascular function, peripheral perfusion, and tissue oxygenation must be improved. Hemodialysis can rapidly remove isopropyl alcohol and acetone but is usually not necessary. It should be reserved for those patients with severe clinical manifestations whose isopropyl alcohol blood levels exceed 100 mg/dl. Although peritoneal dialysis also removes alcohol and acetone, it is much less efficient than hemodialysis.

Paraldehyde Poisoning (5,35)

Chronic paraldehyde overdosage is a rare cause of anion gap metabolic acidosis. Paraldehyde is depolymerized to acetaldehyde and then metabolized to acetyl-CoA and acetic acid (Fig. 5). Although acetic acid levels do increase, the acidosis is caused by multiple organic acids that have not been well characterized. The high acetaldehyde levels can give a positive nitroprusside result, suggesting ketosis, but this is a pseudoketotic reaction. Paraldehyde poisoning usually occurs in patients who chronically abuse alcohol and ingest large amounts of paraldehyde over a long period.

Salicylate Poisoning (2,17,20,29,31,36,38,64,81,85,94)

Salicylate poisoning is a relatively common disorder, which produces a characteristic spectrum of clinical, acid-base, and electrolyte abnormalities. Salicylate may be ingested as salicylic acid, acetylsalicylic acid (aspirin), Na salicylate, or methylsalicylate. Acetylsalicylic acid is rapidly hydrolyzed in the liver to salicylic acid.

At toxic concentration, salicylate uncouples oxidative phosphorylation, which accelerates oxygen use, heat generation, and CO_2 production. Multiple enzyme systems are inhibited by high salicylate levels. Salicylate also directly stimulates the central respiratory center, to increase ventilation. The hyperventilatory response usually exceeds the acceleration of CO_2 production, resulting in a respiratory alkalosis.

The metabolic acidosis produced by salicylate poisoning is multifactorial. As mentioned, a variety of enzymatic reactions are inhibited, and oxidative phosphorylation is uncoupled. Simultaneously, the low P_{CO_2} will increase the intracellular pH and accelerate glycolysis through deinhibition of phosphofructokinase. These effects may contribute to the development of lactic acidosis, which accounts for part of the acidosis. Vomiting and decreased intake can produce volume depletion, and cardiac irregularities may develop as a result of electrolyte abnormalities, especially hypokalemia. These factors also contribute to the development of lactic acidosis. Ketoacidosis also may occur, especially in young children and pregnant women. The anion gap metabolic acidosis that develops results from an accumulation of lactate, ketoacid, salicylate, and other organic acids.

Usually, metabolic acidosis and respiratory alkalosis occur together in salicylate poisoning. The blood pH represents the integrated effect of these two disturbances. Whether acidosis or alkalosis is dominant is influenced by the age of the patient. Metabolic acidosis is generally more severe in infants and young children. Adults with salicylate poisoning usually manifest a normal or alkaline blood pH. The systemic pH importantly affects neurotoxicity and survival. Salicylic acid has a low pK and is >99% ionized at systemic pH. The minute un-ionized fraction of salicylic acid readily penetrates cells, whereas the predominant ionized fraction does not. The concentration of the un-ionized fraction will double if the blood pH falls from 7.4 to 7.1. Thus, acidemia increases the concentration of un-ionized salicylate and its intracellular concentration in brain, liver, and other organs. This probably accounts for the increased mortality rate associated with acidemia.

Many other biochemical abnormalities occur in salicylate poisoning. These patients may develop hypoglycemia. Even when blood glucose levels are normal, brain glucose levels can be reduced. Extreme hypouricemia may occur due to inhibition of renal tubule urate reabsorption by high salicylate levels. Hypokalemia is principally due to enhanced urinary potassium losses caused by alkalinization of distal renal tubule cells (owing to respiratory alkalosis) in a setting where distal delivery of sodium salts (nonreabsorbed salicylate) is increased and sodium reabsorption is enhanced by elevated levels of aldosterone (volume depletion). In addition, starvation and vomiting may induce deficits of potassium. Finally, alkalosis curtails a redistribution of potassium from cells to extracellular fluid.

Clinical manifestations of salicylate poisoning include hyperventilation, confusion, coma, and seizures. Noncardiogenic pulmonary edema may occur, especially with chronic salicylate intoxication. Tinnitus, deafness, and vertigo are common complaints. Hyperthermia without evidence of infection reflects increased heat production. Ecchymoses, petechia, and prolonged bleeding are related to platelet dysfunction and hypoprothrombinemia. A diagnosis of salicylate poisoning should be considered whenever an unexplained anion gap acidosis is present, particularly if it is accompanied by unexplained breathlessness or CNS disturbances. Suspicion is increased if respiratory alkalosis is also identified.

The urinary excretion of salicylate metabolites can cause false-positive reactions for ketones (nitroprusside test) and glucose (reducing reactions). At the same time true ketonuria and glucosuria may be present. The most helpful, sensitive, and rapid clinical screening procedure utilizes ferric chloride to test urine. One milliliter of 10% $FeCl_3$ added to 3 ml of urine produces a purple color if salicylate is present. Since acetone may also produce this reaction, the urine specimen should be boiled to remove acetone.

Blood salicylate levels are readily available. This must be interpreted with respect to the elapsed time from ingestion to the measurement. The blood salicylate level falls with first-order kinetics. Toxicity is usually associated with peak levels above 30 mg/100 ml, while severe toxicity and fatalities occur when levels reach 100 mg/100 ml or more.

Salicylate intoxication is treated by first removing unabsorbed drug from the gastrointestinal tract. Gastric emptying is slowed by salicylism, so that emesis or lavage remains useful for up to 12 hr after ingestion. Activated charcoal should be administered (*see* Methanol Poisoning). Volume depletion, hypokalemia, hypoglycemia, and metabolic acidosis should be aggressively corrected. Hypoprothrombinemia can be corrected with one intramuscular injection of phytonadione (vitamin K), 0.1 mg/kg. Renal salicylate excretion will be accelerated by the induction of an alkaline diuresis. Salicylate is filtered at the glomerulus and both reabsorbed and secreted by the tubules. It is partially reabsorbed as undissociated salicylic acid via the process of nonionic diffusion when the urine pH is lower than the blood pH. Conversely, if urine pH is higher than blood pH, ionized salicylate is trapped in the urine. If the urine pH can be increased to 7.5 or greater, salicylate clearance may increase manyfold above the glomerular filtration rate (GFR). An alkaline diuresis (with urine flows of about 2 ml/min) can be accomplished by $NaHCO_3$ infusion. However, if the patient is already alkalemic, such infusions must be used cautiously, especially because of the danger of tetany.

The potential role for acetazolamide is controversial. By inhibiting carbonic anhydrase, it will reduce the renal bicarbonate reabsorptive capacity, thereby preventing $NaHCO_3$ retention and alkalinizing the urine, an effect that will enhance salicylate excretion. Since acetazolamide can produce acidosis, exogenous $NaHCO_3$ should always be administrated with it. Acetazolamide also tends to elevate plasma free salicylate levels by displacement of salicylate from plasma protein binding sites and inhibition of renal tubular salicylate secretion. Acetazolamide should therefore be used only if exogenous $NaHCO_3$ fails to produce an alkaline diuresis, and then in small amounts. Should sodium retention occur, furosemide may be required.

Intravenous fluids to replete volume, induce diuresis, provide $NaHCO_3$, and replace K^+ must be administered cautiously. Increased capillary permeability occurs in these patients and may predispose to noncardiogenic pulmonary edema and cerebral edema, which will be exacerbated by the intravenous fluids.

If the intoxication is severe and is associated with progressive metabolic and neurologic derangements, hemodialysis may become necessary. Dialysis also will be required if the patient develops acute renal failure or has preexistent chronic renal disease. Hemodialysis very efficiently and rapidly removes salicylate. It also corrects the acidosis, electrolyte abnormalities, and volume status. Peritoneal dialysis is much less effective than hemodialysis. (The peritoneal dialysis clearance rate of salicylate is about 25% that of hemodialysis.)

UNUSUAL ANION GAP METABOLIC ACIDOSES (97,99,104)

Congenital Organic Acidoses (4,7,23,39,71,89,101)

Inborn errors of metabolism can result in organic acidoses because of the accumulation of lactic acid, the classic ketoacids (acetoacetic and βOH-butyric acid), and a variety of other organic acid intermediates, including unusual long-chain ketoacids. Several of these inborn errors have been discussed. Defective glucose production or release as a result of either glucose-6-phosphatase deficiency (von Gierke's disease) or fructose-1,6-bisphosphatase deficiency result in fasting hypoglycemia and lactic and ketoacidosis (*see* Glucose-6-Phosphatase and Fructose-1,6-Bisphosphatase Deficiency). Less well characterized are several defects of phosphoenolpyruvate carboxykinase and pyruvate carboxylase, which also are associated with fasting hypoglycemia and lactic acidosis. Other forms of congenital lactic acidosis (*see* Lactic Acidosis) may be due to a variety of inborn errors of mitochondrial pyruvate metabolism or the electron transport system.

Over the past 20 years, a much larger number of congenital organic acidemias has been identified. The diagnosis and elucidation of these disorders are largely the result of the introduction of gas chromatography–mass spectroscopy (GC–MS) into clinical medicine. This methodology permits the rapid identification of multiple metabolic intermediates, including organic acids, that can potentially accumulate. These intermediates are often analyzed in urine, rather than blood, because they are readily filtered and then concentrated by the kidney.

In many cases, the affected metabolic step is catalyzed by a multiple enzyme complex that may require various cofactors, cosubstrates, or coenzymes. Many different and discrete enzymatic abnormalities, or defects in cofactor or coenzyme metabolism, can produce identical clinical manifestations. Complementation studies using fibroblast cell lines from afflicted patients with clinically similar phenotypes help identify these multiple genotypes.

Most of the congenital organic acidemias are inherited via an autosomal recessive pattern. Children with congenital organic acidemia often have other clinical manifestations, including convulsions, hypotonia, psychomotor retardation, and other neurologic disorders. Feeding difficulties, failure to thrive, and abnormal body and urine odor also are common. In many instances, these disorders result in an acidosis accompanied by a positive urine nitroprusside (ketone) test in a setting where the usual causes of ketoacidosis have been excluded.

The branched-chain amino acids leucine, isoleucine, and valine are essential amino acids. They are catabolized by analogous metabolic sequences (Fig. 6). Each is first transaminated to its respective ketoacid analog, followed by decarboxylation and then dehydrogenation. The subsequent catabolic steps are unique for each branched-chain amino acid.

The inherited defects affecting branched-chain amino acid metabolism also are indicated in Fig. 6. Metabolic blocks at these sites lead to the accumulation of precursors in blood that spill over into the urine.

Hypervalinemia and hyperleucine-isoleucinemia are very rare disorders that usually are not associated with metabolic acidosis or ketosis. Defects at the next metabolic step, the decarboxylation reaction, are more common.

Leucine   Isoleucine   Valine

2-Ketoisocaproic acid   2-Keto-3-methylvaleric acid   2-Ketoisovaleric acid

Isovaleryl-CoA   2-Methylbutyryl-CoA   Isobutyryl-CoA

3-Methylcrotonyl-CoA   Tiglyl-CoA   Methacrylyl-CoA

3-Methylglutaconyl-CoA   2-Methyl-3-hydroxybutyryl-CoA   3-Hydroxyisobutyryl-CoA

3-Hydroxy-3-methyl-glutaryl-CoA   2-Methylaceto-acetyl-CoA   3-Hydroxyisobutyric acid

Acetyl-CoA + Acetoacetic acid   Propionyl-CoA + Acetyl-CoA   Methylmalonyl semialdehyde

Propionyl-CoA

This reaction is catalyzed by a triple enzyme complex which can be affected by at least five distinct defects. Each results in various forms of maple syrup urine disease, named for the characteristic smell of the urine produced by the excreted metabolites. As depicted in Fig. 6, these metabolites include several different ketoacids. The ketoacidosis these patients develop is exacerbated by protein ingestion.

The next metabolic step, dehydrogenation, is defective in patients with isovalemic acidemia, glutaric aciduria II, and ethylmalonic-adipic aciduria. In patients with isovalemic acidemia, a variety of ketoacid products accumulate (Fig. 6). These patients also have a characteristic body odor that resembles sweaty feet. Severe acidosis also occurs in patients with glutaric aciduria II and ethylmalonic-adipic acidemia. The acidosis is caused by a variety of di-carboxylic acids, short-chain fatty acids, and lactic acid. Ketoacidosis does not develop in these disorders.

The other metabolic disorders depicted in Fig. 6 are even rarer and are not well characterized. However, several also may be associated with severe metabolic acidosis and, in some cases, ketoacidosis.

Propionyl-CoA is a metabolic breakdown product of multiple substrates, including valine and isoleucine (Fig. 6), methionine, threonine, cholesterol, and odd chain fatty acids. Propionyl-CoA is metabolized to methylmalonyl-CoA and then to succinyl-CoA, which can enter the Krebs cycle. The metabolic sequence, depicted in Fig. 7, shows the conversion of propionyl-CoA to D-methylmalonyl-CoA, catalyzed by the biotin-requiring enzyme propionyl-CoA carboxylase. The methylmalonyl-CoA is then converted to its L optical isomer and then to succinyl-CoA by the enzyme methylmalonyl-CoA mutase. This enzyme requires the vitamin B_{12}-derived coenzyme adenosylcobalamin. Defects of the enzyme propionyl-CoA carboxylase or methylmalonyl-CoA mutase or abnormalities of the metabolic use of biotin or vitamin B_{12} incorporation into adenosylcobalamin can each block this metabolic sequence.

Defects of propionyl-CoA carboxylase result in the accumulation of propionyl-CoA, propionic acid, and other more proximal metabolites. The accumulation of multiple ketoacids (Fig. 6) as well as long-chain ketones, such as butanone, pentanone, and dexanone, produces severe neonatal ketoacidosis. Defects of biotin metabolism or transport also can block this metabolic step (Fig. 7). Other biotin-dependent enzymes, including pyruvate carboxylase and β-methylcrotonyl-CoA carboxylase (Fig. 6) also are affected by abnormal biotin metabolism. This disorder is called a "multiple carboxylase defect." The

FIG. 6. Metabolic pathways for the branched-chain amino acids. Wavy lines indicate potential blocks. Circled numbers represent the following disorders: (1) hypervalinemia; (2) hyper-leucine-isoleucinemia; (3) maple syrup urine disease; (4) isovaleric acidemia; (5) glutaric aciduria type II, ethyl malonic-adipic aciduria and Jamaican vomiting sickness; (6) 3-methyl-crontonyl-CoA carboxylose deficiency; (7) 3-hydroxyl-3-methylglutaryl-CoA lyase deficiency; (8) 3-ketothiolase deficiency. (From ref. 84.)

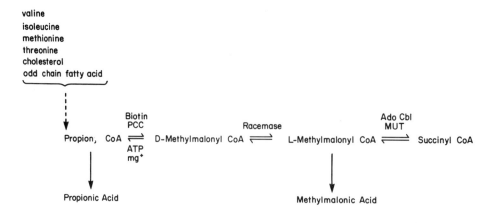

FIG. 7. An overview of the metabolism of propionic and methylmalonic acid showing their major precursors and major catabolic products. The dashed arrow represents several metabolic steps. (Adapted from ref. 71.)

abnormalities may be ameliorated by the administration of pharmacologic doses of biotin.

Defects of methylmalonyl-CoA mutase also produce neonatal ketoacidosis, methylmalonic acidemia, and aciduria. A similar metabolic blockade is produced by defective production or use of adenosylcobalamine, a critical coenzyme for this metabolic reaction. Other vitamin B_{12}-requiring enzymes also may be affected and produce homocysteinuria and megaloblastic anemia. Individuals with adenosylcobalamine defects (at least four different defects have been identified) often improve after pharmacologic doses of vitamin B_{12}.

Other very rare inherited enzymatic disorders that can produce chronic metabolic acidosis include pyroglutamic acidemia (5-oxoprolinemia) and tyrosinemia.

D-Lactic Acidosis (60,73,80)

Lactic acid has L- and D- optical stereo isomers. Higher animals produce and use L-lactate, whereas D-lactate is primarily a product of bacterial metabolism. Normally, D-lactic acid generated by bacteria in the gastrointestinal tract is largely excreted into the stool. However, certain pathologic conditions may result in the systemic absorption of bacterial derived D-lactic acid. The D-lactate can then accumulate in the ECF because of slow metabolic use.

D-Lactic acidosis was well characterized in ruminants, such as cattle and sheep, before it was identified in humans. Ruminants develop D-lactic acidosis after they eat large quantities of carbohydrate-rich grain feeds. Their gastrointestinal motility is impaired, and bacterial D-lactate generation rates are increased. When the disorder occurs in humans, the patients generally have various short bowel syndromes associated with bacterial overgrowth and stasis. Its development may be precipitated by the ingestion of carbohydrates, systemic illnesses, or treatments that alter the enteric bacterial flora (i.e., ingestion of yogurt or L-Lactobacillus tablets for the treatment of diarrhea, or potentially the use of lactulose in patients with hepatic encephalopathy). The development of D-lactic acidosis is commonly associated with CNS abnormalities, including obtundation, confusion, and ataxia. Although these symptoms may be a result of a direct neurotoxic effect of D-lactate, they also may represent a systemic manifestation of some other toxin or toxins that remain unidentified.

D-Lactic acidosis should be considered when patients with gastrointestinal pathology develop an otherwise unexplained anion gap metabolic acidosis. The enzymatic assay for lactic acid uses stereospecific L-lactate dehydrogenase (L-LDH). Therefore, it will not detect D-lactic acid. The diagnosis of D-lactic acidosis can be established with an analogous assay using D-LDH. D-Lactate also can be measured with techniques that are not stereospecific, such as gas–liquid chromatography.

D-Lactic acidosis has been treated successfully with poorly absorbed oral antibiotics (vancomycin, kanamycin), which may beneficially alter the intestinal flora and reduce the D-lactic acid production rate. Dietary manipulations reducing carbohydrate intake also may be helpful.

ACKNOWLEDGMENT

The secretarial support rendered by Ann Drew is very gratefully acknowledged.

REFERENCES

1. Adrogue, H. J., Ekonyan, G., and Suki, W. N. (1984): Diabetic ketoacidosis: Role of the kidney in the acid-base homeostasis re-evaluated. *Kidney Int.*, 25:591.
2. Arene, F. P., Dugowson, C., and Saudek, C.- D. (1978): Salicylate-induced hypoglycemia and ketoacidosis in a nondiabetic adult. *Arch. Intern. Med.*, 138:1153–1154.
3. Baker, L., and Winegard, A. I. (1970): Fasting hypoglycemia and metabolic acidosis associated with deficiency of hepatic fructose-1,6-diphosphatase. *Lancet*, 2:13–16.
4. Bass, J. P. (1983): Inborn errors of pyruvate metabolism. In: *The Metabolic Basis of Inherited Disease*, 5th ed., edited by J. B. Stanbury, J. L. Goldsein, J. B. Wyngaarden, M. S. Brown, and D. S. Fredrickson, pp. 193–203. McGraw-Hill, New York.
5. Beier, L. S., Pitts, W. H., and Gonick, H. C. (1963): Metabolic acidosis occurring during paraldehyde intoxication. *Ann. Intern. Med.*, 58:155–158.
6. Bennett, I. L., Freeman, H. C., Mitchell, G. L., and Cooper, M. N. (1953): Acute methyl alcohol poisoning: A review based on experience in an outbreak of 323 cases. *Medicine*, 32:431–463.
7. Blass, J. P., Schulman, J. D., Young, D. S., and Hom, E. (1972): An inherited defect affecting the tricarboxylic acid cycle in a patient with congenital lactic acidosis. *J. Clin. Invest.*, 51:1845–1851.

8. Bornemann, M., Hill, S. C., and Kidd, G. S. (1986): Lactic acidosis in pheochromocytoma. *Ann. Intern. Med.*, 105:880–882.

9. Bruce, R. A., Jones, J. W., and Strait, G. B. (1964): Anaerobic metabolic responses to acute maximal exercise in male athletes. *Am. Heart J.*, 67:643–650.

10. Buehler, J. H., Berns, A. S., Webster, J. R. Jr., Addington, W., and Cugell, D. W. (1975): Lactic acidosis from carboxyhemoglobinemia after smoke inhalation. *Ann. Intern. Med.*, 82:803–805.

11. Clay, K. L., and Murphy, R. C. (1977): On the metabolic acidosis of ethylene glycol intoxication. *Toxicol. Appl. Pharmacol.*, 39:39–49.

12. Cohen, R. D., and Iles, R. A. (1977): Lactic acidosis: Some physiological and clinical considerations. *Clin. Sci. Mol. Med.*, 53:405–410.

13. Cooper, D. J., and Worthley, L. I. (1987): Adverse haemodynamic effects of sodium bicarbonate in metabolic acidosis. *Intensive Care Med.*, 13:425–427.

14. Cooper, J. R., and Kini, M. M. (1962): Biochemistry of methanol poisoning. *Biochem. Pharmacol.*, 9:145–148.

15. Cooperman, M. T., Davidoff, F., Spark, R., and Pallotta, V. (1974): Critical studies of alcoholic ketoacidosis. *Diabetes*, 23:433–439.

16. Corri, C. F., and Corri, G. T. (1929): Mechanism of epinephrine action. IV. The influence of epinephrine on lactic acid production and sugar utilization. *J. Biol. Chem.*, 84:683–700.

17. Cotton, E. K., and Fahlberg, V. I. (1964): Hypoglycemia with salicylate poisoning. *Am. J. Dis. Child.*, 108:171–173.

18. Craig, G. M., and Craine, C. W. (1971): Lactic acidosis complicating liver failure after intravenous fructose. *Br. Med. J.*, 4:211–212.

19. Dahlquist, N. R., Perreault, J. A., Callaway, C. W., and Jones, J. (1984): D-Lactic acidosis and encephalopathy after jejunoileostomy response to overfeeding and to fasting in humans. *Mayo Clin. Proc.*, 59:141–145.

20. Eichenholz, A., Mulhausen, R. O., and Redleaf, P. S. (1963): Nature of acid-base disturbance in salicylate intoxication. *Metabolism*, 12:164–175.

21. Eldridge, F. (1966): Blood lactate and pyruvate in pulmonary insufficiency. *N. Engl. J. Med.*, 274:878–883.

22. Emmett, M., and Seldin, D. W. (1978): Disturbances in acid-base balance during hypophosphatemia and phosphate depletion. In: *Homeostasis of Phosphate and Other Minerals*, edited by S. G. Massry, E. Ritz, and A. Rapado, pp. 313–325. Plenum, New York.

23. Farrell, D. F., Clark, A. F., Scott, C. R., and Wennbeg, R. P. (1975): Absence of pyruvate decarboxylase activity in man: A cause of congenital lactic acidosis. *Science*, 187:1082–1084.

24. Finch, C. A., Gollnick, P. D., Hlastala, M. P., Miller, L. R., Dillmann, E., and Mackler, B. (1979): Lactic acidosis as a result of iron deficiency. *J. Clin. Invest.*, 64:129–137.

25. Fraley, D. S., Adler, S., Bruns, F. J., and Zett, B. (1980): Stimulation of lactate production by administration of bicarbonate in a patient with a solid neoplasm and lactic acidosis. *N. Engl. J. Med.*, 303:1100–1102.

26. Freireich, A. W., Cinque, T. J., Xanthaky, G., and Landau, D. (1967): Hemodialysis for isopropyl poisoning. *N. Engl. J. Med.*, 277:699–700.

27. Frommer, J. P., and Agus, J. C. (1982): Acute ethylene glycol intoxication. *Am. J. Nephrol.*, 2:1–5.

28. Fulop, M., and Hoberman, H. D. (1975): Alcoholic ketosis. *Diabetes*, 24:785–790.

29. Gabow, P. A., Anderson, R. J., Potts, D. E., and Schrier, R. W. (1978): Acid-base disturbances in the salicylate-intoxicated adult. *Arch. Intern. Med.*, 138:1481–1484.

30. Gennari, F. J. (1984): Serum osmolality. Uses and limitations. *N. Engl. J. Med.*, 301:102.

31. Ghose, R. R. (1967): The significance of acid-base measurements in the management of salicylate intoxication. *Postgrad. Med. J.*, 43:454–457.

32. Gonda, A., Gault, H., Churchill, D., and Hollomby, D. (1978): Hemodialysis for methanol intoxication. *Am. J. Med.*, 64:749–758.

33. Graham, D. L., Laman, D., Theodore, J., and Robin, E. D. (1977): Acute cyanide poisoning complicated by lactic acidosis and pulmonary edema. *Arch. Intern. Med.*, 137:1051–1055.

34. Greene, H. L., Wilson, F. A., Herreran, P., et al. (1978): ATP depletion, a possible role in the pathogenesis of hyperuricemia in glycogen storage disease type I. *J. Clin. Invest.*, 62:321–328.

35. Hayward, J. N., and Boshell, B. R. (1957): Paraldehyde intoxication with metabolic acidosis.

Report of two cases, experimental data and a critical review of the literature. *Am. J. Med.*, 23:965–976.

36. Heffner, J. E., and Sahn, S. A. (1981): Salicylate-induced pulmonary edema. Clinical features and prognosis. *Ann. Intern. Med.*, 95:405–409.

37. Heinig, R. E., Clarke, E. F., and Waterhouse, C. (1979): Lactic acidosis and liver disease. *Arch. Intern. Med.*, 139:1229–1232.

38. Hill, J. B. (1973): Salicylate intoxication. *N. Engl. J. Med.*, 288:1110–1113.

39. Hoppell, C. L., Kerr, D. S., Dahms, B., and Roessmann, U. (1987): Deficiency of the reduced nicotinamide adenine dinucleotide dehydrogenase component of complex I of mitochondrial electron transport. Fatal infantile lactic acidosis and hypermetabolism with skeletal-cardiac myopathy and encephalopathy. *J. Clin. Invest.*, 80:71–77.

40. Huckabee, W. E. (1958): Relationships of pyruvate and lactate during anaerobic metabolism. III. Effect of breathing low-oxygen gases. *J. Clin. Invest.*, 37:264–271.

41. Hurs., H. G., and van Schaftingen, E. (1982): Fructose-2,6-bisphosphate two years after its discovery. *Biochem. J.*, 206:1–12.

42. Jenkins, D. W., Eckel, R. E., and Craig, J. W. (1971): Alcoholic ketoacidosis. *JAMA*, 217: 177–183.

43. Juncos, L., and Taguchi, J. T. (1968): Isopropyl alcohol intoxication. Report of a case associated with myopathy, renal failure, and hemolytic anemia. *JAMA*, 204:732–734.

44. Kane, R. L., Talbert, W., Harlan, J., Sizemore, G., and Catland, S. (1968): A methanol poisoning outbreak in Kentucky. *Arch. Environ. Health*, 17:119–129.

45. Keyvan-Lalgarni, H., and Tannenberg, A. (1974): Methanol intoxication. Comparison of peritoneal and hemodialysis treatment. *Arch. Intern. Med.*, 134:293–296.

46. Kreisberg, R. A. (1972): Glucose-lactate interrelations in man. *N. Engl. J. Med.*, 287:132–137.

47. Lamiere, N., Mussche, M., Baele, G., Kint, J., and Ringor, S. (1978): Hereditary fructose intolerance: A difficult diagnosis in the adult. *Am. J. Med.*, 65:416–423.

48. Levy, L. J., Duga, V., Girgin, M., and Gordon, E. E. (1973): Ketoacidosis associated with alcoholism in nondiabetic subjects. *Ann. Intern. Med.*, 78:213–219.

49. Martin-Amat, G., Tephly, T. R., McMartin, K. E., et al. (1977): Methanol poisoning. II. Development of a model for ocular toxicity in methanol poisoning using the rhesus monkey. *Arch. Ophthalmol.*, 95:1847–1850.

50. McCoy, H. G., Cipolle, R. J., Ehlers, S. M., Sawchuk, R. J., and Zaske, D. E. (1979): Severe methanol poisoning. Application of a pharmacokinetic model for ethanol therapy and hemodialysis. *Am. J. Med.*, 67:804–807.

51. McGarry, J. D., and Foster, D. W. (1976): Ketogenesis and its regulation. *Am. J. Med.*, 61:9–13.

52. McGarry, J. D., and Foster, D. W. (1977): Hormonal control of ketogenesis. Biochemical considerations. *Arch. Intern. Med.*, 137:495–501.

53. McMartin, K. E., Ambre, J. J., and Tephly, T. R. (1980): Methanol poisoning in human subjects. Role for formic acid accumulation in the metabolic acidosis. *Am. J. Med.*, 68:414–418.

54. McMartin, K. E., Makar, A. B., Martin, G., Palese, M., and Tephly, T. R. (1977): Methanol poisoning. I. The role of formic acid in the development of metabolic acidosis in the monkey and the reversal by 4-methyl-pyrazole. In: *Alcohol and Aldehyde Metabolizing Systems, Vol. 2*, edited by R. G. Thurman, J. R. Williamson, H. R. Drott, and B. Chance, pp. 429–440. Academic Press, New York

55. McMartin, K. E., Martin-Amat, G., Noker, P. E., and Tephly, T. R. (1979): Lack of a role for formaldehyde in methanol poisoning in the monkey. *Biochem. Pharmacol.*, 28:645–649.

56. Medalle, R., Webb, R., and Waterhouse, C. (1971): Lactic acidosis and associated hypoglycemia. *Arch. Intern. Med.*, 128:273–278.

57. Morris, R. C. Jr. (1968): An experimental renal acidification defect in patients with hereditary fructose intolerance. I. Its resemblance to renal tubular acidosis. *J. Clin. Invest.*, 47: 1389–1398.

58. Morris, R. C. Jr. (1968): An experimental renal acidification defect in patients with hereditary fructose intolerance. II. Its distinction from classic renal tubular acidosis: Its resemblance to the renal acidification defect associated with the Fanconi syndrome of children with cystinosis. *J. Clin. Invest.*, 47:1648–1663.

59. Morris, R. C. Jr., Nigon, K., and Reed, E. G. (1978): Evidence that the severity of deple-
    tion of inorganic phosphate determines the severity of the disturbance of adenine nucleotide
    metabolism in the liver and renal cortex of the fructose-loaded rat. *J. Clin. Invest.*, 61:
    209–220.

60. Oh, M. S., Phelps, K. R., Traube, M., Barbosa-Saldiar, J. L., Boxhill, C., and Carroll, H. J.
    (1979): D-Lactic acidosis in a man with the short-bowel syndrome. *N. Engl. J. Med.*, 301:
    249–252.

61. Orringer, C. E., Eustace, J. C., Wunsch, C. D., and Gardener, L. B. (1977): Natural history
    of lactic acidosis after grand-mal seizures. A model for the study of an anion-gap acidosis not
    associated with hyperkalemia. *N. Engl. J. Med.*, 297:796–799.

62. Parry, M. F., and Wallach, R. (1974): Ethylene glycol poisoning. *Am. J. Med.*, 57:143–150.

63. Peterson, C. D., Collins, A. J., Hines, J. M., Bullock, M. L., and Keane, W. F. (1981):
    Ethylene glycol poisoning. Pharmacokinetics during therapy with ethanol and hemodialysis.
    N. Engl. J. Med., 304:21–23.

64. Proudfoot, A. T., and Brown, S. S. (1969): Acidaemia and salicylate poisoning in adults. *Br.
    Med. J.*, 2:547–550.

65. Rapoport, A., From, G. L. A., and Hudson, H. (1965): Metabolic studies in prolonged fast-
    ing. I. Inorganic metabolism and kidney function. *Metabolism*, 14:31–46.

66. Rapoport, A., From, G. L. A., and Hudson, H. (1965): Metabolic studies in prolonged fast-
    ing. II. Organic metabolism. *Metabolism*, 14:47–58.

67. Record, C. O., Iles, R. A., Cohen, R. D., and Williams, R. (1975): Acid-base and metabolic
    disturbances in fulminant hepatic failure. *Gut*, 16:144–149.

68. Reichard, G. A., Haft, A. C., Skutches, C. L., Paul, P., Holroyde, C. P., and Owen, O. E.
    (1979): Plasma acetone metabolism in the fasting human. *J. Clin. Invest.*, 63:619–626.

69. Richardson, R. M. A., Little, J. A., Patten, R. A., Goldstein, M. B., and Halperin, M. L.
    (1978): Pathogenesis of acidosis in hereditary fructose intolerance. *Metabolism*, 28:1133–
    1138.

70. Robin, E. D. (1972): Dynamic aspects of metabolic acid-base disturbances: Phenformin lactic
    acidosis with alkaline overshoot. *Trans. Assoc. Am. Physicians*, 83:317–324.

71. Rosenberg, L. E. (1983): Disorders of propionate and methylmalonate metabolism. In: *The
    Metabolic Basis of Inherited Disease*, 5th ed., edited by J. B. Stanbury, J. B. Wyngaarden,
    D. S. Fredrickson, J. L. Goldstein, and M. S. Brown, pp. 474–497. McGraw-Hill, New York.

72. Roth, G. J., and Porte, D. (1970): Chronic lactic acidosis and acute leukemia. *Arch. Intern.
    Med.*, 125:317–321.

73. Schoorel, E. P., Giesberts, M. A. H., Blom, W., and Van Gelderen, H. H. (1980): D-Lactic
    acidosis in a body with short bowel syndrome. *Arch. Dis. Child.*, 55:810–812.

74. Siebert, D. J., and Ebaugh, F. G. Jr. (1967): Assessment of tissue anoxemia in chronic ane-
    mia by the arterial lactate/pyruvate ratio and excess lactate formation. *J. Lab. Clin. Med.*,
    69:177–182.

75. Spechler, J. J., Esposito, A., Koff, R. S., and Hong, W. K. (1978): Lactic acidosis in oat cell
    carcinoma with extensive hepatic metastasis. *Arch. Intern. Med.*, 138:1663–1664.

76. Stacpoole, P. W., Harman, E. M., Curry, S. H., Baumgartner, T. G., and Misbin, R. I.
    (1983): Treatment of lactic acidosis with dichloracetate. *N. Engl. J. Med.*, 309:390–396.

77. Stacpoole, P. W., Lorenz, A. C., Thomas, R. G., and Harman, E. M. (1988): Dichloroacetate
    in the treatment of lactic acidosis. *Ann. Intern. Med.*, 108:58–63.

78. Steinmann, B., and Gitzeemann, R. (1981): The diagnosis of hereditary fructose intolerance
    in childhood. *Helv. Paediatr. Acta*, 36:297–300.

79. Stokes, J. B., and Averon, F. (1980): Prevention of organ damage in massive ethylene glycol
    ingestion. *JAMA*, 243:2065–2066.

80. Stolberg, L., Rolfe, R., Gitlin, N., et al. (1982): D-Lactic acidosis due to abnormal gut
    flora—Diagnosis and treatment of two cases. *N. Engl. J. Med.*, 306:1344–1348.

81. Summitt, R. C., and Etteldorf, J. N. (1964): Salicylate intoxication in children. Experience
    with peritoneal dialysis and alkalinization of the urine. *J. Pediatr.*, 64:803–814.

82. Swanson, R. E., and Thompson, R. B. (1969): Renal tubular handling of glycerol and ethyl-
    ene glycol in the dog. *Am. J. Physiol.*, 217:553–562.

83. Swartz, R. D., Millman, R. P., Billi, J. E., et al. (1981): Epidemic methanol poisoning: Clini-
    cal and biochemical analysis of a recent episode. *Medicine*, 60:373–382.

84. Tanaka, K., and Rosenberg, L. E. (1983): Disorders of branched-chain amino acids and

organic acid metabolism. In: *The Metabolic Basis of Inherited Disease*, 5th ed., edited by J. B. Stanbury, J. L. Goldstein, J. B. Wyngaarden, M. S. Brown, and D. S. Fredrickson, pp. 440–473. McGraw-Hill, New York.

85. Tenney, S. M., and Miller, R. M. (1955): The respiratory and circulatory actions of salicylate. *Am. J. Med.*, 19:498–508.
86. Tobin, M., and Lianos, E. (1979): Hemodialysis for methanol intoxication. *J. Dial.*, 3:97–106.
87. Tonning, D. J., Brooks, D. W., and Harlow, C. M. (1956): Acute methyl alcohol poisoning in 49 naval ratings. *Can. Med. Assoc. J.*, 74:20–27.
88. Transquada, R. E., Bernstein, S., and Grant, W. J. (1964): Intravenous methylene blue in the therapy of lactic acidosis. *Arch. Intern. Med.*, 114:13–25.
89. Tuchman, M., and Tuchman, M. (1985): Organic acids in health and disease. *Adv. Pediatr.*, 32:469–506.
90. Vaziri, N. D., Ness, R., Wellikson, L., Barton, C., and Greep, N. (1979): Bicarbonate buffered peritoneal dialysis. An effective adjunct in the treatment of lactic acidosis. *Am. J. Med.*, 67:392–396.
91. Vincent, J. L., Dufaye, D., Berre, J., Leeman, M., Degaute, J. P., and Kahn, R. (1983): Serial lactate determinations during circulatory shock. *Crit. Care Med.*, 11:449–451.
92. Wacker, W. E. C., Haynes, H., Druyan, R., Risher, W., and Coleman, J. E. (1965): Treatment of ethylene glycol poisoning with ethyl alcohol. *JAMA*, 194:1231–1233.
93. Wainer, R. A., Wiernik, P. H., and Thompson, W. L. (1973): Metabolic and therapeutic studies of a patient with acute leukemia and severe lactic acidosis of prolonged duration. *Am. J. Med.*, 55:255–260.
94. Winters, R. W., White, J. S., Hughes, M. C., et al. (1959): Disturbances of acid-base equilibrium in salicylate intoxication. *Pediatrics*, 23:260–285.
95. Zuppinger, K., and Rossi, E. (1969): Metabolic studies in liver glycogen disease with specific reference to lactate metabolism. *Helv. Med. Acta*, 35:406–422.

General Review Articles

96. Cahill, G. F., Jr. (1981): Ketosis. *Kidney Int.*, 20:416.
97. Cohen, J. J., and Kassirer, J. P. (1982): *Acid-Base*. Little, Brown, Boston.
98. Cohen, R. D., and Woods, H. F. (1976): *Clinical and Biochemical Aspects of Lactic Acidosis*. Blackwell Scientific Publications, Oxford.
99. Emmett, M., and Seldin, D. W. (1985): Clinical syndromes of metabolic acidosis and alkalosis. In: *The Kidney: Physiology and Pathophysiology*, edited by D. W. Seldin and G. Giebish, pp. 1567–1639. Raven Press, New York.
100. Glasser, L., Sternglanz, P. D., Combie, J., and Robinson, A. (1973): Serum osmolality and its applicability to drug overdose. *Am. J. Clin. Pathol.*, 60:695–699.
101. Goodman, S. I., and Markey, S. P. (1981): *Diagnosis of Organic Acidemias by Gas Chromatography–Mass Spectrometry*. Alan R. Liss, New York.
102. Kreisberg, R. A. (1980): Lactate homeostasis and lactic acidosis. *Ann. Intern. Med.*, 92:227–237.
103. McGarry, J. D. (1979): New perspectives in the regulation of ketogenesis. *Diabetes*, 28:517–523.
104. *Metabolic Acidosis*. (1982): *Ciba Symposium 87*. Pitman Books Limited, London.
105. Oliva, P. B. (1970): Lactic acidosis. *Am. J. Med.*, 48:209–225.
106. Relman, A. S. (1978): Lactic acidosis. In: *Contemporary Issues in Nephrology: Acid-Base and Potassium Homeostasis*, edited by B. M. Brenner and J. H. Stein, pp. 65–100. Churchill-Livingstone, Edinburgh.
107. Rose, B. D. (1984): *Clinical Physiology of Acid-Base and Electrolyte Disorders*, 2nd ed. McGraw-Hill, New York.

The Regulation of Acid–Base Balance, edited
by Donald W. Seldin and Gerhard Giebisch,
Raven Press, Ltd., New York © 1989.

17

Chloride-Responsive
Metabolic Alkalosis

Harry R. Jacobson

*Division of Nephrology, Department of Medicine, Vanderbilt University
School of Medicine, Nashville, Tennessee 37232*

Classification of Metabolic Alkalosis
The Body's Response to Metabolic Alkalosis
  Systemic Buffering • Respiratory Compensation • Renal Response to
  Metabolic Alkalosis
Clinical Features of Metabolic Alkalosis
Physiologic Principles: Generation and Maintenance of Metabolic Alka-
  losis
  Generation • Maintenance
Chloride-Responsive Metabolic Alkalosis
  Gastric Acid Loss • Diuretic-Induced Metabolic Alkalosis • Posthy-
  percapnic Metabolic Alkalosis • Congenital Chloride Diarrhea • Vil-
  lous Adenoma of the Large Bowel
References

Metabolic alkalosis is defined as a primary increase in plasma bicarbonate
concentration. Associated with this primary elevation of plasma bicarbonate is
compensatory hypoventilation with elevation of the arterial PCO_2 in an attempt to restore plasma pH toward normal. Generally, respiratory compensation is incomplete, and patients with primary metabolic alkalosis should have
a pH of greater than 7.45, i.e., alkalemia. However, should metabolic alkalosis be part of a mixed acid-base disorder, the arterial pH need not be greater
than 7.45, and the plasma bicarbonate concentration need not be elevated
(*see* Chapter 19).

Understanding the pathogenesis and clinical presentation of metabolic
alkalosis is important for several reasons. First, metabolic alkalosis is the most
common clinical acid-base abnormality observed in hospitalized patients.
Second, the presence of metabolic alkalosis, because of its frequency, is often

a clue to a significant underlying medical disorder and occasionally is the only clue. Third, understanding the pathogenesis of metabolic alkalosis and the specific role of the kidney in its generation and maintenance gives one an excellent background in many major principles in renal physiology.

CLASSIFICATION OF METABOLIC ALKALOSIS (15)

It is practical, both to understand pathogenesis and to approach its treatment, to divide metabolic alkalosis into two broad categories: chloride-sensitive and chloride-resistant. These two broad categories include most of the clinical examples of metabolic alkalosis. However, with respect to pathogenesis, metabolic alkalosis actually can be divided into four categories.

1. Metabolic alkalosis associated with volume contraction known classically as "chloride-responsive alkalosis."

2. Metabolic alkalosis associated with excess secretion of sodium-retaining hormones from the adrenal cortex. These syndromes are associated with

TABLE 1. *Classification of metabolic alkalosis according to cause*

I. Chloride-responsive (volume contracted states)
  A. Vomiting
  B. Nasogastric suction
  C. Diuretic therapy
  D. Posthypercapnea
  E. Villous adenoma
  F. Congenital chloride wasting diarrhea

II. Chloride-resistant (volume expanded states)
  A. Primary hyperaldosteronism
  B. Cushing's syndrome (adrenal, pituitary, ectopic ACTH)
  C. Exogenous steroids or drugs with mineralocorticoid activity (licorice, carbenoxalone)
  D. Secondary hyperaldosteronism (renal artery stenosis, accelerated hypertension, renin-secreting tumors)
  E. Adrenal 11- or 12-hydroxylase deficiency
  F. Liddle's snydrome

III. Alkali administration or ingestion
  A. Milk-alkali syndrome
  B. Oral or parenteral HCO_3 administration in renal failure
  C. Conversion of accumulated potential HCO_3 (lactate, ketones) to HCO_3 after recovery from organic acidoses

IV. Miscellaneous
  A. Refeeding following fasting
  B. Hypercalcemia with secondary hypoparathyroidism
  C. Penicillin (high dose) therapy
  D. Severe K^+ and Mg^{2+} deficiency
  E. Bartter's syndrome

normal or expanded extracellular fluid volume and are classically called "chloride resistant alkalosis."

3. Alkalosis due to accumulation of administered or ingested alkali.

4. A number of less common disorders that cannot be classified conveniently into the above three categories and thus, for convenience, are called "miscellaneous."

Table 1 is a categorical listing of the causes of metabolic alkalosis. This chapter and Chapter 18 deal with the entire issue of metabolic alkalosis. This chapter, after addressing the compensatory response of the body to the development of metabolic alkalosis, the general clinical features of metabolic alkalosis, and certain general physiologic principles addresses in detail the category of chloride-responsive metabolic alkalosis. Chapter 18 addresses in detail the additional major category of metabolic alkalosis, chloride-resistant metabolic alkalosis, and also describes alkalosis due to administration or ingestion of alkali and miscellaneous causes of metabolic alkalosis.

THE BODY'S RESPONSE TO METABOLIC ALKALOSIS (1)

Systemic Buffering (33)

Acute addition of alkali to the extracellular space initiates an immediate buffering response that involves both extracellular and intracellular buffers (Fig. 1). It should be recalled that the major extracellular buffer pair is bicarbonate and CO_2. At equilibrium, the state of the bicarbonate/CO_2 buffer pair reflects the state of all systemic buffers in both the extracellular and the intracellular space. In classic studies, Swann et al. determined the distribution of sodium bicarbonate infused into nephrectomized dogs. They found that approximately one third of the administered bicarbonate was buffered by cellular and skeletal mechanisms, and two thirds remained within the extracellular fluid. Only about 1% of the administered bicarbonate load was buffered in the extracellular space by protein. The remainder of the bicarbonate was retained as bicarbonate in the extracellular fluid. Of the approximately one third of the bicarbonate buffered by intracellular mechanisms, 2% of the administered load was buffered via red blood cell exchange of chloride for bicarbonate, approximately 4% of the administered load was dissipated by lactic acid and other organic acids produced and released by cells in response to an elevation of intracellular pH, and 26% of the administered load was buffered by the exchange of intracellular protons for extracellular sodium and potassium. It should be kept in mind that these quantitative characteristics of the buffering of an acute alkali load are derived from experiments in which a massive acute bicarbonate load was administered, i.e., 20 mEq/kg, raising

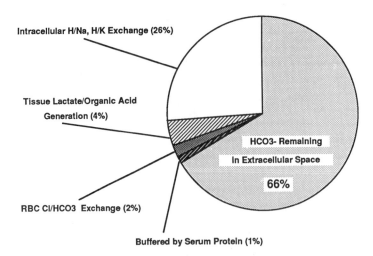

FIG. 1. Schematic illustration of the systemic buffering response to an acute alkali load. Approximately 66% of an acute alkali load remains unbuffered in the extracellular space. Approximately 1% of the alkali is buffered by protons that are bound to various serum proteins, and approximately 2% is buffered via chloride bicarbonate exchange across red blood cells. Four percent of the buffering is accomplished by stimulation of organic acid production by various tissues, with lactic acid being the predominant metabolite. Buffering of 26% of the total alkali load is accomplished by the translocation of the protons from cells to the extracellular environment in exchange for sodium and potassium.

plasma bicarbonate concentration acutely to 60 to 70 mEq/liter. With respect to buffering, it is unclear what quantitative role the skeleton plays in metabolic alkalosis. In the acute setting, it is probably of minimal significance. However, in chronic metabolic alkalosis, bone carbonate content is increased, suggesting that the skeleton may be a potentially important buffer.

Respiratory Compensation (5,35,36)

As opposed to metabolic acidosis in which the ventilatory response is acute, major, and quite predictable, in metabolic alkalosis, the ventilatory response is less predictable and quantitatively smaller. Both central (medulla) and peripheral chemoreceptors are involved in the ventilatory response to acid-base disorders. Although the issue is still controversial and revolves around how rapidly one might expect a change in the central nervous system pH in response to metabolic alkalosis, recent studies suggest that the peripheral chemoreceptors are primarily responsible for the hypoventilation in metabolic alkalosis. The chemoreceptor response is to initiate hypoventilation and CO_2 retention. The hypoventilation requires several hours to produce a steady state change in arterial P_{CO_2}. A rough rule of thumb is that the hypoventilation results in a 0.4 to 0.7 mm Hg rise in the P_{CO_2} for each milliequivalent

TABLE 2. *The impact of respiratory compensation on arterial pH in metabolic alkalosis*

Plasma HCO₃ mEq/liter	pH/Pco₂ Without respiratory compensation		pH/Pco₂ With respiratory compensation[a]
30	7.48/40		7.46/43.5
35	7.56/40		7.49/47
40	7.62/40	Severe alkalemia	7.52/50.5
45	7.67/40	likely to produce	7.54/54
50	7.72/40	major symptoms	7.56/57.5

[a]Calculated using the formula $\Delta Pco_2 = 0.7 \times \Delta HCO_3$

per liter rise in the arterial bicarbonate concentration. Most published reports and suggestions for calculating the expected rise in Pco_2 during chronic metabolic alkalosis suggest that the ΔPco_2 should be $0.7 \times$ the Δ bicarbonate. It is also generally thought that the plasma Pco_2 rarely exceeds 60 mm Hg purely as a compensatory response to metabolic alkalosis. Thus, in a patient with metabolic alkalosis and a Pco_2 of 65 mm Hg, one should be very suspicious of a superimposed primary respiratory acidosis. This issue is discussed in greater detail Chapter 7. Although the respiratory compensation does not restore pH to normal, it does have a major impact on the magnitude of the alkalemia (Table 2).

A final important point with respect to the respiratory response relates to the potential danger of hypoxemia. In the vast majority of patients demonstrating respiratory compensation for metabolic alkalosis, the hypercapnea will not be associated with clinically significant hypoxemia. However, in certain cases, especially in patients with underlying pulmonary disease or in patients receiving additional respiratory depressants, significant degrees of hypoxemia can develop and become dangerous.

Renal Response to Metabolic Alkalosis (29)

In humans, the kidneys filter over 4,500 mEq of bicarbonate per day. Under normal circumstances, virtually all of this bicarbonate is reabsorbed, and about 80 mEq of net acid is excreted. This is discussed in detail in Chapter 10. Normally, the kidney has a limited ability to reabsorb filtered bicarbonate; i.e., the kidney has a tremendous capacity to excrete an excess load of bicarbonate. One can give approximately 1,000 mEq of bicarbonate per day for 2 weeks to normal subjects and produce just a barely detectable increase in plasma bicarbonate concentration. This efficient renal rejection of bicarbonate under normal conditions is in sharp contrast to the circumstances that obtain in most clinical disorders producing metabolic alkalosis. In most of these disorders, during the maintenance phase of metabolic alkalosis, the filtered load of bicarbonate is increased above normal, and thus there must be an associated abnormal increase in renal bicarbonate reabsorption (proton secretion). In our review of the various disorders producing metabolic alkalosis, we discuss the specific role of the kidney in both the generation and maintenance phases of the particular disorders. We comment on how our understanding of the renal response to metabolic alkalosis dictates our therapy.

The integrated response of the body to an acute alkali challenge (either from without or generated from within) incorporates three basic mechanisms that work in conjunction to minimize the resultant pH change in the extracellular and, ultimately, the intracellular fluid. The first of these three mechanisms includes the acute buffering of excess bicarbonate by titration of certain acid buffers in the extracellular and intracellular spaces. The second mechanism is somewhat different in that it takes several hours to develop and does not primarily change the bicarbonate concentration. Rather, it offsets the change in body fluid pH by increasing the PCO_2 via hypoventilation. The third mechanism is quantitatively the most important and involves the renal excretion of excess bicarbonate. Although this is the major mechanism, it is also the one most often interfered with in clinical disorders that result in sustained metabolic alkalosis.

CLINICAL FEATURES OF METABOLIC ALKALOSIS (20–22,24,25,32)

The signs and symptoms of metabolic alkalosis are relatively nonspecific, and most often the clinical picture is dominated by the symptoms of the underlying disorder. However, the alkalosis *per se* may cause a number of potentially important symptoms, especially if it is of major magnitude (i.e., pH greater than 7.55). Symptoms are evident mostly in the central nervous system (CNS), the neuromuscular units, the heart and peripheral circulation, and certain metabolic pathways (Table 3).

Alkalosis *per se* may cause weakness and malaise. In some patients, this may progress to confusion, stupor, or coma. The exact origin of these CNS symptoms is unclear. The possibilities include (1) hypoxia from hypoventilation and decreased oxygen delivery from a combination of hypoventilation and increased oxygen infinity of hemoglobin (Bohr effect), (2) CNS hypoperfusion secondary to volume contraction and hypotension, and (3) the alkalemia itself. Neuromuscular symptoms include muscle weakness and cramping or muscle twitching, which can be observed in the presence of negative Chvostek and Trousseau signs. Cardiovascular symptoms and signs include hypotension secondary to both decreased cardiac output and peripheral vasodilatation. The most worrisome cardiovascular complications are arrhythmias. Both refractory superventricular and ventricular arrhythmias have been noted in critically ill patients with metabolic alkalosis. It should be remembered that with many

TABLE 3. *Symptoms and signs in metabolic alkalosis*

Central nervous system
  Lethargy
  Confusion, disorientation, anxiety
  Stupor, coma
  Convulsions
Neuromuscular
  Muscle weakness
  Cramping
Cardiovascular
  Hypotension
  Supraventicular arrhythmias
  Ventricular arrhythmias
Metabolic
  Increased oxygen affinity of hemoglobin (Bohr effect)
  Increased lactate production (elevated anion gap)
  Eucalcemic tetany (decreased ionized calcium)
  Hypokalemia

---

such patients, potassium depletion almost always accompanies the metabolic alkalosis and obviously may contribute to the arrhythmia. This clinical problem of arrhythmias may be especially prominent in patients who are in the early postoperative period and still on artificial ventilation, which does not allow for respiratory compensation.

There are various symptoms or signs of metabolic alkalosis that can be lumped into a category called "metabolic." Alkalosis can affect the oxygen-carrying capacity of the blood. Metabolic alkalosis shifts the oxyhemoglobin dissociation curve to the left (Bohr effect). This increases the degree of oxygen saturation and theoretically is detrimental to the delivery of oxygen to the tissue. However, in less than 24 hr there is a compensatory increase in the concentration of 2,3-DPG in red cells that shifts the oxyhemoglobin dissociation curve back toward the right. Thus, this altered hemoglobin binding of oxygen is probably only of clinical relevance in acute alkalosis. An additional metabolic response is the increased production of lactate and other organic acids resulting in both pH compensation and an increase in the anion gap (*see* Chapter 11 for discussion of anion gap). Lactate production is increased secondary to stimulation of the enzyme phosphofructokinase, which catalyzes the rate limiting step in glycolysis converting fructose 6-phosphate to fructose 1,6-diphosphate. Generally, the increased lactate production seen in metabolic alkalosis is limited and, at least in humans, does not result in an elevation of plasma lactate to greater than 5 mEq/liter. It should be noted that more than just organic acid production contributes to the elevated anion gap seen in metabolic alkalosis. Volume contraction with hyperconcentration of serum albumin and titration of serum albumin due to the elevated pH results in the higher net negative charge of albumin and thus a greater anion gap.

Alkalosis with alkalemia has two effects on calcium. The first is a pH-induced decrease in ionized calcium concentration owing to increased binding of calcium to plasma proteins. Total plasma calcium concentration remains normal. A second effect of alkalemia on calcium involves a decrease in the excretion of calcium in the urine. Both parathyroid hormone (PTH)-dependent and independent mechanisms have been proposed for this enhanced renal calcium absorption. With marked alkalemia, tetany can occur.

Most patients with significant metabolic alkalosis also have hypokalemia. This relationship between metabolic alkalosis and potassium deficiency has stimulated a number of investigations and hypotheses attempting to provide a cause and effect link between potassium deficiency and metabolic alkalosis. Primary potassium depletion has been invoked as a cause for both the generation and maintenance of metabolic alkalosis. This is related to the hypothesis that potassium depletion is associated with intracellular acidosis and thus enhances proton secretion by renal tubular cells. This theory is discussed in more detail subsequently. Although there is some controversy that primary potassium depletion plays an important causative role in the generation and maintenance of metabolic alkalosis, there is no question that significant potassium losses are induced by primary metabolic alkalosis.

PHYSIOLOGIC PRINCIPLES: GENERATION AND MAINTENANCE OF METABOLIC ALKALOSIS

Although we discuss the clinical syndromes in this chapter and in Chapter 18, from the standpoint of generation, it is convenient to consider metabolic alkalosis as a consequence of either acid loss from the body or excess alkali addition to the body. For metabolic alkalosis to be maintained, generation must be continued indefinitely, or the adaptive renal mechanism for excreting the excess total body alkali must be overcome.

Generation

Negative hydrogen ion balance is a major cause of metabolic alkalosis (Fig. 2). These hydrogen ions may be lost from the gastrointestinal tract or be excreted in the urine. Specific examples are evident in our subsequent discussion of the clinical syndromes. The administration of bicarbonate or precursors of bicarbonate in the form of organic anions, such as lactate, citrate, and acetate, can generate a metabolic alkalosis if the rate of administration or metabolism into bicarbonate is greater than the rate of endogenous acid production and exceeds, for one reason or another, the ability of the kidney to excrete the excess alkali. A third potential mechanism for the generation of metabolic alkalosis is the loss from the body of a significant quantity of fluid with an anion composition that differs from the anion composition in the

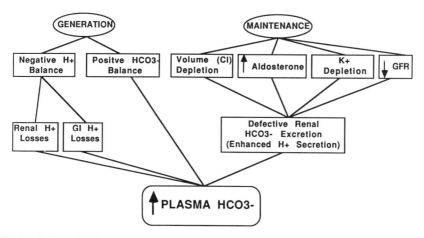

FIG. 2. Schematic diagram depicting the major factors responsible for generation and maintenance of metabolic alkalosis. Generation can be accomplished by either the loss of protons from the body or the gain of bicarbonate. Proton loss can be through either the kidney or the gastrointestinal tract. The maintenance phase of metabolic alkalosis involves four major processes. These processes are quantitatively more or less important in various disorders. Volume depletion, increased plasma aldosterone levels, potassium depletion, and a significant reduction in glomerular filtration rate all contribute to a varying degree to the maintenance phase of metabolic alkalosis in different conditions. All four of these processes have in common their effect on preventing renal bicarbonate excretion.

extracellular fluid. This occurs when the lost fluid chloride concentration is disproportionately high relative to its bicarbonate concentration. This can occur in the acute renal excretion of sodium chloride associated with administration of loop diuretics. However, the metabolic alkalosis associated with potent diuretics includes a significant component of renal loss of hydrogen ion.

Maintenance (2,6,19)

The predominant factor in the maintenance of metabolic alkalosis is the inability of the kidney to excrete the excess bicarbonate load. As illustrated in Fig. 2, at least four factors contribute significantly to this deficiency. The first contributing factor is volume depletion, classically manifested by a reduced urinary chloride excretion (urinary chloride concentration less than 20 mEq/liter). A second important maintenance factor in a number of clinical syndromes is the increased plasma levels of sodium-retaining hormones (i.e., aldosterone or other mineralocorticoid-like substances). This increased mineralocorticoid activity, via several mechanisms, stimulates net renal proton excretion and thus prevents rejection of the increased filtered load of bicarbonate. A third factor, potassium depletion, is thought to contribute significantly to the maintenance of metabolic alkalosis by producing enhanced proximal and distal nephron proton secretion. A fourth factor that can contribute to the maintenance of metabolic alkalosis is significant reduction in glomerular filtration rate (GFR) independent of changes in extracellular fluid volume (i.e., reduced functioning renal mass). Sufficient reduction in functioning renal mass can impair the ability to excrete bicarbonate once metabolic alkalosis has been generated.

It is important to note that in considering the individual disorders producing metabolic alkalosis, it becomes apparent that chloride-responsive and chloride-resistant alkalosis may have similar physiology with respect to the generation and maintenance phases. For example, both metabolic alkalosis associated with vomiting and alkalosis of primary hyperaldosteronism result from negative hydrogen ion balance. In addition both, although to different degrees, are associated with a maintenance phase characterized by enhanced mineralocorticoid activity. The former can be effectively treated by allowing the kidney to excrete the increased plasma bicarbonate, whereas the latter requires interruption of the mineralocorticoid effect on the kidney.

CHLORIDE-RESPONSIVE METABOLIC ALKALOSIS (10–13)

Gastric Acid Loss (3,4,9,16,23,30,31,34,37–39)

Drainage of the stomach through a nasogastric tube and prolonged vomiting are two of the most common causes of chloride-responsive metabolic alkalosis. Patients can have varying degrees of extracellular fluid volume depletion from mild, clinically imperceptible deficits to almost hypovolemic shock. In addition to volume depletion, patients with these disorders almost always demonstrate significant potassium depletion.

Generation

The loss of gastric fluid, via either vomiting or nasagastric drainage, is associated with loss of hydrochloric acid, sodium chloride, and potassium chloride (Fig. 3). It should be remembered that in many of these patients the loss of gastric fluid is superimposed on poor intake of either potassium or sodium or both. The loss of hydrochloric acid is responsible for an acute elevation of the plasma bicarbonate concentration. If the plasma bicarbonate concentration exceeds the then current renal bicarbonate reabsorptive capacity, there will be bicarbonate excretion in the urine. This bicarbonate will be excreted with sodium, thus exacerbating the sodium loss and volume depletion. In addition, the bicarbonate would also be excreted with some potassium, producing potassium depletion. Indeed, urinary potassium losses are probably the major contributor to hypokalemia and potassium depletion in this syndrome. The combination of gastric fluid and urinary sodium losses

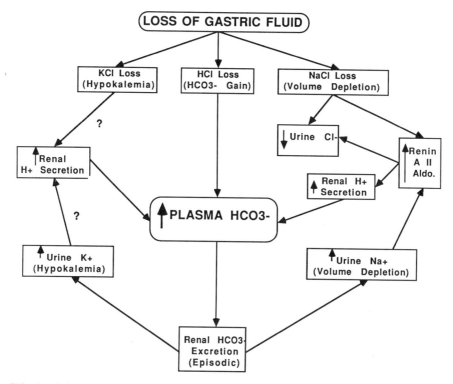

FIG. 3.   Schematic illustration of metabolic alkalosis secondary to loss of gastric fluid. The loss of gastric fluid results in potassium chloride and sodium chloride depletion as well as hydrochloric acid loss from the body. The lost hydrochloric acid directly contributes to the alkalosis because of the untitrated bicarbonate that gains access to the circulation. Sodium chloride loss in the gastric fluid results in volume depletion, which is associated with a low urine chloride concentration and stimulation of the renin angiotensin II-aldosterone access. Aldosterone directly stimulates renal proton secretion, which contributes to the maintenance of an elevated plasma bicarbonate concentration. Acute elevation of the plasma bicarbonate concentration is associated with renal bicarbonate excretion. This bicarbonate is excreted with sodium and potassium, thus contributing to the volume depletion and the hypokalemia. The hypokalemia involves, to a minor extent, the direct loss of potassium in the gastric fluid and, to a major extent, enhanced urinary potassium excretion. There is some evidence that hypokalemia may directly increase renal proton secretion at both the proximal tubule and the collecting duct.

results in stimulation of the renin angiotensin II-aldosterone axis. Volume depletion because of sodium chloride loss in the gastric fluid and sodium bicarbonate loss in the urine, as well as the increased aldosterone action on the kidney, are responsible for the low urinary chloride concentration.

The metabolic alkalosis is also generated in part by the enhanced distal nephron proton secretory rate caused by aldosterone. Possibly (as illustrated by the question mark in Fig. 3), the potassium depletion and hypokalemia contribute to the generation of metabolic alkalosis by stimulating inappropriate proton secretion (due to intracellular acidosis). It should be noted that both potassium depletion and increased aldosterone secretion are thought to contribute significantly to the maintenance of metabolic alkalosis in this disorder, as is discussed subsequently. Urinary bicarbonate excretion and an alkaline urine pH may be only episodic and closely follow periods when plasma bicarbonate is acutely elevated by active losses of gastric fluid. When one evaluates these patients after they have achieved a steady state and the generation phase is over, urine bicarbonate excretion is normal or low in spite of the metabolic alkalosis. There may be a special role for chloride depletion above and beyond its role as the anion associated with sodium in volume depletion. Thus, reduced delivery of chloride to the distal nephron may contribute to generation and possibly to the maintenance of metabolic alkalosis by reducing the GFR and enhancing inappropriate distal nephron proton secretion. Very low levels of distal chloride delivery may prevent bicarbonate secretion, which is dependent on lumen chloride exchange for bicarbonate.

An excellent example of the generation of metabolic alkalosis is shown in Fig. 4 which summarizes plasma and urinary acid base and electrolyte composition in a normal human subject undergoing gastric drainage while on a low sodium chloride diet. This patient illustrates all of the pathophysiologic features summarized in Fig. 3. Drainage of gastric fluid which contains between 60 and 100 mEq/liter of HCl results in the acute and dramatic increase in plasma bicarbonate from 28 to 38 mEq/liter. Simultaneously, plasma chloride is reduced in a reciprocal fashion. During the gastric drainage, urine pH rises, and significant urinary bicarbonate excretion is observed. During this generation phase, the urinary net acid excretion is negative, and urinary chloride excretion falls to almost zero. Simultaneous with the urinary bicarbonate excretion is the increased obligatory urinary sodium excretion. For the remaining 9 days that this subject ingests a low sodium diet, a steady state hypochloremic metabolic alkalosis with a slightly acid urine pH, normal to slightly enhanced urinary net acid excretion, virtual absence of urinary chloride, and low urinary sodium are maintained. If the subject has a major increase in sodium chloride content of the diet, there is complete reversal of these acid-base and electrolyte patterns. Urinary net acid excretion falls, while urine pH and urine bicarbonate concentrations increase. This is associated with normalization of plasma bicarbonate and chloride concentrations and an increase in both urinary chloride and sodium excretion, ultimately reflecting sodium chloride balance. Not illustrated in Fig. 4 is the simultaneous hypokalemia and elevated urinary potassium excretion that is exacerbated during the bicarbonaturia but still significant despite low plasma potassium concentrations during the steady state low sodium chloride intake.

Maintenance

What maintains the metabolic alkalosis in the patient illustrated in Fig. 4? In other words, why in the setting of alkalemia does the kidney excrete an

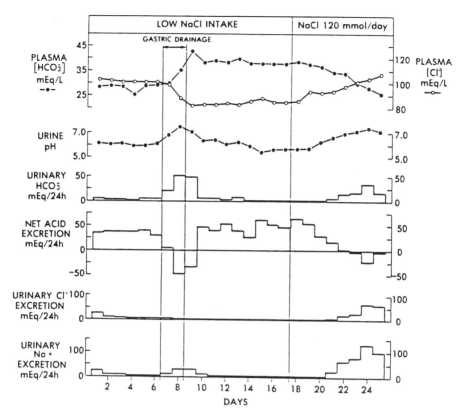

FIG. 4. Balance study on a normal subject undergoing acute gastric drainage during intake of a low sodium chloride diet. Coincident with gastric drainage, plasma bicarbonate increases, with a reciprocal fall in plasma bicarbonate concentration. The acute elevation of plasma bicarbonate exceeds renal capacity for bicarbonate reclamation, resulting in an acute increase in urinary bicarbonate excretion as well as a rise in urine pH. Sodium excretion increases in concert with the bicarbonaturia. Shortly after gastric drainage is discontinued, urinary bicarbonate excretion falls and urine net acid excretion increases to levels at least equal to, and after several days, greater than the predrainage period. Also after gastric drainage, urinary chloride excretion falls to zero. Since bicarbonaturia ceases, urinary sodium excretion also falls to low levels, accurately reflecting, as does urinary chloride, the volume depletion that exists. A steady state of metabolic alkalosis with an acid urine pH is maintained until sufficient sodium chloride is presented in the diet. During recovery, plasma bicarbonate falls, and plasma chloride concentration increases in a reciprocal fashion. The urine pH rises, and the retained plasma bicarbonate is excreted in the urine. For several days, urine chloride and sodium remain zero, representing time during which volume repletion takes place. Subsequently, chloride and sodium both appear in the urine.

acid urine with net acid secretion? Although undoubtedly there are as yet undiscovered contributors to the underlying renal mechanisms for this maintenance, our current understanding of this abnormal situation is illustrated in Table 4, where the renal mechanisms responsible for the maintenance of metabolic alkalosis associated with volume depletion are listed. These factors promoting maintenance are divided into proximal and distal mechanisms,

TABLE 4. *Renal mechanisms contributing to metabolic alkalosis associated with volume depletion*

Proximal mechanisms	Distal mechanisms

Decreased glomerular filtration rate (GFR)
  Volume depletion
  Hypokalemia
Increased proximal tubule
  HCO_3^- reabsorption (reclamation)
  Increased luminal $[HCO_3^-]$
  Angiotensin II
  K^+ depletion with intracellular acidosis
Increased proximal tubule (and loop
  of Henle) Cl^- absorption
  Volume depletion with ↓ GFR
  ? Angiotensin II
Increased ammonia production 2°
  to hypokalemia
	Increased collecting duct H^+ secretion
	  Aldosterone
	  K^+ depletion with intracellular acidosis
	  Decreased $[Cl^-]$ in collecting duct lumen
	Increased NH_4^+ excretion
	  Increased H^+ secretion
	  Increased NH_3 production
	Decreased HCO_3^- secretion 2° to decreased
	  luminal $[Cl^-]$

referring to the region of the nephron in which the mechanisms are located.

First, there is decreased distal delivery of bicarbonate and chloride owing to enhanced reabsorption in the proximal nephron and, in some circumstances, decreased GFR. Whether or not there is an absolute increase in the filtered load of bicarbonate is a function of the magnitude of the reduction in GFR relative to the increase in plasma bicarbonate concentration. The decreased GFR results from a number of mechanisms, with the major ones being extracellular fluid volume depletion and hypokalemia-induced reduction in renal blood flow. In spite of metabolic alkalosis and alkalemia and in spite of an absolute increase in the filtered load of bicarbonate, absolute proximal tubule bicarbonate reabsorption can be increased. This might well be due to a favorable effect of increased luminal bicarbonate concentration on the rate of apical membrane sodium proton exchange. In addition, angiotensin II, which is frequently elevated in this clinical syndrome, may stimulate proximal tubule sodium bicarbonate absorption. Finally, enhanced proximal bicarbonate reabsorption may be caused by intracellular acidosis resulting from potassium depletion. This acidosis can stimulate sodium-proton exchange. Proximal tubule and presumably loop chloride absorption are stimulated in volume depletion and contribute to the very low distal delivery of this anion. It also is possible that angiotensin II stimulated proximal absorption involves stimulation of sodium chloride absorption. Another proximal mechanism that contributes indirectly to enhanced net acid excretion is the hypokalemia-induced increase in ammonia production.

With respect to the distal nephron, there is increased collecting duct proton secretion, which is multifactorial. It involves aldosterone-induced stimulation of proton secretion as well as aldosterone-induced stimulation of the negative potential in the collecting duct lumen, which serves to enhance both proton and potassium secretion. As with the proximal nephron, some have postulated that potassium depletion produces intracellular acidosis and thus stimulates collecting duct proton secretion. In addition, it is possible that a very low lumen chloride concentration favors proton secretion by collecting duct cells, since it has been demonstrated that these cells secrete protons in parallel with chloride. Net acid excretion by the distal nephron is also increased by the increased excretion of ammonia, which results from both increased proximal ammonia production and enhanced collecting duct proton secretion. It is possible that decreased bicarbonate secretion may contribute to the maintenance of metabolic alkalosis. Cortical collecting ducts can secrete bicarbonate under appropriate conditions via chloride bicarbonate exchange at the luminal cell membrane of certain collecting duct cells. If lumen chloride concentration is sufficiently low, this exchange may be inhibited. It is important to note in Fig. 4 that throughout the maintenance phase of metabolic alkalosis, there is virtually no chloride in the urine. Urine pH falls to its lowest level during this maintenance phase.

Diagnosis

The diagnosis of gastric fluid loss-induced metabolic alkalosis, like most other significant metabolic acid-base disorders, is established by a combination of history, physical examination, and important laboratory tests (Table 5). These laboratory tests should include at least a measurement of serum electrolytes and arterial blood gases. At times, determination of urinary chloride will be important in the differential diagnosis. The gastric drainage should be evident from the history, since this occurs almost exclusively in the hospital setting. However, one should be careful not to conclude that all metabolic alkalosis in a patient with a nasogastric tube is secondary to gastric drainage. The serum electrolytes generally demonstrate a normal or slightly reduced sodium, low normal to significantly reduced potassium, low chloride, and high bicarbonate, with the changes in these two anions being reciprocal.

The arterial blood gases demonstrate alkalemia with a pH greater than 7.45 and alkalosis with a bicarbonate concentration greater than 25 mEq/liter. Assuming this is a simple acid-base disorder and not associated with another primary disorder, the P_{CO_2} will be elevated in agreement with the formula presented earlier.

Urine sodium is generally low except during periods when bicarbonate is excreted in the urine. Urine chloride is always low, generally less than 10 mEq/liter, and frequently virtually absent. Urine potassium excretion is inappropriately high for the degree of hypokalemia. The diagnostic features of

TABLE 5. *Diagnosis of metabolic alkalosis associated with volume (Cl) depletion*

History
  Nasogastric drainage
  Vomiting
  Diuretic use
  Diarrhea
  CO_2 retention

Physical examination
  Blood pressure
  Positive tilt test
  Weight loss
  Evidence for chronic obstructive pulmonary disease

Laboratory examination
  Serum electrolytes

Na^+	Variable; frequently $\leq$ 140 mEq/liter in patients with free access to water
K^+	Generally low $\leq$ 3.5 mEq/liter and frequently < 3.0 mEq/liter
Cl^-	Always low; the fall in serum Cl^- matches closely the rise in serum HCO_3^-
HCO_3^-	Always increased
Anion gap	May be increased slightly to moderately (2–8 mEq/liter)
Arterial blood gases	
pH	$\geq$ 7.45 unless a mixed acid-base disorder is present
P_{CO_2}	> 40 unless a mixed acid-base disorder is present
HCO_3^-	> 25 unless a mixed acid-base disorder is present
Urine electrolytes	
Na^+	May be increased or low ($\leq$ 10 mEq/liter) depending on: 1 Recent diuretic use 2 If bicarbonaturia is present (i.e., obligatory urinary Na loss)
Cl^-	Very low ($\leq$ 5 mEq/liter) except for cases with recent diuretic use
K^+	Variable, may be low late in maintenance phase but otherwise is abnormally high despite hypokalemia
HCO_3^-	Absent from urine during maintenance phase but present during generation

metabolic alkalosis associated with extracellular fluid volume (chloride) depletion are listed in Table 5.

Treatment

Treatment of metabolic alkalosis, secondary to loss of gastric fluid, is relatively straightforward. As in all metabolic acid-base disorders, the first consideration should be given to diagnosing and treating the underlying disorder. In this case, removing the nasogastric tube if possible, and diagnosing and treating the cause for vomiting should be attempted. Simultaneously, the clinician must answer four questions.

1. How severe is the volume depletion?

2. What is the magnitude of potassium depletion?

3. How severe is the alkalemia?

4. Are cardiovascular and renal function sufficient to allow for renal correction of the metabolic alkalosis without the major risk of intolerable volume expansion?

Answers to these questions will allow one to determine if there is an immediate need for exogenous acid to titrate the elevated HCO_3^-, if there is a need for immediate intravenous potassium replacement, and what volume of sodium chloride replacement is required. Potassium depletion may be severe and require 100 to 300 or even 400 mEq for replacement. Similarly, the sodium chloride requirements can range from small amounts, which can be replaced with sufficient oral intake provided the patient is capable, to several liters, which must be given intravenously to support blood pressure and to correct the metabolic alkalosis. It should be pointed out that in spite of severe potassium depletion, the alkalosis will be corrected with sufficient sodium chloride replacement. This is not the case when the potassium depletion is so severe that it limits chloride conservation by the kidney.

Should the patient have severe alkalemia, i.e., pH>7.60 to 7.65, or should the alkalemia be associated with major systemic symptoms, the clinician should attempt correction more quickly. In addition, should the cardiovascular and renal status of the patient prevent correction of a severe alkalemia by simple sodium chloride and potassium chloride replacement, exogenous acid administration may be required. There are three major intravenous solutions available for providing exogenous acid: (1) 0.1 to 0.15 N HCl, which contains 100 mEq/liter of hydrogen ion, (2) ammonium chloride at 20 g/liter, which provides 374 mEq of hydrogen ion per liter, and (3) arginine monohydrochloride at 100 g/liter, providing 475 mEq/liter of hydrogen ion. The latter two are precursors for HCl and are also significantly hyperosmotic and irritating solutions that can be infused only in large veins. Similarly, HCl has a very low pH and must be given through a central line into a large vein (not in the heart). It should be stressed that this mode of therapy is only for the severe case. In supplying exogenous acid, one must calculate approximately how much is needed. This can be accomplished by (1) assuming that the space of distribution of bicarbonate in the body is $0.5\times$ the body weight in kilograms, (2) determining the change in bicarbonate concentration desired (present serum bicarbonate minus the serum bicarbonate desired after therapy), and (3) multiplying (1) by (2). For example, a 56-year-old man with significant chronic obstructive lung disease has undergone emergency surgery for a ruptured abdominal aortic aneurysm. A preadmission set of electrolytes from a recent outpatient visit showed, in mEq/liter sodium 139, potassium 3.9, chloride 88, total CO_2 35. You are called to see the patient in the intensive care unit 2 days after surgery and find the following.

The patient is on a ventilator and has a nasogastric tube in place, which over the past day has drained 1500 ml. His urine output has fallen to 400 ml over the past 24 hr. A blood gas shows a plasma bicarbonate of 50 mEq/liter with a pH of 7.72 and a PCO_2 of 40. You decide that the alkalemia is severe and potentially life-threatening and decide to improve the pH to 7.50 by a combined approach. First, you would like to lower the plasma bicarbonate concentration from 50 to 40 mEq/liter, and, second, you would like to modify the artificial ventilation of the patient to allow for elevation of PCO_2 to 50 mm Hg of mercury. The patient weighs 70 kg. To calculate the exogenous acid required, you determine the desired change in plasma bicarbonate concentration (which is 10 mEq/liter) and multiply it by the apparent volume of distribution for bicarbonate, which in this patient is 0.5 times 70 kg, 35 kg. Thus, the patient requires 350 mEq of acid. The patient has no evidence of liver disease, and the serum potassium is 3.6. At this point, the patient is judged to be euvolemic. You elect to infuse ammonium chloride at the rate of 100 ml/hr over 10 hr. An alternative treatment would be to infuse 2 liters of a 0.15 N HCl again at a rate of 100 ml/hr. (*Note*: This patient has a severe alkalosis secondary not only to gastric fluid loss but also to inappropriate hyperventilation. *See* the subsequent section on posthypercapnic alkalosis.)

Intravenous HCl probably has the least problems with respect to complication but, unfortunately, must be given in relatively dilute solution and thus requires large volumes. Intravenous ammonium chloride carries with it the risk of CNS depression, especially in patients with hepatic insufficiency caused by the accumulation of ammonia. Ammonium chloride acutely alkalinizes cells, since, generally, in its extracellular equilibrium with ammonia, the increased ammonia enters cells and buffers intracellular protons. Generally, over a period of several minutes, this alkalinization is minimized. It is possible that some CNS depression seen with ammonium chloride infusions is related to this intracellular alkalinization even in patients without significant liver disease. Arginine monohydrochloride has been associated with severe hyperkalemia because of a presumably strong tendency to cause extracellular shifts of potassium.

In patients undergoing nasogastric drainage, one may decrease the amount of HCl lost in this fluid by histamine receptor antagonists specific for the H_2 receptor. Thus, cimetidine or ranitidine may be useful. If for some reason one cannot maintain plasma bicarbonate at an acceptable level with these maneuvers, acetazolamide, a carbonic anhydrase inhibitor diuretic, can be given if the patient has reasonable renal function (i.e., creatinine clearance of approximately half-normal or better). There is some additional risk of carbonic anhydrase inhibition in the form of enhanced urinary potassium losses. Thus, one must carefully monitor serum potassium and be ready to provide large replacement amounts. With respect to these drugs, cimetidine can be given 300 mg intravenously every 6 hr, or ranitidine can be given 50 mg intravenously every 12 hr, and acetazolamide can be given 250 mg intravenously every 12 hr. These doses should be appropriately adjusted if renal insufficiency is present.

Finally, in the very unusual case, metabolic alkalosis may require therapy with hemodialysis. Thus, a patient with severe metabolic alkalosis with either acute renal failure or chronic renal failure will not be able to correct via renal excretion of the excess bicarbonate. If exogenous provision of acid cannot keep up with the generation rate or significantly improve the alkalemia, hemodialysis using a dialysis bath with a high chloride and low bicarbonate (or acetate) concentration can be used. Alternatively, hemofiltration with infusion of NaCl solutions can be used.

Although one generally does not monitor the urine in patients being treated for metabolic alkalosis, it should be noted (Fig. 4) that the provision of sodium chloride results not only in lowering of the plasma bicarbonate concentration and elevation of plasma chloride concentration but in the appearance of bicarbonate in the urine, the elevation of urine pH, and when sufficient chloride has been administered, the reappearance of chloride in the urine.

Diuretic-Induced Metabolic Alkalosis (7,14,17,18,27)

With the exception of the carbonic anhydrase inhibitors and the potassium-sparing diuretics, all diuretics are capable of producing metabolic alkalosis. The more commonly used agents that can produce this include furosemide, ethracrynic acid, bumetanide, all thiazides, metolazone, and indapamide.

Generation

Alkalosis induced by diuretics is generated by several mechanisms. These include (1) a direct effect of the diuretic on increasing net acid excretion by the kidney, (2) increased proton and potassium secretion by the distal nephron as a result of increased distal sodium delivery, (3) enhanced distal nephron proton and potassium secretion in response to the secondary hypoaldosteronism resulting from volume depletion, (4) contraction of the extracellular fluid space by loss of a chloride-rich fluid, and (5) the possible effect of potassium depletion and hypokalemia on stimulating proton secretion in proximal and distal nephron segments of the kidney. Figure 5 illustrates the generation of metabolic alkalosis by diuretic administration. It should be noted that the specific molecular mechanism whereby diuretics exert a direct effect on renal epithelia to increase proton secretion is unknown. It is possible that inhibition of thick ascending limb sodium/potassium chloride cotransport is associated with enhanced sodium proton exchange in this nephron segment. Similarly, it is possible that certain diuretics might inhibit bicarbonate secretion in the cortical collecting tubule and possibly stimulate net proton secretion in either cortical or medullary collecting ducts.

Maintenance

The important factors maintaining diuretic-induced metabolic alkalosis are the same as those maintaining the alkalosis of gastric fluid loss. The net effect

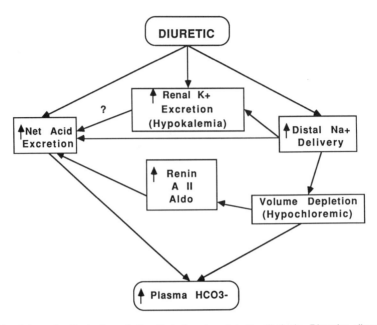

FIG. 5. Schematic illustration of diuretic-induced metabolic alkalosis. Diuretics directly increase net acid excretion (loop diuretics and thiazides), increase renal potassium excretion, and increase the delivery of sodium to the distal nephron. Distal sodium delivery and its subsequent elimination in the urine produce volume depletion. With respect to thiazides and loop diuretics, there is a disproportionately high urinary elimination of sodium with chloride, thus producing hypochloremic volume depletion. Hypochloremic volume depletion can slightly, but significantly, increase plasma bicarbonate concentration via true contraction alkalosis. Volume depletion stimulates the renin angiotensin II-aldosterone axis. The development of hypokalemia, the increased distal delivery of sodium, and the stimulation of aldosterone all result in increased net proton secretion, which when coupled to the increased net acid excretion induced by the diuretic itself, results in significant metabolic alkalosis.

of these maintenance factors is to prevent renal excretion of the accumulated bicarbonate. These factors include, most importantly, volume depletion, with a variable component of reduction in GFR, variable degrees of potassium depletion, and secondary hyperaldosteronism. It is important to note that as long as volume depletion persists, continued administration of diuretics is not necessary to maintain the metabolic alkalosis. Metabolic alkalosis secondary to diuretics is generally not very severe. Indeed, the metabolic alkalosis is roughly proportional to the magnitude of the extracellular fluid volume depletion. Since the latter becomes limiting in diuretic treatment, generally the plasma bicarbonate will not exceed 40 mEq/liter.

Diagnosis

Mild metabolic alkalosis is a common problem in diuretic administration, especially in patients who have underlying edema-forming states, such as nephrotic syndrome, cirrhosis, and congestive heart failure. These patients are predisposed to develop significant metabolic alkalosis during diuretic treatment as opposed to patients who are receiving diuretics for management of hypertension. Marked restriction in dietary sodium chloride intake, which tends to be more common in patients with underlying edema than in patients with hypertension, also contributes to the tendency of diuretics to produce metabolic alkalosis. There is some correlation between the potency of the diuretic and the magnitude of the metabolic alkalosis produced. Thiazides generally produce a metabolic alkalosis that is modest, with elevation of the plasma bicarbonate to above 30 mEq/liter being somewhat unusual. In contrast, the loop diuretics, especially furosemide and ethacrynic acid, as well as the nonthiazide sulfonamide metolazone, may increase plasma bicarbonate by 5 to 10 mEq/liter and, exceptionally, by 10 to 15 mEq/liter. Of interest, generation of metabolic alkalosis with diuretic therapy generally takes several days but can be accomplished virtually overnight if the patient receives a potent diuretic and undergoes a massive diureses.

In most circumstances, diagnosis of diuretic-induced metabolic alkalosis can be confirmed easily by the history. Difficulty arises when the patient denies using diuretic drugs, and the clinician suspects that surreptitious diuretic use is occurring. Suspicion is heightened in the patient who has a history of psychiatric disturbance.

The serum electrolyte pattern in diuretic-induced metabolic alkalosis is similar to that seen in gastric fluid loss alkalosis. Patients may be normonatremic or hyponatremic, the serum bicarbonate is increased, the chloride is reciprocally decreased, and the potassium is generally on the low side. Severe potassium depletion and severe hypokalemia are less likely to be evident in diuretic-induced versus gastric fluid loss alkalosis. With respect to urinary electrolytes, the urine chloride measurement can be helpful but also can be confusing. Urine chloride concentration will be elevated in spite of volume depletion if urine is sampled during a time when diuretic action is present. In general, urine chloride concentration may be elevated for as long as 12 hr after the administration of a thiazide and for as long as 8 hr after the administration of a loop diuretic. For the nonthiazide sulfonamide metalozone, urine chloride concentration may be elevated for up to 24 hr after administration. In some difficult cases of metabolic alkalosis, the clinician has to determine whether or not diuretic agents can be detected in the urine. Occasionally, urinary screening for diuretics must be repeated because of intermittent use by the patient.

Treatment

Treatment of diuretic-induced metabolic alkalosis generally involves cessation of diuretic therapy and sufficient oral intake of salt and potassium chloride to correct the mild to moderate cases. However, in many patients, the metabolic alkalosis is more severe, and it is not desirable to either stop diuretics or liberalize salt intake. In these patients, any potassium depletion must be corrected, and the diuresis can be continued with a regimen that includes agents that prevent renal net acid excretion or even increase bicarbonate excretion in the urine. These agents include the potassium-sparing diuretics, such as spironolactone and amiloride, and the carbonic anhydrase inhibitor acetazolamide. It should be recalled that the potassium-sparing agents spironolactone and amiloride inhibit not only urinary potassium excretion but also proton secretion. Serial determination of serum electrolytes in patients to be diuresed allows the clinician to initiate either potassium-sparing diuretic treatment or carbonic anhydrase inhibitor when the serum total CO_2 exceeds 30 mEq/liter.

Posthypercapnic Metabolic Alkalosis (8,26)

The last major form of chloride-responsive metabolic alkalosis that is generated by the kidney is posthypercapnic metabolic alkalosis. This is a clinical syndrome that occurs in patients who generally have chronic obstructive pulmonary disease with CO_2 retention and a compensatory metabolic alkalosis. For one reason or another, but usually in response to mechanical ventilation, the P_{CO_2} is reduced, resulting in metabolic alkalosis.

Generation

In chronic hypercapnea, the kidney contributes significantly to generating a compensatory metabolic alkalosis. This stems from the stimulation of net acid excretion by the kidney by the elevated plasma and presumably intracellular P_{CO_2}. This enhanced proton secretory rate occurs in both proximal and distal nephron segments. In experimental animals, the induction of stable hypercapnea is associated not only with renal generation of a compensatory metabolic alkalosis but also with a net negative balance with respect to chloride. Indeed, if dogs are made hypercapnic on a high sodium chloride diet, restoration of plasma P_{CO_2} to normal results in prompt excretion of the excess retained bicarbonate and resolution of the metabolic alkalosis. In animals on a low sodium chloride intake, restoration of P_{CO_2} is associated with some bicarbonaturia but only partial correction, which is not completed until dietary salt intake is increased. Many patients who have chronic CO_2 retention on the basis of chronic obstructive pulmonary disease also have recurring medical problems, including hypertension or right-sided heart failure. These patients are on low sodium chloride intakes or possibly diuretic therapy. They may behave functionally like the experimental animals on a low sodium chloride diet and be unable to excrete promptly the retained bicarbonate when plasma P_{CO_2} is acutely reduced.

Maintenance

Maintenance of posthypercapnic metabolic alkalosis is also dependent on the inability of the kidney to excrete the retained bicarbonate. Generally, this is secondary to volume depletion or a decrease in effective arterial blood volume. The physician must be careful not to contribute to this metabolic alkalosis by maintaining volume depletion with diuretic therapy.

Diagnosis

The diagnosis of posthypercapic metabolic alkalosis usually is straightforward. However, to ensure its prompt detection and indeed to avoid its generation, one must always ask if a patient who will be artificially ventilated is normally a CO_2 retainer. One should search for evidence of chronic obstructive pulmonary disease or a history of previous blood gas determinations demonstrating CO_2 retention in any patient who develops a significant metabolic alkalosis while on the ventilator. In patients who are on a ventilator and have unexplained irrational behavior or restlessness or seizures, one must promptly determine blood gases to determine if severe metabolic alkalosis is responsible. The alkalosis of this syndrome can be quite severe and of very rapid onset. For example, consider the patient who has chronic obstructive pulmonary disease with a stable elevated plasma P_{CO_2} of 80 mm Hg and a compensatory plasma bicarbonate concentration of 41 mEq/liter. This patient's control pH would be 7.33. In evaluating these blood gases, the diagnosis of primary respiratory acidosis with compensatory metabolic alkalosis is obvious because of the acidemic pH and the P_{CO_2} elevation much greater than that expected if the CO_2 retention were secondary to a primary metabolic alkalosis. If this patient undergoes artificial ventilation in the recovery room after an uncomplicated appendectomy and the P_{CO_2} is reduced acutely to 25 mm Hg, even if a rapid and normal renal capacity to excrete the previously retained bicarbonate is present, pH can rise to significantly greater than 7.7, and a life-threatening metabolic alkalosis appear.

Treatment

At least four treatment options are available. First, one can and indeed in the very acute setting should adjust the ventilator settings to allow for an elevation of the P_{CO_2}. A second option is to direct treatment at the elevated plasma bicarbonate. This generally will take longer to produce a change in systemic pH and also should be considered in those patients where one suspects that the P_{CO_2} will remain reduced either by artificial ventilation for some significant time or spontaneously by the patient because of some improvement in the patient's respiratory status. Under these conditions, the

treatment of elevated plasma bicarbonate can be accomplished either by
volume expansion with sodium chloride-containing solutions, or in some cases
just increased oral sodium chloride intake. Another way to reduce the elevated plasma bicarbonate is to administer exogenous acid, as discussed in the
section on metabolic alkalosis. An additional useful approach to therapy is to
lower plasma bicarbonate by the administration of a carbonic anhydrase inhibitor diuretic, i.e., acetazolamide 250 to 500 mg twice daily.

Congenital Chloride Diarrhea

The usual large bowel diarrhea is associated with a hyperchloremic metabolic acidosis. There are, however, at least two conditions that are uncommon
but when present may produce metabolic alkalosis as a result of net proton
loss through the lower gastrointestinal tract. These two disorders are the rare
and inherited disorder of congenital chloride diarrhea and the somewhat more
common acquired tumor of the colon, villous adenoma.

Generation

This inherited disorder results in metabolic alkalosis for two major reasons.
First, there is a derangement in the ileum, the colon, or both segments of the
gastrointestinal tract in chloride absorption through a chloride bicarbonate
exchanger. This results in the formation of watery, high chloride concentration diarrhea of 1 to 3 liters/day. In addition, there is loss of hydrogen ions in
the diarrhea (the diarrhea fluid is generally acidic and contains significant
quantities of ammonium salts). This generation mimics very closely that seen
with diuretic administration, the only difference being that the generation
here is accomplished by the gastrointestinal tract as opposed to the kidney.

Maintenance

Maintenance of alkalosis in chloride diarrhea depends on the inability of the
kidney to excrete the excess plasma bicarbonate. In chloride-responsive
alkalosis, this renal inability to excrete the excess bicarbonate is a function of
volume contraction. These patients will, in addition, demonstrate hyperreninemia and hyperaldosteronism and have reductions in GFR, all of which
may contribute to enhance net acid excretion and blunting of the kidneys'
ability to excrete bicarbonate.

Diagnosis

This syndrome usually occurs during infancy. Normally there is a large
increase in daily stool volume and the stool is never formed. Measurement of

stool chloride and analysis of stool electrolytes determine that the chloride concentration is usually between 120 and 150 mEq/liter and that there is an excess of chloride over the sum of sodium and potassium in the diarrhea fluid. Typically, urine chloride concentration is extremely low, and urine sodium concentration can be low or high, depending on the presence of significant renal bicarbonate excretion in response to a recent acute elevation of plasma bicarbonate. Potassium excretion generally is increased. Although perfusion of the intestinal tract, especially the ileum, can demonstrate directly an abnormality of chloride transport, this diagnostic test rarely is necessary. Serum electrolytes demonstrate a hypochloremic metabolic alkalosis with potassium depletion.

Treatment

The approach to treatment in these patients is similar to that described for patients with metabolic alkalosis secondary to gastric fluid loss. One must determine the severity of the volume depletion and alkalosis, as well as the severity of potassium depletion. Thus, one can determine the requirement for parenteral treatment with intravenous normal saline and supplemental potassium chloride. If the patient has a severe metabolic alkalosis, one may also consider intravenous administration of exogenous acid. The chronic management of these patients is difficult. Some combination of supplemental sodium, potassium, and chloride intake is required.

Villous Adenoma of the Large Bowel (28)

Villous adenomas are tumors found almost exclusively in the rectum and the sigmoid colon. Many patients with villous adenomas excrete large volumes of an odorless and colorless fluid isotonic to plasma. This fluid can vary in volume from 1 to 3 liters/day. Electrolyte composition of this fluid confirms that it is predominantly sodium chloride. In addition, there is net acid secretion by the tumor. Interestingly, not all patients with villous adenomas develop this syndrome.

Maintenance

As with all the other chloride-responsive lesions producing metabolic alkalosis, villous adenoma-induced alkalosis is maintained by volume contraction and its attendant prevention of renal bicarbonate excretion. It should be noted that with this and the previous diarrheal etiology for metabolic alkalosis, the major component of the maintenance phase is really the continued loss of sodium chloride and hydrochloric acid in the stool. As a result, the volume depletion and magnitude of the metabolic alkalosis in some of these patients can be profound. Indeed, prerenal azotemia with the BUN greater than 100 mg/dl and volume depletion to the point of shock and profound potassium depletion have all been reported in patients with these disorders.

Diagnosis and Treatment

The history of large volumes of diarrhea fluid in a patient with metabolic alkalosis should immediately trigger consideration of villous adenoma, as well as chloride diarrhea. Such patients require rectal examination and sigmoidoscopy. Generally, these tumors are quite large and not difficult to diagnosis. Surgical removal is the treatment of choice. Before surgery, treatment for villous adenoma, with respect to fluid and electrolyte therapy, is the same as for chloride diarrhea.

REFERENCES

1. Adrogue, J. H., Brensilver, J., Cohen, J. J., and Madias, N. E. (1983): Influence of steady-state alterations in acid-base equilibrium on the fate of administered bicarbonate in the dog. *J. Clin. Invest.*, 71:867–883.
2. Atkins, E. L., and Schwartz, W. B. (1962): Factors governing correction of the alkalosis associated with potassium deficiency: The critical role of chloride in the recovery process. *J. Clin. Invest.*, 41:218–229.
3. Ayus, J. C., Olivero, J. J., and Adrogue, H. J. (1980): Alkalemia associated with renal failure. Correction by hemodialysis with low bicarbonate dialysate. *Arch. Intern. Med.*, 140:513–515.
4. Barton, C. H., Vaziri, N. D., Ness, R. L., et al. (1979): Cimetidine in the management of metabolic alkalosis induced by nasogastric drainage. *Arch. Surg.*, 114:70–74.
5. Bellingham, A. J., Detter, J. C., and Lenfant, C. (1971): Regulatory mechanisms of hemoglobin oxygen affinity in acidosis and alkalosis. *J. Clin. Invest.*, 50:700–706.
6. Berger, B E., Cogan, M. G., and Sebastian, A. (1984): Reduced glomerular filtration and enhanced bicarbonate reabsorption maintain metabolic alkalosis in humans. *Kidney Int.*, 26:205–208.
7. Bieberdorf, F. A., Gorden, P., and Fordtran, J. S. (1972): Pathogenesis of congenital alkalosis with diarrhea. *J. Clin. Invest.*, 51:1958–1968.
8. Brackett, N. C. Jr., Wingo, C. F., Muren, O., and Solano, J. T. (1969): Acid-base response to chronic hypercapnia in man. *N. Engl. J. Med.*, 280:124–130.
9. Bushinsky, D. A., and Gennari, F. J. (1978): Life-threatening hyperkalemia induced by arginine. *Ann. Intern. Med.*, 89:632–634.
10. Cohen, J. J. (1968): Correction of metabolic alkalosis by the kidney after isometric expansion of extracellular fluid. *J. Clin. Invest.*, 47:1181–1192.
11. Galla, J. H., Bonduris, D. N., Dumbauld, S. L., et al. (1984): Segmental chloride and fluid handling during correction of chloride-depletion alkalosis without volume expansion in the rat. *J. Clin. Invest.*, 73:96–106.
12. Galla, J. H., Bonduris, D. N., and Luke, R. G. (1983): Correction of acute chloride-depletion alkalosis in the rat without volume expansion. *Am. J. Physiol.*, 244:F217–F221.
13. Galla, J. H., Bonduris, D. N., Sanders, P. W., and Luke, R. G. (1984): Volume-independent reduction in glomerular filtration rate in acute chloride-depletion alkalosis in the rat. *J. Clin. Invest.*, 74:2002–2008.

14. Gyory, A. Z., and Lissner, D. (1977): Independence of ethacrynic acid-induced renal hydrogen ion excretion of sodium-volume depletion in man. *Clin. Sci.*, 53:125–132.
15. Irsigler, G. B., Stafford, M. J., and Severinghaus, J. W. (1980): Relationship of CSSF pH, O_2, and CO_2 responses in metabolic acidosis and alkalosis in humans. *J. Appl. Physiol.*, 48:355–361.
16. Kassirer, J. P., and Schwartz, W. B. (1966): The response of normal man to selective depletion of hydrochloric acid. *Am. J. Med.*, 40:10–18.
17. Katz, F. H., Eckert, R. C., and Gebott, M. D. (1972): Hypokalemia caused by surreptitious self-administration of diuretics. *Ann. Intern. Med.*, 76:85–90.
18. Khan, M. I. (1980): Treatment of refractory congestive heart failure and normokalemic hypochloremic alkalosis with acetazolamide and spironolactone. *Can. Med. Assoc. J.*, 123:883–887.
19. Kurtzman, N. A., White, M. G., and Rogers, P. W. (1973): The effect of potassium and extracellular volume on renal bicarbonate reabsorption. *Metabolism*, 22:481–492.
20. Lawson, N. W., Butler, G. H., and Ray, C. T. (1973): Alkalosis and cardiac arrhythmias. *Anesth. Analg.*, 52:957–964.
21. Lifschitz, M. D., Brasch, R., Cuomo, A. J., and Menn, S. J. (1972): Marked hypercapnia secondary to severe metabolic alkalosis. *Am. J. Med.*, 77:405–409.
22. Lubash, G. D., Cohen, B. D., Youn, C. W., et al. (1958): Severe metabolic alkalosis with neurologic abnormalities. *N. Engl. J. Med.*, 258:1050–1052.
23. Luke, R. G., and Galla, J. H. (1983): Chloride-depletion alkalosis with a normal extracellular fluid volume. *Am. J. Physiol.*, 245:F419–F424.
24. Madias, N. E., Ayus, J. C., and Adrogue, H. J. (1979): Increased anion gap in metabolic alkalosis. The role of plasma-protein equivalency. *N. Engl. J. Med.*, 300:1421–1424.
25. Mitchell, J. H., Wildenthal, K., and Johnson, R. J. L. (1972): The effects of acid-base disturbances on cardiovascular and pulmonary function. *Kidney Int.*, 1:375–389.
26. Polak, A., Haynie, G. D., Hays, G. M., and Schwartz, W. B. (1961): Effects of chronic hypercapnia on electrolyte and acid-base equilibrium: I. Adaptation. *J. Clin. Invest.*, 40:1223–1237.
27. Rosenblum, M., Simpson, D. P., and Evenson, M. (1971): Factitious Bartter's syndrome. *Arch. Intern. Med.*, 137:1244–1245.
28. Schrock, L. G., and Polk, H. C. Jr. (1974): Rectal villous adenoma producing hypokalemia. *Am. Surg.*, 40:54–59.
29. Schwartz, W. B., and Cohen, J. J. (1978): The nature of the renal response to chronic disorders of acid-base equilibrium. *Am. J. Med.*, 64:417–428.
30. Schwartz, W. B., Hays, R. M., Polak, A., and Haynie, G. D. (1961): Effects of chronic hypercapnia on electrolyte and acid-base equilibrium: II. Recovery with special reference to the influence of chloride intake. *J. Clin. Invest.*, 40:1237–1249.
31. Singer, R. B., Clark, J. K., Barker, E. S., et al. (1979): The acute effects in man of rapid sodium intravenous infusion of hypertonic sodium bicarbonate solution. *Medicine*, 34:51–95.
32. Sutton, R. A. L., Wong, N. L. M., and Dirks, J. H. (1979): Effects of metabolic acidosis and alkalosis on sodium and calcium transport in the dog kidney. *Kidney Int.*, 15:520–533.
33. Swan, R. C., Axelrod, D. R., Seip, M., and Pitts, R. F. (1955): Distribution of sodium bicarbonate infused into nephrectomized dogs. *J. Clin. Invest.*, 34:1795–1801.
34. Swartz, R. D., and Jacobs, J. F. (1978): Modified dialysis for metabolic alkalosis. *Ann. Intern. Med.*, 88:432–433.
35. Tuller, M. A., and Mehdi, F. (1971): Compensatory hypoventilation and hypercapnia in primary metabolic alkalosis. *Am. J. Med.*, 50:281–290.
36. Von Ypersele de Strihou, C., and Frans, A. (1973): The respiratory response to chronic metabolic alkalosis and acidosis in disease. *Clin. Sci.*, 45:439–448.
37. Warren, S. E., Swerdlin, A. R. H., and Steinberg, S. M. (1979): Treatment of alkalosis with ammonium chloride: A case report. *Clin. Pharmacol. Ther.*, 25:624–627.
38. Williams, D. B., and Lyons, J. H. Jr. (1980): Treatment of severe metabolic alkalosis with intravenous infusion of hydrochloric acid. *Surg. Gynecol.*, 150:315–321.
39. Worthley, L. I. G. (1977): The rational use of IV hydrochloric acid in the treatment of metabolic alkalosis. *Br. J. Anaesth.*, 49:811–817.

General Review Articles

40. Cogan, M. G., and Rector, F. C. Jr. (1986): Acid-base disorders. In: *The Kidney*, edited by B. M. Brenner and F. C. Rector, pp. 457–517. W. B. Saunders, Philadelphia.
41. Harrington, J. T. (1984): Nephrology Forum: Metabolic alkalosis. *Kidney Int.*, 26:88–97.
42. Harrington, J. T., and Kassirer, J. P. (1982): Metabolic alkalosis. In: *Acid-Base*, pp. 235–306. Little, Brown, Boston.
43. Hodgkin, J. E., Soeprono, F. F., and Chan, D. M. (1980): Incidence of metabolic alkalemia in hospitalized patients. *Crit. Care Med.*, 8:725–728.
44. Jacobson, H. R., and Seldin, D. W. (1983): On the generation, maintenance and correction of metabolic alkalosis. *Am. J. Physiol.*, 245:F425–F432.
45. Relman, A. S. (1972): Metabolic consequences of acid-base disorders. *Kidney Int.*, 1:347–359.
46. Seldin, D. W., and Rector, F. C. Jr. (1972): The generation and maintenance of metabolic alkalosis. *Kidney Int.*, 1:305–321.

The Regulation of Acid–Base Balance, edited
by Donald W. Seldin and Gerhard Giebisch,
Raven Press, Ltd., New York © 1989.

18

Chloride-Resistant
Metabolic Alkalosis

Harry R. Jacobson

*Division of Nephrology, Department of Medicine, Vanderbilt University,
Nashville, Tennessee 37232*

Pathophysiology
Causes of Chloride-Resistant Metabolic Alkalosis
  Hypertension, High Aldosterone, Low Renin • Hypertension, High
  Aldosterone, High Renin • Hypertension, Low Aldosterone, Low Re-
  nin • Chloride-Resistant Metabolic Alkalosis in Euvolemic or Volume
  Contracted States: Renal Chloride Wasting
References

Chloride-resistant metabolic alkalosis by definition is metabolic alkalosis
that cannot be corrected by the administration of sodium chloride. Although
in most instances this means that there is no evidence of volume or sodium
chloride depletion, some patients with chloride-resistant metabolic alkalosis
have evidence for a mild reduction in extracellular fluid volume as a result of
abnormal renal handling of sodium chloride.

The major disorders producing chloride-resistant metabolic alkalosis are
summarized in Table 1. These disorders are divided into those associated with
volume expansion and those associated with euvolemia or volume contraction.
In those disorders associated with volume expansion, the pathogenesis of the
metabolic alkalosis is tightly linked with the cause of the volume expansion,
i.e., enhanced renal sodium reabsorption and net acid excretion in response
to an endogenous or exogenous substance. Many of these disorders are well
known but uncommon. The prototype for the volume expanded chloride-
resistant metabolic alkalosis is primary aldosteronism. This disorder provides

459

TABLE 1. *Chloride-resistant metabolic alkalosis*

Volume expanded states	Euvolemic or volume contracted states
Hypertension, high aldosterone, low renin 　Conn's syndrome (adrenal adenoma) 　Pseudo-Conn's syndrome (bilateral adrenal 　　hyperplasia) 　Dexamethasone-suppressible hyperaldosteronism Hypertension, high aldosterone, high renin 　Renovascular hypertension 　Accelerated hypertension 　Renin-secreting tumors Hypertension, low aldosterone, low renin 　Cushing's syndrome 　　Adrenal tumor (adenoma, carcinoma) 　　Adrenal hyperplasia 2° to pituitary 　　　overproduction of ACTH (Cushing's disease) 　　Ectopic ACTH 　Elevated adrenal deoxycorticosterone (DOC) 　　production 　　11-Hydroxylase deficiency 　　17-Hydroxylase deficiency 　Liddle's syndrome 　Exogenous mineralocorticoids 　　Fludrocortisone (Florinef) 　　Prednisone, methylprednisolone 　　Glycyrrhizic acid (licorice) 　　Carbenoxolone	Renal chloride wasting 　Bartter's syndrome 　Severe potassium and 　　magnesium depletion Hypercalcemia 　Vitamin D toxicity 　Bony metastases Hyperparathyroidism Exogenous alkali loads 　Milk-alkali syndrome 　Massive transfusions Excretion of nonreabsorbable 　anions Glucose refeeding

a useful framework to discuss in detail the pathophysiology of classic chloride-resistant metabolic alkalosis.

PATHOPHYSIOLOGY (10,12,15)

The general sequence of events in mineralocorticoid excess states producing chloride-resistant metabolic alkalosis is shown in Fig. 1. The mineralocorticoid hormone or substance with mineralocorticoid-like activity exerts most of its direct action at the level of the collecting duct system. In the principal, or light cell, of the collecting duct, mineralocorticoids stimulate both sodium absorption and potassium secretion. At least three major changes occur in the principal cell to produce these alterations in transport. First, there is a significant increase in the apical cell membrane permeability to sodium so that urinary sodium more readily enters the cell. Second, there is an increase in apical cell membrane potassium permeability to allow for greater exit of potassium from the cell into the urine. Third, there is a significant increase in

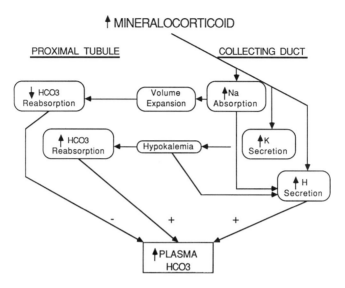

FIG. 1. Pathogenesis of metabolic alkalosis secondary to increased mineralocorticoid activity. This scheme applies to primary aldosteronism as well as other hypermineralocorticoid states. Mineralocorticoids through receptor-mediated actions at the level of the collecting duct stimulate sodium absorption, potassium secretion, and proton secretion. Shown in this diagram is the fact that mineralocorticoid can directly stimulate proton secretion but also stimulates proton secretion through a sodium-dependent mechanism. A similar such sodium-dependent effect on potassium secretion is also present but not illustrated in this diagram. The enhanced distal nephron sodium absorption results in volume expansion and in variable degrees of hypertension. The expanded intravascular volume depresses proximal tubule bicarbonate reabsorption, tending to limit the magnitude of the metabolic alkalosis. The enhanced potassium secretion ultimately leads to hypokalemia, which is thought to stimulate proton secretion in the collecting duct and also to enhance bicarbonate reabsorption in the proximal tubule. Both of these, in combination with mineralocorticoid-induced stimulation of proton secretion, result in metabolic alkalosis.

sodium, potassium ATPase activity at the basolateral membrane of these cells. Sodium, potassium ATPase represents the sodium pump, and its increased activity is necessary for the enhanced absorption of sodium and increased potassium secretion. These changes are in part responsible for the increased lumen-negative electrical potential observed with increased mineralocorticoid activity. However, an additional factor contributing to the enhanced lumen-negative potential difference is the apparent tightening of the cell to cell junctions in the collecting duct, resulting in decreased chloride permeability. This permeability change results in less electrical shunting of the negative potential difference generated by active sodium absorption.

The mineralocorticoid-dependent increase in lumen-negative potential difference is responsible for at least two important secondary events. First, the lumen-negative voltage provides a favorable electrical trap for potassium exit across apical cell membranes of principal cells. In other words, enhanced sodium absorption and its associated increased lumen-negative voltage contribute significantly to potassium secretion by the cortical collecting duct. A similar effect of the lumen-negative voltage is exerted on proton secretion, which is thought to be electrogenic and sensitive to the prevailing transepithelial voltage.

Another primary action of mineralocorticoid is on the intercalated cell of the collecting duct. This cell specializes in proton secretion, which is accomplished by a proton translocating ATPase situated on the apical cell membrane. Although the exact mechanism is unknown, mineralocorticoids stimulate net proton secretion by this cell. It is evident, therefore, that the action of mineralocorticoid hormone on the collecting duct is complex, with direct effects on sodium, potassium, and proton transport and indirect effects on both potassium secretion and proton secretion that are manifested through the action of mineralocorticoids to stimulate the lumen-negative transepithelial voltage. In this regard, it is important to point out that in both experimental animals and in human subjects, it is difficult to generate metabolic alkalosis with supraphysiologic or pharmacologic doses of mineralocorticoid in the setting of dietary sodium restriction. In other words, in the intact organism there appears to be some critical dependence on sodium intake for the generation of metabolic alkalosis through enhanced net acid excretion by the kidney. It has been difficult to reconcile this observation with the clear-cut demonstration of sodium-independent proton secretion in the medullary portion of the collecting duct. However, it may be important for some negative potassium balance to act in synergism with the mineralocorticoid to produce metabolic alkalosis. This is suggested by numerous experimental observations in animals that clearly show that the severity of metabolic alkalosis is directly but inversely related to the potassium balance. In a classic experimental animal model of metabolic alkalosis, dogs given desoxycorticosterone acetate (DOCA) while ingesting a normal sodium chloride diet develop a mild metabolic alkalosis when potassium intake is normal but a more severe metabolic alkalosis during dietary potassium restriction.

Further support for the relationship between potassium balance and the magnitude of the metabolic alkalosis comes from observations in human subjects with primary aldosteronism, where an inverse relationship between plasma bicarbonate concentration and plasma potassium concentration is observed (Fig. 2). As illustrated in Fig. 1 and discussed also in Chapter 17, hypokalemia is thought to contribute to both the generation and maintenance of metabolic alkalosis by promoting proximal bicarbonate absorption and stimulating distal nephron proton secretion. Some have sought to explain this observation by postulating that potassium depletion results in intracellular acidosis that would stimulate sodium proton exchange in proximal tubules, resulting in enhanced bicarbonate absorption, and also stimulate proton secretion in the intercalated cells of the collecting duct. Although this is a plausible hypothesis, more direct proof is required for its acceptance. Recent studies in experimental animals have demonstrated stimulation of an H^+,K^+-ATPase in

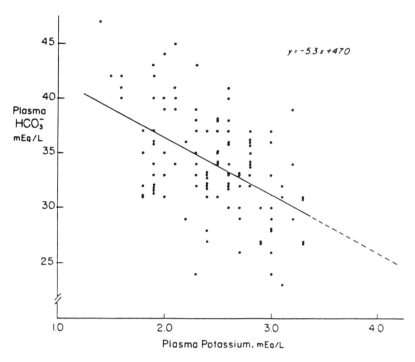

FIG. 2. Relationship between plasma bicarbonate and potassium concentrations in patients with primary aldosteronism. All patients depicted had aldosterone-producing adrenal adenomas. The inverse relationship between plasma potassium and bicarbonate concentration is illustrated. These observations are consistent with the clear-cut dependency of the metabolic alkalosis in excess mineralocorticoid states on the magnitude of potassium depletion. (From ref. 12.)

cortical and medullary collecting duct in response to potassium depletion. This H^+,K^+-ATPase, which may be similar to the gastric H^+,K^+-ATPase responsible for gastric acid secretion, may be responsible for proton secretion and potassium absorption in the collecting duct. Further proof for the functional significance of such an H^+,K^+-ATPase is required. Whether or not mineralocorticoids directly affect a possible H^+,K^+-ATPase in the distal nephron or another adrenal steroid metabolite affects proton secretion in the collecting duct by any action either on proton ATPase or H^+,K^+-ATPase remains to be studied.

It is relevant to note that in human subjects ingesting a normal diet administration of desoxycorticosterone (DOC) or aldosterone in supraphysiologic or pharmacologic doses produces only a modest metabolic alkalosis. However, when these human subjects ingest a diet containing supplemental sodium bicarbonate and reduced chloride content, metabolic alkalosis is more severe. This observation suggests that under normal circumstances, even though mineralocorticoid might stimulate net proton secretion in the distal nephron, counterregulatory processes may be in place that can limit the magnitude of the metabolic alkalosis. These counterregulatory influences are swamped by the addition of exogenous alkali and are somehow interfered with by low dietary chloride. Again, it is important to point out that in these subjects, reducing dietary chloride and increasing dietary bicarbonate results in a greater negative potassium balance during administration of the DOC or aldosterone. Although many factors undoubtedly are responsible for limiting the magnitude of metabolic alkalosis generated under these conditions, it is important to consider that bicarbonate secretion in the collecting duct may be an important compensatory response to metabolic alkalosis. This bicarbonate secretion may be affected negatively by either potassium depletion or chloride restriction, especially since it is known that collecting duct bicarbonate secretion is accomplished via chloride bicarbonate exchange present in the apical cell membrane of certain intercalated cells.

Figure 1 also illustrates that enhanced collecting duct sodium absorption with primary mineralocorticoid excess results in volume expansion, with a resultant tendency to suppress the reabsorption of bicarbonate in the proximal tubule. It is relevant to note in Fig. 1 that the generation of metabolic alkalosis in mineralocorticoid excess appears to be exclusively a function of the kidney. Although there is evidence for transport effects of mineralocorticoid on the gastrointestinal tract, especially the colon, it is the renal action of these substances that is responsible for generating chloride-resistant metabolic alkalosis.

Maintenance of this form of metabolic alkalosis is straightforward. It depends on the persistent action of the mineralocorticoid and the coexisting potassium depletion. In addition, although the latter contributes to the maintenance, its correction will not completely restore normal acid-base balance.

CAUSES OF CHLORIDE-RESISTANT METABOLIC ALKALOSIS

Hypertension, High Aldosterone, Low Renin (1,4,17,20)

This group of disorders producing chloride-resistant metabolic alkalosis has in common an almost identical pathogenesis. The disorders are characterized by primary hypersecretion of aldosterone from the adrenal gland, with resultant metabolic alkalosis and sodium retention, resulting in hypertension and suppression of plasma renin activity. These disorders constitute the classic syndrome of primary aldosteronism.

As a clinical entity, primary aldosteronism was first described by Conn, whose original case was secondary to an aldosterone-producing adenoma of the adrenal gland (Table 2). It is for this reason that primary aldosteronism owing to an adrenal adenoma is called Conn's syndrome. At least 75% of the

TABLE 2. *Clinical features of primary aldosteronism*

Clinical presentation
  Hypertension—usually mild to moderate
  Females/males—2:1
  Age—30–50 years
Laboratory findings
  Metabolic alkalosis—[HCO_3] 30–35 mEq/liter
  Hypokalemia and/or inappropriately high urinary potassium excretion
  Urine [Cl]—> 30 mEq/liter
    Plasma aldosterone or 24 hr urinary aldosterone excretion (not suppressed by high
      salt diet)
    Plasma renin (not stimulated by salt depletion and upright posture)

Differential diagnosis	
Adrenal adenoma	CT scan, adrenal vein sampling, adrenal
Bilateral adrenal hyperplasia	venography, adrenal ^{131}I cholesterol scan
Glucocorticoid-responsive hypertension	Dexamethasone treatment is corrective

---

patients with primary aldosteronism have Conn's syndrome and thus, by definition, have a unilateral adrenal adenoma that is generally small and likely to occur in either adrenal gland. This disorder is twice as common in women as men and is most common in the fourth through sixth decades of life. Although 75% or more of the cases are secondary to an adrenal adenoma, the rest are secondary to bilateral adrenal cortical nodular hyperplasia (pseudo-primary aldosteronism, pseudo-Conn's syndrome). In addition, but extremely rarely, primary aldosteronism has been observed in patients with carcinoma of the adrenal gland. Finally, a rare familial syndrome of dexamethasone-responsive aldosteronism has been described.

Clinical Features

Virtually all patients with primary aldosteronism demonstrate diastolic hypertension. The severity of the hypertension ranges from minimal to malignant but generally is not marked. The patients almost always demonstrate metabolic alkalosis, which can vary in severity but most frequently is mild to moderate, with a plasma bicarbonate concentration that is elevated but usually below 35 mEq/liter. Variable degrees of hypokalemia are present. Although serum potassium may be normal, usually it is decreased and in most instances is below 3.5 mEq/liter. Generally, patients with this disorder are seen when they are in the steady state and, therefore, in the state of mineralocorticoid escape. Thus, urine chloride concentration generally reflects the sodium chloride intake and is virtually always greater than 30 mEq/liter. It is this normal urine chloride concentration that differentiates patients with Cl-resistant metabolic alkalosis from those patients with the disorders described in Chapter 17.

The clinical features and laboratory data should suggest the presence of hyperaldosteronism. To confirm that this is secondary to primary aldosteronism, one must demonstrate increased aldosterone secretion from the adrenal gland and secondary suppression of plasma renin activity. There are a number of ways to go about this, but the preferred method is to demonstrate autonomous aldosterone secretion that is unresponsive to volume expansion. Generally, the volume expansion is accomplished by placing the patient on at least a 10 g sodium chloride containing diet for 3 days. Plasma aldosterone or 24 hr urinary aldosterone excretion is measured before and after the high sodium chloride intake. In the setting of primary aldosteronism, such a high sodium chloride intake may exacerbate potassium wasting. Therefore, before performing this procedure, all patients must have their potassium deficiency corrected. In some patients, there will be a significant fall in either plasma aldosterone or 24 hr urinary aldosterone excretion with a high sodium chloride intake. In other patients who develop significant hypokalemia during the salt loading, plasma and urinary aldosterone may decrease. Usually, however, decreases in plasma and urinary aldosterone under these circumstances still do not result in levels that are in the normal range.

Having demonstrated that the aldosterone secretion rate is elevated by virtue of these procedures does not allow one to distinguish between primary and secondary aldosteronism. One must measure the plasma renin activity, which should be low and generally less than 1 ng/ml/min. Since the renin measurement usually is accomplished after determination of aldosterone, patients generally will be volume replete or expanded. It is, thus, important to determine that the plasma renin activity does not increase to normal or above normal levels when the patient is placed on a low sodium diet (less than 1 g/day for 3 days) or a combination of short-term sodium restriction with acute administration of a loop diuretic. The stimulated plasma renin should be drawn after the patient has assumed the upright posture for at least 2 hr.

Some advocate that a reasonable screening test for aldosteronism in hypertensive patients is the observed response to the administration of spironolactone. Spironolactone is an aldosterone receptor antagonist and will compete with aldosterone for its receptors in various target tissues. Sufficient doses of spironolactone will restore blood pressure and correct the metabolic abnormalities in patients with primary aldosteronism. Generally, the patients require observation on therapy for several weeks before one can determine the response. This test is not specific for primary aldosteronism because patients with low renin hypertension also will respond with respect to their blood pressure, although they should not have a significant metabolic alkalosis before treatment (the exception to this is the patient receiving diuretics). Spironolactone treatment may correct certain metabolic abnormalities in patients with accelerated hypertension and secondary aldosteronism but will not normalize blood pressure. Therefore, reliance on the spironolactone response is not a preferred method of screening for primary aldosteronism.

Differential Diagnosis

Having established the clinical and laboratory criteria for primary aldosteronism, the differential diagnosis really includes three major disorders: adrenal adenoma, which is present in at least three quarters of the cases, bilateral adrenal hyperplasia, and increased adrenal production of aldosterone that is suppressible with dexamethasone treatment. Therefore, the major practical aspect of the differential diagnosis is to identify those patients who will require surgical treatment to obtain a cure, i.e., patients with adrenal adenomas.

A number of differences between primary aldosteronism and an adrenal adenoma versus bilateral adrenal hyperplasia have been proposed to discriminate between these two disorders. For example, basal aldosterone levels tend to be higher with adenoma than hyperplasia, basal renin levels tend to be lower with adenoma than hyperplasia, and a fall in plasma aldosterone has been observed during the assumption of upright posture with an adenoma, whereas a rise in aldosterone is observed in patients with hyperplasia. Such differences are not specific discriminators between these two forms of primary aldosteronism. Similarly, certain suppressive tests to evaluate the change in plasma aldosterone, such as the administration of DOCA or the mineralocorticoid fludrocortisone, that result in a significant fall in plasma aldosterone in patients with hyperplasia but no change in plasma levels of aldosterone in patients with adenoma are poor discriminating factors. The diagnosis of an adenoma versus hyperplasia really depends on five diagnostic techniques. The first is the abdominal computerized axial tomogram (CT) scan, which is helpful only if it is positive by demonstration of a unilateral adenoma. Since these adenomas may be small, the CT scan is not always positive. If there is no adenoma demonstrated on the CT can, one must resort to either adrenal venography, adrenal venous aldosterone measurements, or adrenal scanning with ^{131}I cholesterol. Generally, scanning is accomplished after pretreatment with dexamethasone to suppress pituitary ACTH release and, secondarily, cholesterol uptake by normal adrenal tissue.

The final form of primary aldosteronism, which is very rare and generally familial, is dexamethasone suppressible. This disorder is diagnosed by its familial tendency and by exclusion after evaluation for an adrenal adenoma or bilateral adrenal hyperplasia.

Treatment

Metabolic alkalosis secondary to primary aldosteronism is not responsive to sodium chloride and is only partially responsive to the restoration of potassium stores. The only satisfactory treatment is to remove the source of aldosterone or prevent its action. With adrenal adenomas, the treatment of choice is surgery. Total body potassium deficits between 500 and 1,000 mEq are not uncommon. It is critical in these patients to ensure that potassium stores are replete before surgery. In bilateral adrenal hyperplasia, treatment is medical. Classically, patients are treated with the aldosterone receptor antagonist spironolactone, which prevents the sodium retention and other metabolic effects of aldosterone, thus curing the hypertension as well as the chloride-resistant metabolic alkalosis. Unfortunately, some patients require high doses of spironolactone and thus are exposed to its side effects, which include gynecomastia in males, irregular menses and hirsutism in females, and possible increased risk for carcinoma of the breast. The potassium-sparing diuretic amiloride has been applied with success in the management of patients with bilateral adrenal hyperplasia and primary aldosteronism.

Hypertension, High Aldosterone, High Renin (18)

Metabolic alkalosis in the setting of hypertension with high renin and aldosterone levels is due to three major disorders: renovascular hypertension, accelerated hypertension, and the very uncommon renin-secreting tumors. It should be noted that hypertension with high renin and high aldosterone is also observed in women ingesting estrogen-containing oral contraceptives. However, hypokalemia and metabolic alkalosis are generally not an important component of this disorder. Many patients whose hypertension is not secondary to high renin, high aldosterone may have hypokalemic metabolic alkalosis, high renin, and high aldosterone secondary to diuretic therapy.

Renovascular hypertension and accelerated hypertension are included in this category of chloride-resistant metabolic alkalosis only for historical reasons. Clinically significant metabolic alkalosis is uncommonly seen in patients with renovascular hypertension. Although some of these patients may exhibit a mild metabolic alkalosis, when a significant metabolic alkalosis is found, some additional cause (most often diuretic therapy) is contributing.

In a comparison of clinical characteristics of renovascular hypertension versus essential hypertension, a small but significantly greater percentage of patients with renovascular hypertension demonstrated a serum total CO_2 content of greater than 30 mEq/liter. However, the mean total CO_2 content of the 316 patients with essential hypertension was 26.3 mEq/liter, whereas the mean total CO_2 content of the 164 patients with renovascular hypertension was 27.2 mEq/liter. Similarly, in malignant hypertension, there is little support for the concept that metabolic alkalosis is an important accompanying problem. In an early study of a small number of patients with malignant hypertension, plasma total CO_2 content averaged 29 mEq/liter. Interestingly, the one patient with the highest total of CO_2 content of 35 mEq/liter was found on autopsy to have bilateral nodular hyperplasia of the adrenal glands. There appeared to be no correlation between the aldosterone secretory rate and the magnitude of the mild metabolic alkalosis observed. Thus, significant, i.e., total CO_2 content greater than 35 mEq/liter, chloride-resistant metabolic alkalosis is not a feature of renovascular hypertension or malignant hypertension. Indeed, in renovascular hypertension, there currently is little evidence that even a modest metabolic alkalosis, i.e., a plasma total CO_2 between 26 and 35 mEq/liter, occurs commonly.

The third disorder associated with hypertension, high renin, and high aldosterone, and chloride-resistant metabolic alkalosis is primary renin overproduction. This is because renin-secreting tumors can produce severe hypertension, hyperaldosteronism, and hypokalemic metabolic alkalosis. This disorder can be secondary to a number of tumors, including the classic hemangiopericytoma, which is the single most common tumor, although still quite rare. Since this is an uncommon clinical problem and since many of the patients have not been well studied with respect to their electrolyte status, the true incidence and severity of metabolic alkalosis in this disorder is not known.

Hypertension, Low Aldosterone, Low Renin (3,5,6,8,13)

Cushing's Syndrome

Cushing's syndrome is associated with variable degrees of hypertension, hypokalemia, and metabolic alkalosis. The pathogenesis of the metabolic alkalosis in Cushing's syndrome is similar to that seen in primary aldosteronism. However, the hormones responsible are different. In patients with Cushing's syndrome, the metabolic alkalosis correlates with the plasma cortisol level, suggesting a role for cortisone in the generation and maintenance of this metabolic alkalosis. However, in many patients with Cushing's syndrome, not only is cortisol production by the adrenal gland increased but there is also increased production of DOC and corticosterone. Irrespective of the steroid primarily responsible, it is thought that the alkalosis is generated by stimulation of proton secretion in mineralocortocoid target tissue, i.e., the collecting duct of the kidney.

Clinical Features

The major clinical features of Cushing's syndrome result from the numerous metabolic abnormalities induced by excessive secretion of cortisone. Thus, weight gain, emotional and psychologic changes, alterations in the menstrual cycle in women, glucose intolerance, muscle weakness, osteoporosis, hirsutism, and increased thromboembolic phenomena are common clinical features. About one of three patients with Cushing's syndrome demonstrates a metabolic alkalosis. However, the incidence of clinically significant metabolic alkalosis is much less. Although clinically significant metabolic alkalosis is somewhat more common in patients with carcinoma of the adrenal gland or the syndrome of ectopic ACTH, major metabolic alkalosis also has been observed in patients with classic Cushing's disease, i.e., bilateral adrenal cortical hyperplasias secondary to increased pituitary release of ACTH.

Although one cannot conclude that Cushing's syndrome in a patient with metabolic alkalosis is secondary to an adrenal carcinoma or ectopic ACTH, there is a general tendency for the metabolic alkalosis to be more severe in these two etiologies of Cushing's syndrome. With respect to an adrenal carcinoma, it is known that these tumors are relatively deficient in 11 β-hydroxylation, which results in the excessive secretion of deoxycorticosterone, a compound with mineralocorticoid effects. In addition, other steroid metabolites with mineralocorticoid activity can be produced by these tumors. In patients with ectopic ACTH, metabolic alkalosis may appear more frequently or be more severe because of the profoundly high ACTH levels that are sometimes observed. Although an elevated plasma ACTH is found in patients with bilateral adrenal hyperplasia and Cushing's disease, these levels do not approach those sometimes seen in patients with ectopic ACTH production.

Differential Diagnosis

It is unlikely that chloride-resistant metabolic alkalosis will be the primary feature bringing a patient with Cushing's syndrome to the attention of the physician. Occasionally, however, especially in the patient with ectopic ACTH production, metabolic alkalosis will be a presenting feature. Interestingly, these patients with ectopic ACTH are somewhat atypical in their clinical presentation in that there is an overwhelming male predominance and a striking absence of cushingoid habitus as compared to Cushing's syndrome secondary to primary adrenal tumors or hyperplasia in response to excess pituitary ACTH release. Although a detailed discussion of the differential diagnosis of Cushing's syndrome is beyond the scope of this chapter, Table 3 outlines the major diagnostic features of the three primary types of disorders producing Cushing's syndrome, i.e., adrenal hyperplasia secondary to pituitary ACTH release, primary adrenal tumors, benign or malignant, and ectopic ACTH production. One must confirm the presence of Cushing's syndrome by documenting overproduction of glucocorticoids. This is best accomplished by measuring 24 hr urine-free cortisol, which should be greater than 125 μg. Other diagnostic tests include an elevated plasma cortisol with failure to demonstrate diurnal fluctuations, i.e., highest level of plasma cortisol on awakening in the morning and decreased plasma cortisol in the afternoon with minimum during the first hour or two of sleep. Having demonstrated the presence of hyperadrenocorticism, the differential diagnosis outlined in Table 3 will dictate the most likely cause and the approach to therapy.

TABLE 3. *Differentiation of various types of hyperadrenocorticism*

Observation[a]	Hyperplasia	Tumor	Ectopic ACTH
Sex, female/male	9:1	1:1	1:10
Cushingoid habitus	Yes	Yes	Usually not
Masculinization	Absent	Often present	Absent
Pigmentation	Mild	Absent	Severe
Plasma ACTH concentration	60–200 pg/ml	Usually absent	Over 100 pg/ml
ACTH concentration ratio, petrosal			
sinus/peripheral venous	> 2.0	< 1.5	
Type of ACTH	Normal	Not found	Large
Dexamethasone suppression			
Low dose	No	No	No
High dose	Yes	No	No
Metyrapone response	Exaggerated	None	None
(plasma 11-desoxycortisol)	> 10 μg/dl	< 10 μg/dl	> 10 μg/dl
Adrenal scintiscan with			
dexamethasone suppression	Low uptake	Unilateral	Symmetrical
CT scan of adrenal	? Enlarged, symmetrical	Tumor	? Enlarged, symmetrical
CT scan, pituitary	Tumor (50% ?)	Normal	Normal

[a]Indicates typical responses to tests, but there are exceptions in each category on rare occasions.
From ref. 20.

Treatment

As with most disorders producing metabolic acid-base disturbances, treatment of the underlying disease is the best approach to therapy. Thus, adrenal hyperplasia secondary to oversecretion of ACTH by the pituitary is managed by direct attack on the pituitary gland. This is accomplished surgically or with radiotherapy depending on the clinical circumstance. In patients with adrenal tumors, a surgical approach is taken after careful noninvasive imaging to determine the unilateral location of an adenoma or carcinoma. If noninvasive studies indicate bilateral adenomas, generally the patient has pituitary hypersecretion of ACTH and is not treated by surgical adrenalectomy. Patients with ectopic ACTH are treated according to their primary illness, which generally is a malignancy, the most common being those of the lung and pancreas.

Elevated Adrenal Deoxycorticosterone Production

Two inherited disorders of enzyme deficiencies in the adrenal gland resulting in a block in the production of cortisol and resultant ACTH-stimulated overproduction of cortisol precursors are rare causes of chloride-resistant metabolic alkalosis. These disorders are 11-hydroxylase deficiency and 17-hydroxylase deficiency. Both disorders are associated with hypertension, salt retention, renal potassium wasting, and metabolic alkalosis. In 11-hydroxylase deficiency, there is an accumulation of 11-deoxycortisol and 11-DOC. The enzyme deficiency prevents formation of cortisol, corticosterone, and aldosterone. These patients are volume expanded secondary to the salt retention produced by excess DOC secretion. Renin levels are generally low. The only additional clinical features are the occasional development of gynecomastia in men and variable degrees of masculinization in women. Generally, the enzyme defect is not complete, and the disorder is inherited as an autosomal recessive. The hypertension and the other clinical features, such as hirsutism, respond to exogenous glucocorticoid replacement.

The 17-hydroxylase deficiency is associated with more profound clinical features. This is because the enzyme defect is present in the adrenal gland and gonads, so that formation of sex hormones, estrogen and androgen, is affected. Thus, patients with 17-hydroxylase deficiency are phenotypic females irrespective of their genotype. Patients are usually recognized at puberty, when primary amenorrhea and development of secondary sex characteristics, such as pubic and axillary hair, are absent. Thus, hypokalemic metabolic alkalosis and hypertension in a young phenotypic female with primary amenorrhea are likely due to 17-hydroxylase deficiency. Diagnosis is made by very low levels of 17-ketosteroids and 17-hydroxysteroids in the urine. In this disorder as well as in 11-hydroxylase deficiency, plasma ACTH levels are elevated. 17-Hydroxylase deficiency requires not only glucocorticoid replacement but also exogenous estrogens to treat the sexual immaturity.

Liddle's Syndrome

This very uncommon disorder is characterized by hypertension, renal potassium wasting, and metabolic alkalosis with hypoaldosteronism and low renin. This disorder affects both males and females and is associated with measurable abnormalities in sodium transport in nonrenal cells (erythrocytes). There is a presumed abnormality in renal sodium and potassium transport, with enhanced sodium and potassium secretion. There is no definitive proof that Liddle's syndrome results from a primary defect in renal epithelial sodium transport. The lack of response of patients to inhibitors of adrenal gland mineralocorticoid synthesis (metyrapone) and the lack of response to mineralocorticoid receptor blockade by spironolactone suggest that an adrenal steroid with mineralocorticoid activity (expressed through the renal mineralocorticoid receptor) is not responsible. Patients exhibit a natriuretic response and resolution of their hypertension and potassium wasting when treated with triamterene, a potassium-sparing diuretic with a mechanism of action similar to that of amiloride.

Exogenous Mineralocorticoids

For certain patients, physicians prescribe high doses of glucocorticoid, such as prednisone, or physiologic amounts of the mineralocorticoid fludrocortisone to treat a number of inflammatory diseases or disorders associated with deficient aldosterone production or action. Pharmacologic concentrations of glucocorticoids will occupy mineralocorticoid receptors in the kidney and result in sodium retention, potassium excretion, and a tendency to develop metabolic alkalosis. Numerous studies have demonstrated significant elevation of plasma bicarbonate by up to, and occasionally over, 10 mEq/liter with chronic ingestion of high doses of glucocorticoid. With respect to the mineralocorticoid fludrocortisone, significant metabolic alkalosis will develop only if inappropriate ingestion of this compound occurs. Generally, patients are prescribed relatively low physiologic replacement doses of 0.1 to 0.3 mg/day. It requires deliberate or inadvertent ingestion of significantly greater amounts of fludrocortisone to produce a clinically significant metabolic alkalosis.

In certain patients, metabolic alkalosis may develop secondary to renal actions of mineralocorticoid-like substances that are not prescribed by the physician. Two compounds, glycyrrhizic acid and carbenoxolone, have typical mineralocorticoid properties producing sodium retention and potassium excretion by the kidney. There is also enhanced net acid excretion by the kidney and, therefore, the development of metabolic alkalosis. Volume expansion results in suppression of renin and, secondarily, aldosterone secretion. In many patients, hypertension also is present.

Glycyrrhizic acid is obtained from the root of the plant *Glycyrrhiza glabra* and has been used in the food (licorice) and pharmaceutical industries as a flavoring agent. One of the first reports of important metabolic sequelae resulting from the ingestion of licorice described the development of edema and congestive heart failure in patients treated with extract of glycyrrhiza for peptic ulcer disease. Subsequently, it was demonstrated that the compound responsible for this sodium retention was glycyrrhizic acid and that it had metabolic activity similar to DOC. Since then, a number of reports have described the syndrome of hypertension with low renin and low aldosterone in patients, who, on careful questioning, report the ingestion of large quantities of licorice usually in the form of licorice candy. Metabolic alkalosis seen in these patients can be moderate, with serum total CO_2 content frequently exceeding 30 mEq/liter. Most often, however, the major clinical presentation is severe hypokalemia, with paralysis or rhabdomyolysis. Serum potassium concentrations not uncommonly are less than 2 mEq/liter. A similar clinical picture is seen in subjects ingesting carbenoxolone, a drug used to treat gastric ulcers. The diagnosis of this disorder requires a specific detailed history for the possible ingestion of these compounds. Generally, one does not diagnose this disorder through a comprehensive metabolic workup including measurement of renin and aldosterone. However, low renin, low aldosterone hypertension in a patient with metabolic alkalosis should immediately bring this disorder to mind. Treatment is accomplished by discontinuing the ingestion of these mineralocorticoid-like compounds.

Chloride-Resistant Metabolic Alkalosis in Euvolemic or Volume Contracted States: Renal Chloride Wasting (2,7,9,14,16,19)

Bartter's Syndrome

Bartter's syndrome is listed under the category of renal chloride wasting. It is really the dominant disorder in a group of uncommon diseases associated with renal potassium wasting and variable amounts of renal chloride or salt wasting. In addition to hypokalemia and metabolic alkalosis, the hallmarks of Bartter's syndrome include hyperreninemia, hyperaldosteronism, normal blood pressure, and hyperplasia of the juxtaglomerular apparatus (Table 4). In most if not all patients, there is an associated increase in the urinary excretion of prostaglandins. In addition, most patients have relative resistance to the pressor effects of infused angiotensin II and norepinephrine. There are several hereditary potassium-wasting disorders that are very uncommon but have a clinical picture similar to that of Bartter's syndrome. The important differences include the fact that some of these potassium-wasting disorders are associated with suppression of aldosterone or normal aldosterone, some are associated with a decrease in urinary prostaglandin excretion, some are associated with a specific HLA antigen, but most importantly, none are associated with hyperplasia of the juxtaglomerular apparatus.

Much has been written about the physiology of Bartter's syndrome, and a number of patients thought to have this disorder have been investigated

TABLE 4. *Clinical and laboratory features of Bartter's syndrome*

Major Features	Minor Features
Hypokalemia 2° to renal K$^+$ wasting	Salt craving
Metabolic alkalosis	Polydipsia
Renal Cl$^-$ wasting	Polyuria
Hyperreninemia	Elevated plasma bradykinin and urine
Hyperaldosteronism	kallikrein excretion
Increased urinary prostaglandins	Increased urinary catecholamines
Justaglomerular apparatus hyperplasia on	(epinephrine and norepinephrine)
renal biopsy	Defect in platelet aggregation
Decreased pressor response to angiotensin II	Hyperuricemia
and catecholamines	Hypercalcemia
Stunted growth	Hypomagnesemia
Progressive renal failure	Nephrocalcinosis

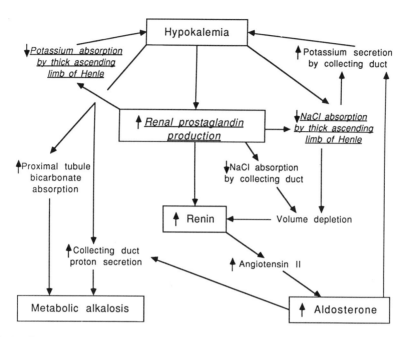

FIG. 3. Pathogenesis of Bartter's syndrome. This figure illustrates the major components of Bartter's syndrome: hypokalemia, metabolic alkalosis, elevated aldosterone and renin levels in plasma, and enhanced renal prostaglandin production. The underlined derangements represent candidates for the primary disorder in Bartter's syndrome.

extensively from the standpoint of balance studies and clearance studies designed to define the primary defect. The three most commonly proposed hypotheses to explain this syndrome include (1) a primary defect in renal chloride transport, resulting in chloride wasting, (2) a primary defect in renal potassium handling, with resultant hypokalemia and secondary renal chloride wasting as well as secondary stimulation of renal prostaglandin production, and (3) a primary increase in intrarenal prostaglandin production, resulting in inhibition of sodium chloride reabsorption and enhanced potassium secretion. The pathophysiology of Bartter's syndrome is illustrated in Fig. 3. Ignoring for the moment which is the primary defect, one can summarize the pathogenesis as renal potassium wasting presumably by both the thick ascending limb of Henle and collecting duct, with the development of significant hypokalemia. The hypokalemia may be responsible for at least three additional features of the syndrome, including (1) inhibition of sodium chloride absorption in the loop of Henle, (2) increased renal prostaglandin production, and (3) enhanced bicarbonate absorption and proton secretion in the proximal and distal nephron, respectively, resulting in metabolic alkalosis. The enhanced intrarenal prostaglandin production may contribute to volume depletion by inhibiting sodium chloride absorption in the loop of Henle as well as the collecting duct. Volume depletion may then result in increased renin secretion, increased production of angiotensin, and increased angiotensin II-induced synthesis and release of aldosterone from the adrenal gland. The aldosterone in concert with the hypokalemia helps to generate and maintain the metabolic alkalosis, and, of course, the elevated aldosterone may also maintain the hypokalemia. The increased prostaglandin produced may stimulate renin release.

Differential Diagnosis

The major disorders one must differentiate from Bartter's syndrome include chronic diuretic abuse and the rare causes of primary renal potassium wasting. Surreptitious vomiting and laxative abuse can be excluded by their association with low urine chloride and, occasionally, by a thorough history. The disorder of renal potassium wasting actually may be made up of a group of heterogeneous disorders that demonstrate several features of Bartter's syndrome but are not associated with juxtaglomerular cell hyperplasia. With respect to differentiation between Bartter's syndrome and diuretic abuse, key features include low urinary potassium excretion rates in diuretic abuse when diuretics are not administered and, more importantly, documentation of diuretic abuse by the measurement of diuretic agents in the urine. The latter may require testing of multiple urines. Frequently, one may not be able to diagnose Bartter's syndrome in the setting of severe potassium deficiency because the latter may produce renal salt wasting and many other features similar to Bartter's syndrome. Potassium deficiency can suppress aldosterone synthesis in patients with Bartter's syndrome, and plasma aldosterone levels may be normal or low. In order to diagnose Bartter's syndrome, one must have the clinical features, place the patient on an adequate sodium intake, restore potassium deficits, and then measure aldosterone and renin as well as the urinary potassium excretion response to restriction in dietary potassium intake. Measurement of urinary prostaglandin excretion and renal biopsy also may be required.

Treatment

The major clinically important manifestation of Bartter's syndrome is hypokalemia. Restoration of normal potassium stores and maintenance of potassium balance are critical. However, this cannot be accomplished with just potassium supplementation. The hypokalemia and most of the other abnormalities associated with Bartter's syndrome are ameliorated significantly by prostaglandin synthetase inhibition. Generally this is accomplished with indomethacin given at 100 to 200 mg/day. Indomethacin is not capable of completely correcting the hypokalemia and appears to have no major effect on the renal chloride wasting. This latter observation has suggested to some that the primary abnormality in Bartter's syndrome is not overproduction of prostaglandins but an intrinsic transport defect producing chloride wasting. In many patients, the combined use of potassium supplements and indomethacin can maintain a serum potassium of 3 mEq/liter or greater. However, two additional forms of treatment also have been helpful. The first involves the use of potassium-sparing diuretics, specifically amiloride. This diuretic, which inhibits sodium absorption and potassium secretion in the distal tubule and collecting duct, along with potassium supplementation, has been effective in maintaining serum potassium above 3 mEq/liter even in the absence of prostaglandin synthetase inhibition. Some experience has been reported with the use of angiotensin-converting enzyme inhibitors, specifically captopril.

Potassium and Magnesium Depletion

A Bartter's-like syndrome caused by primary renal potassium wasting has been described. Its clinical features are very similar to those of Bartter's syndrome and will not be discussed further. It has been demonstrated that magnesium depletion, either by severe dietary magnesium deficiency or secondary to disorders that cause renal magnesium wasting, results in hypokalemia and, in some cases, modest metabolic alkalosis. This hypokalemia is secondary to magnesium depletion-induced potassium wasting by the kidney. In experimental animals and in humans, there is some suggestion that magnesium depletion results in elevation of plasma aldosterone and increases in 24 hr urine aldosterone excretion. This elevated aldosterone may be present even though there is an associated hypokalemia. The specific nephron site responsible for the potassium wasting seen with magnesium depletion is unknown but may very well be the thick ascending limb of Henle. Presumably, this site of potassium wasting and magnesium depletion would not be dependent on hyperaldosteronism. What role elevated aldosterone production plays in the potassium wasting of magnesium deficiency is unclear. However, both hypokalemia and elevated aldosterone may contribute to the generation and maintenance of metabolic alkalosis.

Numerous disorders that produce magnesium depletion are associated with independent effects on acid-base balance. Thus, in many of these disorders, an independent effect of magnesium is difficult to identify. For example, diabetic ketoacidosis, chronic alcoholism, and chronic diuretic use (especially loop diuretic) are all causes of magnesium depletion that independently produce obvious systemic acid-base changes. Renal potassium wasting occurring concurrently with magnesium wasting or resulting from severe magnesium depletion is seen in acquired defects of renal tubule transport secondary to various drugs, especially aminoglycosides and cisplatin. The simultaneous renal wasting of both cations and their interrelation becomes evident when one attempts to correct potassium depletion by administering only potassium supplements. In some patients, restoration of potassium stores cannot be accomplished until simultaneous magnesium depletion is corrected. Congenital renal magnesium wasting is a rare disorder that is not always associated with renal potassium wasting. In some patients, there also appears to be an abnormality in renal calcium handling with hypercalciura. Some of these patients actually demonstrate a metabolic acidosis that appears to be secondary to distal renal tubular acidosis. In all patients with unexplained hypokalemic metabolic alkalosis, one must exclude coexistent magnesium depletion, which may be secondary to the same disorder that produced the potassium wasting or may be primary. Magnesium depletion can be treated emergently with parenteral magnesium sulfate or, more commonly, through oral magnesium salts or magnesium oxide.

Hypercalcemia

Hypercalcemia secondary to vitamin D ingestion and hypercalcemia secondary to malignancies have been associated with metabolic alkalosis. The pathogenesis of this alkalosis is unclear. In experimental animals, infusion of calcium acutely to produce hypercalcemia results in an increase in net acid excretion and an apparent increase in proximal tubule bicarbonate absorption. These changes are independent of parathyroid hormone alterations but remain mechanistically unexplained. Thus, it remains to be established if chronic hypercalcemia produces alterations in either proximal tubule bicarbonate reabsorption or distal nephron proton secretion independent of changes in parathyroid hormone or vitamin D. Similarly, effects of vitamin D on bicarbonate absorption in the proximal tubule or proton secretion in the distal nephron are unexplored. It should be noted that metabolic alkalosis is not uniformly associated with these disorders and generally is not a major clinical problem.

Hyperparathyroidism

Although there have been some reports of hyperchloremic metabolic acidosis in patients with hyperparathyroidism, the more common acid-base abnormality observed is metabolic alkalosis. Parathyroid hormone has been shown to inhibit bicarbonate absorption in proximal tubule, presumably through a cyclic AMP-dependent effect. It has also been shown to stimulate acidification by the distal nephron. Although it is logical to assume that the balance of these two effects might determine whether or not parathyroid hormone excess results in enhanced net acid excretion, careful studies involving segmental analysis of acidification have not been performed. A complicating feature of hyperparathyroidism is hypercalcemia, which may have independent effects on renal bicarbonate handling. However, there is some evidence that hyperparathyroidism produces metabolic alkalosis irrespective of the serum calcium, since an animal model of hyperparathyroidism associated with hypocalcemia also results in metabolic alkalosis. In an animal model, chronic hypocalcemia and secondary hyperparathyroidism are maintained by the infusion of a calcium-chelating agent. A mild to moderate metabolic alkalosis follows in spite of the hypocalcemia. It is important to note that hyperparathyroidism results in calcium mobilization from bone. In addition to mobilization of bone calcium, alkali buffers from bone also are released and thus may contribute to the generation of metabolic alkalosis. With prolonged hypercalcemia either from hyperparathyroidism or from vitamin D toxicity or tumor-related hypercalcemia, a renal concentrating defect may appear. In such patients, there may be some component of extracellular fluid volume depletion and possibly secondary hyperaldosteronism. These latter two factors may contribute to the metabolic alkalosis, and they also render the metabolic alkalosis partially responsive to the administration of sodium chloride.

Exogenous Alkali Loads

There are two major disorders associated with metabolic alkalosis and exogenous alkali loads. The classic milk-alkali syndrome has three major clinical components, including hypercalcemia, variable degrees of renal failure, and metabolic alkalosis. Generally, patients with this disorder are ingesting excessive quantities of alkali and calcium. Some patients may also be ingesting vitamin D. The most commonly ingested calcium-containing alkali is calcium carbonate, which is available as a calcium supplement but also is present in preparations designed to treat peptic ulcer symptoms. The associated renal failure in these patients may be secondary to the long-term chronic calcium ingestion, with resultant nephrocalcinosis, or may be secondary to some coexisting or underlying primary renal disease. The reduced renal function contributes to the metabolic alkalosis, since normally functioning kidneys would allow for excretion of the excess alkali under most circumstances. Thus, in this disorder, the maintenance of metabolic alkalosis is complex and involves continued exogenous supply, reduced renal bicarbonate excretory capacity, and possibly an independent effect of the hypercalcemia to enhance renal bicarbonate absorption and stimulate net acid excretion.

This is an important syndrome to diagnose, although it is uncommon. Whether patients have nephrocalcinosis secondary to milk-alkali syndrome or another underlying renal disease, progressive renal insufficiency may lead to end-stage renal disease. Recognizing this syndrome and stopping the excess calcium intake or the unnecessary vitamin D ingestion will not only correct the metabolic alkalosis but may also stabilize renal function.

Another uncommon cause of metabolic alkalosis secondary to the provision of exogenous alkali has been described in patients receiving massive transfusions. This syndrome is seen in patients given blood with citrate as the anti-coagulant. The citrate is ultimately metabolized to form bicarbonate. The metabolic alkalosis is usually short-lived if patients have normal renal function and can excrete the excess bicarbonate. In patients who have reduced renal function or who are volume depleted, this transfusion-induced metabolic alkalosis may persist and may respond to expansion of intravascular volume.

Excretion of Nonreabsorbable Anions

It has been thought that delivery of nonreabsorbable anions to the distal nephron, at a time when the distal nephron is avidly reabsorbing sodium, results in enhanced lumen-negative voltage. This is believed to be secondary to distal delivery of sodium with an anion that is less effective than chloride in shunting the lumen-negative voltage associated with active sodium absorption. This enhanced lumen-negative voltage, therefore, provides a greater electrical driving force to trap both potassium and protons in the lumen. Thus, both urinary potassium wasting and an increase in net acid excretion with the development of metabolic alkalosis ensue. Depending on the volume status of the patient and on the magnitude of the potassium depletion, correction of this disorder requires discontinuation of the administered nonreabsorbable anion, restoration of intravascular volume, and correction of potassium depletion. The most commonly implicated nonreabsorbable anions are drugs, especially the penicillins. Thus, very large doses of sodium penicillin or semisynthetic penicillin, such as carbenicillin, can result in this disorder.

Glucose Refeeding

This uncommon cause of metabolic alkalosis is observed in patients who eat after a prolonged period of starvation. Metabolic alkalosis produced is multi-factorial. First, there is increased generation of bicarbonate from the conversion of ketoacids to bicarbonate. Second, there is an increased bicarbonate reabsorptive capacity by the kidney. However, both the generation of the metabolic alkalosis and the renal bicarbonate reabsorptive capacity changes are short-lived. Thus, the alkalosis resolves spontaneously as the kidney excretes the excess alkali. Usually the alkalosis is mild, i.e., plasma bicarbonate less than 35 mEq/liter and lasts for no more than 2 or 3 days.

REFERENCES

1. Bravo, E. L., Tarazi, R. C., Dustan, H. P., et al. (1983): The changing clinical spectrum of primary aldosteronism. *Am. J. Med.*, 74:641–651.

2. Brunner, F. P., and Frick, P. G. (1968): Hypokalemia, metabolic alkalosis and hypernatra-emia due to "massive" sodium penicillin therapy. *Br. Med. J.*, 4:550–552.
3. Christy, N. P., and Laragh, J. H. (1961): Pathogenesis of hypokalemic alkalosis in Cushing's syndrome. *N. Engl. J. Med.*, 265:1083–1088.
4. Conn,, J. W. (1955): Primary aldosteronism: A new clinical syndrome. *J. Lab. Clin. Med.*, 45:3–17.
5. Conn, J. W., Rovner, D. R., and Cohen, E. L. (1968): Licorice-induced pseudoaldosteron-ism. *JAMA*, 205:492–496.
6. Ganguly, A. (1982): New insights and questions about glucocorticoid-suppressible hyperal-dosteronism. *Am. J. Med.*, 72:851–854.
7. Garella, S., Chazan, J. A., and Cohen, J. J. (1970): Saline-resistant metabolic alkalosis of "chloride-wasting nephropathy." *Ann. Intern. Med.*, 73:31–38.
8. Gold, E. M. (1979): The Cushing syndrome: Changing views of diagnosis and treatment. *Ann. Intern. Med.*, 90:829–844.
9. Hulter, H. N., Sebastian, A., Toto, R. D., Bonner, E. L. Jr., and Elnicki, L. P. (1982): Renal and systemic acid-base effects of the chronic administration of hypercalcemia-producing agents: Calcitriol, PTH, and intravenous calcium. *Kidney Int.*, 21:445–458.
10. Hulter, H. N., Sigala, J. F., and Sebastian, A. (1978): K^+ deprivation potentiates the renal alkalosis-producing effect of mineralocorticoid. *Am. J. Physiol.*, 235:F298–F309.
11. Jacobson, H. R., and Seldin, D. W. (1983): On the generation, maintenance, and correction of metabolic alkalosis. *Am. J. Physiol.*, 245:F425–F432.
12. Kassirer, J. P., London, A. M., Goldman, D. M., and Schwartz, W. B. (1970): On the patho-genesis of metabolic alkalosis in hyperaldosteronism. *Am. J. Med.*, 49:306–315.
13. Liddle, G. W., Bledsoe, T., and Coppage, W. S. Jr. (1963): A familial renal disorder simu-lating primary aldosteronism but with neglible aldosterone secretion. *Trans. Assoc. Am. Physicians*, 76:199–213.
14. Litwin, M. S., Smith, L. L., and Moore, F. D. (1959): Metabolic alkalosis following massive transfusion. *Surgery*, 45:805–813.
15. Luke, R. G., Wright, F. S., Fowler, N., Kashgarian, M., and Giebisch, G. H. (1978): Effects of potassium depletion on renal tubule chloride transport in the rat. *Kidney Int.*, 14:414–427.
16. Orwoll, E. S. (1982): The milk-alkali syndrome: Current concepts. *Ann. Intern. Med.*, 97:242–248.
17. Schambelan, M., Slaton, P. E. Jr., and Biglieri, E. G. (1971): Mineralocorticoid production in hyperadrenocorticism. Role in pathogenesis of hypokalemic alkalosis. *Am. J. Med.*, 51:299–303.
18. Simon, N., Franklin, S. S., Bleifer, K. H., and Maxwell, M. H. (1972): Clinical characteris-tics of renovascular hypertension. *JAMA*, 220:1209–1218.
19. Stinebaugh, B. J., and Schloeder, F. X. (1972): Glucose-induced alkalosis in fasting subjects. Relationship to renal bicarbonate reabsorption during fasting and refeeding. *J. Clin. Invest.*, 51:1326–1336.
20. Wilson, J., and Foster, D. (eds.) (1985): *Textbook of Endocrinology*, p. 866. W. B. Saun-ders, Philadelphia.

General Review Articles

21. Cogan, M. G., and Rector, F. C. Jr. (1986): Acid-base disorders. In: *The Kidney*, edited by B. M. Brenner and F. C. Rector, pp. 457–517. W. B. Saunders, Philadelphia.
22. Harrington, J. T. (1984): Nephrology Forum: Metabolic alkalosis. *Kidney Int.*, 26:88–97.
23. Harrington, J. T., and Kassirer, J. P. (1982): Metabolic alkalosis. In: *Acid-Base*, pp. 235–306. Little, Brown, Boston.
24. Hodgkin, J. E., Soeprono, F. F., and Chan, D. M. (1980): Incidence of metabolic alkalemia in hospitalized patients. *Crit. Care Med.*, 8:725–728.

25. Jacobson, H. R., and Seldin, D. W. (1983): On the generation, maintenance and correction of metabolic alkalosis. *Am. J. Physiol.*, 245:F425–F432.
26. Relman, A. S. (1972): Metabolic consequences of acid-base disorders. *Kidney Int.*, 1:347–359.
27. Seldin, D. W., and Rector, F. C. Jr. (1972): The generation and maintenance of metabolic alkalosis. *Kidney Int.*, 1:305–321.

The Regulation of Acid–Base Balance, edited
by Donald W. Seldin and Gerhard Giebisch,
Raven Press, Ltd., New York © 1989.

19

Clinical Syndromes of Respiratory Acidosis and Alkalosis

C. Gregory Elliott and Alan H. Morris

*Department of Medicine, University of Utah School of Medicine,
and Pulmonary Division, LDS Hospital,
Salt Lake City, Utah 84143*

Respiratory Acidosis
　　Definition • Systemic and Metabolic Consequences • Pathophysiologic
　　Approach to Respiratory Acidosis • Clinical Evaluation • Clinical
　　Syndromes
Respiratory Alkalosis
　　Definition • Systemic and Metabolic Consequences • Pathophysiologic
　　Approach to Respiratory Alkalosis • Clinical Evaluation • Clinical Ap-
　　proach to Treatment
References

RESPIRATORY ACIDOSIS
(1,2,4,5,8,10,13,14,17,20,22,24,25,26,29,32)

Definition

Respiratory acidosis is usually defined by an inappropriately elevated arterial P_{CO_2}. This definition allows the clinician to recognize the inadequate matching of alveolar ventilation ($\dot{V}_A$) to metabolic rate ($\dot{V}_{CO_2}$), alveolar hypoventilation, which results in hypercapnia, and the more subtle inadequate respiratory compensation for metabolic acidosis in which alveolar hyperventilation (hypocapnia) occurs but is less marked than the expected response (Table 1). With hypercapnic respiratory acidosis, the pHa falls below 7.4 as the Pa_{CO_2} increases above 40 mm Hg. In uncomplicated respiratory acidosis, the Pa_{CO_2} is always greater than 40 mm Hg and inappropriately high. When the onset of hypercapnia is rapid (within minutes to hours), there is not suffi-

TABLE 1. *Abbreviations and terms*

Symbol	Term	Units
$\dot{V}_E$	Minute ventilation	liters/min
$\dot{V}_A$	Alveolar ventilation	liters/min
$\dot{V}_D$	Dead space ventilation	liters/min
f	Ventilatory rate	min^{-1}
V_T	Tidal volume	liters
V_D	Dead space per breath	liters
V_D/V_T	Dead space to tidal volume ratio ($= \dot{V}_D/\dot{V}_E$)	
FEV_1	Forced expiratory volume in 1 sec	liters
$\dot{V}_{CO_2}$	Carbon dioxide production	liters/min
Pa_{O_2}	Arterial O_2 pressure	mm Hg
Pa_{CO_2}	Arterial CO_2 pressure	mm Hg
pHa	Arterial pH	

cient time for compensatory renal regeneration and reabsorption of bicarbonate. This situation is termed "acute respiratory acidosis." In contrast, when the retention of carbon dioxide is gradual or persistent (i.e., days, weeks, or months), there is a compensatory increase in renal regeneration and reabsorption of bicarbonate, which increases blood $[HCO_3^-]$ and reduces the fall in pHa that otherwise would have occurred. This disorder is termed "chronic respiratory acidosis."

When inadequate respiratory compensation compounds metabolic acidosis, the pHa often is well below 7.4, but the Pa_{CO_2}, although lower than normal, remains inappropriately high for the degree of acidemia (Fig. 1, metabolic acidosis with inadequate respiratory compensation area). The inappropriately elevated Pa_{CO_2} correctly identifies respiratory acidosis because it is above the confidence limits for Pa_{CO_2} in metabolic acidosis. A respiratory acidosis with a Pa_{CO_2} below normal always indicates a mixed acid-base disorder. Although the primary acid-base disorder is metabolic acidosis, identification of the respiratory contribution to the acidosis is necessary for the recognition and treatment of underlying clinical problems.

Systemic and Metabolic Consequences

The systemic effects of hypercapnic respiratory acidosis are numerous and of critical importance to the clinician. Evaluation of patients with known or suspected hypercapnic acidosis should include careful neurologic assessment as well as cardiovascular examination. Increasing Pa_{CO_2} directly increases cerebral blood flow. Hypercapnic acidosis increases intracranial pressure and may cause papilledema. In addition, stupor and coma may occur at very high Pa_{CO_2} levels (>80 mm Hg). Headache, confusion, disorientation, and asterixis represent valuable, although frequently late and inconstant, signs of respiratory failure.

SEA LEVEL

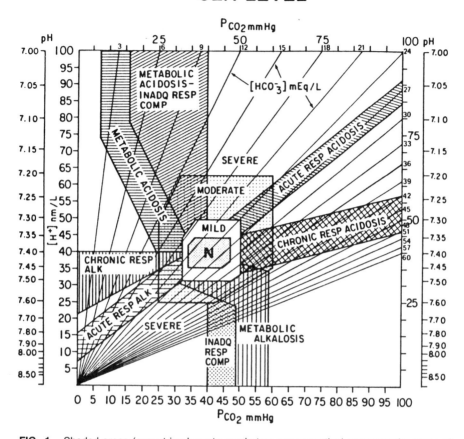

FIG. 1. Shaded areas (except inadequate respiratory compensation) represent the range of variability observed in selected populations with pure acid-base disorders. In general, patients whose measurements are not within the shaded areas have more than one acid-base disorder. (From ref. 23.)

Cardiovascular effects of hypercapnic acidosis depend to a large extent on the autonomic response to hypercapnia. Even in the absence of hypoxemia, hypercapnia stimulates the release of epinephrine and norepinephrine. These endogenous catecholamines may produce hypertension and tachycardia. However, profound hypercapnia may be associated with hypotension because of depression of myocardial contractility and increases in pulmonary vascular resistance.

Renal blood flow and glomerular filtration rate (GFR) may be reduced at high levels of Pa_{CO_2}. Chronic hypercapnia produces increased regeneration and reabsorption of bicarbonate by the renal tubule. An increase in ammonium chloride excretion results in the hypochloremia characteristic of chronic respiratory acidosis.

The effects of hypercapnic acidosis on the individual patient may be highly variable. Numerous clinical observations reinforce the time-honored principle of treating the patient and not the arterial blood gas measurement.

Pathophysiologic Approach to Respiratory Acidosis

Once the clinician has recognized the presence of respiratory acidosis, it is appropriate to consider a differential diagnosis based on pathophysiologic mechanisms (Table 2). This approach encourages the clinician to coordinate clinical, functional, and laboratory information and seek physiologic mechanisms that can best explain the respiratory acidosis. For example, a patient with stable chronic obstructive pulmonary disease (COPD) may develop acute respiratory acidosis after surgery because of atelectasis, retained secretions, narcotic-induced hypoventilation, and prolonged neuromuscular blockade. The identification of each of these different elements requires consideration of elastic work of breathing (atelectasis), resistive work of breathing (retained secretions), ventilatory drive (narcotic-induced hypoventilation), and respiratory muscle strength (neuromuscular blockade).

TABLE 2. *Pathophysiologic assessment of respiratory acidosis*

I. Increased CO_2 production ($\dot{V}CO_2$)
    A. Activity
        e.g., Seizures, shivering, work of breathing, exercise
    B. Bicarbonate buffering of H^+ in metabolic acidosis
        e.g., Anaerobic exercise, exogenous bicarbonate administration
    C. Basal metabolism
        e.g., Fever, hyperthyroidism
    D. Lipogenesis
        e.g., Parenteral nutrition
II. Decreased alveolar ventilation ($\dot{V}_A$)
    A. Decreased minute ventilation ($\dot{V}_E$)
        1. Impaired ventilatory control
            a. Medullary CO_2 receptors (e.g., narcotics)
            b. Carotid body Pao_2 receptors (e.g., surgical removal)
        2. Mechanical limitations
            a. Advanced neuromuscular disease
            b. Ventilatory muscle exhaustion
    B. Increased dead space ventilation ($\dot{V}_D$)
        1. Pulmonary vascular obstruction (e.g., pulmonary thromboembolism)
        2. Decreased cardiac output (e.g., hypovolemic shock and advanced pulmonary
           disease)
        3. Maldistribution of ventilation and perfusion associated with lung disease (e.g.,
           air trapping)
        4. Decreased tidal volume (V_T) with increased V_D/V_T owing to rapid shallow
           breathing pattern
            a. Impaired bellows (e.g., neuromuscular disease)
            b. Chest wall disease (e.g., kyphoscoliosis)
            c. Increased work of breathing (e.g., airway obstruction *or* lung edema *or*
               fibrosis)

The concept of the matching of alveolar ventilation ($\dot{V}_A$) to CO_2 production ($\dot{V}CO_2$) is central to the pathophysiologic assessment of respiratory acidosis.

$$Paco_2 = \dot{V}co_2 \; k/\dot{V}_A \qquad [1a]$$

$$Paco_2 = \dot{V}co_2 \; k/(\dot{V}_E - \dot{V}_D) \qquad [1b]$$

where k is a constant, $\dot{V}_E$ is minute ventilation, and $\dot{V}_D$ is dead space ventilation. Increased $Paco_2$ results either from an increase in Vco_2, a decrease in V_A, or both. It can be a result of pulmonary or nonpulmonary problems, since CO_2 elimination from the lung depends on the function of other organ systems as well (including the central and peripheral nervous systems, the musculoskeletal system, and the cardiovascular system).

Increased CO₂ Production

Increased CO_2 production ($\dot{V}co_2$) alone is an uncommon cause of respiratory acidosis. The large ventilatory reserve of most patients allows alveolar ventilation to increase proportionately as additional CO_2 is produced by increases in activity or basal metabolism. Therefore, increases of CO_2 production can only play a role in the pathophysiology of respiratory acidosis when alveolar ventilation is fixed, e.g., in a patient receiving controlled mechanical ventilation or when alveolar ventilation is markedly limited by one or more disease processes. Increases in activity require increased use of oxygen and substrate, such as carbohydrates, fatty acids, or amino acids. This aerobic metabolism releases chemical energy and liberates CO_2, which must be eliminated by the lungs (Fig. 2).

Increases in metabolic activity without a concomitant increase in tissue O_2 supply results in the anaerobic production of ATP and the generation of lactic acid. The lactic acid is buffered by tissue stores of bicarbonate, with the generation of additional quantities of CO_2 (Fig. 3).

Increases in basal metabolism, as may occur with fever or hyperthyroidism,

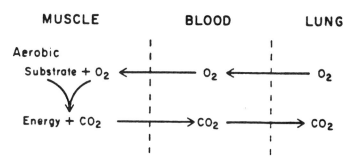

FIG. 2. Aerobic metabolism of carbohydrates produces CO_2, which the respiratory system must eliminate. (Modified from ref. 31.)

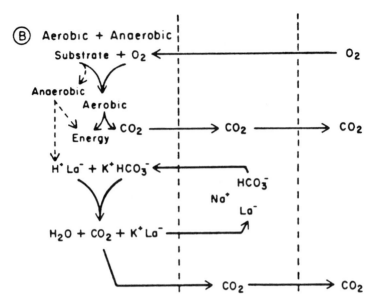

FIG. 3. Anaerobic metabolism generates lactic acid. CO_2 is liberated from bicarbonate as the lactic acid is buffered. (From ref. 31.)

may increase the production of CO_2 through aerobic or anaerobic pathways. CO_2 production increases approximately 13% for each degree centigrade increase in temperature.

Lipogenesis is not easy to induce in humans. However, excessive glucose administration to a critically ill patient (e.g., hyperalimentation), particularly in the setting of adequate glycogen stores, may lead to lipogenesis. This process uses pyruvate from the metabolism of glucose coupled with acetylcoenzyme A, with resultant generation of CO_2 (Fig. 4).

Decreased Alveolar Ventilation

If the described disorders that result in excessive CO_2 production can be excluded or are unlikely, an increased $PaCO_2$ indicates a decreased $\dot{V}_A$. Decreased minute ventilation ($\dot{V}_E$) or increased dead space ventilation ($\dot{V}_D$), may individually or collectively contribute to decreased alveolar ventilation (Table 2).

Both disordered ventilatory control and mechanical limitations can decrease $\dot{V}_E$. Ventilatory control for CO_2 elimination depends on the medullary chemoreceptors. A reduction in the sensitivity of these receptors to increasing PCO_2 and decreasing cerebrospinal fluid pH can result in an inappropriately low $\dot{V}_E$ and, therefore, a low $\dot{V}_A$. This pathophysiologic mechanism can be

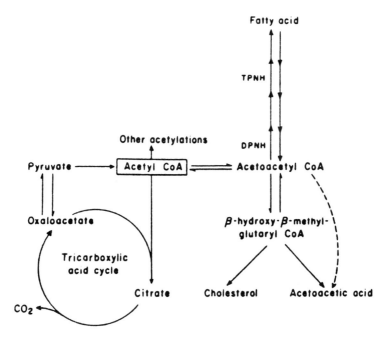

FIG. 4. When excess glucose is stored in tissues as fat, the tricarboxylic acid cycle generates CO_2, which the respiratory system must eliminate. (Modified from ref. 18.)

difficult to recognize when the patient has advanced pulmonary dysfunction but is easily recognized when the vital capacity and the lungs are close to normal.

The other pathophysiologic category that results in decreased alveolar ventilation ($\dot{V}_A$) is increased dead space ventilation ($\dot{V}_D$). The volume of gas in the trachea and conducting airways (anatomic dead space) approximates 1 ml/lb of ideal body weight. In addition to anatomic dead space, the lungs may contain many regions where alveolar ventilation ($\dot{V}_A$) greatly exceeds blood flow ($\dot{Q}$) (Fig. 5C). These high $\dot{V}_A/\dot{Q}$ regions behave as if some of the ventilation is excessive and wasted. This wasted ventilation constitutes physiologic dead space.

Increases in arterial P_{CO_2} should not be attributed solely to increases in dead space ventilation unless the dead space/tidal volume ratio (V_D/V_T) exceeds 0.6 (normal V_D/V_T is approximately 0.3). Because this requires substantial pulmonary vascular obstruction, increased dead space alone is seldom responsible for respiratory acidosis. However, an increase in $\dot{V}_D$ may lead directly to respiratory acidosis in a patient with other processes that impair CO_2 elimination. For example, patients with airway obstruction and hyperinflation are susceptible to increases in $\dot{V}_D$ owing to decreased pulmonary perfusion, e.g., due to hypovolemia. They would also be more suscepti-

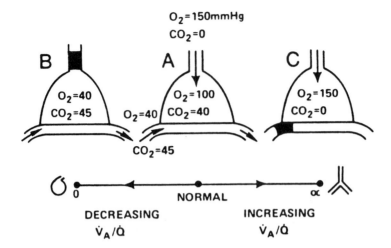

FIG. 5. The lung contains a spectrum of $\dot{V}_A/\dot{Q}$ units, which may range from no ventilation **(B)** to no perfusion **(C)**. Conditions that convert more $\dot{V}_A/\dot{Q}$ units to high V_A relative to $\dot{Q}$ make CO_2 elimination more inefficient by requiring a larger $\dot{V}_E$. (From ref. 34.)

ble to increases in $\dot{V}_D$ caused by pulmonary vascular occlusion, e.g., pulmonary embolus, or by decreases in capillary perfusion caused by air trapping or by application of high airway pressure during mechanical ventilation.

A decrease in tidal volume (V_T) alone can be associated with a large enough increase in the ratio of dead space to tidal volume (V_D/V_T) to produce a significant increase in $\dot{V}_D$. Anatomic dead space is approximately constant. Thus any disorder that decreases the V_T leads to a concomitant increase in V_D/V_T. An increase in V_D/V_T can be viewed as a relative inefficiency of ventilation; i.e., additional work and ventilation ($\dot{V}_E$) are required to maintain the same alveolar ventilation ($\dot{V}_A$) (Table 3). This increase in V_D/V_T is believed to be a common mechanism in COPD patients with acute exacerbations, since they usually develop tachypnea with a rapid shallow breathing pattern (high f, low V_T).

A decreased V_T may result from neuromuscular disease that decreases the

TABLE 3. *Effect of decreasing tidal volume upon dead space ventilation when dead space volume and minute ventilation are constant*

$\dot{V}_E$ (liters/min)	V_D (liter)	V_T (liter)	f (min^{-1})	$\dot{V}_D$ (liters/min)	$\dot{V}_A$ (liters/min)
8.0	0.15	1.00	8	1.2	6.8
8.0	0.15	0.50	16	2.4	5.6
8.0	0.15	0.25	32	4.8	3.2

Modified from ref. 4.

contractile force developed by respiratory muscles, from chest wall disorders that diminish the chest wall and lung displacement produced by normally contracting muscles, and from adjustments to increased work of breathing that may result in reductions in V_T designed to decrease the work of breathing. Increased work of breathing may result from increased lung stiffness (decreased lung compliance) produced by pulmonary edema or to increased airway resistance (bronchospasm or retained secretions). Patients with airway obstruction can also encounter difficulty because often they increase their breathing frequency when in distress. This reduces exhalation time and leads to air trapping with consequent overinflation. The overinflated lungs change the position and contour of the diaphragms from a highly arched to a flattened muscle bed. In the hyperinflated chest, diaphragm contraction may pull the rib cage inward and narrow the costal angle with inspiration (Hoover's sign).

Clinical Evaluation (3,9,16,30,33)

Although the definitive documentation of respiratory acidosis remains largely a blood gas diagnosis, it is not exclusively so, and the evaluation of respiratory acidosis rests heavily on the physician's fundamental tools—history and physical examination. It is the data obtained from a competently performed history and physical examination that provide the basis from which the physician establishes the likelihood (prior probability) of specific problems. Basic laboratory tests, e.g., spirometry, can aid by allowing quantitative confirmation of clinical hypotheses. Specialized laboratory tests, such as the assessment of ventilatory response to CO_2, are only occasionally necessary to provide confirmation of clinical impressions.

Importance of Prior Probability in Minimizing Errors

Clinical decisions are based on an analysis of data. The database consists of information from the history, physical examination, laboratory, and published literature. Since all decisions are associated with a significant probability of error, it is important to review the following basic principles that, when applied to the analysis of data, can minimize interpretive errors. An understanding of the role of prior probability (likelihood, frequency, or incidence are frequent synonyms) can lead to an increased appreciation of the value of history and physical examination data and lead to improvement in clinical decision making.

The most useful way to draw conclusions about change from any test result is by comparing it with a previous result in the same patient. The comparison of two estimations on the same patient eliminates much of the uncertainty involved in comparing a particular patient's measurement with an estimate obtained from a population. Although a comparison of sequential measurements within the same patient allows the physician the most confident interpretations, it is usually necessary to draw conclusions from a single patient measurement for which only comparison with population-derived estimates is possible. Any such approach, including the 95% confidence interval (CI) approach (*see* Chapter 6), is based on characteristics of a population of identified individuals already known to be normal. Clinical decisions, in contrast, are never made with foreknowledge of the normal or abnormal state of the patient; they involve knowledge only of a test result (e.g., the answer to a question, the presence or absence of a physical finding, or a Paco2 value within or without the normal range) from which we must deduce whether a patient is normal or abnormal. The probability that a positive result predicts that the condition being sought is, in fact, present is defined by the predictive value of a positive test and is strongly influenced by the pretest or *a priori* likelihood (prior probability) that the hypothesis being evaluated (e.g., that the patient is normal) is actually true. These concepts are illustrated in Fig. 6.

Sensitivity and specificity are characteristics of the test only and are independent of the population being tested. Sensitivity and specificity are defined by studying the test results in a known population. In contrast, the predictive values of + or − test results are a function of both the test characteristics and the characteristics of the population within which the test is applied. The predictive value of a positive response to the question "Are you short of breath?" will be dramatically influenced by the character of the population to which the patient belongs. For example, a patient who responds positively and belongs to the population of individuals with known heart disease and recurrent lung edema will very likely have pulmonary congestion, whereas a patient who belongs to the population of marathon runners is more likely to have just run 10 miles than to be suffering from pulmonary congestion.

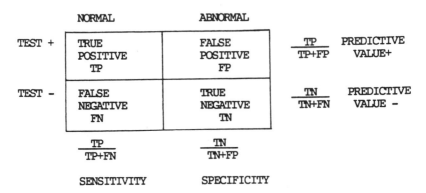

FIG. 6. (Test + and Test −) Positive and negative test results; (Predictive Value +) predictive value of a positive test; (Predictive Value −) predictive value of a negative test.

Figure 6 displays the results of a test in individuals in a well-defined population for which the prior probability of the condition being tested is known. For an individual from this population, the sensitivity, specificity, predictive value +, and predictive value − are calculated as illustrated. For an individual from another population, calculation of predictive values (+ or −) would require knowledge of the prior probability of the condition being tested in the new population.

The predictive value + is the probability, given a positive test result (Test +), that this represents a true positive. In a population with a very low prior probability for the condition being sought, most positive test results will be false positives, and the predictive value + will be extremely low. In contrast, when the prior probability is very high, very few positive tests will be false positives, and the predictive value of a positive test will be very high. The sensitivity and specificity, on the other hand, describe only the probability that the people with the condition will have a positive test (true positives) and that those without the condition will have a negative test (true negatives). Both sensitivity and specificity are independent of population distribution of the condition, since they describe the response of the test in those people already known to either have or not have the condition being sought. In clinical decision making, the interpretation of a test result usually is made for a patient in whom the condition may or may not be present (i.e., it is usually not known). It is for this reason that the predictive value of a positive or negative test result (and not the sensitivity or specificity) is the germane expression of the usefulness of the test in clinical diagnosis.

If the hypothesis being evaluated by the test has a prior probability of 2%, it is extremely unlikely to be true or present (Table 4). If the prior probability is 2%, a test with a sensitivity and specificity of 95% (a very good test) would yield a positive result with a predictive value of only 28%, that is, with only a 28% chance of being a true positive (72% chance of being a false positive). Even with an increase in sensitivity and specificity to 99% ($p=0.01$), the

TABLE 4. *Predictive value as a function of sensitivity and specificity when prior probability is low*

Prior probability = 2%		
Sensitivity and specificity	Positive predictive value (%)	Negative predictive value (%)
50	2	98
70	5	99
90	16	100
95	28	100
99	67	100

Modified from ref. 30.

TABLE 5. *Predictive value as a function of sensitivity and specificity when prior probability is high*

Prior probability $= 98\%$		
Sensitivity and specificity	Negative predictive value (%)	Positive predictive value (%)
50	2	98
70	5	99
90	16	100
95	28	100
99	67	100

Modified from ref. 30.

predictive value of a positive test (positive predictive value) would only increase to 67%, leaving about 1 chance in 3 that the positive result is a false positive. Therefore, a hypothesis with a low prior probability cannot be confirmed with confidence by any positive test result. In contrast, almost any negative test result can be used to reject the hypothesis (the negative predictive value is always very high).

The converse is true if the prior probability is 98%, and the hypothesis is, therefore, extremely likely to be true or present (Table 5). If the prior probability is 98%, a test with a sensitivity and specificity of 95% would yield a negative result with a predictive value of only 28%, that is, with only a 28% chance of being a true negative (72% chance of being a false negative). A hypothesis with a high prior probability cannot be excluded with confidence by any negative test result. In contrast, almost any positive test result can be be used to confirm the hypothesis (the positive predictive value is always very high).

The prior probability of any hypothesis (e.g., that the patient is normal or that the patient has acute respiratory acidosis) is estimated from many sources of information. Foremost among these are the history and physical examination. Each response to a question during acquisition of the patient history, and each result of a search for a specific physical finding during physical examination, alter the prior probability for the next question, the next physical finding, or the next laboratory test (e.g., $Paco_2$).

Even though the p value for the 95% CI is always 0.05, the predictive value of a positive test result (e.g., a $Paco_2$ that exceeds the 95% CI) can vary from extremely low to extremely high as the prior probability of the condition sought (e.g., respiratory acidosis) varies from very low (2%; Table 4) to very high (98%; Table 5). In fact, any test (such as the $Paco_2$) is most useful when the prior probability is neither very low nor very high. The predictive value of a positive test is shown in Fig. 7 as a function of the prior probability of the hypothesis being examined. Note that even though p is always 0.05, the predictive value+ varies greatly for the same test result. When prior proba-

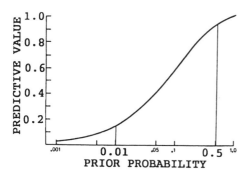

FIG. 7. Predictive value of a positive test as a function of the prior probability that the condition being sought (or hypothesis being tested) is true. $p = 0.05$ (α error), power = 0.80 (β error = 0.20). Multiply values by 100 to obtain probabilities in percent. (Modified from ref. 3.)

bility is 1% (0.01), the predictive value + is only about 14% (0.14); when the prior probability is 50% (0.50), the predictive value + is about 94% (0.94).

Measurements such as $PaCO_2$ can, therefore, be meaningfully interpreted, and reasonable conclusions relative to the question of normality or abnormality can be drawn only when the test result is placed within the clinical context. This means only when an attempt has been made to estimate the prior probability for the condition being evaluated. An isolated test result (e.g., $PaCO_2$) frequently is not helpful when the prior probability is either extremely high or extremely low unless the test is performed for the purpose of monitoring or titration.

History

The primary cause of respiratory acidosis is often readily apparent from a consideration of historical data. Knowledge of the patient's underlying medical condition frequently leads directly to diagnosis and treatment. Examples of such direct diagnoses include patients with long-standing and progressive COPD, patients with progressive neuromuscular disorders, such as muscular dystrophy, or patients who have recently undergone cardiopulmonary resuscitation and mechanical ventilation. The history of cardiopulmonary resuscitation provides a high prior probability (likelihood) that CO_2 retention and respiratory acidosis result from a defect of the chest wall (flail chest). The diagnosis can be confirmed by physical examination (inward sternal movement with spontaneous breaths, costochondral crepitation, and subcutaneous ecchymoses).

Historical information is essential to the recognition of each pathophysiologic cause for respiratory acidosis (Table 6). Increased CO_2 production contributes to respiratory acidosis only if the patient requires mechanical ventilation or has advanced pulmonary dysfunction. The clinical suspicion of excess CO_2 production derives directly from historical information; for example, exercise, seizures, and shivering are all associated with increased aerobic and anaerobic CO_2 production. Lipogenesis with concomitant increases in

TABLE 6. *Useful historical information for evaluation of respiratory acidosis*

Pathophysiologic mechanism	Historical information	Therapeutic suggestions
Increased CO_2 production ($\dot{V}_{CO_2}$)	Severely limited alveolar ventilation, e.g., advanced chronic lung disease, mechanical ventilation	Decrease CO_2 production and/or increase alveolar ventilation
Aerobic metabolism	Exercise, seizure, shivering, agitation, fever, hyperthyroidism	Sedation, paralysis, antipyretics, β-blockade
HCO_3^- buffering of acidosis	Anaerobic exercise, exogenous bicarbonate administration	Decrease acid production
Lipogenesis	Parenteral glucose administration	Decrease glucose load
Decreased alveolar ventilation($\dot{V}_A$) Decreased minute ventilation ($\dot{V}_E$)	Medications: sedatives, narcotics Malnutrition Hypothyroidism	Discontinue sedatives or narcotics Nutritional support Thyroid replacement Ventilatory support
Medullary chemoreceptors	Brainstem injury, vascular accident Infection, history of sleep disorder	
Carotid chemoreceptors	Carotid body resection	Respiratory stimulants
Increased dead space ventilation (V_D)		
Pulmonary vascular obstruction	Recent abdominal, thoracic, or orthopedic surgery, venous thrombosis, or thrombophlebitis Recent immobility	Anticoagulant or thrombolytic therapy

Cause	Clinical features	Treatment
Decreased perfusion	Hypovolemia 2° vomiting, diuretics, diarrhea, gastrointestinal blood—melena ↓ Myocardial contractility—ischemic heart disease, arrhythmia	Replace volume Increase cardiac output Inotropes—digoxin
Decreased tidal volume (V$_T$)	Dyspnea while supine, relieved sitting up or standing or any positionally determined dyspnea	
Neuromuscular	Myasthenia gravis, drugs that block neuromuscular junction, muscle pain—polymyositis, muscular dystrophy	Discontinue drugs Specific therapy
Chest wall	Recent cardiopulmonary resuscitation or chest trauma, pathologic rib fractures	Support ventilation, deep breathing therapy
↑ Work of breathing (↑ resistance)	Stridor, hoarseness, narrow endotracheal tube present Wheezing, asthma, chronic airflow obstruction	Relieve upper airway obstruction Bronchodilator, antibiotic, anti-inflammatory therapy Support ventilation
↑ Work of breathing (↓ compliance)	Paroxysmal nocturnal dyspnea (cardiac pulmonary edema) Fever, chills, cough (pneumonia) Cough, exertional dyspnea, medications (alveolitis, fibrosis)	Deep breathing therapy Specific therapy

CO_2 production is likely only if the patient is receiving parenteral glucose in excess of 2,000 calories daily.

The history is also central to recognizing alveolar hypoventilation caused by an impaired ventilatory drive. The absence of historical information about advanced pulmonary dysfunction strongly suggests a disorder of ventilatory drive. Narcotics, benzodiazepines, and other drugs that depress the central nervous system decrease the ventilatory response to increasing $PaCO_2$. For this reason, a careful review of medications is essential. Not only are sedatives and analgesics commonly prescribed for patients with underlying cardio-respiratory diseases, they are also commonly overlooked contributors to respiratory acidosis. In addition to medications, a history of hypothyroidism, brainstem injury, malnutrition, or carotid body resection provides an appropriate background for impaired ventilatory drive.

The history also can establish the likelihood that an increase in $\dot{V}_D$ contributes to respiratory acidosis. Although pulmonary embolism characteristically increases dead space, the usual acid-base derangement in patients with pulmonary embolism is respiratory alkalosis ($\downarrow PaCO_2$) because of the increased ventilatory drive that markedly increases $\dot{V}_E$. When other diseases that may limit $\dot{V}_E$ are present (e.g., severe airway obstruction), respiratory acidosis may be the result of pulmonary embolism. Historical clues to the diagnosis of thromboembolism include both symptoms (e.g., dyspnea, pleuritic chest pain, or hemoptysis) and the clinical setting (e.g., recent major surgery, deep vein thrombosis or thrombophlebitis, adenocarcinoma).

Historical information aids in the recognition of a decreased cardiac output that results in increased $\dot{V}_A/\dot{Q}$ ratios. A common clinical setting for such a problem is the intensive care unit. Patients with underlying cardiac disease and lung edema often receive positive end expiratory pressure (PEEP). This may increase $\dot{V}_D$ (by decreasing cardiac output as a result of increasing airway pressure) in a patient with fixed minute ventilation ($\dot{V}_E$). Gastrointestinal bleeding, vomiting, and diarrhea may reduce intravascular volume and cardiac output. Each of these conditions may increase $\dot{V}_A/\dot{Q}$ ratios, leading to increased $\dot{V}_D$ and respiratory acidosis in patients with limited ventilatory reserve or fixed $\dot{V}_E$.

Finally, historical data enhance the prior probability of respiratory acidosis caused by decreased tidal volume. Generalized muscle weakness or supine dyspnea suggests diaphragm failure; cough and exertional dyspnea suggest interstitial disease, such as heart failure or pulmonary fibrosis; and wheezing and cough suggest asthma. Paroxysmal nocturnal dyspnea may be an historical clue to lung edema in a decompensating patient with chronic lung disease.

Physical Examination

A systematic physical examination provides important information with respect to both the cause and the severity of respiratory acidosis. The exam-

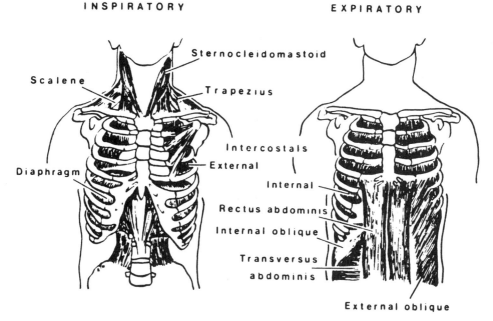

FIG. 8. The diaphragm is the principal inspiratory muscle. The observation of contraction by accessory inspiratory muscles is strong evidence for the presence of neuromuscular disease or advanced pulmonary dysfunction. Exhalation normally is passive. Active contraction of expiratory muscles provides strong evidence for advanced neuromuscular or pulmonary disease. (From ref. 32.)

iner should pay particular attention to the state of consciousness, the pattern of ventilation, and the functional state and activity of the respiratory muscles. Patient and examiner position are extremely important. Proper orientation is essential for the evaluation of body symmetry and symmetry of movement during breathing. For example, failure to examine the patient in both the upright and supine positions may allow diaphragmatic paralysis to go unrecognized. In the upright position, the paradoxical movement (inward movement during inspiration) of the abdomen may not be apparent.

Knowledge of the accessory muscles of respiration is basic. The diaphragm is the principal inspiratory muscle. When the work of breathing is increased or the diaphragm is ineffective, the physician can observe active contractions of the scalenus medius, parasternal and external intercostal, sternocleidomastoid, and trapezius muscles, usually in that order (Fig. 8).

Flaring of the alae nasae and descent of the trachea (thyroid cartilage) with quiet inspiration at rest is an indication of increased ventilatory drive. In the presence of diaphragm failure, severe airway obstruction, or a driven ventilation (>40 liters/min $\dot{V}_E$), the accessory expiratory muscles actively contract. These muscles include the rectus abdominis, the transversus abdominis, and the internal and external oblique muscles of the abdomen (Fig. 8). Patient position and abdominal configuration assessment are critical here, since the rectus is an expiratory muscle only when the anterior abdominal wall presents a convex surface to the atmosphere. This is the case when subjects are upright. In some supine patients, however, the abdomen is scaphoid, and the anterior abdominal wall presents a concave surface to the atmosphere. In this case, the rectus becomes an inspiratory muscle!

The physical examination also contributes to the assessment of the severity of respiratory acidosis. The observation of stupor or coma in association with profound hypercapnia and acidosis is a strong indication for intubation and mechanical ventilation. Conversely, although the pH may be greatly depressed and the P_{CO_2} greatly elevated, if the patient is alert and oriented, it is likely that the clinician has time to pursue other therapeutic interventions. In addition to assessing the patient's mental status, the clinician should look for signs of a failing ventilatory pump. Recruitment of accessory inspiratory and expiratory muscles and evidence of fatigued inspiratory muscles commonly precede severe ventilatory muscle failure. Common signs of inspiratory muscle fatigue include (1) rapid shallow breathing followed by bradypnea, (2) alternation between abdominal and rib cage displacement during inspiration, and (3) paradoxical abdominal motion; i.e., the abdominal wall moves in rather than up and out during inspiration.

The physical examination also identifies signs that characterize each of the pathophysiologic mechanisms outlined for respiratory acidosis (Table 7). For example, the observations of shivering or involuntary muscle contractions strongly suggest increased CO_2 production. Similarly, the observation of a flail chest or severe kyphoscoliosis increases the likelihood of impaired function of the thoracic bellows.

Basic Laboratory Tests

Measurement of pHa and Pa_{CO_2} is central to the diagnosis of respiratory acidosis. This readily available laboratory test detects respiratory acidosis in many patients even when careful history and physical examination do not suggest its presence. Among the explanations for the observation of decreased pH and increased P_{CO_2}, in the absence of historical and physical examination findings to suggest respiratory acidosis, are compensatory metabolic alkalosis and altered ventilatory drive, which reduce the respiratory distress usually associated with respiratory acidosis.

Acute hypercapnia can be recognized easily by the comcomitant decrease of arterial pH. However, worsening hypercapnia in a patient with preexistent chronic respiratory acidosis is most easily recognized by comparison with previous measurements of Pa_{CO_2}, pH, and serum bicarbonate.

Basic laboratory tests (Table 8) are useful in elucidating the etiology of respiratory acidosis. Chest roentgenography and spirometry are particularly

TABLE 7. *Useful physical examination observations for evaluation of respiratory acidosis*

Pathophysiology	Physical examination observation
Increased CO_2 production ($\dot{V}CO_2$)	Fever
	Parenteral glucose administration
	Piloerection and shivering
	Involuntary motor activity
Decreased alveolar ventilation ($\dot{V}_A$)	
Impaired ventilatory control	Bradypnea and decreased $\dot{V}_E$, apnea
Increased dead space	
Pulmonary vascular obstruction	Increased intensity of the second (pulmonic) component of a physiologically split second heart sound
Decreased cardiac output	S_3 gallop, orthostatic hypotension
Hyperinflation	Hoover's sign (lateral rib margins move in rather than out, and costal angle narrows on inspiration)
Decreased tidal volume (V_T)	
Neuromuscular	Paradoxical abdominal motion (suggests diaphragm dysfunction)
	Active contraction of accessory inspiratory and expiratory muscles
	Apnea
Musculoskeletal	Flail chest (paradoxical movement of sternum or ribs), kyphoscoliosis, Hoover's sign
Increased work (↑ resistance)	Stridor over trachea, internal diameter of tracheal tube < 7.5 mm, prolonged inspiration
	Expiratory wheezing, early or paninspiratory medium rales
Increased work (↓ compliance)	Chest strapping
	Late inspiratory fine crepitant rales (edema or fibrosis)

TABLE 8. *Basic and specialized laboratory assessment of respiratory acidosis*

Pathophysiologic mechanism	Basic laboratory measurement	Specialized laboratory
Increased CO_2 production ($\dot{V}CO_2$)		Measure $\dot{V}CO_2$
Decreased alveolar ventilation ($\dot{V}_A$) Impaired ventilatory control		Ventilatory response to CO_2 or hypoxia; sleep study Mouth occlusion pressure
Increased dead space		Direct measure of V_D or V_D/V_T during exercise
Decreased tidal volume (V_T) Neuromuscular disorders	Maximal inspiratory pressure 0 to -30 cm H_2O Vital capacity $< 1,000$ ml	
Chest wall, e.g., kyphoscoliosis	Vital capacity $< 1,000$ ml, but maximal inspiratory pressure -30 cm H_2O to -60 cm H_2O	Chest wall compliance Chest (total) compliance
Increased work (↑ resistance)	Decreased inspiratory flow on spirogram (upper airway) Decreased FEV_1/FVC (< 0.6) and FEV_1 (< 1.0 liter) on the spirogram (peripheral airways)	Airway resistance
Increased work (↓ compliance)	Lung edema (chest roentgenogram) Lung fibrosis (chest roentgenogram) and vital capacity < 1.0 liter (spirogram) Chest compliance (during mechanical ventilation)	Lung compliance Chest (total) compliance

useful for the recognition of advanced pulmonary disease. For example, from the chest x-rays, increased apex to diaphragm distance, eversion of the hemidiaphragms, increased retrosternal clear space, and an angle between the anterior diaphragm and the sternum of more than 90 degrees indicate overinflation. The radiographic distribution of edema helps distinguish among heart failure, excessive fluid therapy, and increased permeability lung edema. Chest roentgenograms also allow recognition of specific disorders that are difficult to appreciate by physical examination (e.g., tension pneumothorax, bullae).

Spirometry provides quantitative assessment of airway obstruction or chest restriction. The quantitative data provided by spirometry help the clinician to distinguish patients with respiratory acidosis caused by severe pulmonary dysfunction ("Can't breathe") from those with respiratory acidosis and impaired ventilatory drive ("Won't breathe"). Studies of patients with acute asthma attacks have demonstrated that CO_2 retention does not usually occur unless the forced expired volume in 1 sec (FEV_1) is less than 20% of predicted. Respiratory acidosis accompanying COPD generally occurs when airway obstruction is severe (e.g., FEV_1 less than 1.0 liter). Similarly, CO_2 retention accompanying neuromuscular diseases or kyphoscoliosis would not be expected unless the vital capacity is <1.0 liter, although a reduction of vital capacity to <50% of predicted is a warning that frank respiratory acidosis may rapidly supervene.

Special Laboratory Tests

In addition to basic laboratory studies, there are several special laboratory studies that occasionally are useful in the evaluation of respiratory acidosis (Table 8). Before these tests are performed, severe mechanical impairment associated with pulmonary, thoracic cage, and neuromuscular disorders must be carefully excluded. In general, these studies should be performed in a laboratory experienced with these tests, after consultation with a pulmonary specialist.

Clinical Syndromes

Respiratory acidosis can be a consequence of diseases that alter brainstem, nerve, neuromuscular, muscle, chest cage, airway, or pulmonary parenchymal function. Therapeutic need is dictated primarily by the hydrogen ion concentration (or pH) of body fluids, the most commonly assessed of which is arterial blood (pHa) (*see* Chapters 7, and 20). Therein lies one of the major clinical differences between acute and chronic respiratory acidosis, since for the same $PaCO_2$, only the acute problem will, because of the low pHa,

TABLE 9. *Causes of respiratory acidosis*

I. Asthma and asthma variants (↑ $\dot{V}_D$) (acute and/or chronic)
  A. Status asthmaticus
    1. Asthma without identifiable cause
    2. Asthma secondary to irritant stimulus, e.g., sodium metabisulfite
  B. Churg Strauss vasculitis
II. Upper airway obstruction (↓ $\dot{V}_E$) (usually acute)
  A. Foreign body
  B. Angioneurotic edema
  C. Epiglottitis
  D. Laryngotracheal stenosis
  E. Relapsing polychondritis
  F. Occlusive sleep apnea
III. Spontaneous tension pneumothorax (↓ V_T, ↓ $\dot{V}_E$) (acute)
  A. Histiocytosis X
  B. Bullous emphysema
  C. Cystic fibrosis
  D. Trauma
  E. Lymphangioleiomyomatosis
  F. Idiopathic
IV. Acute respiratory acidosis superimposed on chronic obstructive pulmonary disease (↑ $\dot{V}_D$) (acute and chronic)
  A. Bronchospasm
  B. Retained secretions
  C. Lung edema due to occult left ventricular failure
  D. Inflammation with or without infection
V. Neuromuscular disease with acute decompensation (↓ V_T, ↓ $\dot{V}_E$) (acute or chronic) (*see* Table 13)

---

require ventilatory support. The clinical responses of the patient, however, may be the major determinant of therapy.

We have listed (Table 9) the causes of respiratory acidosis with the corresponding pathophysiologic category (*see* Table 2) and an indication of its usual acute and/or chronic nature. The selected clinical syndromes that follow were chosen either because they are common (e.g., asthma, COPD) or are frequently overlooked (e.g., decreased ventilatory drive, neuromuscular disorders).

Acute Respiratory Acidosis

Decreased alveolar ventilation

Acute central nervous system from drug overdose. Any drug that can produce brainstem (CNS) depression is capable of decreasing both V_T and f, thereby decreasing $\dot{V}_E$, leading to decreased $\dot{V}_A$, which produces hypercapnia (increased $PaCO_2$) and acidemia (low pHa). For example, the data in Table 10 were obtained from a patient suffering from a barbiturate overdose. After

TABLE 10. *Acute respiratory failure in central nervous system depression[a]*

	Time (hr)	V_T (liter)	f (min^{-1})	$\dot{V}_E$ (liters/min)	$Paco_2$ (mm Hg)	pHa
A	07:45	0.5	16	8	75	7.13
B	08:00	0.5	24	12	50	7.30
C	08:15	0.75	16	12	33	7.50
D	08:30	0.75	14	10.5	39	7.42

[a]Data obtained from a patient following barbiturate overdose.

emergency endotracheal intubation and institution of mechanical ventilation, the hypercapnia ($Paco_2 = 75$) indicates inadequate matching of $\dot{V}_A$ to $\dot{V}co_2$, but it is the acidemia (pHa = 7.13) that requires therapy in the form of assisted ventilation (A, Table 10). The subsequent measurements (B,C,D, Table 10) indicate three changes in the mechanical ventilation pattern (V_T, f, $\dot{V}_E$) made before the pattern associated with an appropriate $\dot{V}_A$—one that yielded normal $Paco_2$ and pHa—was established (D, Table 10). Note that the same $\dot{V}_E$ (12 liters/min) is associated with both hypoventilation (B, Table 10) and hyperventilation (C, Table 10) because of the difference in ventilatory pattern (V_T and f).

Correction of life-threatening acidemia resulting from acute ventilatory failure is only one of the two major therapeutic goals that need to be addressed. The other is direct treatment of the drug overdose. This may take the form of specific antagonists (e.g., Naloxone for opiate overdose), elimination (e.g., hemodialysis for dialyzable drugs), or purely supportive therapy (e.g., mechanical ventilation and waiting for drug dissipation).

Acute asthma. Isolated acute respiratory acidosis secondary to pulmonary disease alone is usually due to asthma and is rarely produced by other pulmonary disorders. Acute asthma attacks lead to respiratory acidosis only when airway obstruction is extreme. Airway obstruction by mucous plugs constitutes the major cause of alveolar hypoventilation. Increased respiratory muscle work and bicarbonate buffering of lactic acid may produce small increases of $\dot{V}co_2$. Hypercapnia is seldom observed until the FEV_1 falls below 20% of its predicted value (Fig. 9). This corresponds to a measurement of peak expiratory flow rate, which is less than 100 liters/min. Since many clinicians do not have spirometers or peak flow meters readily available when they assess patients with acute asthma, evidence from the history and physical examination that supports the presence of severe airflow obstruction should be sought.

Severe dyspnea represents the principal historical clue that has been associated with respiratory acidosis during acute asthma attacks. A number of physical observations suggest the possibility of respiratory acidosis. Most of these can be quickly determined without specialized equipment (Table 11). These

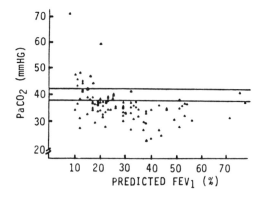

FIG. 9. Relationship between percent predicted FEV$_1$ and Paco$_2$ in acute asthma. The two horizontal lines represent upper and lower limits of normal for this study. Note that Paco$_2$ increases occur when FEV$_1$ is <20% of predicted. (Modified from ref. 20.)

include tachypnea, hypertension, and tachycardia. The presence of a pulsus paradoxus and the use of accessory muscles of respiration also increase the likelihood of acute respiratory acidosis. Obtundation in the presence of severe airflow obstruction makes severe respiratory acidosis highly likely and should lead to immediate intubation and assisted mechanical ventilation.

In general, the detection of acute respiratory acidosis by arterial blood gas analysis of a patient with physiologic evidence of severe airflow obstruction should lead to hospital admission. A normal Paco$_2$ in a patient with acute asthma and persistent respiratory distress suggests impending acute respiratory failure. Although the clinical course may vary considerably, these patients require careful observation in an intensive care unit until the signs of a severe asthma attack have resolved.

The significance of acute respiratory acidosis on the response to sympathomimetic bronchodilators should be considered. Hyporesponsiveness of the bronchial β$_2$-receptor to β-agonist therapy has been demonstrated under

TABLE 11. *Physical findings that indicate severe asthma likely to be complicated by hypercapnia*

Sign	Definition
Stupor or coma	Patient does not interact with environment
Tachycardia	Heart rate ≥ 115 min^{-1}
Tachypnea	Ventilatory rate ≥ 30 min^{-1}
Pulsus paradoxus	Systolic blood pressure decreases ≥ 17 mm Hg during inspiration
Hypertension	Blood pressure > 140/90

Modified from ref. 13.

conditions of systemic acidosis. However, the administration of β-agonists to patients with acute respiratory acidosis caused by asthma is usually effective. Since the acidosis is predominately related to CO_2 retention, bicarbonate should not be administrated in an attempt to restore the effectiveness of the $β_2$-receptor. If the patient does not respond clinically, intubation and assisted mechanical ventilation are the appropriate therapy.

Once intubation and mechanical ventilation are required, total correction of hypercapnic respiratory acidosis may be undesirable. Since barotrauma, i.e., pneumothorax and acute circulatory failure represent severe and potentially fatal complications of mechanical ventilation, strong consideration should be given to correcting arterial hypoxemia and pHa and improving but not necessarily fully correcting the hypercapnea ($Paco_2$) with mechanical ventilation. Correction of arterial hypoxemia can be undertaken while limiting peak airway pressure to less than 50 cm H_2O and thereby reducing the risk of cardiocirculatory failure and pneumothorax. Since mucous plugging of airways, rather than bronchospasm, is the major contributor, therapy and hospitalization may have to be prolonged. A measure of 24 hr sputum production and a daily measure of maximum expiratory flow (e.g., peak flow, FEV_1) are useful complements to the physical examination in defining the patient's response to therapy.

Acute exacerbation of respiratory acidosis in chronic obstruction pulmonary disease. Acute respiratory acidosis is commonly superimposed on chronic respiratory acidosis. Inflammation, hypersecretion of mucus, bronchospasm, respiratory muscle fatigue, and anxiety with tachypnea (decreased expiratory emptying time can lead to a sudden decrease in $\dot{V}_A$ in the patient with an already limited $\dot{V}_A$ as a result of chronic airway obstruction. In addition, acute left ventricular decompensation with lung edema may increase airway obstruction and cause a superimposed acute respiratory acidosis. Pulmonary edema secondary to left ventricular failure may produce similar decompensation in patients with kyphoscoliosis whose pulmonary function is limited but otherwise stable.

In all of these acute exacerbations of chronic respiratory disease, the predominant mechanism leading to the acute decrease in $\dot{V}_A$ may be the consequence of a simple change in spontaneous ventilation pattern. In the circumstances listed immediately above, the patient's ventilatory pattern is usually changed to one with an increased rate and decreased volume (V_T). This decrease in V_T in spite of a maintained or even increased $\dot{V}_E$ usually increases the V_D/V_T ratio (and the $\dot{V}_D$) and leads to a decrease in $\dot{V}_A$.

Increased CO_2 production. Continuous enteral or parenteral feeding creates a new metabolic problem, intraprandial thermogenesis. Three factors affect the physiologic response to the intraprandial state: (1) rate of formula infusion, (2) fuel composition of the formula, and (3) the patient's health. High infusion rates of glucose are particularly likely to increase Vco_2 in the malnourished patient, but even increasing infusion rates of blended food will

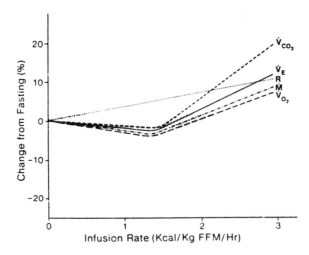

FIG. 10. Infusion of glucose and other energy sources in excess of 2 Kcal/kg of fat-free body mass/hr increases CO_2 production above fasting levels. Compensatory increases of $\dot{V}_E$ occur. Increases of $\dot{V}_{O_2}$ are proportionately less than increases of $\dot{V}_{CO_2}$, with a resultant increase of respiratory quotient (R). (From ref. 17.)

increase $\dot{V}_{CO_2}$ (Fig. 10). The resulting increase in $PaCO_2$ stimulates an increase in alveolar ventilation that can be accomplished easily by patients without cardiopulmonary disease. However, the patient with advanced pulmonary disease or the patient whose alveolar ventilation is fixed by a ventilator cannot compensate. Respiratory acidosis may ensue within hours of infusing the high carbohydrate load in parenteral solution.

Exercise poses a similar stress for the patient with limited ventilatory capacity. Increased CO_2 production is a direct result of increased aerobic work. Furthermore, if the energy demands of exercise exceed oxygen delivery, bicarbonate buffering of lactic acid generates additional CO_2. Most patients with advanced COPD are able to increase $\dot{V}_A$ sufficiently to lower $PaCO_2$ during exercise. However, some patients with advanced pulmonary disease may not be able to increase $\dot{V}_A$ in proportion to the increase in $\dot{V}_{CO_2}$ (Eq. la; Table 12), and respiratory acidosis may occur.

TABLE 12. *Acute respiratory acidosis precipitated by exercise in a patient with advanced COPD*

	FEV_1 (liter)	PaO_2 (mm Hg)	pHa	$PaCO_2$ (mm Hg)	$\dot{V}_E$ (liters/min)	$\dot{V}_{CO_2}$ (liters/min)
Rest	0.69	68	7.36	41	8	0.20
Exercise	—	62	7.30	48	49	1.78

Chronic Respiratory Acidosis

Chronic obstructive pulmonary disease

The most common cause of chronic respiratory acidosis is chronic airway obstruction due to chronic bronchitis or emphysema. When chronic hypercapnia supervenes in these conditions, the FEV_1 is usually less than 1 to 1.3 liters (we use a 1.0 liter FEV_1 as a guideline, since it is convenient to remember). If the pHa is well defended (i.e., the chronic respiratory acidosis is adequately compensated by renal [HCO_3^-] retention), no therapy is indicated for the mild acidemia. The hypercapnia by itself is not an indication for therapy but rather a compensation for the mechanical derangement of the lung that limits $\dot{V}_A$. The elimination of the large volatile acid load (CO_2) with a reduced $\dot{V}_A$ requires that the concentration of CO_2 in this $\dot{V}_A$ increase (i.e., that the $Paco_2$ increase). In fact, if it were not for the obligatory decrease in Pao_2 that occurs as $Paco_2$ rises, the hypercapnia, at any but severe levels, would usually be unimportant. (The reduced $Paco_2$ may require supplemental O_2 therapy.) The increased $Paco_2$ that occurs as a physiologic compensation for the reduced $\dot{V}_A$ is analogous to the increased blood urea nitrogen (BUN) that occurs as a physiologic compensation for a reduced GFR.

Therapy for COPD should be directed at maximizing lung function through treatment of the mechanical limitations of $\dot{V}_A$ (the increased airway resistance and dynamic airway collapse) with bronchodilators, antibiotics, anti-inflammatory agents, breathing training, and postural drainage. Therapy should not be directed at normalizing the elevated $Paco_2$, which, after mechanical lung function has been optimized, is the necessary physiologic compensation that allows the patient to maintain life.

Decreased ventilatory drive

When the history, physical examination, and laboratory database do not suggest severe airway obstruction (i.e., no history of exercise intolerance, wheezing, cough and sputum production, no physical examination evidence of wheezing, narrowing of the costal angle with inspiration, use of accessory respiratory muscles, and no evidence of severe airway obstruction [an FEV_1 in excess of 1.3 liters]), careful consideration should be given to decreased ventilatory drive as the cause of the elevated $Paco_2$. One of the common causes of decreased ventilatory drive is respiratory compensation for a metabolic alkalosis. A history of diuretic therapy, nasogastric suction, or severe vomiting or other causes of metabolic alkalosis should alert the clinician to this possibility. Although the underlying metabolic alkalosis may be difficult to discern, successful therapy will provide a specific correction of the hypercapnia.

The adequacy of respiratory drive can be evaluated by several tests. One simple measure is to determine the arterial Pco_2 before and after voluntary hyperventilation. Patients with severe mechanical limitation (often referred to as patient who "can't breathe") usually cannot decrease their $PaCO_2$ by more than 10 mm Hg. A second method is the measurement of ventilatory response to inhaled CO_2. The patient rebreathes from a bag containing 4 to 6 liters of 7% carbon dioxide, 50% oxygen, and 43% nitrogen, (the increased oxygen avoids arterial hypoxemia and stimulation of carotid body chemoreceptors). Patients with impaired ventilatory drive do not increase their minute ventilation normally in response to increases in $PaCO_2$. The clinician must be certain that no mechanical impairment (e.g., airway obstruction) exists before performing a CO_2 rebreathing test.

Neuromuscular disease

Neuromuscular diseases cause respiratory acidosis by progressively decreasing alveolar ventilation. The locus of pathology helps to differentiate these disorders (Table 13), and specific tests (e.g., muscle biopsy for polymyositis) are necessary for definitive clinical diagnosis. However, each of these disorders progressively decreases vital capacity, tidal volume, and alveolar ventilation. Respiratory acidosis does not usually complicate neuromuscular diseases or restrictive pulmonary disease until the vital capacity is less than 1 liter. However, some patients can experience rapid decreases in vital capacity. Therefore, if the neuromuscular disorder is progressing rapidly, caution is advised when the vital capacity falls to 50% of predicted. In general, patients with neuromuscular disease can maintain a normal pHa and $PaCO_2$ if their

TABLE 13. *Neuromuscular diseases that cause respiratory acidosis*
(↓ V_T, ↓ V_E, ↓ V_A)

I. Peripheral nervous system (acute and/or chronic)
   A. Cervical fracture C3–5
   B. Amyotrophic lateral sclerosis
   C. Multiple sclerosis
   D. Poliomyelitis
   E. Guillain-Barré syndrome
   F. Bilateral phrenic denervation

II. Neuromuscular junction (usually acute)
   A. Myasthenia gravis
   B. Drug-induced neuromuscular blockade
      1. Aminoglycoside antibiotics
      2. Lidocaine
      3. Quinidine
      4. β-blockers
      5. D-Penicillamine
      6. Phenytoin
      7. Trimethapan

III. Muscle disease (acute and/or chronic)
   A. Muscular dystrophy
   B. Polymyositis

vital capacity exceeds three times the normal tidal volume. Therefore, respiratory acidosis associated with a neuromuscular disease and a well-preserved vital capacity should trigger a search for disordered ventilatory drive or an increased dead space/tidal volume ratio. In contrast, respiratory acidosis associated with marked reduction of vital capacity may be caused by neuromuscular disease with or without concomitant restrictive (e.g., lung edema) or obstructive (e.g., asthma) lung disease.

RESPIRATORY ALKALOSIS
(4,6,7,11,12,15,19,21,27,28)

Definition

Excessive $\dot{V}_A$ relative to $\dot{V}CO_2$ defines respiratory alkalosis. This commonly results from increased alveolar ventilation (V_A) and rarely results from reduction of CO_2 production. An increased pHa and decreased $PaCO_2$ confirm the diagnosis of respiratory alkalosis. When the onset of respiratory alkalosis is sudden, increased renal excretion of bicarbonate cannot compensate. The serum bicarbonate concentration is, therefore, usually greater than 18 mEq/liter in acute respiratory alkalosis. Conversely, when excessive CO_2 elimination occurs over a prolonged period of time, renal compensation leads to a decrease of serum bicarbonate and reduces the rise in pHa that would otherwise occur. This constitutes chronic respiratory alkalosis.

It is uncommon for a respiratory alkalosis to occur concomitantly with a metabolic alkalosis. Arterial pH often exceeds 7.55, and the $PaCO_2$, although higher than normal, remains inappropriately low for the degree of alkalosis (Fig. 1, inadequate respiratory compensation). Such a disorder occurs most commonly in patients receiving mechanically assisted ventilation.

Systemic and Metabolic Consequences

The principal effects of respiratory alkalosis are increased neuromuscular excitability and vasoconstriction of arteriolar smooth muscle of selected organs. Respiratory alkalosis causes cerebral vasoconstriction and reduces cerebral blood flow. The reduction in cerebral blood flow is greatest at $PaCO_2$ levels of 20 to 25 mm Hg. Lower levels of $PaCO_2$ cause cerebral ischemia (hypoxia), which produces an offsetting vasodilator effect. Respiratory alkalosis also shifts the oxyhemoglobin dissociation curve, with a resultant increase of hemoglobin affinity for oxygen. Furthermore, hypocapnia ($PaCO_2$ <25 mmHg) reduces myocardial blood flow. The combined reduction of myocardial blood flow and enhanced neuromuscular irritability may cause ventricular arrhythmias, especially when coupled with hypokalemia, hypomagnesemia, and hypophosphatemia.

Fatigue, headache, light headedness, and inability to concentrate are nonspecific symptoms associated with respiratory alkalosis. Numbness and tingling of the hands, feet, mouth, or tongue, with or without muscle spasms, more specifically characterize increased neuromuscular excitability that respiratory alkalosis causes. More severe respiratory alkalosis can contribute to seizures and serious cardiac arrhythmias.

Physical signs that may indicate the presence of respiratory alkalosis include Chvostek's sign (tapping the facial nerve just anterior to the ear results in contraction of facial muscles) and Trousseau's sign (compression of the brachial artery for 1–5 min leads to muscle spasm of the hand and wrist). These signs also occur in patients who are hypocalcemic or hypomagnesemic.

Pathophysiologic Approach to Respiratory Alkalosis

The pathophysiologic approach to respiratory alkalosis is based on the matching of V_A to $\dot{V}CO_2$ (Table 14). Increased ventilatory drive is the pathophysiologic mechanism most commonly responsible for respiratory alkalosis. Medullary chemosensitivity to CO_2 may be altered by pain, anxiety, systemic disease (e.g., sepsis or liver failure), and a number of medications. In addition, pulmonary stretch receptors reflexly alter medullary chemosensitivity. When lung volume is decreased by fibrosis or pulmonary edema, the medullary centers become more sensitive to CO_2, V_E and V_A increase, and respiratory alkalosis follows. Arterial hypoxemia ($\downarrow PaO_2$) stimulates peripheral chemoreceptors (carotid bodies) to increase V_A and lower $PaCO_2$. In general, minute ventilation does not increase appreciably unless PaO_2 is <50 mm Hg.

Mechanical ventilation also is commonly associated with respiratory alkalosis. Excessive CO_2 elimination can occur when the patient's V_E is controlled by a ventilator. Under such circumstances, the ventilatory rate and tidal volume may be decreased to correct respiratory alkalosis. In contrast, when the ventilator assists the patient who spontaneously initiates ventilation, augmented ventilatory drive usually is responsible for respiratory alkalosis.

TABLE 14. *Pathophysiologic approach to respiratory alkalosis*

I. Increased alveolar ventilation ($\uparrow \dot{V}_A$)
   A. Increased ventilatory drive
      1. Medullary chemoreceptors,
         e.g., pain, anxiety, drugs, systemic diseases
      2. Carotid body chemoreceptors,
         e.g., arterial hypoxemia acidosis
   B. Mechanical ventilation
      1. Controlled mode
II. Decreased CO_2 production ($\downarrow \dot{V}CO_2$)
   A. Activity, e.g., sedation, paralysis
   B. Basal metabolism, e.g., hypothermia

Therefore, changes of ventilator settings will not usually correct this respiratory alkalosis. Sedation and paralysis may be necessary to reduce ventilatory drive, when correction of an underlying disorder which increases ventilatory drive is not possible.

Clinical Evaluation (3,9,16,30,33)

In general, respiratory alkalosis is less threatening to the patient than is respiratory acidosis. This fact reflects the nonprogressive nature of most respiratory alkaloses and contrasts sharply with the frequently progressive nature of respiratory acidosis. Arterial pH remains less than 7.55 for most disorders that cause respiratory alkalosis. This degree of alkalosis does not result in seizures or cardiac arrhythmias unless other factors concomitantly affect neuromuscular irritability (e.g., hypoxia, hypocalcemia). For these reasons, the presence of mild respiratory alkalosis usually should be viewed as an important laboratory marker for the detection of underlying disease rather than as an indication for therapeutic intervention. The need to treat respiratory alkalosis changes dramatically when the pH exceeds 7.55. Blood pH greater than 7.70 is rarely tolerated for prolonged periods without serious cardiac arrhythmias or seizures.

The history and physical examination are central to evaluating the cause of respiratory alkalosis. Historical information and physical findings can often identify conditions that cause respiratory alkalosis with sufficient certainty to enable the physician to initiate specific therapy. For example, a comatose patient with chronic liver disease with a pH of 7.50 and a $PaCO_2$ of 22 almost certainly has respiratory alkalosis secondary to the effects of hepatic encephalopathy on ventilatory drive. Because of the high prior probability of hepatic encephalopathy-induced alkalosis from the history, a negative laboratory test cannot confidently exclude this diagnosis, and a positive test adds little to the diagnostic certainty (*see* Table 5).

Basic laboratory studies are extremely helpful for the detection of other conditions that may cause or contribute to respiratory alkalosis. For example, the history and physical examination often fail to detect arterial hypoxemia. Measurement of PaO_2 in a sample of arterial blood can detect a decreased PaO_2 when the patient is not cyanotic. Similarly, respiratory alkalosis caused by pulmonary thromboembolism usually requires laboratory confirmation, since the history and physical examination lack sensitivity, specificity, and predictive value for this diagnosis.

History

Historical information provides diagnostic information that can alter the prior probability for a number of disorders that contribute to respiratory alkalosis (Table 15). The history should focus on symptoms of diseases commonly associated with respiratory alkalosis and on medications known to increase ventilatory drive. For example, a clinical setting of acute or chronic liver disease accompanied by confusion, stupor, or coma strongly suggests respiratory alkalosis associated with hepatic encephalopathy. Similarly, fever, chills, and confusion in an elderly patient suggest that sepsis underlies an acute respiratory alkalosis. Although pain and anxiety can cause alveolar hyperventilation and respiratory alkalosis, routine unanesthetized arterial punctures do not usually alter pH or $PaCO_2$.

Respiratory alkalosis can be a manifestation of pulmonary diseases as well. Pulmonary emboli, mild asthma, pulmonary edema, pulmonary fibrosis, and primary pulmonary hypertension have all been associated with respiratory alkalosis. Recent surgery, prolonged bedrest, increased age, and thrombophlebitis represent well-established risk factors for pulmonary thromboembolism. Episodic wheezing, dyspnea, and cough are common symptoms of asthma. Primary pulmonary hypertension is characterized by exertional dyspnea or syncopal attacks. Pulmonary fibrosis can result from a variety of causes (asbestosis, sarcoidosis, drug therapy, illicit drug abuse, extrinsic allergic alevolitis, rheumatoid arthritis), all of which are commonly associated with exertional dyspnea and a dry, nonproductive cough. Pulmonary edema that results from cardiac failure should be suspected when the patient describes paroxysmal nocturnal dyspnea, but heart failure-induced pulmonary edema may occur more subtly, with only a nonproductive cough.

Commonly prescribed medications contribute to respiratory alkalosis by increasing ventilatory drive. Therapeutic doses of salicylate induce respiratory alkalosis in proportion to the dose and duration of salicylate therapy. Other symptoms of salicylism, such as tinnitus, hearing loss, nausea, and vomiting, may accompany salicylate-induced respiratory alkalosis. Hydralazine and progesterone also can stimulate ventilatory drive and produce a mild respiratory alkalosis. Aminophylline stimulates alveolar ventilation, principally by increasing hypoxic ventilatory drive.

Physical Examination

The physical examination also provides diagnostic information that can alter the prior probability for a number of disorders that can cause respiratory alkalosis (Table 16). Because respiratory alkalosis caused by hepatic failure only occurs with advanced liver disease, signs of severe liver disease must be present in order to suggest respiratory alkalosis secondary to liver disease. Ascites, asterixis, confusion, stupor, or coma is usually present. Other stigmata of chronic liver disease may be present as well. When respiratory alkalosis accompanies septic shock, tachycardia, cutaneous vasodilation, and hypotension represent important signs that buttress the clinical diagnosis before

TABLE 15. *Useful historical information for evaluation of respiratory alkalosis*

Pathophysiologic mechanism	Historical information	Therapeutic outcome
Increased alveolar ventilation ($\dot{V}_A$)		
Medullary chemoreceptors		
Pain	Trauma, inflammation	Analgesics
Anxiety	Anxiety	Sedatives and/or supportive care
Pregnancy	Third trimester of pregnancy	
Drugs	Salicylate ingestion, progesterone	Discontinue or ↓ dose
Systemic disease	Severe acute or chronic liver disease	↓ Diet protein, remove fecal material from colon
	Sepsis	Antimicrobial Rx and drain infected tissue
Carotid body chemoreceptors		
Hypoxemia	Cardiopulmonary disease, confusion,	O_2 Rx to ↑ $Pao_2 > 60$ torr
Aminophylline	Muscle tremor	
Pulmonary stretch receptors		
Lung edema	Cardiac or renal disease, ARDS	Diuresis or dialysis
Lung fibrosis	Exertional dyspnea, cough	
Pulmonary disease		
Asthma, mild	Episodic cough, wheeze	Bronchodilator
Pulmonary embolism	Dyspnea, recent surgery, venous disease	Anticoagulants, thrombolysis
Primary pulmonary hypertension	Dyspnea, syncope	Vasodilators
Mechanical ventilation	Intermittent mandatory ventilation or assisted ventilation	Sedate or paralyze if necessary
	Controlled by ventilator	Decrease ventilator rate and tidal volume
Decreased CO_2 production ($\dot{V}_{CO_2}$)	Alcoholism, hypothermia	Rewarm

TABLE 16. *Useful physical examination observations for evaluation of respiratory alkalosis*

Pathophysiology	Physical examination observations
Increased alveolar ventilation ($\dot{V}_A$)	
Medullary chemoreceptors	
Pain	Inflammation, tenderness
Anxiety	Tremor, diaphoresis
Pregnancy	Gravid uterus
Drugs—Salicylates	
Systemic disease	
Hepatic failure	Ascites, asterixis, confusion, stupor, coma
Sepsis	Temperature > 38°C, hypotension, cutaneous vasodilation
Carotid body chemoreceptors	
Hypoxemia	Cyanosis
Aminophylline	Muscle tremor
Pulmonary stretch receptors	
Lung edema	End inspiratory rales, S_3 gallop
Lung fibrosis	End inspiratory fine crepitant rales
Pulmonary disease	
Thromboembolism	Tachypnea (f > 18 min^{-1}), ↑ P_2, pleural rub
Asthma, mild	Hyperinflation, prolonged exhalation, expiratory wheezing
Primary pulmonary hypertension	↑ P_2, palpable P_2, right ventricular heave
Decreased CO_2 production ($\dot{V}_{CO_2}$)	
Sedation, paralysis	Flaccid paralysis
Hypothermia	Temperature < 36°C

blood culture results are available. If respiratory alkalosis is a result of primary pulmonary hypertension or chronic recurrent pulmonary embolism, the second component of a physiologically split second heart sound (P_2) usually is as loud or louder than the first component of the second heart sound (A_2).

The physical examination is less helpful when respiratory alkalosis results from arterial hypoxemia. Cyanosis of the extremities may result from venous stasis rather than arterial hypoxemia. Conversely, central cyanosis (usually detected by inspection of the tongue) does not always accompany arterial hypoxemia. Since the visual detection of cyanosis requires 5 g/dl of reduced hemoglobin, cyanosis will not be detectable if severe anemia is present. If alkalosis produces a marked left shift of the oxyhemoglobin dissocation curve, cyanosis may be absent when PaO_2 is low. Therefore, measurement of PaO_2 usually is useful when evaluating a patient in whom respiratory alkalosis is suggested, for example, by the presence of tachypnea or dyspnea.

Basic and Specialized Laboratory Tests

Basic laboratory tests, such as the chest roentgenogram, the spirogram, the electrocardiogram, and arterial blood gases, contribute to the diagnosis of conditions that cause respiratory alkalosis (Table 17). However, these tests also have limitations. The chest roentgenogram usually shows thickened interstitial spaces (Kerley's lines) in patients with pulmonary fibrosis or pulmonary edema. However, as many as 10% of patients with chronic diffuse infiltrative lung disease proven on lung biopsy have normal chest roentgenograms.

The chest roentgenogram and the electrocardiogram are usually abnormal when primary pulmonary hypertension or chronic recurrent pulmonary embolism is severe enough to cause respiratory alkalosis. In these cases, the chest roentgenogram reveals enlarged main pulmonary arteries and hilar vessels, and the electrocardiogram reveals a pattern of right ventricular hypertrophy and strain. In contrast, both chest x-ray and electrocardiogram are often normal when acute pulmonary thromboembolism is the cause of acute respiratory alkalosis.

Specialized laboratory studies may dramatically increase the diagnostic certainty when the clinician remains uncertain of the cause for respiratory alkalosis after history, physical examination, and basic laboratory tests. A common cause of respiratory alkalosis, pulmonary thromboembolism, frequently requires laboratory confirmation. For example, consider a middle-aged woman who has dyspnea (history) and tachypnea (physical examination) 1 week after undergoing a cholecystectomy (history). A chest roentgenogram reveals decreased aeration of both lower lobes. Arterial blood gas analysis reveals acute respiratory alkalosis and a slightly decreased PaO_2. Pulmonary thromboembolism is a likely diagnosis, but the diagnosis remains uncertain.

TABLE 17. *Basic and specialized laboratory tests for evaluating respiratory alkalosis*

Pathophysiology	Basic laboratory tests	Specialized laboratory tests
Increased alveolar ventilation ($\dot{V}_A$)		
Medullary chemoreceptors		
Pain	X-ray (e.g., unsuspected bone fracture)	Myelogram, CT spine
Anxiety		
Drugs	Thyroid function studies	Serum salicylate level 350–500 mg/ml
Systemic diseases		
Hepatic encephalopathy		
Sepsis	Blood cultures	
Carotid body chemoreceptors		
Hypoxemia	$Pao_2 < 55$ mmHg	Hypoxic ventilatory drive tests
Aminophylline		Theophylline level > 10 mg/liter
Pulmonary stretch receptors		
Lung fibrosis	Chest x-ray	↓ Pao_2 during exercise
		↓ CO diffusing capacity
Lung edema	Chest x-ray	Pulmonary capillary wedge pressure measurement
Pulmonary disease		
Asthma, mild	Spirogram, ratio of FEV_1/FVC ↓	Bronchoprovocation test
Pulmonary embolism		Ventilation and perfusion lung scan
		Pulmonary arteriogram
Primary pulmonary hypertension	Chest roentgenogram	Pulmonary artery pressure
	ECG	
Decreased CO_2 production ($\dot{V}co_2$)		Measure $\dot{V}co_2$

The observation of a lobar perfusion defect in an area where the inhalation of radioactive xenon remains normal greatly increases the likelihood that the respiratory alkalosis results from pulmonary thromboembolism.

Clinical Approach to Treatment

Disorders that cause acute or chronic respiratory alkalosis may be divided into those causing mild alkalosis (pHa 7.46–7.54) and those causing severe alkalosis (pHa≥7.55) (Table 18). Mild respiratory alkalosis rarely requires treatment *per se*, but it often signals an underlying primary disorder that requires specific therapy. Acute pulmonary thromboembolism characteristically results in mild acute respiratory alkalosis, whereas chronic pulmonary embolism and pulmonary hypertension cause chronic respiratory alkalosis. Specific therapy for pulmonary embolism includes anticoagulation or thrombolysis. Thromboendarterectomy is indicated for selected patients with chronic thrombotic occlusion of the pulmonary arteries. Anticoagulant or thrombolytic therapy cannot be expected to correct the respiratory alkalosis that accompanies pulmonary embolism. However, successful treatment of arterial hypoxemia with oxygen should immediately decrease alveolar ventilation resulting from the carotid body response to arterial hypoxemia. Similarly, reversal of respiratory alkalosis should accompany successful treatment of hepatic encephalopathy. In each instance of mild respiratory alkalosis, the need for treatment of the underlying disorder far outweighs the need for treatment of the associated respiratory alkalosis.

Severe respiratory alkalosis requires immediate therapy because the risks of untreated severe respiratory alkalosis are substantial. Tachypnea, confusion, anxiety, hypotension, seizures, and coma have been associated with severe

TABLE 18. *Categorization of respiratory alkalosis according to severity*

I. Disorders associated with mild respiratory alkalosis
   (pHa = 7.46–7.54)
   A. Hepatic cirrhosis
   B. Salicylate intoxication
   C. Pregnancy
   D. Hypoxia
   E. Pulmonary fibrosis
   F. Asthma
   G. Aminophylline
   H. Lung edema
   I. Pulmonary thromboembolism
II. Disorders associated with severe respiratory alkalosis
   (pHa ≥ 7.55)
   A. Excessive mechanical ventilation
   B. CNS lesion (tumor, encephalitis)
   C. Psychiatric disorder

acute respiratory alkalosis (pHa≥7.55). Severe respiratory alkalosis may be induced easily in patients with chronic respiratory acidosis if they are initially overventilated in an attempt to reduce the $PaCO_2$ to normal. Physical signs that may precede coma and death include asterixis and myoclonus. When mechanical overventilation is the cause of severe respiratory alkalosis, treatment consists of allowing the hypercapnea to persist by decreasing the ventilation provided by the ventilator. Arterial pH should be maintained between 7.35 and 7.50. In the rare circumstance when a CNS lesion or a psychiatric disorder induces life-threatening respiratory alkalosis, immediate treatment consists of sedation or paralysis with sedation to decrease ventilatory drive. Controlled mechanical ventilation supports the patient until the primary disorder can be treated.

REFERENCES

1. Argov, Z., and Mastaglia, F. L. (1979): Disorders of neuromuscular transmission caused by drugs. N. Engl. J. Med., 301:409–413.
2. Brackett, N. C. Jr., Cohen, J. J., and Schwartz, W. B. (1965): Carbon dioxide titration curve of normal man: Effect of increasing degrees of acute hypercapnia on acid-base equilibrium. N. Engl. J. Med., 272:6–12.
3. Browner, W. S., and Newman, T. B. (1987): Are all significant P values created equal? The analogy between diagnostic tests and clinical research. JAMA, 257:2459–2463.
4. Cherniak, R. M., Cherniak, A. L., and Naimark, A. (1972): Respiration in Health and Disease, 2nd ed. W.B. Saunders, Philadelphia.
5. Covelli, H. D., Black, W. J., Olsen, M. S., and Peekman, J. F. (1981): Respiratory failure precipitated by high carbohydrate loads. Ann. Intern. Med., 95:579–581.
6. Culpepper, J. A., Rinaldo, J. E., and Rogers, R. M. (1985): Effect of mechanical ventilator mode on tendency towards respiratory alkalosis. Am. Rev. Respir. Dis., 132:1075–1077.
7. Dantzker, D. R., and Bower, J. S. (1979): Mechanisms of gas exchange abnormality in patients with chronic obliterative pulmonary vascular disease. J. Clin. Invest., 40:828–835.
8. Darioli, R., and Perret, C. (1984): Mechanical controlled hypoventilation in status asthmaticus. Am. Rev. Respir. Dis., 129:385–387.
9. Diamond, G. A., and Forrester, J. S. (1983): Clinical trials and statistical verdicts: Probable grounds for appeal. Ann. Intern. Med., 98:385–394.
10. Dulfano, M., and Ishikawa, S. (1965): Hypercapnia: Mental changes and extra pulmonary complications. Ann. Intern. Med., 63:829–841.
11. Epler, G. R., McLoud, T. C., Gaensler, E. A., et al. (1978): Normal chest roentgenogram in chronic diffuse infiltrative lung disease. N. Engl. J. Med., 298:934–939.
12. Farber, H. R., Yiengst, M. J., and Shock, N. W. (1949): The effect of therapeutic doses of aspirin on the acid-base balance of the blood in normal adults. Am. J. Med. Sci., 217:256–262.
13. Fischl, M. A., Pitchenik, A., and Gardner, L. B. (1981): An index predicting relapse and need for hospitalization in patients with acute bronchial asthma. N. Engl. J. Med., 305:783–789.
14. Gilbert, R., Keighley, J., and Auchincloss, J. H. (1965): Mechanisms of chronic carbon dioxide retention in patients with obstructive pulmonary disease. Am. J. Med., 38:217–225.
15. Goodland, R. L., Reynolds, J. G., and Pommerenke, W. T. (1954): Alveolar carbon dioxide tension levels during pregnancy and early puerperium. J. Clin. Endocrinol., 14:522–530.
16. Griner, P. F., Mayewski, R. J., Mushlin, A. I., and Greeland, P. (1981): Selection and interpretation of diagnostic tests and procedures: Principles and applications. Ann. Intern. Med., 94:553–600.
17. Heymsfield, S. B., Erbland, M., Casper, K., et al. (1986): Enteral nutritional support. Clin. Chest Med., 7:41–67.

18. Hoffman, W. S. (1970). *The Biochemistry of Clinical Medicine*, 4th ed., p. 152. Year Book, Chicago.
19. Kilburn, K. H. (1966): Shock, seizures, and coma with alkalosis during mechanical ventilation. *Ann. Intern. Med.*, 65:977–984.
20. McFadden, E. R. Jr., and Lyons, H. A. (1968): Arterial blood gas tension in asthma. *N. Engl. J. Med.*, 278:1027–1032.
21. Morgan, E. G., Baidwan, B., Petty, T. L., and Zwillich, C. W. (1979): The effects of unanesthetized arterial puncture on P_{CO_2} and pH. *Am. Rev. Respir. Dis.*, 120:795–798.
22. Morris, A. H. (1987): Acute respiratory failure: Therapeutic strategies. In: *Current Therapy in Critical Care Medicine*, edited by J. E. Parillo. B. C. Decker, Philadelphia.
23. Morris, A. H., Kanner, R. E., Crapo, R. O., and Gardner, R. M. (1984): *Clinical Pulmonary Function Testing: A Manual of Uniform Laboratory Procedures*, 2nd Ed. Intermountain Thoracic Society, Salt Lake City, UT.
24. Newsom, D. J., Goldman, M., Loh, L., and Casson, M. (1976): Diaphragm function and alveolar hypoventilation. *Q. J. Med.*, 45:87–100.
25. Pontoppidan, H., Geffin, G., and Lowenstein, P. (1972): Acute respiratory failure in the adult. *N. Engl. J. Med.*, 287:743–752.
26. Read, D. J. C. (1967): A clinical method for assessing the ventilatory response to CO_2. *Aust. Ann. Med.*, 16:20–32.
27. Sanders, J. S., Berman, T. M., Bartlett, M. M., and Kronenberg, R. S. (1980): Increased hypoxic ventilatory drive due to administration of aminophylline in normal men. *Chest*, 78:279–282.
28. Sasahara, A. A., Hyers, T. M., Cole, C. M., et al. (1973): The urokinase pulmonary embolism trial. *Circulation*, 47:1–108.
29. Smith, P. E. M., Calverley, P. M. A., Edward, R. H. T., Evans, G. A., and Campbell, E. J. M. (1987): Practical problems in the respiratory care of patients with muscular dystrophy. *N. Engl. J. Med.*, 316:1197–1205.
30. Vecchio, T. J. (1966): Predictive value of a single diagnostic test in unselected populations. *N. Engl. J. Med.*, 274:1171–1173.
31. Wasserman, K., Hansen, J. E., Sue, D. Y., and Whipp, B. J. (1987): *Principles of Exercise Testing and Interpretation*, p. 7. Lea & Febiger, Philadelphia.
32. Weber, K. T., and Janicki, J. S. (eds.) (1986): *Cardiopulmonary Exercise Testing*, chap. 1, p. 4. W.B. Saunders, Philadelphia.
33. Weinstein, M. C., and Fineberg, H. V. (1980): *Clinical Decision Analysis*. W.B. Saunders, Philadelphia.
34. West, J. B. (1977): *Ventilation/Blood Flow and Gas Exchange*, 3rd ed., p. 36. Blackwell, Oxford.

The Regulation of Acid–Base Balance, edited by Donald W. Seldin and Gerhard Giebisch, Raven Press, Ltd., New York © 1989.

20

Special Circumstances of Acid-Base Balance

Jeffrey R. Thompson and William L. Henrich

Departments of Internal Medicine, The University of Texas Southwestern Medical Center at Dallas, and Dallas Veterans Administration Medical Center, Dallas, Texas 75216

ACID-BASE CHANGES DURING HEMODIALYSIS AND PERITONEAL DIALYSIS (10,12,15,18,32)

Hemodialysis (10,12,15,18,32)

A mild metabolic acidosis is characteristic of stable patients treated with maintenance hemodialysis. The usual predialysis serum bicarbonate concentration ranges from 16 to 23 mEq/liter and is associated with acidemia in the range of 7.30 to 7.36. In one survey of the acidemia of end-stage renal disease

(ESRD), mean hydrogen ion concentration was 46 mEq/liter, and pH was 7.34 (Fig. 1). The respiratory response to the decline in serum bicarbonate concentration is typical of other metabolic acidoses, falling approximately 1 mm Hg for each mEq/liter decline in bicarbonate.

In most dialysis patients, the predialysis bicarbonate concentration is stable, suggesting that long-term acid-base balance has occurred. This balance is achieved from an interplay of several factors: endogenous acid production (usually 1 mmole/g protein ingested per day), gastrointestinal losses or gains, organic anion loss during dialysis (up to 100 mmoles/treatment), and alkali addition (from dialysate buffer) during the dialysis treatment (in one study using an acetate dialysate bath of 37 mm, about 178 mmoles of alkali were gained during each treatment). This relationship may be summarized as

Net alkali = Bicarbonate input during dialysis[1] − organic anion loss[2]

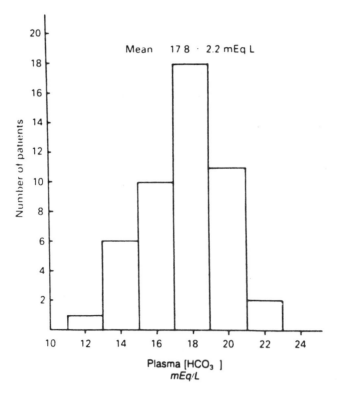

FIG. 1. Distribution of serum bicarbonate concentrations in patients on maintenance hemo-dialysis. (From ref. 10.)

---

[1] From either acetate metabolism or a bicarbonate bath.

[2] Loss of pyruvate, acetoacetate, β-hydroxybutyrate, and citrate from patient to dialysate.

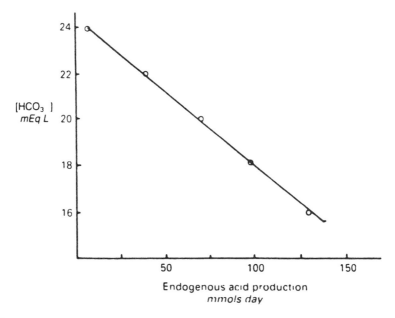

FIG. 2. Relationship between endogenous acid production and serum bicarbonate concentration in hemodialysis patients. (From ref. 10).

The result of this pattern of acid addition during the interdialytic interval and net alkali gain during dialysis results in a relatively stable predialysis bicarbonate concentration. The level at which the bicarbonate stabilizes depends on several factors, including the amount of protein consumed, the protein catabolic rate (both of which determine, in large measure, endogenous acid production), the presence or absence of glucose in the dialysate (both aceto-acetate and hydroxybutyrate losses are greater without glucose), and the type and concentration of dialysate buffer used (acetate or bicarbonate). Of course, the rate of exchange between buffers is also influenced by the characteristics of dialysance across the dialysis membrane and the concentration gradient across the membrane. The rates of ultrafiltration, dialysate flow rate, and blood flow rate all influence transfer of buffer to the patient and anions from the patient. The net result is that, given unchanging dialysis characteristics, the predialysis serum bicarbonate concentration remains stable and is inversely proportional to endogenous acid production (Fig. 2).

Changes in Serum Bicarbonate During Hemodialysis

Acetate dialysis

Originally, bicarbonate was used as the source of alkali in dialysis. This practice required the cumbersome task of bubbling CO_2 into the dialysate to lower the pH to prevent the precipitation of calcium and magnesium salts. The rapid conversion of acetate to bicarbonate during infusion studies led to its use as a practical buffer for large dialysis units servicing a greater number of patients.

During a routine hemodialysis procedure using acetate dialysate, the dialytic process will result in bicarbonate transfer to the dialysate and acetate transfer to the blood. Hence, blood returning to the patient from the dialyzer contains a high concentration of acetate (10–15 mmoles/liter) but a low concentration of bicarbonate (5–10 mmoles/liter). The pH of the returning blood does not fall because CO_2 diffuses into the dialysate during the exchange. Acetate is rapidly metabolized in the body to bicarbonate (primarily in muscle) so that blood returning to the dialyzer has a higher bicarbonate concentration and a lower steady state acetate concentration (usually around 5 mmoles/liter). The dialysance of acetate across standard dialysis membranes is less than for bicarbonate; therefore, the usual acetate dialysate concentration ranges between 35 and 37 mmoles/liter. Normally, the majority of acetate is metabolized in muscle to acetyl-CoA, and then consumption of a proton yields CO_2 and water. This generates a bicarbonate ion. The upper limit of acetate metabolism is about 4.5 mmoles/kg/hr, with a range of between 2.5 and 3.5 mmoles/kg/hr in dialyzed subjects. Usually, 90% of infused acetate is metabolized to bicarbonate, the remainder being directed to fatty acid and cholesterol synthesis. Worsening of hyperlipidemia has not been a consequence of acetate dialysate in long-term studies. The metabolism of acetate also results in about 200 Kcal/mole and may provide 60 to 70% of basic caloric needs during dialysis. One characteristic of standard acetate dialysis is that serum bicarbonate concentration tends to rise gradually during the procedure and will continue to increase for 1 to 2 hr after discontinuation as acetate is fully metabolized.

Bicarbonate dialysis

Bicarbonate dialysate has increased in use in the past several years for several reasons. First, several reports have linked some of the adverse symptoms and signs encountered in dialysis to acetate buffer. These adverse events range from increased bouts of hypotension and more cramping to a reduction in cognitive abilities. Bicarbonate dialysate has ameliorated these adverse events in some studies. There is still debate over the precise role of acetate in these dialysis-related complications, since acetate blood levels and hypotension have been dissociated and because controlled, blinded comparisons have not yielded compelling differences between the buffers. One group of patients potentially at risk for delayed or impaired conversion of acetate to bicarbonate is those with a reduced muscle mass (e.g., cachectic, malnourished individuals or women with a small body surface area).

In one large survey of this problem, Vinay et al. demonstrated 10% of the dialysis population to be acetate intolerant, i.e., not able to increase serum

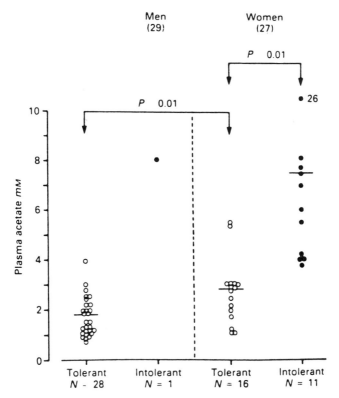

FIG. 3. Plasma acetate concentrations after dialysis in men and women on hemodialysis. In general, a higher acetate concentration was associated with intolerance to acetate dialysate. (From ref. 32.)

bicarbonate concentration after dialysis. Moreover, intolerant patients were shown to have a much higher plasma acetate concentration than tolerant individuals (Fig. 3). Although a decrease in muscle mass did not account fully for the differences in acetate metabolism, it is of interest that 11 of 27 women were intolerant as compared to only 1 of 29 men. A second reason for the increased use of bicarbonate dialysate is the growing popularity of short-time, rapid ultrafiltration dialysis. This procedure has a goal of reducing dialysis time to between 120 and 150 min/treatment. To achieve this goal, dialysate and blood flow rates must be very high, and large surface area dialyzers with greater ultrafiltration characteristics must be used. This combination results in much greater acetate flux and higher serum acetate concentrations because the metabolic rate of acetate is exceeded. Since acetate acts locally as a peripheral vasodilator, blood pressure may be compromised, particularly if large volumes are concomitantly being removed during the process. The third factor that has led to a renewed enthusiasm for bicarbonate dialysate is the availability of central delivery bicarbonate dialysate systems and the reduced cost differential between bicarbonate and acetate dialysate in systems using an individual proportioning device. The bicarbonate dialysate concentration may be varied to meet the requirements of individual patients, usually over a range of 29 to 38 mEq/liter. One characteristic of bicarbonate dialysate is that serum bicarbonate concentration increases more rapidly during dialysis than with acetate. Hence, the end-dialysis serum bicarbonate concentration is the peak concentration, since no delayed metabolism will occur.

Acid-Base Balance Considerations in High-Flux, Reduced-Time Dialysis

The concept of reducing hemodialysis time recently has gained popularity for several reasons. First, the procedure may greatly reduce dialysis time, a fact that has caused great enthusiasm among ESRD patients. Second, the shorter procedure theoretically allows for an increased turnover of dialysis patients during the regular shift, a result that could increase dialysis unit capacity. Whether this increased patient capacity will lead to greater profit (and thus provide a third motive for short-time procedures) is, at present, unclear because more expensive equipment is needed to monitor patients during the procedure. The critical element in the performance of short-time dialysis is the use of high-flux, high surface area dialyzers, typically constructed from biocompatible membranes, such as polysulfone (instead of cuprophane or cellulose acetate). Also implicit in the implementation of the shorter procedure is the performance of individualized dialysis by prescription. This concept of kinetic modeling of dialysis prescription has been stressed by Gotch et al., who incorporate dialyzer urea clearance, blood and dialysate flow, and treatment time into the formula to determine adequacy. Using a similar approach, Keshaviah et al. reported adequate clearances and volume control with a reduced incidence of adverse symptomatology during short-time dialysis. Serum bicarbonate concentration can be maintained above 20 mEq/liter in virtually all patients on the high-flux procedure as long as bicarbonate dialysate is used.

The reason bicarbonate dialysate is required in lieu of acetate dialysate during the high-flux, short-time procedure is apparent when one considers that acetate flux from the dialyzer (J) is 2.5-fold greater than the metabolic conversion rate at $t = 2$ hr. During conventional hemodialysis, acetate dialysance and blood acetate concentration do not usually exceed E (rate of acetate metabolism, a constant of approximately 3.3 mM/min). However, with high-flux, short-time hemodialysis, blood acetate concentration sharply increases due to increased acetate flux and delayed metabolism of acetate. The blood bicarbonate concentration declines because of bicarbonate flux from the patient's blood to the dialysate and delayed metabolic conversion of acetate to bicarbonate so that after 2 hr the blood bicarbonate may fall to 12 mEq/liter and acetate concentration may exceed levels seen with conventional hemodialysis. This combination of bicarbonate loss across the dialyzer coupled with the delay in acetate conversion may lead to a transient acidemia. With time, acetate metabolism will result in generation of bicarbonate, but the best way to provide a more stable serum bicarbonate concentration is by employing bicarbonate dialysate.

Effects of Hemodialysis on Respiratory Function

Since ESRD patients on hemodialysis have frequent bouts of hypotension and cardiac arrhythmias, attention has logically been focused on reversible factors that might contribute to adverse signs and symptoms. In this regard, hypoxemia has been recognize as an accompanying feature of the procedure, and efforts to understand the mechanism and reduce the magnitude of hypoxemia have been ongoing for the last decade. Several features characterize dialysis hypoxemia: (1) it occurs within the first hour of the procedure (with acetate bath), (2) it occurs independently of the dialysis membrane in use and occurs only when blood is exposed to dialysate, and (3) usually a 10 mm Hg decline in Po_2 occurs in the first hour of the procedure, which gradually returns to base-line (predialysis) levels over the course of the procedure. The exact mechanism of dialysis hypoxemia is not entirely clear; however, with acetate dialysate the loss of CO_2 from blood across the dialyzer results in a sharply reduced Pco_2 in the blood returning to the patient. This results in some degree of compensatory hypoventilation, restoring Pco_2 to near predialysis values but lowering Po_2 in the process.

Bicarbonate dialysate initially was reported by some to abolish hypoxemia on dialysis. However, more recent investigations suggest that significant hypoxemia, albeit a slightly lesser degree than with acetate dialysate, still occurs with bicarbonate dialysate. The hypoxemia associated with bicarbonate dialysate usually occurs later in the procedure and may persist through the end of the procedure. Again, the precise mechanism for the hypoxemia is unknown but may be related to the mentioned rapid rise in both the serum bicarbonate concentration and arterial pH.

Although more work is needed to elucidate the mechanisms responsible for dialysis hypoxemia, the salient features are that (1) the hypoxemia is mild to modest, (2) it occurs early in the procedure with acetate dialysate, later with bicarbonate, and (3) it probably is reduced slightly by bicarbonate dialysate.

Peritoneal Dialysis

Most peritoneal dialysis performed today is performed using the technique of either chronic ambulatory peritoneal dialysis (CAPD) or continuous cyclic peritoneal dialysis (CCPD). In these techniques, a mixture of D ($-$) and L ($+$)

stereoisomers of lactate is used. Although acetate buffer may be used for reverse osmosis machines, widespread use is not common. Bicarbonate peritoneal dialysate may be used in specialized circumstances, which will be discussed.

Lactate Peritoneal Dialysis

During both intermittent peritoneal dialysis (IPD) and CAPD, lactate is metabolized to bicarbonate in the body, whereas bicarbonate is lost into the dialysate. A mixture of D- and L-lactate exists in peritoneal dialysis solutions; the L form is rapidly metabolized by L-lactate dehydrogense, and the D form is metabolized much more slowly. The molecular weight of sodium lactate is 112 daltons, and the pK is 3.9. The low pK assures that almost all sodium lactate is dissociated at body pH. The buffering effect of sodium lactate occurs when it reacts with carbonic acid to produce bicarbonate and lactic acid. Catabolism of lactate occurs via acetyl-CoA with conversion to pyruvate in the Krebs cycle; later transamination to alanine (at multiple sites) or carboxylation to glucose (liver and kidney only) occurs. About 50% of lactate metabolism occurs in the liver, whereas 30% occurs in the kidneys. The normal turnover rate of lactate ranges between 0.77 and 0.87 mmoles/kg/hr. At the completion of the TCA cycle, CO_2 and water are generated, and oxidative decarboxylation can eliminate the H^+ generated during the interdialytic period. Lactate ions, rather than lactic acid, may enter the hepatic cell. The subsequent H^+ consumption, through the Krebs cycle or gluconeogenesis, results in an alkaline cell and restores the bicarbonate consumed in the periphery. It should be noted that patients with severe liver disease may be unable to metabolize lactate normally, although this is unusual.

During IPD with lactate (dialysate concentration 45 mEq/liter, 1 hr dwell time, 2 liter dialysate volume), blood lactate concentration rose to 10.4 mg/dl, and pyruvate concentration rose to 0.56 mg/dl over 43 hr. About 70 mEq of lactate was absorbed during a single exchange, as 25 to 30 mEq of bicarbonate was lost into the dialysate. With a 5 liter/hr dialysate flow rate and a zero dwell time, similar results were obtained.

During the usual CAPD procedure, using a dialyate lactate concentration of 38.5 mEq/liter, 75 to 95% of the lactate is absorbed and metabolized during a 4 to 6 hr dwell time. The blood lactate level may reach 1.5 mEq/liter. The total bicarbonate removed during CAPD ranges from 190 to 250 mEq/day and depends on the base-line serum bicarbonate concentration and the number of exchanges performed. The majority of patients on CAPD have a serum bicarbonate concentration between 24 and 26 mEq/liter on a dialysate lactate concentration of 35 mEq/liter. If dialysate lactate concentration is increased to 40 mEq/liter, an increase in serum bicarbonate concentration of 2 to 3 mEq/liter may be anticipated. In fact, as many as 15 to 20% of CAPD patients treated with the higher lactate dialysate may have an elevated serum bicarbonate. In any case, it is clear that a higher and more constant serum bicarbonate level is maintained in most CAPD patients compared to hemodialysis. Serum bicarbonate levels are comparable to hemodialysis patients in the IPD procedure (around 22 mEq/liter).

Bicarbonate Peritoneal Dialysis

Bicarbonate may be used as the base buffer for peritoneal dialysis in some circumstances. Most often, the use of bicarbonate peritoneal dialysate has been in the setting of acute renal failure, severe metabolic acidosis, hypotension (which may preclude hemodialysis), peripheral vasoconstriction, and liver disease (which may impair lactate metabolism). The clinical circumstances under which this constellation of signs occurs is usually acute renal failure associated with severe lactic acidemia. This therapy has the benefit of preventing volume overload as correction of acidemia with bicarbonate occurs. In addition, the therapy is constant, providing the bicarbonate infusion over several days and avoiding precipitous changes in blood pressure, volume, and pH. The bicarbonate peritoneal dialysis mixture is not available commercially but is easily prepared from intravenous solutions (Table 1).

One feature of bicarbonate dialysate is that calcium and magnesium are not included in the mixture to prevent precipitation of salts. Thus, parenteral injections of calcium (usually as calcium gluconate) and magnesium sulfate should be provided as needed. Close monitoring of the changes of serum calcium and magnesium concentrations are required during the procedure. The use of bicarbonate peritoneal dialysate for CAPD has been explored with

TABLE 1. *Bicarbonate peritoneal dialysate*[a]

Additives (for 2 liter exchange)	
1 liter 0.9 N saline	
1 liter 0.45 N saline	
60 ml $D_{50}W$[b]	
50 mEq Na HCO_3[b]	
Concentrations	
Na (mEq/liter)	137
Cl (mEq/liter)	112
HCO_3 (mEq/liter)	25
Glucose (g)	1.5%

[a]Calcium and magnesium must be monitored and administered parenterally; potassium may be added as indicated.
[b]May be adjusted to achieve desired amount of ultrafiltration (glucose) or bicarbonate administration.

the use of compartmentalized dialysis bags (to separate the calcium and magnesium from the bicarbonate), but these formulations are not yet available.

Peritoneal Dialysis for Metabolic Alkalosis

One final and unusual application of peritoneal dialysis in the acute oliguric or anuric renal failure setting is in the treatment of severe alkalemia unresponsive to acetazolamide or dilute hydrochloric acid therapy. In this circumstance, volume repletion with saline may be precluded by concomitant pulmonary edema from capillary membrane damage (adult respiratory distress syndrome or noncardiac pulmonary edema). A low acetate or low bicarbonate peritoneal dialysate may be prepared in this case, and volume removal may be adjusted as needed with short dwell times and the addition of hypertonic glucose to the dialysate.

ACID-BASE DISORDERS WITH PARENTERAL NUTRITION (8,13,14,16,20,22,30,31)

Since its introduction in clinical practice, total parenteral nutrition (TPN) has been recognized to be associated with acid-base disorders. TPN is never administered to a normally healthy person, however, so the specific effects of TPN on acid-base balance are often difficult to discern. Patients are frequently starving or malnourished; they may be catabolic from surgery, burns, trauma, or sepsis; some may have a diseased gastrointestinal tract with resultant loss of HCl or bicarbonate. These underlying problems are the usual cause of acidosis and alkalosis in patients receiving TPN and are discussed elsewhere in this text. Therefore, while evaluating an acid-base disorder in a parenterally alimented patient, the clinician should always keep the underlying disease in mind, implicating the TPN as the cause only after other causes are excluded.

The acid-base problems of TPN are those that occur with alimentation in general (e.g., glucose-induced alkalosis occurring on refeeding), those that are due to a greatly increased nutrient delivery (beyond that possible enterally), those that are caused by any relative disproportion or deficiency among the delivered nutrients, and those that result from problems unique to the formulation and delivery of nutrients parenterally.

Acid-Base Changes with Starvation (13,30)

Since patients due to receive TPN are starving, malnourished, or catabolic, a brief description of the acid-base changes that take place during starvation is warranted to understand some of the changes that subsequently occur with the institution of TPN.

In subjects who have adequate fat stores, total caloric deprivation results in increased hepatic ketoacid production (starvation ketosis). This results in a mild metabolic acidosis during the first 3 to 7 days of fasting: $pH = 7.30$ to 7.35, total CO_2 is 18 to 20 mEq/liter, $P_{CO_2} = 30$ to 35 mm Hg. The increase in serum ketoacid concentration is roughly proportional to the increase in anion gap (5–7 mM) and to the decrease in serum total CO_2. As fasting continues, the acidosis disappears or becomes less pronounced because of an increased renal excretion of net acid. Renal net acid excretion during the first several days of fasting is increased because of an increase in titratable acidity (from increased urinary phosphate and ketoacid excretion) and renal ammoniagenesis. The urine pH falls during this time period. As renal ammoniagenesis continues to increase, titratable acidity returns to base line, and urine pH rises. Net acid excretion is frequently triple or quadruple that in the fed state, 180 to 240 mmoles/day (versus 60 mmoles/day). This adaptive increase is not as complete in a previously malnourished person who begins to fast, since his or her capacity to increase renal ammoniagenesis is inhibited, and titratable acidity frequently is reduced due to prior phosphate depletion. The reason that renal ammoniagenesis cannot be stimulated in states of malnutrition as much as when well fed is not clear. Glutamine (the precursor to renal ammonia) is found in normal amounts in the serum.

The acidosis and increased ammonium excretion occurring with fasting have important physiologic effects. The acidosis serves as a feedback signal, inhibiting further ketogenesis. The increased urinary ammonium excretion comprises about 50% of the nitrogen loss during fasting and is, therefore, detrimental. Bicarbonate administration during fasting will disinhibit ketogenesis and will reduce body nitrogen losses.

When a fast is terminated by refeeding with a carbohydrate, ketogenesis is halted abruptly, and a mild metabolic alkalosis occurs that lasts a few days. The exact cause of the alkalosis is not known. The sodium diuresis that occurs on fasting tends to enhance renal sodium avidity and, hence, bicarbonate avidity, which might explain the maintenance of the alkalosis but not its generation. A continued enhanced net acid excretion, when it is no longer needed, has not been shown to occur.

Acid-Base Changes with Malnutrition (20)

In practice, patients likely to begin TPN have not been totally fasted. Typically, they have been in the hospital a few days to weeks with poor or no oral intake and have been receiving dextrose 5% intravenously, 1 to 3 liters/day, supplying 50 to 150 g of dextrose monohydrate, about 170 to 510 Kcal (3.4 Kcal/g). This amount of carbohydrate is more than adequate to limit ketogenesis (as little as 15 g/day will reduce ketogenesis by 50%). Where ketogenesis has been eliminated, no acid-base disturbance (attributable to the diet) is seen. The blood pH and plasma bicarbonate concentrations in malnourished individuals are normal in the absence of other acid-base stressors. When protein calorie malnutrition is present, acid-base homeostasis is nevertheless disturbed. The kidney's ability to increase net acid excretion, both as titratable acidity and ammonium excretion, is impaired so that an acid load, which would ordinarily be easily eliminated, might produce acidemia. There is a reduced titratable acidity, explained by phosphate depletion and hypophosphaturia. Although ammonium excretion may increase in response to an acid load, the increase is substantially less than which would occur when in a protein-replete state. The cause of the impaired adaptation in ammonia production has not been identified but is reversed by protein-calorie refeeding.

Constituents of Total Parenteral Nutrition Solutions (8,14,16,22,31)

Total parenteral nutrition solutions are a combination of carbohydrates, fats, proteins, electrolytes, vitamins, and a preservative or solvent (Table 2). The individual components may be responsible for an acid-base disorder. As well, a disproportion between components may precipitate a problem.

Proteins

Fibrin hydrolysates and casein enzymatic digests were the primary sources of amino acids used in TPN solutions through the mid 1970s. Acid-base disorders were rarely described with these preparations. When described, the disorder was typically a metabolic acidosis of the increased anion gap variety and tended to occur in premature neonates, in severely malnourished patients, and in patients with intercurrent renal disease. All these patients have an impaired renal capacity to increase net acid excretion. The acidosis can be explained by the usual principles of endogenous acid production; i.e., with metabolism or incorporation of certain amino acids, acid is liberated. The sulfur-containing amino acids, methionine and cysteine, generate sulfuric acid, urea, and CO_2. Arginine, lysine, and histidine liberate a proton, urea, and CO_2 during their metabolism. A proton also is generated during the *de novo* synthesis of anionic amino acids (aspartate, glutamate) that are needed in approximate equimolar quantities to cationic amino acids during protein synthesis (to establish overall protein net charge). If the anionic amino acids are provided in the TPN, they can be incorporated into a protein with one of the cationic amino acids (without the liberation of a proton), or they can generate a bicarbonate during their catabolism. Although these solutions also typically have a high titratable acidity (the amount of alkali needed to raise the pH to 7.4 is

TABLE 2. *Composition of four commercial amino acid solutions (8.5% concentrations)*

	Aminosyn 8.5% (Abbott)	Freamine III 8.5% (McGaw)	Novamine 8.5% (Cutter)	Travasol 8.5% (Travenol)
L-Amino acids (g/100 ml)	8.5	8.5	8.5	8.5
Total nitrogen (g/100 ml)	1.3	1.3	1.35	1.4
Osmolarity (mOsm/liter)(calculated)	850	810	785	860
Approximate pH	5.3	6.5	5.6	6.0
Essential amino acids (mg/100 ml)				
L-Leucine	810	770	590	526
L-Isoleucine	620	590	420	406
L-Valine	680	560	350	590
L-Phenylalanine	380	480	590	526
L-Tryptophan	150	130	140	152
L-Methionine	340	450	420	492
L-Threonine	460	340	420	356
L-Lysine	624	620	673	492
Nonessential amino acids (mg/100 ml)				
L-Alanine	1,100	600	1,200	1,760
L-Arginine	850	810	840	880
L-Histidine	260	240	500	372
L-Proline	750	950	500	356
L-Serine	370	500	340	—
L-Tyrosine	44	—	20	34
L-Glutamic acid	—	—	420	—
L-Aspartic acid	—	—	250	—
Glycine (AAA, USP)	1,100	1,190	590	1,760
Cysteine	—	20	40	—
Electrolytes				
Sodium (mEq/500 ml)	—	5	—	—
Potassium (mEq/500 ml)	2.7	—	—	—
Magnesium (mEq/500 ml)	—	—	—	—
Chloride (mEq/500 ml)	17.5	1.5	—	17
Acetate (mEq/500 ml)	45	36	—	26
Phosphate (mM/liter)	—	5	—	—

Adapted from ref. 22.

about 20–60 mmoles/liter), it is the eventual metabolism of the solution's constituents that determines its relative acidifying or alkalinizing potential. The relative proportions of the cationic and sulfur-containing amino acids versus the anionic amino acids determine the eventual acidifying or alkalinizing potential of the amino acid mixture. That administration of protein digests resulted in an acidosis infrequently, and then only in special circumstances, is due to the presence of just a slight excess of cationic over anionic amino acids (a cation gap), equivalent to the usual acid-ash diet.

Protein digests, however, caused other problems. There are dipeptides and tripeptides that are poorly metabolized, a significant ammonia load, a varying amount of amino acids from lot to lot, and the glutamate present in these preparations was associated with brain damage in experimental animals when administered parenterally. For these reasons, crystalline amino acid solutions came into use. Their introduction resulted in a much more frequent occurrence of metabolic acidosis. This was a hyperchloremic, nonanion gap type of metabolic acidosis. Investigations excluded extrarenal causes and indicated a normal renal response to the acidosis; i.e., net acid excretion was increased. The titratable acidity of the solutions was one-half to one-quarter that of fibrin hydrolysates, suggesting that the acidity of the solution itself was not the cause. The exclusion of the anionic amino acids from the mixture resulted in greater overabundance of cationic amino acids, a larger cation gap. The cationic amino acids were formulated as the hydrogen chloride salt. Once metabolized or incorporated into protein, hydrochloric acid was liberated. In addition, hydrochloric acid was deliberately added to the mixture to enhance the solution's stability. Thus, the infusion of the crystalline amino acid solution was equivalent to an infusion of hydrochloric acid and produced a hyperchloremic acidosis.

Deleting the acid-producing amino acids from the mixture was contemplated. However, methionine and lysine are essential amino acids and could not be omitted from the TPN solution. In addition, although arginine is not an essential amino acid, its absence greatly retards activity of the urea cycle (causing elevated serum ammonia levels), and histidine has been found to be a relative requirement for the attainment of a positive nitrogen balance. By administering the arginine, lysine, and histidine as acetate salts or as the free base, however, the cation gap and chloride excess acidosis was avoided. The acetic acid generated is metabolized completely to CO_2 and H_2O or incorporated into fat. With these changes, the protein preparations used in TPN rarely cause an acidosis in the absence of other factors influencing renal tubular acidification. The absence of an acid-base disorder does not necessarily mean that renal acidification is normal in patients receiving TPN. There is an influence of the prior nutritional state, and it has been suggested that the TPN may itself inhibit renal ammoniagenesis. It is postulated that generation of ATP from nonglutamine sources (such as would be available with administration of TPN) will impair glutamine deamination and thus lead to a decreased renal ammonia production. Direct proof of this theory is lacking.

In terms of acid-base effects, essential amino acid formulas offer no benefit over formulas containing both essential and nonessential amino acids.

The administration of amino acids tends to enhance the hypercarbic drive to ventilation; i.e., ventilation is stimulated to a greater degree for any given level of PCO_2. This may be important in patients with compromised hypoxemic ventilatory drive, such as occurs during starvation, especially since administration of carbohydrates may dramatically increase CO_2 production. In this sense, amino acid solutions may actually prevent a respiratory acidosis.

Carbohydrates

Dextrose is the usual carbohydrate added to TPN solutions, usually supplying 50 to 100% of all the nonprotein calories.

Fructose had been considered as a useful source of calories for TPN, since it has a higher caloric density than dextrose and can move intracellularly even in the absence of insulin. Infusion at rates greater than 0.5 g/kg/hr or administration to patients with hereditary fructose intolerance, however, resulted in serious and occasionally fatal episodes of lactic acidosis. This lactic acidosis may be explained by a depletion of hepatic ATP levels (from rapid intracellular phosphorylation of fructose) and by an increase in glycolysis due to the increased fructose-1-phosphate levels. In addition, even at slower rates of infusion, some degree of lactic acidosis occurs. The use of fructose in TPN is absolutely contraindicated in states in which a metabolic acidosis is likely to develop and, given the availability of high calorie lipid solutions, should probably not be used at all.

Any carbohydrate administration will tend to raise the respiratory quotient (RQ = moles CO_2 produced/moles O_2 consumed) toward 1.0. So long as carbohydrate is being catabolized, the ratio will be less than 1.0, but if carbohydrate is administered in excess of need, fatty acid synthesis will occur, with an RQ of about 8, so that an RQ of >1 might be found. Coincident with the change in RQ, there is also a change in energy consumption (moles O_2 consumed). If a patient with simple nutritional depletion is supplied glucose in excess of need, conversion to fat occurs with little increase in O_2 consumption. However, as the RQ is increased, there will be a definite increase in CO_2 production. In the hypermetabolic patient who has ongoing fat oxidation, provision of excess glucose does not result in net lipogenesis, and the RQ may not change much, but O_2 consumption does increase greatly and, with it, CO_2 production. Both types of patients experience an increase in CO_2 generated (although their RQs are different).

In patients with a relatively fixed ventilation, a respiratory acidosis could develop. This has been reported to occur in intubated patients suddenly given a large glucose load. They experienced a rise in PCO_2 and a fall in arterial pH during concentrated dextrose infusion, which abated on discontinuing the infusion. The glucose load of 5% dextrose is not enough to cause marked changes in CO_2 production, so this effect is usually seen only with hyperalimentation.

These problems can be circumvented by several simple measures. (1) Gradually increase the glucose load over several days. (2) Do not administer glucose in excess of caloric requirements. (3) Administer at least 20 to 30% of the nonprotein calories as fat; they are burned at a lower RQ and thus, for an equivalent energy expenditure, will generate less CO_2. (4) Monitor patients at risk (ventilator patients, COPD patients) frequently during the introduction of TPN or during a change in its dose. (5) Use the assist-controlled ventilation mode in patients being ventilated (as opposed to intermittent-mandatory ventilation) during introduction or change of TPN. Patients are better able to excrete the extra CO_2 with the increased ventilator assistance.

An unusual circumstance of acidosis has occurred in several cancer patients given dextrose. These patients developed a lactic acidosis that was not attributable to other causes. It resolved after discontinuing the dextrose infusion. In the tumor cells, pyruvate is not metabolized via the Krebs cycle but rather is converted to lactate, which then has to be transported to the host's organs for gluconeogenesis or aerobic metabolism to occur (Cori cycle). Under basal conditions, hepatic metabolism can keep up with this excess lactate load, but with the infusion of large loads of glucose, lactate production by the tumor exceeds the lactate clearance capacity of the liver, and a lactic acidosis develops. These patients typically have leukemia or lymphoma, increased basal O_2 consumption, increased glucose turnover, and increased Cori cycling. Since these measurements are not made routinely, the clinician cannot predict if this response will occur in any given patient, and a trial and error approach is used; that is to begin the TPN and monitor the patient carefully for clinical deterioration. If this occurs, the glucose infusion is discontinued. Lactic acidosis is not severe and is readily reversible if one is aware of this potential complication and monitors the patient closely.

Fat

Currently used lipid emulsions are high in caloric density and are iso-osmotic (and so can be administered by peripheral vein), but lipid emulsions do not usually cause appreciable acid-base problems. A mild degree of ketogenesis may be induced with their use, especially if medium-chain triglycerides are used in the absence of concomitant carbohydrate administration.

Vitamins

Parenteral vitamin formulas containing the minimum daily requirements are administered routinely on a daily basis to a patient being given TPN. Because this item may be overlooked when ordering the TPN and because there may be some inactivation of vitamins in the solution, it is still useful to consider the acid-base disorders occurring with vitamin deficiencies.

Thiamine deficiency with severe acute metabolic acidosis has been reported as a complication of TPN administered without vitamins. Patients receiving TPN may already have preexisting thiamine depletion (especially alcoholics), and the large glucose load given with TPN may serve to precipitate thiamine deficiency. In the reported cases, the disorder started after 1 to 2 weeks of TPN with features characteristic of Shoshin beriberi: hypotension, tachypnea and dyspnea, tachycardia, high-output heart failure, and a profound lactic acidosis unresponsive to large amounts of bicarbonate but rapidly responsive to intravenous thiamine. It is, therefore, important to always administer thiamine with TPN, probably in excess of that usually present in multivitamin preparations (they all contain the minimum recommended dose: 3 mg for adults and 1.2 mg for children less than 11 years old). An excess is suggested because hydrolytic cleavage of thiamine to an inactive form has been described to occur in TPN solutions, especially when the pH of the solution is greater than 6 and if bisulfite (a preservative) is present in concentrations greater than 160 mg/liter. Up to 97% inactivation of the thiamine present in TPN has been described. Since standard intravenous vitamin preparations have only the minimum required, any inactivation will result in an inadequate supplement. Given the serious consequences of thiamine deficiency, it would be wise to consider additional supplemental thiamine administration, e.g., 100 mg daily, especially in alcoholics or other patients predisposed to thiamine deficiency.

Biotin is a vitamin essential for carboxylation. Its absence results in a decreased pyruvate carboxylase activity, which results in a modest lactic acidosis. In the absence of biotin, there also is an increased production and excretion of organic acid intermediates. Biotin deficiency and metabolic acidosis have been reported to occur in patients receiving TPN. These patients had received multiple courses of broad-spectrum antibiotics, probably depleting the bowel flora (intestinal bacteria produce biotin). The patients were usually infants and also had other features believed to be related to the biotin deficiency: alopecia totalis, hypotonia, and developmental delay as well as a scaly periorificial dermatitis. In adults, the recommended minimum daily dose is 60 μg and in children (less than 11 years), 20 μg.

Vitamin D deficiency is associated with a mild hyperchloremic, nonanion gap, metabolic acidosis resembling a proximal renal tubular acidosis (RTA). Although hypocalcemia and secondary hyperparathyroidism frequently are present, the metabolic acidosis seems to occur independently of these changes. No instance of a metabolic acidosis attributable to vitamin D deficiency in patients receiving TPN has been reported, despite the usual practice of not administering vitamin D with the TPN. Vitamin D is usually not given to avoid hypercalcemia.

Other Additives

The other major constituents of TPN that may affect acid-base balance are basically two: phosphate and the relative amount of organic anion added. Hypophosphatemia is one of the more frequent metabolic complications of TPN, occurring in about 25% of all patients in some series. The risk of hypophosphatemia is greatest when phosphate supplements are less than 10 mmoles/liter, when there is concomitant use of insulin, diuretics, or antacids, and when there is a history of alcoholism or chronic malnutrition. Phosphate depletion results in hypophosphaturia, which consequently limits urinary titratable acidity. In addition, severe hypophosphatemia may impair proximal renal tubular cell function, with consequent bicarbonaturia and decreased ammoniagenesis. Therefore, it is imperative that phosphate be monitored daily during the initiation of TPN. A supplement of 10 mmoles/liter is a beginning guideline. Doses several times that amount may be required.

The organic anion usually added to TPN is acetate. It is present in the protein formulations as the conjugate base of arginine, lysine, or histidine. Acetic acid is sometimes used to titrate the pH of the solution, and sodium acetate may be added. Only sodium acetate has any affect on acid-base balance; it consumes a proton during metabolism and thus exerts an alkalinizing influence. Acetic acid, whether present with an amino acid or added separately to the solution, eventually will be metabolized to CO_2 and H_2O and, therefore, will have no ultimate acid-base influence. The supplemental sodium acetate serves to temper the acidifying effect of any added HCl and of the sulfur-containing amino acids, methionine and cysteine. Currently available amino acid-dextrose solutions use less than 9 mEq HCl to buffer each liter, and approximately 30 to 45 mEq of H^+ are released during the metabolism of the 15 to 22 mEq of methionine and cysteine present in each liter. Thus, generally less than 40 to 50 mEq of sodium acetate is needed to completely balance the acid load. In cases where the acid content of the diet cannot be tolerated, the diet can be made alkaline-ash by substituting sodium acetate for sodium chloride or by simply adding sodium acetate. Conversely, HCl can be added to the TPN to combat a metabolic alkalosis resistant to the usual measures of treatment.

ACID-BASE DISTURBANCES ASSOCIATED WITH BLOOD TRANSFUSIONS (6,7,17,21)

Acid-base disturbances may occur after massive blood transfusions, but these disturbances usually are secondary to the underlying condition rather than to the transfused blood itself. Nevertheless, banked blood can alter acid-base homeostasis if given very rapidly or in very large quantities.

Constituents of Banked Blood

Transfused blood differs from normal blood because it has been mixed with an anticoagulant–preservative solution and because metabolic changes have occurred during storage. The anticoagulant–preservative solutions in current use are shown in Table 3. Acetate-citrate-dextrose (ACD) was the first of these. Citrate had been recogized as an effective anticoagulant, but red blood cell (RBC) viability was limited in the absence of added dextrose. The added dextrose, however, tended to caramelize when the solution was autoclaved. It was found that caramelization could be prevented by acidification of the solution. Acidifying the solution also served to increase RBC viability. Citrate, phosphorus, dextrose (CPD) differs from ACD because there is slightly less

TABLE 3. *Composition of anticoagulant–preservative solutions per unit of whole blood*

		ACD-A[a]	CPD[b]	CPD-A1[c]	Adsol AS-1
Trisodium citrate (dihydrate)	g	1.485 (15.1 mEq)	1.656 (16.9 mEq)	1.656 (16.9 mEq)	d
Citric acid (monohydrate)	g	0.540	0.206	0.206	d
Monobasic sodium phosphate (monohydrate)	g	—	0.139	0.139	d
Dextrose (hydrose)	g	1.687	1.606	2.00	2.20
Adenine	g	—	—	0.017	0.027
Mannitol	g	—	—	—	0.75
Sodium chloride	g	—	—	—	0.90
Volume	ml	67.5	63	63	100

[a]ACD-A, acid citrate dextrose-A.
[b]CPD, citrate phosphate dextrose.
[c]CPD-A1, citrate phosphate dextrose adenine-1.
[d]The RBC present in Adsol are collected in CPD. Assuming a donor hematocrit of 40%, packed cells of 90%, and that the added solutes remain in the plasma, Adsol has 0.10 g trisodium citrate (1.0 mEq), 0.012 g citric acid, and 0.008 g sodium phosphate.

citrate and because of the presence of sodium phosphate. The solution has a higher pH, and the added inorganic phosphate aids in the formation of organic phosphate esters. Thus, when preserved in CPD, RBCs have improved viability. CPD supplanted ACD as the major anticoagulant preservative solution in general use soon after its introduction in the early 1970s. The addition of adenine to the CPD solution (CPD-A1) further improved posttransfusion RBC viability, probably by providing a precursor for continued nucleotide (ATP) synthesis.

A more recently introduced preservative system, AS-1 (Adsol), uses RBCs that have been collected in standard CPD and concentrated by removal of plasma. To these cells is added 100 ml of normal saline containing dextrose, adenine, and mannitol. This results in a unit of blood with a hematocrit of about 58% (a compromise between the flow characteristics of whole blood and the reduced volume load of packed RBC units). It also dramatically reduces the amount of sodium citrate present per unit of blood. This is of benefit when large volumes are being transfused.

Changes in Blood During Storage

The changes that take place in blood as a result of banking are referred to as the "storage lesion" of RBCs (Table 4). These metabolic and acid-base disturbances associated with blood transfusions rank low on the list of problems

TABLE 4. *Storage lesion of red blood cells*

Decreased RBC viability
Viscosity changes
Hemoglobinemia
Decreased RBC ATP level
Decreased RBC 2,3-DPG level
No functional platelets
Low factor V and VIII
Hypothermia
Hypercalcemia
Hyperkalemia
Acid–base stress
Citrate load

Adapted from ref. 6.

associated with transfusions (Table 5). When massive transfusions became possible with the ability to store blood for prolonged periods, however, the possibility of metabolic complications was recognized. The ACD anticoagulant has a pH of 5, and CPD has a pH of 5.6. When blood is stored in ACD or CPD, the pH of the solution is immediately lowered. When first collected, blood in ACD has a pH of about 6.9, slightly lower than in CPD (7.1). With storage, as RBC metabolism continues, there is a progressive production of lactic acid, a decline in red cell ATP and 2,3-DPG, and a leak of intracellular potassium into the supernatant. Red cell ATP falls to about 60% of base line by the end of the storage period. Levels of 2,3-DPG begin to decrease after about a week of storage, becoming less than 20% of base line by the end of the second week. This shifts the O_2 dissociation curve to the left and lowers the P_{50}, thereby decreasing O_2 offloading to the tissues. Supernatant potassium concentration increases, reaching 20 to 30 mEq/liter, or approximately 5 to 10 mEq/unit of whole blood by the end of the storage period.

The production of lactic acid results in a lactate concentration of 10 to 15 mEq/liter, or 5 to 8 mEq/unit. The H^+ produced is titrated by HCO_3^-, forming H_2CO_3, which is converted to CO_2 and H_2O via carbonic anhydrase. Bicarbonate concentration falls to 5 to 10 mEq/liter (depending on the length

TABLE 5. *Problems with blood transfusions*

Inadequate supply
Transfusion reaction
Transmission of infection
Volume load
Storage lesion
Iron load
Microaggregates

Adapted from ref. 6.

of storage), and PCO_2 rises to 150 to 200 mm Hg. The pH progressively decreases and by the end of the storage period is 6.6 to 6.7 when measured at 37°C. Measured at 4°C the pH is considerably higher because of the difference in pK and solubility of CO_2 at the lower temperature. A variable amount of base (11–21 mEq/unit) is required to titrate banked blood to a pH of 7.4, depending on the study conditions.

Effects of Transfusions on Acid-Base Balance

Based on the above considerations, one might expect banked blood to produce a significant acidemia. However, such an effect is unusual, even in clinical situations where blood is massively transfused, e.g., with trauma, surgery, and exchange transfusions. This acid-base tolerance to large transfusions could have been predicted by a different analysis of the acid-base information. When collected, blood has a pH of 7.4; the progressive accumulation of lactic acid (or any other acidic intermediary metabolite) causes a fall in pH. Once transfused, however, the lactate is rapidly metabolized in the liver and kidney, producing CO_2 and H_2O and consuming a hydrogen ion. Unless the conjugate base is excreted into the urine as an organic anion (e.g., as sodium lactate) leaving behind the proton, there is no net addition of acid. The same holds true for any added organic acid. The citric acid added to the blood is eventually metabolized to CO_2 and H_2O, with no net acid-base effect. The metabolism of the organic anions, however, generates bicarbonate. Inasmuch as metabolism is required to consume a proton (and generate a bicarbonate), there will be a temporal lag between the time when the acidic infusion is administered and when it is cleared. This lag is inconsequential in patients with adequate liver and renal perfusion. Patients who require massive transfusions, however, are those who have poor tissue perfusion, but even in those with hemodynamic instability, the acid load of the transfusion proves to be easily handled. The transfusion volume itself serves to restore tissue perfusion. Those who have hypoperfusion to the extent that exogenously administered citrate and lactate cannot be rapidly metabolized also cannot handle endogenous lactate loads and invariably have a preexistent lactic acidosis. The administration of bicarbonate on a routine basis to neutralize the acidity of the banked blood should be avoided.

The ultimate acid-base stress, which the unit of blood poses, is an alkalosis. The added citric acid and generated lactic acid are metabolized with no net effect on acid-base balance, but metabolism of the citrate added as trisodium citrate consumes a proton and generates a new bicarbonate. A unit of ACD whole blood contains 15.1 mEq of potential bicarbonate as trisodium citrate. CPD and CPD-A1 have 16.9 mEq/unit. The transfusion of 20 to 30 units, once metabolized, therefore, proves a significant alkaline load.

Clinical studies of the effect of massive transfusions on acid-base balance have been carried out in neonates (exchange transfusions) and in adults (trauma, gastrointestinal hemorrhage, extensive surgery). The effects of the blood transfusion itself on the acid-base status are difficult to discern. Hemodynamic instability and intercurrent lactic acidosis, nasogastric suction with loss of H^+, blood volume contraction, and hypocapnia or hypercapnia are factors that could not be controlled in most of these studies.

Exchange transfusions in neonates represent a clinical circumstance in which massive blood transfusions are given. During exchange transfusions, a volume twice the estimated blood volume is used, which results in the replacement of about 85% of the neonate's blood. In infants transfused within 24 hours of birth, the pH typically fell to between 7.1 and 7.25. The presence of respiratory distress syndrome confounded the acid-base balance because the infants frequently also developed a respiratory acidosis. Empiric trials showed that adding 1 to 2 mEq of sodium bicarbonate or THAM for every 100 ml of blood transfused could prevent the development of this acidosis. Infants 3 days or older exhibited a much less pronounced acidosis in response to exchange transfusions, reflecting a more developed metabolic capacity. Regardless of the age of the neonate, the pH progressively increased after transfusion so that within 1 to 2 hr, any acidosis that might have developed was replaced by a mild alkalosis. This alkalemia peaked between 12 and 24 hr postexchange transfusion. A pH as high as 7.54 and a bicarbonate of 33 have been reported.

It was noted that routine administration of bicarbonate, although ameliorating the fall in pH during the exchange tended to worsen the alkalosis after the exchange. The alkalosis persisted for as long as 3 days. The duration of the alkalosis was reduced by administering saline, suggesting that some contraction in blood volume contributed to the maintenance of the higher pH. In more recent studies in which CPD anticoagulated blood has been used, the decline in pH has been less marked in newborns undergoing exchange transfusions (there is 62% less citric acid added per unit in CPD blood). The current approach with exchange transfusion is to administer the blood as recently collected, packed RBCs suspended in saline, largely eliminating the acid and alkaline load. Routine administration of sodium bicarbonate is no longer a recommended practice.

In contrast to the studies on acid-base status during exchange transfusion, those studies describing adults who underwent massive transfusions are fraught with even more difficulty in interpretation. Patients requiring massive transfusions are, or have been, massively bleeding and consequently have a number of metabolic stresses. Two studies examining these issues are shown in Tables 6 and 7. The patients who had progressive acidemia during the transfusion also had rapid blood loss and could be identified by the usual clinical criteria of low blood pressure, minimal urinary output, tachycardia, pallor, and altered mental state.

Those studies that evaluated the acid-base status of massively transfused

TABLE 6. *Massively transfused surgical patients at Memorial Sloan-Kettering Cancer Center*

| | CPD blood used, no liver disease ($n = 53$) | |
	$[H^+]$ mM/L	pH
Baseline	41.7 ± 0.73	7.380 ± .008
At peak transfusion rate	42.2 ± 1.11	7.375 ± .011
End of surgery	39.7 ± 1.10	7.401 ± .012

Adapted from ref. 17.

patients on the first to third posttransfusion day all showed a tendency toward metabolic alkalosis, with the pH usually in the 7.45 to 7.50 range but occasionally greater than 7.6. Since humans have a tremendous capacity to excrete administered bicarbonate with little increase in plasma $[HCO_3]$, any persistent alkalosis seen posttransfusion in adults usually reflects an ongoing stimulus to alkalosis (such as nasogastric suction) or a state of volume contraction that maintains alkalosis. In the case of massive transfusions, the alkalosis may be generated by the bicarbonate that was administered as citrate.

One group of patients at some risk of developing alkalemia after transfusions are those with ESRD. Lacking renal function, they do not have the ability to excrete any added bicarbonate equivalents. A significant degree of alkalemia has developed in ESRD patients who have received massive transfusions, who have undergone thoracic duct drainage with an acetate-containing protein fraction used for volume replacement, and who have had plasmapheresis in which fresh frozen plasma (as replacement) and citrate (as anticoagulant) were used. Dialysis and endogenous acid production resulted in normalization of pH once the bicarbonate load was discontinued.

The development of an alkalosis posttransfusion is difficult to find in pa-

TABLE 7. *Combat casualties in Vietnam: ACD blood used, usually stored 2–3 weeks*

Group	I	II	III	IV
Blood pressure at end of transfusion	< 90	> 90	< 90	> 90
No. of units	17.6 ± 2.2	14 ± 2.3	35.2 ± 7.9	26.4 ± 1.6
Duration of transfusion (hr)	1.9 ± 0.4	1.9 ± 0.3	11.4 ± 2.7	8.3 ± 1
n	7	10	5	14
Pre-pH	7.26 ± 0.05	7.27 ± 0.06	7.33 ± 0.07	7.39 ± 0.02
Post-pH	7.21 ± 0.05	7.36 ± 0.03	7.40 ± 0.04	7.39 ± 0.03
Pre-CO_2	39 ± 3	34 ± 3	34 ± 6	33 ± 3
Post-CO_2	46 ± 2	42 ± 3	44 ± 8	44 ± 3

Adapted from ref. 7.

tients with normal renal function. A positive correlation between the number of units transfused and the posttransfusion pH has not been found.

In summary, the acid-base disturbances with massive transfusion are:

Early: Tendency toward acidosis during the infusion, since the banked blood is acidic, and there is a finite lag time between the infusion of the acid and its metabolism. This may be important in day-old neonates and preterm babies. In adults, at the usual transfusion rates (less than 1 unit every 5 min), acidosis fails to develop unless there is coexistent shock or severe hepatic impairment.

Late: Tendency toward alkalosis, since the citrate present in the anticoagulant is metabolized, yielding bicarbonate. The development of alkalosis depends on the failure of renal excretion of the extra bicarbonate, because of either volume contraction or renal insufficiency. The relative alkalinizing effects of the various anticoagulant solutions and systems, in descending order, reflect their relative sodium citrate content: CPD>ACD>>>Adsol.

ACID-BASE DISTURBANCES ASSOCIATED WITH RENAL TRANSPLANTATION (4,9,16,23,24,29,33)

The development of acid-base disturbances in patients undergoing renal transplantation and in patients who have a renal allograft is well recognized. As in any other patient, extrarenal disorders affecting acid-base balance are prominent, such as hypoventilation and hyperventilation, diarrhea, and vomiting or nasogastric suction. Acute renal failure, commonly present in the immediate posttransplant period, is associated with a metabolic acidosis, just as in the nonrenal transplant patient with acute renal failure. This section examines the abnormalities in renal excretion of acid that are out of proportion to any reduction in functioning renal mass, RTAs, as they occur in the patient with a transplanted kidney.

A normally functioning renal allograft exhibits normal handling of sodium, water, potassium, and protons. Volume, tonicity, potassium, and acid-base balance, respectively, are normal. Thus, the development of an RTA in a patient with a renal allograft should be considered abnormal and should prompt an investigation into its cause. Fortunately, clinically evident RTAs are uncommon in renal transplant patients.

The varieties of RTA that are clinically evident and well characterized in renal transplant patients are shown in Table 8. The relative frequencies are estimates based on the relative frequency of their descriptions in the literature and thus may not reflect a true frequency. These disorders are not mutually exclusive and may not always be completely manifested. In addition, there are some caveats that should be observed when considering if an RTA is present in a patient. First, the patient should be acidemic. It should be kept in mind that another cause for a low serum bicarbonate concentration is the

TABLE 8. *Renal tubular acidosis in the renal transplant patient*

| Type, location | Azathioprine treated | | Cyclosporine A treated |
| | Time after transplantation | | |
	Early	Late	
Distal RTA (classic, type I)	+ + + +[a]	+ + + +	?
Fanconi syndrome, proximal RTA (type II)	+	—	—
Hyporeninemic, hypoaldosteronism	+	?	?
Hyperkalemic RTA, mineralocorticoid resistant	+ +	—	+ + + +

[a] + to + + + +, relative frequency, from least to most frequent.

metabolic compensation for a primary respiratory alkalosis. Second, extrarenal acidoses should be rigorously excluded. Third, urinary net acid excretion should be low or inadequate. The finding of an elevated urinary pH after administration of an acid load may be due to an impaired renal net acid excretion. However, it must be remembered that an adaptive increase in urinary ammonium excretion will lead to a higher urine pH. This may be especially true in instances where there is a diminished excretion of titratable acid, e.g., due to hypophosphatemia from a phosphate-restricted diet or the use of phosphate-binding antacids.

The advent of the widespread use of cyclosporine A as the mainstay of immunosuppression for renal transplant patients has altered the frequency of occurrence and the types of RTA seen. This is probably a result of the decreased incidence of allograft rejection seen with the use of cyclosporine A but may also be caused by other effects of the medication. For this reason, the discussion is divided into those disorders described in patients being treated with azathioprine and steroids and those being treated with cyclosporine A.

Renal Tubular Acidosis in Patients Being Treated with Azathioprine (4,9,23,33)

Hypokalemic or Normokalemic, and Hyperchloremic Nonanion Gap Metabolic Acidosis

The most frequently described RTA in these patients is a hypokalemic or normokalemic, hyperchloremic, nonanion gap metabolic acidosis. This resembles a type I or classic distal RTA. The patients do not have bicarbonaturia to any appreciable degree but fail to lower their urinary pH to less than 5.5 during an acidosis. Urinary net acid excretion is low. In one detailed study, five patients studied failed to lower their urinary pH despite a sodium sulfate infusion at a time when they were sodium avid. They also failed to increase their urine-minus-blood Pco_2 difference (during a neutral phosphate infusion when the final urine pH had been adjusted to 6.8 by a bicarbonate infusion). This suggests a defect in distal hydrogen ion secretion. Hyperkalemia was absent, supporting the notion that the dysfunction of the distal tubule was not universal. An incomplete form of this distal RTA has been described, characterized by a normal acid-base balance under basal conditions and thus not usually clinically noted. When patients with this disorder are challenged with an acid load, however, they fail to adequately acidify the urine (the urine pH remains above 5.5), indicating a decreased reserve for distal hydrogen ion secretion.

This RTA has been found both early after transplantation and late in the posttransplantation period. Frequently, the disorder is transient and may remit without any specific therapy other than continued immunosuppression. Relapses have been described. The RTA may become permanent.

The cause of this RTA is not known with certainty; however, the strong association of acute and chronic rejection with the appearance of the RTA suggests that immunologic renal tubular damage is responsible. A mononuclear cell interstitial infiltrate is common to systemic lupus erythematosus, hyperglobulinemia, Sjögren's syndrome, other autoimmune diseases, and renal transplant rejection. All of these disorders have been associated with the development of a hypokalemic, distal RTA. One study, in which renal transplant patients were followed-up by performing serial urine acidification tests, found that of the 13 patients who had either complete or incomplete distal RTA in the late posttransplant period, 10 had clinical evidence of chronic rejection (hypertension, proteinuria, or a declining creatinine clearance). Another study found hyperchloremic acidosis in 33.6% of 122 rejection episodes treated and found the hyperchloremia useful in both the early diagnosis of the rejection and in assessing the response to therapy; i.e., resolution of the RTA occurred with resolution of the acute rejection episode.

Fanconi Syndrome

The Fanconi syndrome, both complete and incomplete, has been described to both occur *de novo* and to recur in renal transplant patients. The complete Fanconi syndrome is found less frequently than are combinations of the individual components, such as isolated renal glycosuria or phosphaturia (isolated renal bicarbonaturia, however, has not been described). Patients reported to have the complete Fanconi syndrome associated with renal transplantation were all discovered by the fifth week posttransplant. Instances of isolated renal glycosuria, aminoaciduria, and phosphaturia have been reported occurring both soon after transplantation and late in the posttransplant course. These incomplete variants were isolated findings or were associated with another RTA, such as the hypokalemic, hyperchloremic RTA described previously. The proximal tubular dysfunction in these patients tends to persist. Only one patient has been reported to have had a partial remission (bicarbonaturia persisted despite resolution of renal glycosuria and phosphaturia). The infrequency of the occurrence of this disorder prevents firm conclusions about its pathogenesis, however, the development and continued presence of these disorders appears to be independent of allograft rejection.

Hyporeninemic Hypoaldosteronism

This disorder, characterized by a low plasma renin activity and a low plasma aldosterone despite attempts to stimulate their production, is known to cause a hyperkalemic, hyperchloremic, nonanion gap metabolic acidosis in nonrenal transplant patients, especially those with diabetes mellitus. This disorder has also been described in renal transplant patients, although caution is required in interpreting the reports. In one instance, exogenous mineralocorticoid was being administered during the attempt to stimulate endogenous production. In another, the patient was volume overloaded and so had appropriately suppressed plasma renin activity and aldosterone. One patient was believed to have a second RTA coexisting, and several patients were not even shown to be acidemic. Some instances of this disorder, however, may have been overlooked. Earlier reports in which serum potassium and renin and aldosterone levels were not mentioned contained patients with a hyperchloremic acidosis with an intact ability to lower the urinary pH during an acidosis.

One well-described patient who did have a hyporeninemic hypoaldosteronism documented, had a hyperkalemic, hyperchloremic metabolic acidosis and was diabetic. This patient had a low urinary pH during acidosis, a high urine-blood P_{CO_2} during a neutral phosphate infusion, and did not increase urinary potassium excretion during a sodium bicarbonate infusion while being treated with acetazolamide. It is conceivable that this man's acidosis would have been substantially improved simply by lowering his serum potassium concentration, since hyperkalemia is known to inhibit renal ammoniagenesis. Indeed, that hyperkalemia might play a significant role in the acid-base balance of renal transplant patients was suggested by one study in which a strong inverse correlation was found between the serum potassium level and the whole blood base excess; i.e., the higher the serum potassium, the lower the pH. The infrequency of the occurrence of hyporinemic hypoaldosteronism, at least as reported in the literature, precludes conclusions about the pathogenesis or permanence of this disorder.

Mineralocorticoid-resistant Hyperkalemic Renal Tubular Acidosis

There is one series in the literature describing patients who developed hyperkalemia in the first 3 months postrenal transplantation while being treated with azathioprine. Seventy-five patients were studied, and an unexplained, persistent hyperkalemia was found in 23. Eleven of these 23 patients also had a hyperchloremic acidosis. Further studies were performed on 4 of the nonacidemic patients, who had suppressed plasma renin activity but normal aldosterone levels (the latter were likely inappropriately low for the degree of hyperkalemia). They failed, however, to increase their urinary potassium excretion or to correct their hyperkalemia in response to exogenous mineralocorticoid administration and thus can be characterized as mineralocorticoid-resistant. They did increase their urinary potassium excretion however, when hydrochlorothiazide, a diuretic acting primarily in the distal tubule and having a long duration of action, was administered. In patients followed for at least a year, the hyperkalemia was shown to resolve spontaneously. No mention was made in the report about whether serum bicarbonate or pH returned to normal. This disorder has not been described to occur later after renal transplantation, nor has it been described to occur in association with renal allograft rejection. The pathogenesis may involve renal tubular ischemic damage that frequently occurs in the immediate posttransplant period.

Possible Role of Hyperparathyroidism (16)

Hyperparathyroidism may persist in many patients after transplantation. The acid-base effects of hyperparathyroidism, in this instance, are likely to parallel those seen in men experimentally infused with PTH rather than the acid-base disturbances seen in primary hyperparathyroidism because nephrocalcinosis should not be present in the newly transplanted kidney. With an infusion of PTH, a transient renal acidosis develops and lasts for about 2 days, followed by a persistent, mild, chloride-resistant metabolic alkalosis. PTH both decreases proximal bicarbonate reabsorption and enhances distal acidification. In the setting of renal transplantation, the intercurrent problems of renal insufficiency from ischemia and rejection, hypophosphaturia from decreased oral intake and the continued use of phosphate-binding antacids, and uremic osteodystrophy (possibly retarding extrarenal acid buffering) are several reasons this metabolic alkalosis is not seen. A decreased phosphate intake will cause hypophosphaturia, limiting net acid excretion as titratable acidity. With persistent phosphate deprivation, proximal bicarbonate reabsorption and renal ammoniagenesis also seem to be impaired. Thus, decreased phosphate intake may offset the direct effect of PTH to stimulate distal acidification. Although hyperparathyroidism may be operative in the immediate posttransplant period and could explain a proximal bicarbonate wasting, it does not explain the distal RTA most commonly seen in renal transplant patients (the distal RTA of primary hyperparathyroidism occurs coincident with the development of nephrocalcinosis).

Renal Tubular Acidosis in Patients Being Treated with Cyclosporine A (24,29)

As mentioned earlier, the use of cyclosporine A has changed the character of RTA in transplant patients. Hyperkalemia has been noted to be a frequent occurrence in all patients treated with cyclosporine A. This has been shown in bone marrow and cardiac transplant patients and in patients with uveitis or rheumatoid arthritis treated with cyclosporine A. The serum potassium concentration is increased an average of 0.5 to 1.0 mEq/liter in different studies and is out of proportion to any decrement in GFR.

The hyperkalemia tends to decrease in frequency with time after transplantation. One study, in which a serum potassium concentration greater than 5 mEq/liter was used as the criterion for diagnosing hyperkalemia, found a frequency of 26%, 18%, and 10% at 1, 3, and 6 months posttransplantation, respectively, despite a creatinine clearance greater than 20 ml/min. Other series report similar experiences. In all patients, however, the average serum potassium remains elevated when compared to similar patients being treated with azathioprine. A lower GFR and PAH excretion, hypertension, hyperuricemia, and an impaired ability to excrete a water load are also reported with greater frequency in renal transplant patients treated with cyclosporine A.

Tests of renal tubular function in a group of patients with uveitis who were treated with cyclosporine failed to show evidence of amino aciduria, glycosuria, hypokalemia, hypophosphatemia, hypouricemia, or an altered renal tubule threshold for phosphate, suggesting that proximal tubular function was not impaired by cyclosporine A. Tests of renal acidification were not performed, but the average total CO_2 was only minimally decreased, from 28 to 26 mEq/liter, without any change in serum chloride. One group of bone marrow transplant patients treated with cyclosporine A (who had normal serum electrolytes) had normal urinary acidification after the short ammonium chloride loading test.

There are, nevertheless, reports of the occurrence of a hyperchloremic metabolic acidosis developing along with hyperkalemia in cyclosporine A-treated renal transplant patients. Of 66 patients in two reports, 11 (17%) had the disorder. Of these 11, 7 had a minimum urinary pH less than 5.5. The plasma renin activity was suppressed or in the low normal range in 10 patients with a normal aldosterone level (although it was low when factored for the hyperkalemia). Eight of the patients were taking a β-blocker for hypertension, however, complicating the interpretation of the plasma renin activities. In those patients in whom it was tried, administration of a bicarbonate supplement to raise the blood pH to 7.4 resulted in a partial correction of the hyperkalemia. Another report, in which plasma renin activity (PRA) and aldosterone levels were examined but that did not evaluate acid-base balance, found that base-line PRA was lower in cyclosporine A-treated renal transplant patients compared with azathioprine-treated renal transplant patients and nontransplant patients with renal insufficiency. The PRA could be stimulated by administering lasix and restricting sodium intake to a level comparable to that achieved by azathioprine-treated renal transplant patients. Blood pressure also was decreased by this treatment. Plasma volume, measured as the volume of distribution of ^{99m}Tc-DTPA, tended to be higher in the cyclosporine A-treated patients.

Rats that received 25 mg cyclosporine A per kilogram per day for 8 days (a large dose compared with that currently used for renal transplant patients) developed a hyperkalemic, hyperchloremic metabolic acidosis. Fractional bicarbonate excretion was low, indicating normal proximal tubular bicarbonate reabsorption. GFR was decreased to less than half control values. Urine minus blood P_{CO_2} was abnormally low in the presence of an alkaline urine. After 3 days of treatment, the response of the urine pH to ammonium chloride administration and sodium sulfate infusion (while sodium avid) was determined. The urine pH was appropriately low after ammonium chloride (although urine ammonium excretion and, therefore, net acid excretion was considerably lower in cyclosporine A-treated rats), and the sodium sulfate infusion caused an appropriate decrease in urine pH and increase in net acid excretion. It is noteworthy, however, that the abnormality in urine minus blood P_{CO_2} was much worse after treatment for 8 days than after 3 days, so the ability to acidify the urine and respond to a sodium sulfate infusion, not reported in those rats treated for 8 days, may not necessarily be normal after this length of treatment. Rats may not be a good model for cyclosporine A nephrotoxicity, however, since they have stimulated PRA and aldosterone levels after being treated with cyclosporine A, in distinction to the findings in humans.

These experimental findings and case studies in transplanted patients treated with cyclosporine A are compatible with a voltage-dependent type of distal RTA, i.e., an impairment in the generation of a lumen-negative transepithelial electrical gradient in the distal nephron. This could be the result of a direct effect of the drug on the renal tubular cell, or it could the result of alterations in renal hemodynamics or prostaglandins.

In vitro studies have shown cyclosporine A to be directly toxic to the S3 segment of the proximal tubule. *In vivo*, however, distal tubular effects are most prominent, suggesting that the main mechanism of toxicity is not that of a direct tubular toxin. Cyclosporine A nephrotoxicity is thought to be primarily vascular in origin, with many features akin to those occurring with the use of nonsteroidal anti-inflammatory agents. Indeed, cyclosporine A has been shown to reduce papillary, glomerular, and vascular prostaglandin synthesis. Inhibition of renal prostaglandin synthesis with indomethacin has been shown to increase chloride reabsorption in the cortical thick ascending limb of Henle and in the late distal tubule and cortical collecting duct. This enhanced chloride reabsorption could be a mechanism for the postulated decrease in transepithelial electrical gradient and explain the similarity of the cyclosporine A RTA with type II pseudohypoaldosteronism (the chloride shunt hypothesis). The enhanced chloride reabsorption would tend to cause volume expansion, with secondary hypertension and suppression of renin. The renin also may be directly suppressed because of decreased prostaglandin synthesis. Patients would be expected to acidify the urine in response to ammonium chloride and sodium sulfate and to maintain a normal urine minus blood PCO_2. If this is not found, an additional direct proton secretory defect, either toxic or immunologic (as in the distal RTA associated with rejection), may be present.

The lack of occurrence of a hyperchloremic acidosis in nonrenal transplant patients treated with cyclosporine A would then be ascribed to their better overall renal function (greater renal ammoniagenesis and absence of immunologic renal damage). It is also possible, however, that the tendency to a hyperchloremic RTA in cyclosporine A-treated patients is the result of a hyperkalemic inhibition of renal ammoniagenesis, with the overt RTA only becoming manifest when there is renal tubular damage, as in the hyperchloremic RTA associated with renal transplant rejection. The hypertension also could be ascribed to a directly enhanced vascular tone rather than to an expanded extracellular fluid volume.

Additional explanations of the clinical and experimental findings are possible. Careful balance studies in nonrenal transplant patients before and at the initiation of therapy with cyclosporine A, e.g., patients who will be treated for uveitis or other immunologically mediated disease, are needed to sort out any direct effect of this medicine.

Therapeutic Considerations

There is no specific treatment for any of the RTAs associated with renal transplantation. Rejection, both acute and chronic, should be considered and treated if present. Inasmuch as hyperparathyroidism is associated with proximal bicarbonate wastage, one should evaluate patients with all variants of the Fanconi syndrome for this possibility. Cyclosporine A toxicity also should be considered, and if possible, dose reductions should be made. As with many other aspects of transplant patient management, the use of cyclosporine A makes the differential diagnosis of RTA complicated. As mentioned earlier, one group of investigators equated the development of a hyperchloremic metabolic acidosis with rejection. A patient taking cyclosporine A who develops a hyperchloremic acidosis may be experiencing drug toxicity, not rejection. Current literature does not suggest that any of the features of the RTA are helpful in distinguishing between rejection and cyclosporine A nephrotoxicity. Since some of the effects of cyclosporine A are readily reversible, especially the vascular–prostaglandin-induced ones, decreasing the dose should be expected to improve the GFR and correct the hyperkalemic RTA. Once interstitial fibrosis and tubular atrophy occur, however, at least some renal function has probably been permanently lost, and a decreased GFR and RTA may persist at that time in spite of dose reductions.

The routine reduction in cyclosporine A dosing, as currently practiced, may explain the decrease in prevalence of hyperkalemia that occurs with time after transplantation. Nonsteroidal anti-inflammatory agents should be avoided in renal transplant patients taking cyclosporine A, since the inhibition of renal prostaglandins may be profound. Since there is usually no proximal bicarbonate wasting, 1 mEq/kg/day bicarbonate administration should be adequate to control the acidosis unless the patient is catabolic. Hypokalemia and hyperkalemia should be treated, particularly since the latter tends to decrease the ability of the kidney to excrete acid as ammonium. For chronic potassium control, sodium exchange resins or a kaliuretic diuretic can be used. If renal function is adequate, thiazide diuretics seem especially useful, probably because of their prolonged duration of action and possibly because they work at a site where the chloride shunt may be operative.

Hypophosphatemia also should be treated. Tubular lumen phosphate is the major titratable acid, and decreased phosphate delivery will thereby impair net acid excretion. Hypophosphatemia also retards proximal tubular bicarbonate reclamation and decreases renal ammoniagenesis.

ACID-BASE DISORDERS ASSOCIATED WITH COLD

Temperature Effects on pH *In Vitro* (1–3,5,11,19,25–28)

The hydrogen ion concentration of all solutions is affected by changes in temperature. At a temperature of 25°C, water has a dissociation constant (equal to $[H^+][OH^-]/[H_2O]$) of 10^{-14} M. Neutrality exists when $[H^+]$ equals $[OH^-]$, so that at 25°C, neutrality is at a $[H^+]$ of 10^{-7} M and a pH of 7.0. Increasing the temperature of water to 37°C increases the dissociation constant to 2.4×10^{-14} M, so that the pH of neutrality at 37°C is 6.81 (Figs. 4 and 5).

Blood is a more complex solution than water, having numerous buffer systems. The major nonbicarbonate buffer system is that provided by hemoglobin, specifically the imidazole group of the histidine residues. The changes in the pK of this buffer, as temperature changes, parallel the temperature-dependent changes in the dissociation constant of water (Fig. 5). Bicarbonate is

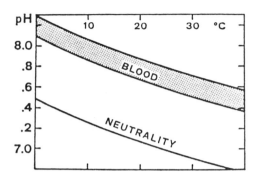

FIG. 4. The pH of neutral water (solid line) and blood shown as a function of temperature. (From ref. 25.)

the major blood buffering system *in vivo*, in large part because of the independent regulation of P_{CO_2}. Changes in temperature affect both the pK of the buffer system and the solubility of the CO_2. A decrease in temperature increases the solubility of gases in solution. Thus, as temperature is lowered, more CO_2 is dissolved in plasma. Changes in the solubility of CO_2 (S) with temperature are shown in Table 9. In a closed system, such as a specimen of blood in a syringe, in which total CO_2 content is constant, an increase in solubility of CO_2 in plasma with a decrease in temperature means that the CO_2 tension (P_{CO_2}) will be decreased (Table 10). Blood with a P_{CO_2} of 40 mm Hg at 37°C will have a P_{CO_2} of 29 mm Hg when cooled anaerobically to 30°C. The change in pK of the bicarbonate–CO_2 buffer, as a function of temperature, is shown in Figs. 5 and 6. For identical changes in temperature, this change is small in comparison to the change in the pH of neutrality of water.

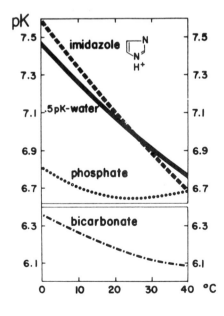

FIG. 5. Changes in the dissociation constants, pK′, of CO_2/bicarbonate, phosphate, and imidazole with temperature. The 0.5 pK of water, or neutrality, is also shown. (From ref. 25.)

TABLE 9. Solubility of CO_2 in plasma

Temperature °C	S^a	Temperature °C	S
40	0.0288	32	0.0345
39	0.0294	30	0.0362
38	0.0301	28	0.0381
37.5	0.0304	26	0.0402
37	0.0308	24	0.0425
36	0.0315	22	0.0450
35	0.0322	20	0.0478
34	0.0320	15	0.0554
33	0.0337		

^{a}S = [H_2CO_3 (mM/liter)] / [P_{CO_2} (mm Hg)].
Adapted from ref. 27.

Phosphate is the other major buffering system in blood, but it has little temperature-dependent change in the pK (Fig. 5). The *in vitro* change in the pH of whole blood as temperature is changed is depicted in Fig. 4. It is evident that the change parallels the change in the pH of neutrality of water and the change in the pK of imidazole.

Temperature-induced changes in plasma are the same as those in whole blood; i.e., changes in temperature do not cause a net transmembrane movement of hydrogen ion, hydroxyl ion, or bicarbonate. The chloride distribution between red cells and plasma is unchanged, as is the volume of the RBC during changes in temperature. Thus, the ratio of hydrogen ions inside to outside the cell is unchanged. Direct measurements of intracellular pH using both DMO and pH electrodes have shown that the intracellular pH changes that occur during changes in temperature parallel those that occur in plasma.

TABLE 10. Factors (s) for computing the ratio of gas tensions of CO_2 and O_2 in blood sealed in vitro at two temperatures, b (body) and m (measured), according to the equation: $Pb/Pm = 10^{s(b-m)}$

pH	Oxygen Temperature range (°C)			Carbon dioxide Temperature range (°C)		
	20–26	26–34	34–40	20–26	26–34	34–40
7.0	0.0252	0.0243	0.0235	0.0201	0.0188	0.0175
7.2	0.0258	0.0250	0.0241	0.0206	0.0193	0.0180
7.4	0.0265	0.0256	0.0247	0.0212	0.0197	0.0185
7.6	0.0272	0.0263	0.0254	0.0218	0.0201	0.0190
7.8				0.0222	0.0207	0.0194

From ref. 5.

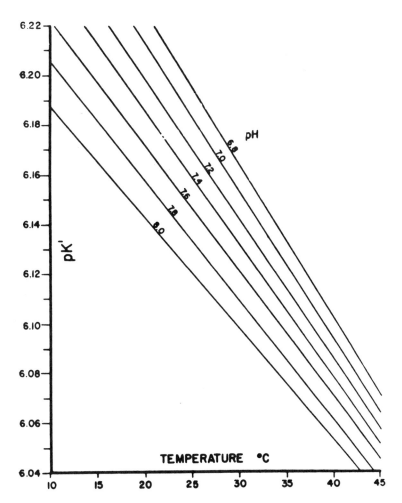

FIG. 6. pK plotted against temperature at various pH isopleths. (From ref. 28.)

Temperature Effects on pH *In Vivo* (19,25,26)

The effects of temperature on pH in humans represent those that are physicochemical in nature, as described previously, and those that are the consequence of pathophysiologic events. Hypothermia in man is, in itself, distinctly abnormal. Because of the pathologic events that take place, there is no consensus about normal blood pH and P_{CO_2} at hypothermic temperatures.

The closest one can come to finding a state of normal in hypothermia is the hypothermia induced for the performance of surgery. In this setting, normal is best defined as optimal, i.e., that state inducing the least amount of morbidity and mortality. Hypothermia is usually induced for the performance of cardiac surgery. In this condition, immediate mortality is usually related to the development of ventricular fibrillation, although asystole or respiratory failure occasionally is the terminal event. The primary morbidity relates to cardiac dysfunction and neurologic abnormalities. Thus, the optimal pH and Pco_2 should be those that decrease the risk of ventricular fibrillation, result in improved cardiac function postoperatively, and cause the least amount of CNS dysfunction.

Early pioneers of hypothermic surgery were impressed by the decreased blood flow to the brain that occurred during hypothermia. They also noted that hypothermia shifted the oxygen-hemoglobin saturation curve to the left, which could result in greater tissue hypoxia. In addition, it was well known that hypocarbia caused CNS vasoconstriction. On theoretical grounds then, it was concluded that hypocapnia and alkalosis should be strictly avoided. The pH and Pco_2, measured at the patient's hypothermic temperature, were kept at 7.40 and 40 mm Hg, respectively. This translates to a pH of <7.40 and a Pco_2 of >40 mm Hg when measured at a temperature of 37°C. In some cases, the use of 5 to 10% CO_2 in the inhaled gas mixture was required to keep the PCO_2 at 40 mm Hg without causing a decrease in Po_2 from hypoventilation. Clinical studies using this regimen were largely uncontrolled or used historical controls; nevertheless, this technique became accepted practice.

As more information became known about the cardiovascular consequences of changes in acid-base balance, some clinicians began to modify their acid-base management during hypothermic surgery. It was shown that both acidemia and alkalemia have a depressant effect on myocardial contractility and that acidemia exacerbates coronary vasospasm and causes changes in pulmonary vascular tone. Ventricular excitability was shown to be very sensitive to sudden changes in pH and was increased with a decrease in pH. Most important, it was shown that the practice of maintaining the pH at 7.40 and the PCO_2 at 40 mm Hg, as measured at the patient's temperature, resulted in a greater tendency to ventricular fibrillation than if the pH was allowed to increase and the PCO_2 to decrease during the hypothermia as blood does *in vitro*. Trials of hypocarbia parallelling the changes in PCO_2 and pH that take place *in vitro* have shown either an improvement or no change. They have never shown the practice to be deleterious. One recent study evaluated the effects of hyperventilation in dogs subjected to hypothermic cardiopulmonary bypass (PCO_2 of 10 mm Hg and pH 8.20 when measured at body temperature; PCO_2 of 24 mm Hg and pH 7.85 when measured at 37°C). The hyperventilated dogs had improved postoperative cardiac function and better intraoperative brain blood flow. No follow-up studies have been done to confirm this observation.

In nature, there are two groups of animals that normally experience hypothermia: hibernating mammals and poikilotherms. The hibernating ground squirrel has a temperature of about 5°C. Its blood pH and PCO_2, at body temperature, are 7.3 to 7.4 and 30 to 40 mm Hg, respectively. This translates to a pH of 6.5 to 6.6 and a Pco_2 of 140 to 190 mm Hg were the blood measured at a temperature of 37°C. Poikilotherms, as exemplified by the diving sea turtle, demonstrate an increasing pH and falling Pco_2 with hypothermia, much like blood *in vitro*, so that at 5°C the pH is about 8.0 and the Pco_2 is 12 mm Hg (a pH of 7.4 and a Pco_2 of 40 mm Hg when measured at 37°C). Although the hibernating ground squirrel is in a state of torpor and the diving sea turtle is engaged in normal activities, one cannot tell if either of these patterns of acid-base changes can be extrapolated to man.

A final point in considering the effect of hypothermia on pH and Pco_2 is that a patient's body temperature is not uniform throughout. For example, the rectal temperature is unlikely to be the same as the temperature of the blood drawn from the radial artery at the wrist because of differences in insulation and countercurrent heat exchange. This means that blood is continuously undergoing the physicochemical changes described.

In summary, blood undergoes changes in pH with changes in temperature that are largely the result of temperature-dependent changes in the K_m of the imidazole group of the histidine residues of hemoglobin. With decreases in temperature, there is an increase in pH. These changes are reversible and are roughly parallel to the change in the pH of neutrality of water with changes in temperature. The increasing solubility of CO_2 as the temperature decreases accounts for the decrease in Pco_2 with hypothermia. The normal (or optimal) pH and Pco_2 are not known. However, from a practical standpoint, the correction of pH and Pco_2 for temperature need not be performed. It is likely that the normal pH curve parallels that of the pH of neutrality of water as temperature is varied. This parallels the changes in pH that occur in blood *in vitro*, so that measuring the pH of blood at 37°C allows one to use the norms at that temperature for making therapeutic decisions. It also eliminates the need to know the patient's temperatures for interpretation of the pH and Pco_2. This latter point is very helpful, especially as one cannot know what a patient's temperature is throughout the body.

Measurement of pH and Pco_2 (1)

Blood gas analyzers in current use are calibrated at 37°C. The pH, Pco_2, and Po_2 are measured directly, and the $[HCO_3^-]$ and O_2 saturation are calculated. If the specimen were obtained from a hypothermic patient, the blood would first be warmed to a temperature of 37°C and analyzed, and the result would be adjusted to the temperature that was specified by programming the analyzer. Different blood gas analyzers use different adjustment formulas. Representative examples are given in Tables 10 and 11, and more complete information can be found in reference 1. Calibrating the electrodes to the temperature of the patient would yield similar values. However, this process

TABLE 11. *Temperature-correction formulas used by blood gas analyzers*

pH

1. $pH = pH_m + [- 0.0146 + 0.0065(7.4 - pH_m)](t - 37)$
2. $pH = pH_m - 0.015(t - 37)$
3. $pH = pH_m + [- 0.0147 + 0.0065(7.4 - pH_m)](37 - t)$
4. $pH = pH_m - 0.0146(t - 37)$

P_{CO_2}

1. $P_{CO_2} = P_{CO_{2m}} 10^{0.021(t-37)}$
2. $P_{CO_2} = P_{CO_{2m}} 10^{0.019(t-37)}$
3. $P_{CO_2} = P_{CO_{2m}} 10^{0.019(37-t)}$
4. $P_{CO_2} = P_{CO_{2m}} 10^{0.019(t-37)}$

P_{O_2}

1. $P_{O_2} = P_{O_{2m}} 10^{\left(\left(\dfrac{0.0252}{[0.243 \ (P_{O_2}/100)^{3.88}] + 1}\right) + 0.00564\right)(t-37)}$

2. $P_{O_2} = P_{O_{2m}} 10^{(0.0052 + 0.27[1 - 10^{-0.13(100 - Sat)}])(t-37)}$

3. $P_{O_2} = P_{O_{2m}} 10^{\left(\dfrac{(5.49 \times 10^{-11} P_{O_2}{}^{3.88}) + 0.071}{(9.72 \times 10^{-9} P_{O_2}{}^{3.88}) + 2.30}\right)(37-t)}$

4. Sat $\leqslant$ 95%
   $P_{O_2} = P_{O_{2m}} 10^{0.031(t-37)}$
   Sat > 95%
   $P_{O_2} = P_{O_{2m}} 10^{[0.032 - 0.0268 \ e^{(0.3 \ Sat - 30)}](t-37)}$

These temperature-correction formulas are used in these instruments: 1. Radiometer ABL-3.2. Corning Models 178, 170, 168, and 158. 3. Instrumentation Laboratory Models 1301 and 1303. 4. Instrumentation Laboratory Model 813.

Adapted from ref. 1.

would be too cumbersome for clinical practice. Thus, the following two sets of data are equivalent.

	Temperature	pH	P_{CO_2}	HCO_2	T_{CO_2}	pK	S_{CO_2}
1.	37°C	7.40	40 mm Hg	25.2	26.4	6.09	0.0308
2.	30°C	7.50	29 mm Hg	25.3	26.4	6.12	0.0362

When interpreting the blood gas, one needs to be aware of the temperature that was specified in calculating the results (37°C is the default setting), and one needs to remember that normality at temperatures other than 37°C is not known. In the example given, one could erroneously interpret the second set of values as indicating a respiratory alkalosis and make therapeutic changes, such as changing ventilator settings, if one were not aware that the values were being reported for a temperature of 30°C. As mentioned previously, using the uncorrected (37°C) values will allow one to make appropriate comparison (with the norms at 37°C).

Clinical States of Hypothermia (2,3,11,19)

Accidental Hypothermia

Accidental hypothermia is any state of hypothermia that has not been induced deliberately for therapeutic reasons. It may be due to water immersion, cold exposure, illness, drugs, or intoxication. Commonly associated illnesses are bronchopneumonia, cerebrovascular accidents, hypoglycemia, Addison's disease, hypopituitarism, and myxedema. Medications or drugs frequently associated are phenothiazines, alcohol, and barbiturates or other sedatives. Thus, other than in cases of immersion and perhaps in cases of exposure, any acid-base imbalance found in a hypothermic individual is largely multifactorial, and the hypothermic aspect is only one component of the problem.

During the initiation of hypothermia, the metabolic rate and O_2 consumption increase, and increased ventilation and heart rate occur. Catecholamines are released, which results in elevations of plasma free fatty acids and ketone bodies. Peripheral vasoconstriction also occurs. Shivering appears at a temperature of about 36°C, is maximal at about 35°C, and is replaced by muscular rigidity at about 33°C. By 33°C, the initially increased metabolic activity and ventilation are decreasing. Heart rate, O_2 consumption, and CO_2 production also begin to decline. Shivering, the mechanism for protecting the core temperature, disappears at about 27°C, coinciding with a complete loss of consciousness and impending ventricular fibrillation (Fig. 7).

Vasoconstriction and shivering are prime factors in the development of a metabolic acidosis during hypothermia. At a time when muscle O_2 demand is increasing because of shivering, O_2 delivery is limited because of vasoconstriction. This relative tissue hypoxia leads to a lactic acidosis. If shivering were avoided, e.g., by the use of muscle paralyzing agents, much of the metabolic acidosis observed in hypothermia would be avoided. Inhibition of vasoconstriction ameliorates the acidosis seen with hypothermia. A recent investigation showed that the use of the α-blocker phentolamine resulted in cooling and rewarming that was more uniform, so that less lactic acidosis and less morbidity occurred. Once hypothermia is established, the depression in ventilation assumes greater importance than the decrease in CO_2 production. Because of the increased solubility of CO_2 at lower temperatures, any increase in PCO_2 during hypothermia produces a more profound decrease in pH than would be observed at 37°C. This physicochemical occurrence led Axelrod and Bass to suggest the term "cold acidosis." Ventilation would have to be markedly suppressed, however, for there to be an increase in PCO_2

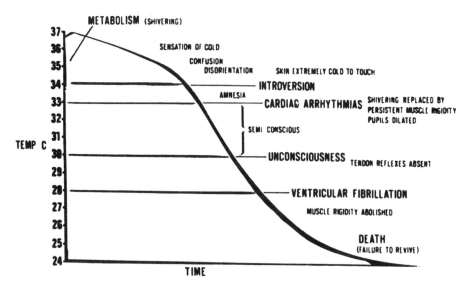

FIG. 7. Relation of signs and symptoms to the temperature at which they develop. Note that body temperature begins to fall more rapidly once shivering is abolished. (From ref. 11.)

(because of the decreased CO_2 production). In fact, the dogs studied by Axelrod and Bass were heavily sedated. Impaired pulmonary CO_2 exchange during hypothermia has not been demonstrated.

The hypoventilation that occurs does contribute to the decrease in Po_2 seen during hypothermia. Other causes of hypoxia in hypothermia are increased bronchiolar secretions at a time when there is decreased ciliary activity and an impaired alveolar–arteriolar gas exchange. Any hypoxemia will obviously contribute to tissue hypoxia and acidemia.

If the patient has become hypothermic without shivering and, therefore, has minimal or no metabolic acidosis (e.g., from alcohol intoxication, which tends to suppress shivering), acidemia may still occur during warming, i.e., a rewarming acidosis. This occurs because shivering ensues as the patient is warmed, and the metabolic rate and CO_2 production, therefore, increase. The amount of shivering depends in part on the manner of rewarming. External heat suppresses shivering when compared with passive or core rewarming. External heat, however, tends to warm the periphery first. It has been shown that rewarming the periphery without rewarming core organs, such as the liver, results in a more profound lactic acidosis. This occurs because the increased lactate production from warm muscles cannot be metabolized by the cold liver (Fig. 8).

In instances in which there has been complete circulatory arrest, there tends to be impaired liver function after the restoration of circulation. This prevents efficient clearance of the accumulated organic acids, so the acidemia

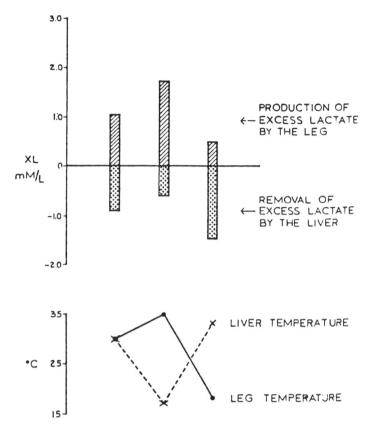

FIG. 8. During cooling of the liver, lactate removal from the blood decreases. With warming of an extremity, lactate production is increased. (From ref. 3.)

will tend to worsen with warming. The acidosis resulting from impaired hepatic metabolism has been prevented in dogs by hepatic vein decompression during circulatory arrest. Amelioration of the acidosis correlated with improved liver histology and galactose clearance, establishing the importance of hepatic function in acid-base homeostasis during hypothermia.

The rapidity with which hypothermia develops also determines the severity of the acidemia. In the case of immersion hypothermia, both experimental and accidental, overt biochemical changes are not conspicuous because of the rapidity of cooling. When development of hypothermia is prolonged, as occurs in exposure, a more severe metabolic acidosis occurs as a result of prolonged shivering and hypovolemia. The latter feature may be related to a cold-induced diuresis.

Metabolic alkalosis is not a usual feature of hypothermia unless HCO_3 has been parenterally administered or there is some loss of HCl (e.g., by nasogastric suction or vomiting). Since hypothermic patients are typically volume depleted, the kidney tends not to excrete the administered bicarbonate appropriately.

Either a true respiratory acidosis or alkalosis may develop on warming, since CO_2 production is dramatically increased. The patient might hypoventilate because of drug-induced sedation, and a respiratory acidosis could then occur. Conversely, there might be primary pulmonary disease, such as pneumonia, or an underlying reason for central hyperventilation (as seen in chronic alcoholics). This hyperventilation would then cause a respiratory alkalosis.

Hypothermia has several direct effects on the kidney. A decrease in renal blood flow occurs. Outer cortical blood flow is decreased more than juxtamedullary and medullary blood flow. GFR declines proportionally to renal plasma flow, and filtration fraction remains constant. Urine flow in short-term studies does not decrease. A decrease in osmolar clearance and an increase in free water clearance occur because hypothermia suppresses ADH secretion. The fractional excretion of both sodium and potassium is increased, and urinary concentrations of sodium, potassium, chloride, and creatinine approach those of plasma. Urinary ammonium content is decreased. There is a decrease in the ability of the proximal tubule to reabsorb bicarbonate, but the urine remains bicarbonate free, since the GFR is depressed and there is less filtered bicarbonate. These findings are consistent with a decreased renal tubular cell activity. Individual tubular cells, however, can maintain cellular integrity and transmembrane potential gradients (although the gradient is decreased compared with that maintained at 37°C). The ability of the kidney to acidify the urine or excrete an acid load during hypothermia has not been studied. There is no permanent change in renal function with hypothermia.

The P_{CO_2} and pH have been measured in only a few clinical studies of accidental hypothermia. The average pH in 31 patients in three series was 7.30 (in two of the series, the temperature at which the blood pH was measured was not stated). In one study of 8 patients, pH and P_{CO_2} were measured at 37°C, and the results were corrected to the patient's hypothermic temperature.

Temperature	pH	P_{CO_2}
37°C	7.29 ± 0.07	59 ± 18
Actual body temperature	7.43 ± 0.07	29 ± 7

In this study, increased ventilation would be the appropriate management (all 8 patients also had a P_{O_2} less than 53 mm Hg). Interpreting the blood gas using the pH and P_{CO_2} adjusted to the patient's body temperature would have dictated that no therapy be given directed to altering the acid-base status. Interpretation of the blood gas result is important. In the 8 patients discussed, increasing the ventilation would have restored the pH to greater than 7.33 and, in most cases, to normal.

There are no treatments specifically directed to the acid-base disturbances associated with hypothermia. If the circulation can be restored, acidemia usually corrects without administration of bicarbonate. In fact, administration of bicarbonate usually results in a metabolic alkalosis after rewarming, which can be prolonged and severe enough to interfere with ventilatory drive. However, in cases where the acidemia is likely to prevent the restoration of the circulation (e.g., below a pH of 7.10), bicarbonate administration is warranted. Clinical decisions regarding treatment should be based on the pH and P_{CO_2} measured at 37°C.

Cardiopulmonary Bypass

Cardiopulmonary bypass is the most common procedure that uses intentional hypothermia. Cardiopulmonary bypass was introduced shortly after the introduction of surgical hypothermia. Early investigations into the acid-base disturbances that occur with normothermic cardiopulmonary bypass demonstrated that the lower the extracorporeal perfusion rate, the more likely the development of a metabolic acidosis. At extracorporeal flow rates less than 40 ml/kg/min, metabolic acidosis invariably develops. This was an increased anion gap lactic acidosis caused by tissue hypoxia. The high flow rates needed to avoid tissue hypoxia were disadvantageous, however, since they were associated with an increased amount of RBC trauma as the blood traversed the oxygenator and cannulae. With the use of hypothermia, extracorporeal flow rates that are slower and cause less RBC trauma are tolerated. The amount of safe circulatory arrest time is increased in hypothermia.

There are a number of differences between accidental hypothermia and hypothermia induced for surgery, in terms of acid-base balance: (1) In surgery, shivering may be completely blocked by the use of neuromuscular blocking agents so that lactate production by shivering muscles during the induction and recovery from hypothermia is blunted. (2) The use of anesthetic agents causes less peripheral vasoconstriction. (3) Ventilation–respiration is controlled throughout surgery. (4) In general, circulatory hemodynamics are better maintained and periods of cardiac arrest are better tolerated. (5) The duration of the hypothermia is generally short and occurs in a controlled and monitored environment. (6) Intercurrent problems, such as infections and intoxications, are usually absent. Some deleterious effects of hypothermia and cardiopulmonary bypass are additive. For example, both cause a disproportionate decrease in renal cortical blood flow. The poor tissue perfusion of cardiopulmonary bypass is aggravated by the vasoconstriction and increased blood viscosity of hypothermia. Hemodilution to a hematocrit of 25% with moderate hypothermia or to 20% with profound hypothermia improves renal cortical flow and reduces blood viscosity, with consequent improved micro-circulatory perfusion. It does, however, decrease O_2-carrying capacity, and, depending on the composition of the priming solution, oncotic pressure may be decreased with consequent tissue edema. Hemodilution also tends to decrease the buffer capacity of the blood. Dilute blood *in vitro*, however, undergoes changes in pH with changes in temperature that parallel the change in the pH of neutrality of water, similar to undiluted blood.

During the performance of hypothermic cardiopulmonary bypass, there is either no acid-base disturbance or a mild metabolic acidosis due to tissue hypoxia. On resumption of normal circulation with adequate cardiac function, the metabolic acidosis quickly resolves as the organic acids are aerobically metabolized, regenerating bicarbonate. Ventilation during hypothermic surgery should be managed according to a poikilothermic scheme; i.e., pH and P_{CO_2} should be measured at 37°C regardless of body temperature, and adjustments should be made based on an optimal pH of 7.40 and an optimal P_{CO_2} of 40 mm Hg.

Metabolic alkalosis frequently develops postoperatively. This metabolic alkalosis is usually a consequence of bicarbonate administration during cardiopulmonary bypass either as $NaHCO_3$ or as citrate from banked blood. There is usually a high circulating level of renin and aldosterone intraoperatively and postoperatively as a consequence of the stress of the procedure and decreased renal perfusion during cardiopulmonary bypass. The elevated aldosterone concentration promotes increased distal renal tubule sodium reabsorption with increased potassium and hydrogen ion secretion. The cardiac output may be low in the immediate postoperative period, resulting in a state of depressed effective arterial blood volume. This enhances proximal tubule reabsorption of HCO_3. The decreased GFR postcardiopulmonary bypass also promotes maintenance of the metabolic acidosis by decreasing the filtered HCO_3 load. The combination of the physiologic changes results in a paradoxical aciduria (the presence of a low urine pH during systemic alkalemia).

Postoperative alkalosis can be prevented by restricting bicarbonate administration during the procedure and by attempting to optimize cardiac output postoperatively. If metabolic alkalosis develops, it is usually mild and is resolved by postoperative day 3. The alkalosis may be severe (pH greater than 7.55), however, when an excessive amount of bicarbonate is administered (as sodium bicarbonate, citrate in banked blood, or as lactate in intravenous fluids), or when renal function is inadequate to excrete the bicarbonate load because of intrinsic renal insufficiency or because of a contracted effective arterial blood volume, e.g., from poor cardiac output. If the alkalemia is severe enough to inhibit ventilation so that ventilator weaning is difficult or if arrhythmias occur, specific corrective measures should be taken (Table 12). Frequently, poor cardiac function precludes the administration of fluids and cannot be corrected with inotropic or unloading agents. If renal function is

TABLE 12. *Management of severe metabolic alkalosis*

1. Correct volume and potassium deficits
2. Ensure adequate cardiac output with unloading agents and/or positive inotropic agents
3. Acetazolamide, 250–500 mg intravenously every 6–12 hr
4. Dilute hydrochloric acid infusion.
   a. Delivered into large-diameter central vein for rapid dilution and decreased incidence of thrombophlebitis
   b. 0.1–0.2 N solution prepared in water, 5% dextrose, normal saline or added to an amino acid or amino acid/lipid preparation
   c. Quantity needed (conservative-low estimate) mEq H^+ = $([Tco_2]_s - 24) \times$ body weight $\times$ 20%
   d. Infuse slowly over 6–24 hr, then reassess and repeat if needed
   e. Careful monitoring of electrolytes, pH, Pco_2, hematocrit, and clinical status of the patient (including infusion site)
5. High chloride–low acetate/bicarbonate dialysis.

adequate, acetazolamide may be used. In a small controlled study, one group of investigators was able to significantly ameliorate the postperfusion alkalosis by administering acetazolamide, 250 mg intravenously, at the end of the surgery and on the morning of the first postoperative day. In patients with impaired renal function, however, acetazolamide may not be effective, and infusion of dilute hydrochloric acid may be used to correct the alkalosis. Hydrochloric acid is preferred over L-arginine monohydrochloride, L-lysine hydrochloride, and ammonium chloride because of their nitrogen and ammonium load. In addition, ammonium chloride and L-arginine monohydrochloride frequently cause flushing, nausea, vomiting, and headache on infusion. Hemodialysis and peritoneal dialysis also may be used to correct the alkalemia. In this case, a low bicarbonate–high chloride bath or dialysate is used.

REFERENCES

1. Ashwood, E. R., Kost, G., and Kenny, M. (1983): Temperature correction of blood-gas and pH measurements. *Clin. Chem.*, 29:1877–1885.
2. Axelrod, D. R., and Bass, D. E. (1956): Electrolytes and acid-base balance in hypothermia. *Am. J. Physiol.*, 186:31–34.
3. Ballinger, F. W. II, et al. (1961): Acidosis of hypothermia. *Ann. Surg.*, 154:517–523.
4. Batlle, D. C., Mozes, M. F., Manaligod, J., Arruda, J. A. L., and Kurtzman, N. A. (1981): The pathogenesis of hyperchloremic metabolic acidosis associated with kidney transplantation. *Am. J. Med.*, 70:786–796.
5. Bradley, et al. (1956): Effect of temperature on Pco_2 and Po_2 of blood *in vitro*. *J. Appl. Physiol.*, 9:201–204.
6. Collins, J. A. (1976): Massive blood transfusion. *Clin. Haematol.*, 5:201–222.

7. Collins, J. A., et al. (1971): Acid-base status of seriously wounded combat casualties: II. Resuscitation with stored blood. *Ann. Surg.*, 173:6–18.
8. Covelli, H. D., Black, J. W., Olsen, M. S., and Beekman, J. F. (1981): Respiratory failure precipitated by high carbohydrate loads. *Ann. Intern. Med.*, 95:579–581.
9. DeFronzo, R. A., Goldberg, M., Cooke, C. R., Barker, C., Grossman, R. A., and Gus, Z. S. (1977): Investigations into the mechanisms of hyperkalemia following renal transplantation. *Kidney Int.*, 11:357–365.
10. Genari, J. F. (1985): Acid-base balance in dialysis patients. *Kidney Int.*, 28:677–688.
11. Golden, C. (1973): Recognition and treatment of immersion hypothermia. *Proc. R. Soc. Med.*, 66:1058–1061.
12. Gotch, F., and Sargent, J. A. (1985): A mechanistic analysis of the National Cooperative Dialysis Study (NCDS). *Kidney Int.*, 28:526–534.
13. Halperin, M. L., Jeejeebhoy, K. N., and Levine, D. Z. (1986): Acid-base, fluid and electrolyte aspects of parenteral nutrition. In: *Fluids and Electrolytes*, edited by J. P. Kokko and R. L. Tannen, pp. 817–831. W. B. Saunders, Philadelphia.
14. Heird, W. C., Dell, R. B., Driscoll, J. M., Jr., Grebin, B., and Winters, R. W. (1972): Metabolic acidosis resulting from intravenous alimentation mixtures containing synthetic amino acids. *N. Engl. J. Med.*, 287:943–948.
15. Henrich, W. L. (1986): Hemodynamic stability during hemodialysis. *Kidney Int.*, 30:605–612.
16. Hulter, H. N. (1985): Effects and interrelationships of PTH, Ca^{2+}, vitamin D, and Pi in acid-base homeostasis. *Am. J. Physiol.*, 248:F739–F752.
17. Kahn, R. C., et al. (1979): Massive blood replacement: Correlation of ionized calcium citrate, and hydrogen ion concentration. *Anesth. Analg.*, 58:274–278.
18. Keshaviah, P., Leuhmann, D., Illstrup, K., and Collins, A. (1986): Technical requirements for rapid high-efficiency therapies. *Artif. Organs*, 10:189–194.
19. Kirklin, J. W., Kirklin, J. K., and Lell, W. A. (1983): Cardiopulmonary bypass for cardiac surgery. In: *Surgery of the Chest*, edited by D. C. Sabiston Jr., and F. C. Spencer, pp. 909–925. W. B. Saunders, Philadelphia.
20. Klahr, S., Tripathy, K., and Lotero, H. (1970): Renal regulation of acid-base balance in malnourished man. *Am. J. Med.*, 48:325–331.
21. Litwin, M. S., Smith, L. L., and Moore, F. D. (1959): Metabolic alkalosis following massive transfusion. *Surgery*, 45:800–813.
22. Loule, N., and Niemiec, P. W. (1986): In: *Parenteral Nutrition*, edited by J. L. Rombean and M. D. Caldwell, p. 278. W. B. Saunders, Philadelphia.
23. Mookerjee, B., Gault, H. M., and Dossetor, J. B. (1969): Hyperchloremic acidosis in early diagnosis of renal allograft rejections. *Ann. Intern. Med.*, 71:47–58.
24. Myers, B. D. (1986): Cyclosporine nephrotoxicity. *Kidney Int.*, 30:964–974.
25. Rahn, H. (1974): Body temperature and acid-base regulation (review article). *Pneumonologie*, 151:87–94.
26. Rahn, H., Reeves, R. B., and Howell, B. J. (1975): Hydrogen ion regulation, temperature, and evolution. *Am. Rev. Respir. Dis.*, 112:165–172.
27. Severinghaus, J. W. (1956): Accuracy of blood pH and Po_2 determinations. *J. Appl. Physiol.*, 9:189–196.
28. Severinghaus, J. W., et al. (1956): Variations of serum carbonic acid pK^1 with pH and temperature. *J. Appl. Physiol.*, 9:197–200.
29. Stahl, R. A. K., Kanz, L., Maier, B., and Schollmeyer, P. (1986): Hyperchloremic metabolic acidosis with high serum potassium in renal transplant recipients: A cyclosporin A associated side effect. *Clin. Nephrol.*, 25:245–248.
30. Stinebaugh, B. J., and Schloeder, F. X. (1972): Glucose-induced alkalosis in fasting subjects. *J. Clin. Invest.*, 51:1326–1335.
31. Velez, R. J., Myers, B., and Guber, M. S. (1985): Severe acute metabolic acidosis (acute beriberi): An avoidable complication of total parenteral nutrition. *J. Parenter. Enter. Nutr.*, 9:216–219.
32. Vinay, P., Prud'homme, M., Vinet, B., et al. (1987): Acetate metabolism and bicarbonate generation during hemodialysis: 10 years of observation. *Kidney Int.*, 31:1194–1204.
33. Wilson, D. R., and Siddiqui, A. A. (1973): Renal tubular acidosis after kidney transplantation. *Ann. Intern. Med.*, 79:352–361.

The Regulation of Acid–Base Balance, edited by Donald W. Seldin and Gerhard Giebisch, Raven Press, Ltd., New York © 1989.

21

Diuretics

Thomas D. DuBose, Jr.

Division of Nephrology, University of Texas Medical Branch, Galveston, Texas 77550

A diuretic is any agent that can increase urine output above the normal rate of 1 to 2 ml/min and represents one of the most widely used groups of drugs prescribed by physicians. A vast array of drugs with different properties is available, and these have been classified in numerous ways based on similarities in chemical structure, nephron site of action, clinical efficacy, and pattern of electrolyte excretion. The specific nephron site of action of diuretics employed clinically is outlined in Table 1 and Fig. 1. Most diuretics directly affect ion transport by the kidney. In this chapter, the clinically important effects of diuretics, both therapeutic and toxic, are emphasized. In addition, a number of acid-base disturbances commonly induced by diuretics are outlined in detail.

To appreciate the means by which acid-base disturbances occur in association with diuretic therapy, the nephron site of action of diuretics is first reviewed.

TABLE 1. *Nephron site of action of diuretic drugs*

Nephron site	Mechanism of action	Drug type
Proximal tubule	Inhibits carbonic anhydrase	Acetazolamide
	Inhibits Na^+ transport	Thiazides (weak)
		Metolazone
	Osmotic effect	Mannitol
Loop of Henle	Inhibits luminal $Na^+/2Cl^-/K^+$ cotransporter	Furosemide
		Bumetanide
		Ethacrynic acid
Early distal tubule	Inhibits Na^+ transport	Thiazides
Late distal tubule and cortical collecting duct	Reduces Na^+ permeability at luminal membrane (K^+ sparing)	Spironolactone
		Amiloride
		Triamterene

INHIBITORS OF TRANSPORT IN THE PROXIMAL TUBULE (9)

It is important to recall that although the proximal tubule is responsible for reabsorption of approximately 50% of the filtered load of Na^+ and H_2O, any agent that selectively reduces the reabsorptive process in this segment owes its diuretic properties to the ability of the more distal nephron segments to increase reabsorption as delivery of salt and water from the proximal tubule is increased. This series of events explains why, as a general rule, proximal diuretics, when used alone, result in only a modest diuresis.

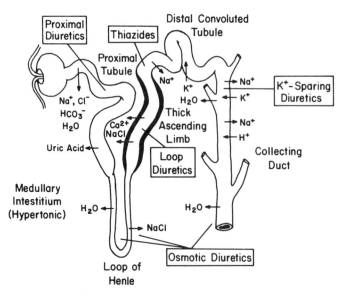

FIG. 1. Nephron site of action of diuretic drugs by class (see boxes). Major electrolyte transport processes are displayed for each nephron segment.

Inhibition of Sodium Bicarbonate Reabsorption: Acetazolamide (1,5,8)

Carbonic anhydrase is present in a number of cells of the nephron and is either distributed in the cytoplasm or bound to the luminal and basolateral membranes. In the proximal tubule, a segment of the nephron responsible for reabsorption of 80 to 90% of the filtered load of bicarbonate, carbonic anhydrase is abundantly distributed in all three locations. The luminal enzyme is associated with the brush border membrane and is in functional contact with proximal tubule fluid. This important association endows the proximal tubule with the ability to accomplish a high degree of bicarbonate reabsorption while avoiding limiting pH gradients. This is achieved since carbonic anhydrase facilitates the conversion of carbonic acid (H_2CO_3) (produced when filtered HCO_3^- reacts with secreted H^+) to CO_2 and H_2O virtually instantaneously. Inhibition of carbonic anhydrase in the proximal tubule results in inhibition of a large portion of bicarbonate reabsorption, therefore (Table 1). Because of the ability of nephron segments beyond the proximal tubule to reabsorb bicarbonate, the effect of a standard inhibitor of carbonic anhydrase in the proximal nephron (85–90% inhibition) exceeds the effect of the inhibitor on whole kidney bicarbonate reabsorption (30%).

Acetazolamide, the prototypical carbonic anhydrase inhibitor, will induce a bicarbonate diuresis, a mild hyperchloremic metabolic acidosis, and a modest depletion of body potassium. Chloride reabsorption also is reduced in the proximal tubule as a result of inhibition of sodium bicarbonate reabsorption, but chloride reabsorption in the loop of Henle obviates any appreciable increase in urinary chloride excretion. The increase in potassium excretion, however, occurs because of the increase in flow rate and delivery of HCO_3^- to the cortical collecting tubule, the nephron site responsible for regulation of K^+ secretion.

Therapeutic Uses of Acetazolamide (9)

Acetazolamide may be employed orally for the treatment of glaucoma by decreasing aqueous humor formation and reducing intraocular pressure (Table 2). This represents the most common use of acetazolamide therapy chronically. Aqueous humor secretion involves hydration of CO_2, the reaction catalyzed by carbonic anhydrase. As an inhibitor of this enzyme, acetazolamide reduces aqueous fluid secretion and, thereby, intraocular pressure.

The urinary alkalinization that occurs as a result of acetazolamide therapy decreases the solubility of uric acid and cystine in acid urine. In addition, the urinary excretion of aspirin can be enhanced transiently by urinary alkalinization.

For the treatment of metabolic alkalosis, particularly chronic metabolic alkalosis in the hospitalized patient receiving chronic nasogastric suction, acetazolamide therapy can be beneficial. It should be emphasized, however, that

TABLE 2. *Therapeutic uses of acetazolamide*

Glaucoma
Cystinuria
Hyperuricosuria
Metabolic alkalosis
Salicylate intoxication
Hyperphosphatemia
Acute mountain sickness
In combination with loop diuretics for oliguria

the initial approach to such a patient should include correction of intravascular volume depletion with isotonic saline. In patients with severe cardiac decompensation, saline therapy may be contraindicated, and acetazolamide, either intravenously or by mouth, may be adequate alone.

Hyperphosphatemia also may respond to the phosphaturic action of acetazolamide. Among the diuretics, acetazolamide is the most potent phosphaturic agent. The mechanism of the increase in phosphate excretion induced by carbonic anhydrase inhibition appears to result from activation of adenylate cyclase and to inhibition of oxidative phosphorylation in the proximal tubule, not alkalinization of tubule fluid as was once assumed. However, marked hyperphosphatemia in patients with renal failure may require renal replacement therapy. If renal function is adequate, a brisk bicarbonate diuresis induced by saline and sodium bicarbonate plus acetazolamide (250–500 mg every 6 hr) may rapidly increase renal phosphate excretion, but hypocalcemia may occur during such therapy and the serum calcium should be followed closely, therefore.

Acute mountain sickness may be prevented by administration of oral acetazolamide before and during ascent to altitude in healthy individuals prone to develop this syndrome. Metabolic acidosis via stimulation of the chemoreceptor–respiration pathway induces an increase in minute ventilation and improves hypoxemia.

The toxic effects of acetazolamide therapy include a tendency toward formation of calcium phosphate stones, renal potassium wasting, and chronic hyperchloremic metabolic acidosis. This latter disorder is discussed in the section on acid-base disturbances. Acetazolamide, when used in patients with severe liver disease, may contribute to the development of hepatic encephalopathy by alkalinization of the urine, thus preventing urinary ammonium excretion and elevating blood ammonia levels. This drug should be avoided in advanced liver disease, therefore.

Inhibition of Proximal Reabsorption by Osmotic Agents: Mannitol

Although mannitol generally is classified as a proximal diuretic (Table 1) because of an osmotic effect that obligates solute-dependent water reabsorption, it should be emphasized that mannitol inhibits the formation of concentrated urine primarily by interrupting countercurrent multiplication in the inner medulla (Fig. 1). Specifically, this agent limits water reabsorption in those nephron segments freely permeable to water (proximal tubule, thin descending limb of Henle, and collecting ducts when ADH is present) and facilitates the washout of medullary solute in the normally hypertonic medulla by dramatically increasing inner medullary blood flow (vasa recta).

Therapeutic Uses of Mannitol (9)

Mannitol commonly is employed as initial therapy in oliguric states, especially if associated with prerenal azotemia as a result of intravascular volume depletion (Table 3). This agent also is used in the prevention of acute renal failure in high-risk patients, e.g., before administration of contrast media in Type I diabetics with mild renal insufficiency, during nephrotoxic antibiotic therapy (amphotericin-B, aminoglycosides), and during extensive vascular or cardiovascular surgery. This drug is a convenient and inexpensive method for treatment of dialysis-related hypotension. Contraindications to use include congestive heart failure and overt volume overexpansion.

TABLE 3. *Therapeutic uses of mannitol*

Oliguric states
Prerenal azotemia
Prevention of acute renal failure
Prevention of nephrotoxicity
Dialysis-induced hypotension

INHIBITORS OF LOOP OF HENLE TRANSPORT (9)

The loop diuretics (furosemide, bumetanide, and ethacrynic acid) inhibit active NaCl transport in the thick ascending limb of the loop of Henle (Table 1 and Fig. 1). This group of diuretics induces a prompt diuresis and has been referred to as high-ceiling diuretics because of the magnitude of the natriuresis achieved. The site of NaCl entry at the luminal membrane of the thick ascending limb is inhibited specifically, perhaps as a result of direct binding of the drug to the $Na^+/2Cl^-/K^+$ cotransporter. Hypovalemia, hypochloremia, and hypokalemia may occur during vigorous diuresis, therefore. Since this nephron segment also is responsible, in part, for Mg^{2+} and Ca^{2+} reabsorption, chronic use of these agents can produce hypomagnesia and hypocalcemia. This latter effect is of advantage in treating severe hypercalcemia, especially when combined with isotonic saline infusion. The most common uses of

TABLE 4. *Therapeutic uses of loop diuretics*

Acute pulmonary edema
Edema with renal insufficiency
Hypertension with renal insufficiency
Oliguric states with volume overload
Hyponatremia (combined with 3% NaCl)
Hypercalcemia (combined with isotonic NaCl)
Edema unresponsive to thiazides
Severe hyperkalemia
Hyporeninemic hypoaldosteronism with hyperkalemia
Acute urate nephropathy

loop diuretics include the treatment of acute volume overload with or without pulmonary edema, acute hyponatremia (if combined with replacement of sodium chloride deficits), hypercalcemia, chronic edema unresponsive to thiazide diuretics, and hypertension in patients with renal insufficiency (GFR<25 ml/min) (Table 4). These drugs may also result in ototoxicity, especially when combined with other ototoxic agents. Loop diuretics as a group exert effects on cochlear and vestibular transport and function. Ototoxicity has been reported more frequently with ethacrynic acid than furosemide and less frequently with bumetanide. Predisposing factors include impaired renal function, rapid administration, pregnancy and concomitant administration of other ototoxic drugs. Acute allergic or idiosyncratic reactions, reported rarely, include acute allergic interstitial nephritis, hepatic dysfunction, myelosuppression, and rash.

INHIBITORS OF DISTAL TUBULE TRANSPORT: THIAZIDES (2,9)

The thiazides inhibit sodium chloride transport in the early segments of the distal convoluted tubule, not the thick ascending limb. As a result, the diuresis and natriuresis are less marked than those observed with loop agents. A modest effect on proximal tubule reabsorption has been identified, and some of the thiazides are weak inhibitors of carbonic anhydrase. Hypokalemia can occur as a result of increased Na^+ and fluid delivery to the cortical collecting tubule, especially if volume depletion has resulted in secondary hyperaldosteronism. The tendency to develop hypokalemia is enhanced by continued high dietary intake of NaCl and low intake of K^+. Thiazides also augment calcium reabsorption in the distal tubule and may result in hypercalcemia. These agents, unlike loop diuretics, lower urinary calcium and are, thus, ideal agents for therapy of idiopathic hypercalciuria.

Metolazone, another sulfonamide diuretic, resembles the thiazides in its effect on the distal tubule but has a more potent effect, independent of carbonic anhydrase, on the proximal tubule.

The general uses of thiazides (Table 5) include the edematous states, hyper-

TABLE 5. *Therapeutic uses of thiazide diuretics*

Hypertension (as step I therapy)
Edema
Idiopathic hypercalciuria
Nephrogenic diabetes insipidus
Proximal renal tubular acidosis (type II)
Combined with loop agents in acute oliguria

tension without renal insufficiency, idiopathic hypercalciuria, nephrogenic diabetes insipidus, and proximal renal tubular acidosis. The last two disorders may benefit from the mild volume depletion and accompanying reduction in GFR, which enhances NaCl and bicarbonate reabsorption in the proximal tubule.

Patients with severe refractory edema or oliguria may, at times, benefit from combined administration of thiazides (especially metolazone) and loop diuretics. The synergistic effect of this combination can result in a marked diuresis and severe hypokalemia if appropriate precautions are not taken, however.

The toxic manifestations of thiazide therapy include impaired carbohydrate metabolism with aggravation of previously controlled diabetes mellitus, hyperuricemia, hyperlipidemia, hyponatremia, hypokalemia, and metabolic alkalosis. Skin rashes may be observed, but rarer allergic manifestations include cholestatic jaundice, interstitial nephritis, thrombocytopenia, and hemolytic anemia. These agents should be avoided in renal insufficiency (plasma creatinine>2.0) because of augmentation of azotemia and should be used with caution in severe liver disease.

POTASSIUM-SPARING DIURETICS (9)

Potassium-sparing diuretics act primarily on the cortical collecting tubule to decrease potassium secretion by one of three mechanisms: (1) competitive inhibition of aldosterone receptor binding, (2) occupancy of the sodium conductive pathway, or (3) reduction of sodium permeability at the luminal membrane (Table 6). Examples of each of these specific drug effects include (1) spironolactone, (2) amiloride, and (3) triamterene (Table 1).

TABLE 6. *Therapeutic uses of potassium-sparing diuretics*

Hypokalemia
Prevent hypokalemia in cardiac patient
In combination with thiazide/loop diuretics
Primary aldosteronism
Bartter's syndrome

Since no more than 3% of the filtered load of sodium is reabsorbed in the cortical collecting tubule, even total inhibition of this process would result in only a modest natriuresis. Thus, these drugs are primarily adjuvant diuretic agents.

In general, in the normal state, potassium secretion in the cortical collecting tubule is a result of sodium reabsorption that generates a lumen-negative potential difference, favorable for K^+ diffusion into tubule fluid. Aldosterone increases the permeability of sodium at the luminal membrane, which increases intracellular Na^+ and stimulates Na^+, K^+-ATPase, thus enhancing K^+ secretion. K^+-sparing diuretics, therefore, interfere with the determinants of K^+ secretion and are used to prevent or treat hypokalemia during states of either primary or secondary mineralocorticoid excess, such as during therapy with thiazide or loop diuretics. Since these drugs may cause hyperkalemia, they should not be prescribed routinely for all patients receiving conventional diuretics. Spironolactone may be employed in the treatment of primary aldosteronism and amiloride in the treatment of Bartter's syndrome and K^+ depletion of diverse causes. Triamterene appears to be equally effective in potassium depletion. Adverse effects include triamterene-induced acute renal failure and crystalluria. Gynecomastia is a frequent side effect with high doses of spironolactone.

Potassium-sparing drugs are contraindicated in hyperkalemia, renal insufficiency (plasma creatinine >2.0), or any circumstance in which potassium balance or renal function is not appreciated. Patients with diabetes mellitus and renal insufficiency are predisposed to hyporeninemic hypoaldosteronism and may develop severe hyperkalemia with metabolic acidosis (type IV RTA) when administered one of these agents. Potentiation of the tendency to develop hyperkalemia is observed during combined therapy with nonsteroidal anti-inflammatory drugs.

EFFECTS OF DIURETICS ON ACID-BASE BALANCE (3,6,7)

That diuretic therapy can result in deranged acid-base homeostasis has been appreciated for at least 50 years. The tendency for mercurial diuretics to induce a hypochloremic metabolic alkalosis that, in turn, compromises the diuresis and, conversely, the potentiation of the diuretic action of mercurials during metabolic acidosis has been investigated extensively. The carbonic anhydrase inhibitors routinely produce metabolic acidosis, an observation first made in 1937, and the use of acetazolamide also can result in respiratory acidosis. It is recognized today that almost every modern diuretic agent employed clinically, especially the loop agents and the thiazides, has as a potential side effect the development of metabolic alkalosis (Table 7). Indeed, because of the wide use of these agents, diuretic therapy is the most common cause of metabolic alkalosis encountered in clinical medicine. Although usu-

TABLE 7. *Pathophysiology of diuretic-induced metabolic alkalosis (loop agents)*

Direct effects
  Contraction alkalosis
  Increased Na^+ delivery to distal exchange sites
  Increase in H^+ secretion—Medullary collecting tubule
Secondary effects
  Hypokalemia
  Volume depletion
  Secondary hyperaldosteronism
  Hypercapnia
  Increase in renal ammoniagenesis

---

ally mild in degree, the metabolic alkalosis can at times be severe and life-threatening. Paradoxically, it is in the setting of the edematous disorders, such as severe congestive heart failure, cirrhosis with ascites, and the nephrotic syndrome, all characterized by deranged volume homeostasis and effective intravascular volume depletion, that this complication may be most serious and recognized latently.

PATHOPHYSIOLOGY OF EFFECTS OF DIURETICS ON ACID-BASE BALANCE

Proximal Tubule (5,8)

The carbonic anhydrase inhibitors were developed as a result of a search for agents with the capacity to inhibit carbonic anhydrase. As discussed earlier, acetazolamide decreases the rate of proton secretion and, thus, bicarbonate reabsorption in the proximal tubule. Thus, metabolic acidosis is a commonly observed side effect produced by this drug. A direct relationship between the magnitude of proximal inhibition and the serum bicarbonate concentration has been observed. This finding parallels the well-known reduction in clinical effectiveness of these drugs as the filtered load of bicarbonate declines (metabolic acidosis). It should be pointed out that carbonic anhydrase also may be inhibited by the absorption of topical mefenide acetate (Sulfamylon) when applied to the skin of patients with extensive burns and result in respiratory and metabolic acidosis. Acetazolamide is only rarely used in the treatment of heart failure and edema but may be employed in combination with loop diuretics when dual inhibition of proximal and loop function is desirable (severe edematous states or severe oliguria with volume expansion). An important application of acetazolamide is for the treatment of metabolic alkalosis when volume overexpansion or heart failure precludes infusion of large volumes of isotonic NaCl.

Loop Agents (3,11)

The loop agents, furosemide, bumetamide, and ethacrynic acid, inhibit NaCl transport in the thick ascending limb of Henle. It is assumed widely that these drugs produce metabolic alkalosis by virtue of secondary effects of the drugs that are removed from the primary site of action. There are several ways in which bicarbonate reabsorption may be increased during administration of these diuretics (Table 7). A reduction in extracellular fluid (ECF) volume results in contraction of ECF around a constant amount of extracellular bicarbonate and results in an increase in plasma $[HCO_3^-]$ (contraction alkalosis). It seems unlikely, however, that this mechanism alone plays a major role in diuretic-induced alkalosis. This view is supported by the observation that a marked increase in plasma $[HCO_3^-]$ is prevented during volume contraction by the rapid uptake of $[HCO_3^-]$ by bone. ECF volume contraction *per se* may then increase the renal reabsorption of bicarbonate in the proximal tubule. When loop inhibition of NaCl transport is accompanied by increased Na^+ delivery to the cortical collecting tubule, the secondary hyperaldosteronism of volume contraction will cause an increase in H^+ secretion by this segment (Table 7). Net acid excretion increases, and, therefore, more bicarbonate is added to renal venous blood. Increased Na^+ reabsorption also increases potassium secretion, and hypokalemia ensues. Thus, the increase in H^+ and K^+ secretion may be maintained and serve to perpetuate the metabolic alkalosis, which is characterized additionally by hypochloremia and hypokalemia (i.e., hypochloremic-hypokalemic metabolic alkalosis). Potassium depletion, volume depletion, and hypercapnia all serve to maintain the alkalosis (Table 7). There is evidence that furosemide directly increases H^+ secretion in the distal nephron independent of aldosterone. This effect may result in a particularly severe metabolic alkalosis when large doses of furosemide or combinations of furosemide and metolazone are administered.

Loop diuretics frequency are overused in edematous states when effective intravascular volume is already reduced. These disorders include the nephrotic syndrome, cirrhosis with ascites, and congestive heart failure, all of which have in common a marked reduction in renal blood flow and GFR. Consequently, proximal bicarbonate reabsorption is increased, and distal salt delivery is reduced. Metabolic alkalosis usually does not occur, therefore, until distal sodium delivery is increased by diuretic administration resulting in increased H^+ and K^+ secretion driven additionally by secondary hypermineralocorticoid state. Potassium deficiency can further enhance the metabolic alkalosis by stimulating renal ammoniagenesis and ammonia excretion. Particular care is required in treating patients with severe intravascular volume depletion to avoid excessive diuresis and potassium depletion. As a general rule, patients with these disorders should not be rendered edema-free but should be allowed to maintain trace levels of edema.

Distal Tubule (4,9)

The sites and mechanism of action of the thiazides and the quinethazone derivative metolazone have been discussed previously (Table 1). Thiazides are similar to the loop diuretics in that both agents reduce effective intravascular volume as a result of renal chloride loss. Since bicarbonate is retained in the reduced extracellular compartment, the concentration of bicarbonate in plasma will rise. With time, the continued delivery of salt to the distal exchange site results in enhanced H^+ and K^+ secretion, causing an increase in net acid excretion, potassium clearance, and as a result of volume depletion, hyperaldosteronism, which further perpetuates the hypokalemia and alkalosis. Secondary hyperaldosteronism as a result of effective intravascular volume contraction prohibits repair of the metabolic alkalosis until chloride balance is restored. Potassium loss tends to be modest in the absence of significant volume depletion but, when present, clearly enhances the renal input of new bicarbonate by enhancing H^+ secretion.

Metabolic alkalosis *per se* is a potent stimulus to distal potassium secretion. Nevertheless, it should be emphasized that in most patients receiving thiazides, the incidence of hypokalemia appears to be low. This may occur because hypokalemia decreases aldosterone secretion, whereas volume depletion enhances proximal reabsorption of NaCl and diminishes distal Na^+ delivery. Both events tend to reduce K^+ secretion and ameliorate severe hypokalemia. Although controversy exists about the need for routine potassium supplements in patients receiving thiazides, it is clear that when indicated (digitalized patient, patients with arrhythmia, ischemic heart disease, or $[K^+]<3.0$ mEq/liter), potassium supplement must be in the form of the chloride salt (KCl), not potassium citrate or potassium bicarbonate. Alternatively, potassium-sparing diuretics may be administered, but because of the development of hyperkalemia in a significant number of patients, these agents should be employed for the same indications noted for potassium supplements. Hypokalemia often may be accompanied by hypomagnesemia when induced by thiazide or loop diuretics. Therefore, the magnesium-sparing effect of amiloride may indicate that drugs in this class are preferable (as well as more convenient) in treating diuretic-induced hyerkalemia. The potassium-sparing drugs should not be used, however, unless renal function is known to be normal because of the potential complication of severe hyperkalemia in patients with renal insufficiency.

Collecting Tubule (10)

Metabolic acidosis can occur in patients receiving spironolactone, amiloride, or triameterene when hyperkalemia ensues. In most cases, a hyperkalemic, hyperchloremic metabolic acidosis is observed and mimics the findings

TABLE 8. *Pathophysiology of metabolic acidosis from diuretics*

Potassium-sparing diuretics (amiloride, spironolactone, triamterene)
  Hyperkalemic, hyperchloremic metabolic acidosis with normal anion gap
    Hyperkalemia reduces renal ammoniagenesis
    Inhibition of acidification by collecting tubule
Carbonic anhydrase inhibitors (acetazolamide)
  Normokalemic, hyperchloremic metabolic acidosis with normal anion gap
    Inhibition of proximal tubule bicarbonate reabsorption

---

seen in selective aldosterone deficiency (Table 8). In part, the metabolic acidosis results from a reduction in ammoniagenesis and ammonia transport due to hyperkalemia *per se*. Nevertheless, selective aldosterone deficiency may be more common in diabetes mellitus, a disorder known to be associated with hyporeninemic hypoaldosteronism. Spironolactone, amiloride, and triamterene are contraindicted in Type I diabetics, especially when renal insufficiency is present and also in patients receiving nonsteroidal anti-inflammatory drugs. The potassium-sparing agents all appear to be capable of inhibiting distal nephron hydrogen ion secretion. We recently demonstrated in our laboratory that amiloride reduces net H^+ secretion in the collecting duct.

SPECIFIC ACID-BASE DISORDERS ASSOCIATED WITH DIURETIC THERAPY

Metabolic Alkalosis (13)

The pathophysiology of metabolic alkalosis in association with thiazide and loop diuretic administration has been described in detail. In summary, these diuretics increase the renal input of new bicarbonate, contract ECF volume, and result in chloride depletion (Table 7). Although the former mechanism generates metabolic alkalosis, additional factors, such as hypokalemia, hypercapnia, volume depletion with reduced GFR, mineralocorticoid excess, and continued distal Na^+ delivery all serve to maintain the alkalosis (Table 7). Clinically, this form of metabolic alkalosis may be recognized as a hypokalemic, hypochloremic form of metabolic alkalosis. The plasma chloride concentration will be reduced by a greater percentage than the plasma sodium concentration. Typical electrolyte and blood gas values are shown in Table 9. Note that [Cl⁻] is reduced 10% but that [Na^+] is unchanged. Thus, the decrease in [Cl⁻] is disproportionate to [Na^+]. This occurs because the plasma [Cl⁻] changes in two types of disorders: (1) acid-base disorders and (2) disorders of hydration (overhydration or dehydration). The plasma [Na^+] changes only in disorders of hydration (hypoosmolality or hyperosmolality). Thus a disproportionate decrease in [Cl⁻], as seen in Table 9, heralds an acid-base disorder. This disorder could be either metabolic alkalosis or respiratory acidosis. Since an alkalemia is evident in this example, the diagnosis of metabolic alkalosis can be made. The resulting alkalemia depresses the respiratory center and peripheral chemorecepters and increases $Paco_2$, reducing the $HCO_3^-/$ $Paco_2$ ratio toward, but not to, normal. The hypoventilatory response to metabolic alkalosis is limited by hypoxemia, so that the $Paco_2$ rarely exceeds 55 to 60 mm Hg. Respiratory compensation may be impaired commonly in patients with chronic obstructive pulmonary disease, heart failure, and severe cirrhosis, especially with hepatic coma. When hypoxemia limits the compensatory response, administration of oxygen may allow a further compensatory increase in $Paco_2$. Potassium depletion, which frequently accompanies metabolic alkalosis, has been implicated as an additional cause for failure of respiratory compensation, but the role of hypokalemia remains controversial.

Metabolic alkalosis not only is very common as a pure disturbance but also may occur frequently in association with other acid-base disorders. The presence of an associated disorder may be suspected when the $Paco_2$ is greater (respiratory acidosis) or far less than (respiratory alkalosis) the expected or predicted respiratory compensation. The combination of respiratory and metabolic alkalosis may result in severe alkalemia and is recognized by the coexistence of an elevated bicarbonate concentration and reduced Pco_2. The anion gap (Na^+-$[Cl^- + HCO_3^-]$) is slightly elevated (above the normal value of 10 mEq/liter) because of the direct effect of alkalosis on the level of anionic proteins in plasma and of alkalosis and hypocapnia on glycolysis (lactate production). This combined disturbance is associated with a poor prognosis and is not uncommon in critically ill surgical patients on mechanical ventilators receiving diuretics, massive blood transfusions (citrate), or continuous nasogastric suction. Patients with severe liver disease and ascites may have chronic respiratory alkalosis, which, when superimposed on diuretic therapy, can be combined with metabolic alkalosis. This may result in profound alkalemia and, in patients with liver disease, can precipitate hepatic coma because of an

TABLE 9. *Typical electrolyte and acid-base values during chronic diuretic therapy*

	Normal	Diuretic
Na^+	140	140
K^+	4.0	3.0
Cl^-	105	94
HCO_3^-	25	32
pH	7.40	7.48
$Paco_2$	40	47
AG	10	14

increase in input of ammonia to the blood from the kidney. Inappropriately elevated arterial CO_2 tensions and plasma bicarbonate concentrations may occur in patients with chronic obstructive lung disease receiving diuretics and salt restriction for cor pulmonale. If alkalemia ensues, diminished respiratory drive may aggravate the underlying pulmonary insufficiency and result in respiratory failure.

The presence of combined metabolic alkalosis and metabolic acidosis can be suspected in the patient with a high anion gap acidosis but an inappropriately low serum chloride, a near normal pH, and a decrement in plasma bicarbonate that does not match the increment in the anion gap. This type of disorder could occur, for example, if a patient receiving thiazide diuretics causing metabolic alkalosis then develops superimposed diarrhea and volume depletion.

The differential diagnosis of metabolic alkalosis is diverse, and the patient taking diuretics may have other explanations for alkalemia as well. Since the appropriate therapy depends on the correct diagnosis, the initial approach should include a careful assessment of volume status and blood pressure. Particularly important is the assessment of volume status by testing for orthostatic hypotension. Since volume depletion and hypokalemia can maintain metabolic alkalosis, the patient in such a category must have volume reexpansion and chloride and potassium replacement as 0.9% NaCl plus KCl either orally or parenterally (not to exceed 20 mEq/hr). Additional information may be derived from measurement of the urine chloride concentration $[Cl^-]_u$. Metabolic alkalosis can be divided into two broad categories based on the urine chloride concentration: (1) chloride-responsive (urine $[Cl^-]$ below 5 mEq/liter) and (2) chloride-resistant (urine $[Cl^-] > 10-15$ mEq/liter). Patients who have metabolic alkalosis as a result of diuretic therapy should be evaluated after cessation of the diuretic for 12 hr. If the diuretic is being administered to the patient at the time of study, a high $[Cl^-]_u$ will be measured, suggesting, erroneously, that the patient will not respond to chloride. Patients with persistently elevated urine chloride concentrations, metabolic alkalosis, and hypertension (after cessation of the diuretic) should be evaluated for mineralocorticoid excess or hyperreninemic states, such as renal artery stenosis.

Therapy of Metabolic Alkalosis

Using the diagnostic approach outlined, patients who should be treated with saline infusion can then be selected (Table 10). Most patients with diuretic-induced metabolic alkalosis will respond to simple cessation of diuretic therapy and correction of hypokalemia by potassium supplementation. More severe volume depletion and metabolic alkalosis usually requires intravenous isotonic saline infusion to facilitate renal bicarbonate excretion (Table

TABLE 10. *Therapy of metabolic alkalosis induced by diuretics*

All patients:
  Stop diuretic, correct hypokalemia (oral KCl)
Volume-depleted patient
  0.9% NaCl IV to restore volume deficit
  KCl to correct K^+ deficiency
Heart failure, severe oliguria, or volume-expanded patient
  Acetazolamide PO or IV
  NH_4Cl PO or IV (rare indication)
  0.1 N HCl IV via central line (rare)

---

10). Quantities of fluid adequate to replace volume deficits and to repair potassium depletion are necessary. This approach often requires monitoring of hemodynamics. In patients in whom saline administration is considered hazardous because of cardiac decompensation, alternative measures may be necessary (Table 10). Acetazolamide is often effective in such patients in only small doses (250–500 mg orally, once or twice). Patients with renal disease or volume overexpansion and continued generation of metabolic alkalosis may require acidifying salts, however.

Metabolic Acidosis (7,10)

The diuretic most commonly associated with metabolic acidosis is acetazolamide. In general, the degree of metabolic acidosis is mild and self-limiting and requires no specific therapy. However, the concomitant development of metabolic acidosis from other disorders in patients receiving acetazolamide can result in a mixed metabolic acidosis that can be severe. Such an example was reported recently in an elderly patient with diabetes mellitus receiving acetazolamide. This patient had a non anion gap (hyperchloremic) acidosis and impaired renal function. Other similar cases have been reported and support the view that diabetic patients receiving acetazolamide should be followed closely and that the presence of renal insufficiency should be cause to discontinue or reduce the dose of acetazolamide.

Metabolic acidosis as a result of inhibition of carbonic anhydrase occurs also when para-aminomethylbenzene sulfonamide acetate (Sulfamylon) is absorbed from the skin of burned patients. This cream and its metabolites are potent carbonic anhydrase inhibitors that also may inhibit RBC carbonic anhydrase, causing respiratory acidosis. Patients with large area burns, renal failure, and mechanical ventilation are at risk, therefore, for the development of severe mixed metabolic-respiratory acidosis.

Metabolic acidosis and hyperkalemia have been reported during administration of potassium-sparing diuretics especially in diabetics and in patients with mild renal insufficiency. In general, potassium-sparing diuretics are contraindicated in the presence of renal insufficiency because of the potential for life-threatening hyperkalemia. Moreover, because of the frequent association of hyporeninemic hypoaldosteronism with diabetes mellitus and chronic tubulointerstitial disease, these drugs should be given only if necessary and with great caution. Patients with metabolic acidosis of the hyperchloremic-non anion gap variety usually require sodium bicarbonate therapy. In the presence of hyperkalemia, the acidosis may respond to a reduction in serum potassium alone. Detailed information on the therapy of metabolic acidosis is available in Chapter 14.

REFERENCES

1. DuBose, T. D. Jr., and Lucci, M. S. (1983): Effect of carbonic anhydrase on superficial and deep nephron bicarbonate reabsorption in the rat. *J. Clin. Invest.*, 71:55–65.
2. Fernandez, P. C., and Puschett J. B. (1973): Proximal tubular actions of metolazone and chlorthiazide. *Am. J. Physiol.*, 225:954–961.
3. Garella, S., Chang, B. S., and Kahn, S. I. (1975): Ammonia and bicarbonate transport by thick ascending limbs of rat kidney. *Kidney Int.*, 8:279–283.
4. Harrington, J. T., Isner, J. M., and Kassirer, J. P. (1982): Our national obsession with potassium. *Am. J. Med.*, 73:155–159.
5. Kunau, R. T. (1972): The influence of the carbonic anhydrase inhibitor benzolamide [Cl-11366] on reabsorption of chloride, sodium, and bicarbonate in the proximal tubule of the rat. *J. Clin. Invest.*, 51:294–302.
6. Levy, R. I., Weiner, I. M., and Mudge, G. H. (1958): The effects of acid-base balance on the diuresis produced by organic and inorganic mercurials. *J. Clin. Invest.*, 37:1016–1023.
7. Liebman, P. R., Kinnelly, M. M., and Hirsch, E. F. (1981): Hypercarbia and acidosis associated with carbonic anhydrase inhibition: A hazard of topical mafenide acetate use in renal failure. *Burns*, 8:395–398.
8. Lucci, M. S., Tinker, J. P., Weiner, I. H., and DuBose, T. D. Jr. (1983): Function of proximal tubule carbonic anhydrase defined by selective inhibition. *Am. J. Physiol.*, 245: F440–F463.
9. Rose, X., and Burton, D. (1986): Clinical use of diuretics. In: *Body Fluid Homeostasis*, edited by B. M. Brenner and J. H. Stein, pp. 409–438. Churchill-Livingstone, New York.
10. Schambelan, M., Sebastian, A., and Biglieri, E. G. (1980): Prevalence, pathogenesis, and functional significance of aldosterone deficiency in hyperkalemic patients with chronic renal insufficiency. *Kidney Int.*, 17:89–101.
11. Tannen, R. L. (1972): The effect of uncomplicated potassium deficiency on urine acidification. *J. Clin. Invest.*, 49:813–827.

General Review Articles

12. Berger, B. E., and Warnock, D. G. (1986): Mechanisms of action and clinical uses of diuretics. In: *The Kidney*, edited by B. M. Brenner and F. C. Rector Jr., pp. 433–456. W. B. Saunders, Philadelphia, PA.
13. DuBose, T. D. Jr. (1986): Effect on acid-base balance. In: *The Physiological Basis of Diuretic Therapy in Clinical Medicine*, edited by G. Eknoyan and M. Martinez-Maldonado, pp. 125–138. Grune & Stratton, Orlando, FL.

14. Francisco, L. L., and Ferris, T. F. (1982): Use and abuse of diuretics. *Arch. Intern. Med.*, 142:28–32.
15. Knox, F. G., Hammond, T. G., and Haramati A. (1986): Sites and mechanisms of action in the kidney and effects on monovalent ion excretion. In: *The Physiological Basis of Diuretic Therapy in Clinical Medicine*, edited by G. Eknoyan and M. Martinez-Maldonado, pp. 95–108. Grune & Stratton, Orlando, FL.
16.. Seely, J. F., and Dirks, J. H. (1977): Site of action of diuretic drugs. *Kidney Int.*, 11:1–8
17. Suki, W. N., Stinebaugh, B. J., Frommer, J. P., and Eknoyan, G. (1985): Physiology of diuretic action. In: *The Kidney: Physiology and Pathophysiology*, edited by D. W. Seldin and G. Giebisch, pp. 2127–2162. Raven Press, New York.

Subject Index

587